S0-BJL-740

Physiology of Man

Reinhold Books in the Biological Sciences

Consulting Editor: Professor Peter Gray
Andrey Avinoff Professor of Biology
University of Pittsburgh
Pittsburgh, Pennsylvania

The Encyclopedia of the Biological Sciences, edited by Peter Gray
Biophysics: Concepts and Mechanisms, by E. J. Casey
Cell Function, by L. L. Langley
Chordate Morphology, by Malcolm Jollie
Concepts of Forest Entomology, by Kenneth Graham
Ecology of Inland Waters and Estuaries, by George K. Reid
Environmental Measurement and Interpretation, by Robert B. Platt and
    John F. Griffiths
Evolution: Process and Product, Revised Edition, by Edward O. Dodson
Experimental Biology: Measurement and Analysis, by R. H. Kay
Experimental Entomology, by Kenneth W. Cummins, Lee D. Miller, Ned
    A. Smith, and Richard M. Fox
General Zoology, by Clarence J. Goodnight, Marie L. Goodnight, and
    Peter Gray
Introduction to Comparative Entomology, by Richard M. Fox and Jean
    Walker Fox
Macromolecular Structure of Ribonucleic Acids, by A. S. Spirin and A.
    N. Bakh
Management of Artificial Lakes and Ponds, by George W. Bennett
Manual of Insect Morphology, by E. Melville DuPorte
Natural History, by Richard A. Pimentel
Paramedical Microbiology, by Stanley E. Wedberg
The Plant Community, by Herbert C. Hanson and Ethan D. Churchill
Principles in Mammalogy, by David E. Davis and Frank B. Golley

Consulting Editor's Statement

IT IS RARELY that a consulting editor has the opportunity of welcoming an old friend to his series. Langley and Cheraskin's book, though new to our series, is not new either to me or to my students, for this outstanding physiology text, here completely revised, has been a classic through two previous editions.

The authors' approach is fundamentally the same; that is, it concentrates on the organ more than the chemistry and on the organism more than the molecule. It is, of course, completely up to date, without bewildering the student seeking information about physiology by a pyrotechnic display of chemistry. Emphasis is placed throughout on the integration of the different systems. This purpose is rendered easier by placing the nervous system at the beginning and the endocrine system at the end, thus permitting the circulatory, respiratory, and alimentary systems to join them.

This is indeed a welcome addition to REINHOLD'S BOOKS IN THE BIOLOGICAL SCIENCES.

PETER GRAY

Physiology of Man

THIRD EDITION

L. L. LANGLEY, **Ph.D., LL.B.**
National Institutes of Health

E. CHERASKIN, **M.D., D.M.D.**
University of Alabama

REINHOLD PUBLISHING CORPORATION New York
Chapman & Hall Ltd., London

This book is dedicated
to the proposition that
learning can be fun

Preface to the Third Edition

THE FIRST EDITION of this textbook was published in 1954; the second in 1958. The present edition, then, represents the third generation, so to speak, and just as a grandchild usually differs markedly from his grandparent, this edition differs markedly from the first.

The dedication remains the same, that is, that learning can be fun. In fact, we contend that the acquisition of knowledge can and should be one of the most enjoyable of all human endeavors. Accordingly, the first edition was written and illustrated in what the authors thought was an entertaining style. Most of the students who used the text agreed, but our peers found that style flippant. They contended that the learning of physiology is a serious undertaking which should not be made light of. With that admonishment ever before us, this textbook has, through subsequent generations, become more serious, more responsible, more mature. We also hope it is more authoritative. Though youth thinks otherwise, age and maturity can still be enjoyed.

The original goal—to provide a textbook in physiology for the student with minimal preparation in anatomy, mathematics, physics, and chemistry—has been maintained. Difficult concepts must then either be omitted, or explained in a manner understandable to the reader. We have attempted the latter.

Knowledge of physiology continues to grow; thus each revision of a basic textbook tends to become longer. Length is a factor because the longer the book, the more expensive. In addition, the time allotted for such a course is limited. With these limitations in mind, we have attempted to keep the length the same as in previous editions. Since new material had to be added, something had to be deleted. Concepts no longer tenable in the light of new information were removed. In addition, background anatomical discussions had to be shortened. As a result, we believe a better balance has been achieved.

All suggestions to document each statement in the text have been resisted. Beyond question complete documentation has great value, but it also has a major disadvantage and that is it not only markedly lengthens the book but also makes the text immeasurably more difficult to read and to comprehend. For this reason, and because it is an introductory textbook, documentation has not been added. The references, however, at the end of each chapter have been maintained and updated. They provide additional reading, selected because of content as well as the style of presentation.

Years of teaching experience have taught us that it is best to tell the student what you are going to tell him, tell him, and then tell him what you told him. This plan is carried out in each chapter which starts with a brief introduction, then a detailed discussion, and closes with a succinct summary of the major points presented in that chapter. In addition, pertinent questions are provided at the end of each chapter.

In any field that is rapidly growing and changing, frequent revisions of textbooks are necessary. Physiology is no exception. Accordingly, we have altered basic concepts that recent research has shown need revision, we have deleted views that no longer seem tenable, and we have added new theories that have adequate significance. Because there is at least one year between reviewing the subject and the publication of the textbook, the very latest information cannot be included. Nonetheless, we trust that physiology instructors will find each section reasonably current.

All of the new illustrations were prepared by Frances Langley. She also improved many from previous editions. It will be noted that the legends beneath the illustrations have been greatly lengthened. The authors have long felt that an illustration should be so pertinent, so clear, and so simple, that it saves a thousand words. Thus, the legends were, in the first and second editions, kept short. It finally occurred to us that even though an illustration is obvious and self-explanatory, the legend can be used for emphasis and repetition; and repetition is undeniably essential to learning.

Another major change has been made. We have a new publisher. The change was brought about by several factors, but in so far as the reader is concerned we believe that he will find the change has resulted in very obvious improvement. Major credit for this improvement is gratefully given by the authors to Mr. John Hart; truly a knowledgeable, incredibly meticulous, and indefatigable editor.

Finally, to the many students and instructors who have written to us, whether to criticize or compliment, we express our sincere appreciation. It is understandably enjoyable to be complimented, but it is more helpful to receive criticism. We have earnestly tried to satisfy each complaint, to embody your helpful suggestions into the present edition. We continue to solicit your reactions.

L. L. LANGLEY
E. CHERASKIN

January, 1965

Contents

PART

1

Orientation

Basic Physiological Principles

1

BEFORE THE BASIC PHYSIOLOGICAL PRINCIPLES ARE ANALYZED, it is well for the reader to have a clear understanding of the field encompassed by the term **physiology.** It is correctly stated that anatomy refers to the study of the **structure** of an organism, while physiology is concerned with **function.** Put in most simple terms, physiology *is the study of what makes us tick.* Although this expression may vividly convey the concept in its broadest connotation, it also includes the field of psychology. Physiology, strictly speaking, is the study of function, of the mechanisms characteristic of living organisms. Some of these properties are basic and underlie so many facets of the subject that it is well to discuss them first in this orientation section.

HOMEOSTASIS

By far the most important single concept in the entire field of physiology concerns the *constancy of the internal environment.* The internal environment is determined by conditions within the body, for example, temperature, blood pressure, and the concentration of the constituents in the body fluids. Obviously there must be highly sensitive and exquisitely integrated mechanisms charged with the responsibility of maintaining a delicate state of balance. Physiology is concerned with the study of these systems, which have been termed by the eminent American physiologist, Walter Cannon, **homeostatic mechanisms.** The constancy of the internal environment Dr. Cannon labeled **homeostasis.** This word is derived from the Greek *homoios,* meaning "like" or "similar," and *stasis,* a "standing still." In other words, there is a balance, a constancy of the internal state of the human being. Clearly, the word is well chosen.

EXAMPLES OF HOMEOSTASIS

There are many common, everyday illustrations of homeostasis. For example, every mother knows that her child's temperature should be

3

about 98.6°F (37°C). If it is more than that, she apprehensively summons the doctor. She does not stop to think whether it is an icy December morning or a hot and humid August afternoon. She expects her child's temperature to be about the same at all times, and she is right! Physiological research has shown that a human being may be exposed to wide variations of climate and yet the temperature of the inside of the body remains remarkably close to 98.6°F. Certainly we heat our homes and wear heavy clothing in the winter, but these precautions are taken to protect us against the extremes of weather variations. Over a relatively wide temperature range, one need do nothing. The mechanisms which maintain a constant body temperature swing into action rapidly and automatically. They function to accomplish results comparable to that of the modern automatic heating and air-conditioning plants.

Another example of homeostasis is the constancy of the blood-sugar level. It can be easily demonstrated that the blood sugar is rapidly returned to within the normal range despite the fact that one eats, for example, three pieces of chocolate cake at one meal. On the other hand, if the subject were to starve for several days, the blood sugar would still be close to its average value. This is accomplished by the interaction of diet and the functioning of the liver, kidneys, and hormones—all of which will be studied in due course.

The examples just cited are by no means the only ones. As each of the body systems, such as the nervous, circulatory, respiratory, alimentary, excretory, and endocrine systems, is analyzed it will be seen that there are countless homeostatic mechanisms functioning to maintain the integrity of the organism despite an ever-changing external environment.

DYNAMIC PROCESSES

It is important to note that this constancy of the internal environment in the face of an ever-changing external world is dependent on **dynamic processes**. It should be the student's goal to gain a working knowledge of the mechanisms which maintain this static state. The importance of homeostasis is more dramatically underlined when the dynamic processes fail to maintain a balanced relationship. A failure of temperature regulation may result in fever; a collapse of sugar regulation may lead to diabetes mellitus.

Everyone is familiar with the steady state which is often referred to as "second wind." All athletes know that, during exercise, at first breathing is heavy and difficult, the heart pounds, and fatigue or even collapse seems imminent. They soon learn, however, that following this initial period breathing becomes less labored and the pounding of the heart actually disappears. The athlete then feels as though he has been magically converted into an effortless machine with boundless energy.

When exercise is initiated, the heart and respiratory rates do indeed rise, heavy breathing carries more oxygen into the blood, and the increased rate of blood flow brings the oxygen to the tissues more rapidly. In addition, the elevated circulatory rate also furnishes the tissues with vital foodstuffs such as sugar. Concurrently, rapid and efficient alterations are taking place which divert the blood from inactive areas, such as the intestinal tract, to the actively contracting muscles. And, since exercise produces heat, other changes take place which serve to eliminate the excess heat and maintain a constant temperature. The net result of these and other adjustments is to allow the athlete to expend energy at a high rate with a modicum of fatigue and with strikingly small deviations in the internal environment.

These few examples serve to demonstrate that physiology is concerned with the dynamic mechanisms by which the body functions under conditions of rest and how these processes are altered in order to maintain the constancy of the body under other circumstances. The sensitive mechanisms which maintain this constant internal state permit the individual to live under a wide variety of conditions.

SEQUENCE OF EVENTS

One goal of physiology is to discover and analyze the homeostatic mechanisms. In the case of the athlete, actively contracting muscles surely require more oxygen than muscles at rest. But the student should understand at the outset that merely stating that the heart pumps more blood and the lungs take in more air because the muscles need more oxygen does not explain *how* these changes occur. It is true that a physiological change may be desirable, that is, it may result in benefits to the body. But recognizing the utility of a change does not explain the sequence of events by which the end result is accomplished.

It is often assumed that each physiological mechanism must serve some useful purpose for the body. This type of **teleological** reasoning may prove very helpful to the research worker to provide him a broad concept as to the mechanism under investigation. The term teleology implies *end*, that is, the character of being shaped or designed toward an end or purpose. In the example just presented, it would be teleological reasoning to state that in exercise more blood is required and therefore the heart increases its output (Fig. 1-1). This is true, but it is the ultimate goal of the physiologist to elucidate the precise sequence of events by which this desirable end result is produced (Fig. 1-2).

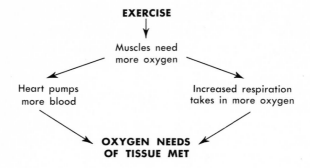

FIG. 1-1 A layman's explanation of the changes that occur during exercise.

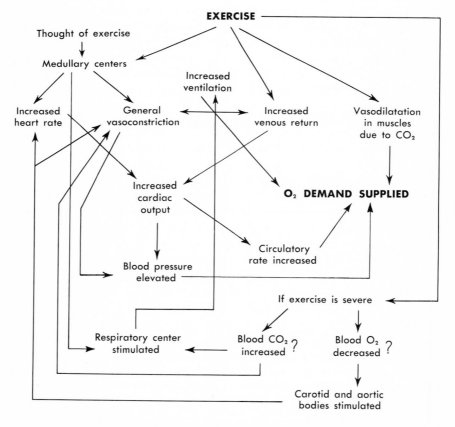

FIG. 1-2 A physiologist's explanation of the changes that occur during exercise.

The student must first comprehend the normal function of the body. Secondly, he must understand the sequence of events by which those functions are altered. The student of physiology must always ask himself, What are the mechanisms? What is the sequence of events?

ELECTRICAL PHENOMENA

It is interesting to observe that perhaps all animals and plants are sources of **electrical activity** or energy. This phenomenon is undoubtedly due to the electrolytes found in all living protoplasm. It can be easily demonstrated that small but very definite quantities of electricity are generated when solutions of electrolytes are separated by a membrane, provided that the solutions differ in the quality or concentration of the electrolytes. Although in many cases the exact mechanism is not clear, it may be stated as a general rule that all protoplasmic activity is associated with electrical phenomena. The details concerning the exact mechanism by which living cells generate electrical activity will be discussed in Chap. 3.

Knowledge concerning the electrical activity associated with living organisms has progressed with developments in the electronic sciences. The recent great strides in this field parallel the considerable knowledge

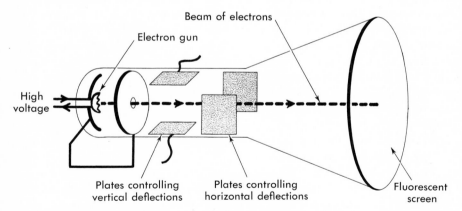

FIG. 1-3   Cathode-ray oscillograph. The electron gun produces a stream of electrons, which are focused on to the fluorescent screen in the form of a visible dot. By altering the voltage on the plates, one can make the beam move up or down, or from side to side. Usually the beam is made to sweep from left to right by an internal oscillating voltage mechanism by means of which the rate and frequency of the sweep can be controlled. The electrical phenomenon being analyzed is led to the plates controlling vertical deflections. Thus, as the beam sweeps from left to right, changes of voltage will cause the beam to move up or down, thereby describing a characteristic configuration.

gained in the physiology of electrical phenomena. The apparatus currently used for these purposes is highly complex and beyond the scope of this book. Suffice it to say that for much of the basic investigation the **cathode-ray oscillograph** is used (Fig. 1-3). In order to obtain a permanent record, a photograph is taken of the oscillographic screen, as one would photograph a picture on the television screen.

TRANSFER THROUGH MEMBRANES

There are at least five ways in which transfer through membranes may occur. They are (1) **diffusion,** (2) **filtration,** (3) **osmosis,** (4) **active transport,** and (5) **pinocytosis.**

DIFFUSION

If common table salt, NaCl, is placed in the bottom of a glass and water added carefully so as not to stir up the salt, the salt nonetheless goes into solution. After a period of time, chemical analysis reveals that the salt is now evenly dispersed throughout the water. Actually, the top of the salt layer in contact with the water quickly dissolves, and once in solution the individual ions—that is, the sodium and chloride ions—dance off in all directions. One of the basic properties of molecules and ions is this constant movement in solution. The rate of movement is a function of temperature. At absolute zero ($-273°C$), all ionic and molecular movement ceases. The warmer the solution, the more rapid is the movement. Thus in water at room temperature, the sodium and chloride ions move in all directions at a relatively rapid rate. As each particle of salt dissolves, it passes into the solvent, leaving another layer of salt exposed to the water. Eventually all the salt is in solution. The individual ions collide and rebound from one another until finally there is an even distribution of ions throughout the solution. This process of distribution is termed **diffusion.**

Figure 1-4 shows that diffusion of particles will take place not only through a solution but across a permeable membrane as well. If such a membrane (of either synthetic or physiological source) divides the container into two compartments and a solution is placed on one side and pure water on the other, after a few minutes the water will contain salt. Eventually the concentration of salt on both sides of the membrane will be identical because the unequal solutions attain equilibrium. In other words, the salt has diffused through the membrane. This is explicable on the basis of ionic and molecular movement. The salt ions move at random, and when they happen upon a membrane pore, they can pass through it.

DIFFUSION THROUGH A SOLUTION
Even distribution

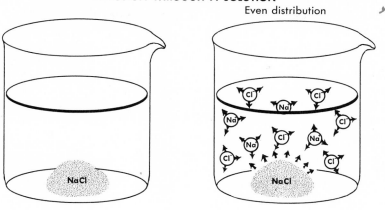

DIFFUSION THROUGH A MEMBRANE
Permeable membrane

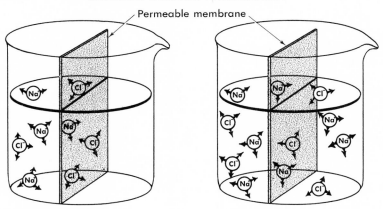

FIG. 1-4   Diffusion. In the pair of upper beakers the mass of salt is seen to ionize and the ions distribute themselves throughout the solution. In the lower beakers the ions, due to random movement, find pores in the membrane and pass through it. Accordingly, in time there is an equal number of ions on both sides of the membrane.

If a membrane separates two solutions containing the same solute, but in different concentrations, the particles of both solutions will diffuse through the membrane. However, because a larger number of particles are in the more concentrated solution, there is a greater probability of those particles finding and passing through openings in the membrane.

In other words, more particles pass from the higher concentration into the lower than vice versa. The difference between the two concentrations is termed a **concentration gradient.** For the reasons just stated, particles will diffuse "down" the concentration gradient. The rate of diffusion is proportional to the difference in concentration.

The concentration gradient, however, may not be the sole factor which determines the rate, or even the direction, of diffusion. Another factor is the electrical charge of the particle. There is attraction between ions of opposite charge. Accordingly, positive ions will move in the direction of a negative area and negative ions will move toward a positive region. This difference in negativity or positivity is termed the **electrical gradient.** Ions will move "down" the electrical gradient at a rate proportional to the potential difference of the two solutions.

FILTRATION

In the chemistry laboratory, the student has probably had occasion to filter many substances. To do this he places a permeable piece of paper in a funnel and pours a solution into it (Fig. 1-5). The solution slowly

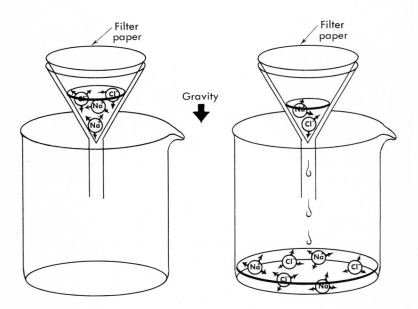

FIG. 1-5 Filtration. Due to the force of gravity, the water and the salt pass through the filter paper as shown in the beaker to the right. However, if the solute particles were larger than the filter paper pores, the solvent would pass through, but the solute would not.

passes through, leaving behind molecules which are too large to escape through the small openings in the filter paper. If the chemist desires to speed the process, he reduces the pressure in the container below the filter (by applying suction). The lower the pressure, the faster is the filtration process. **Filtration** then differs from diffusion. Filtration takes place *not* by virtue of molecular and ionic movement but rather as a result of an external force which literally impels the substance through the filter. For example, when suction is applied, the atmospheric force on the top side of the filter is greater than the pressure within the container. This pressure differential is the force which causes the fluid to pass through the filter. If no suction is employed, then the only force is gravity. The rate of filtration depends upon the degree of external energy which tends to drive the substance through the filter. In the living organism the fluid component of blood, for example, filters through the capillary wall. The force in this substance is supplied by the blood pressure. The same is true in the kidneys where substances filter through the glomerulus into the tubule.

OSMOSIS

The term **osmosis** is derived from the Greek *osmos* meaning, broadly, "pressure laden." Solvents of differing molecular dimensions, separated by a membrane, will traverse the membrane at different rates, thus establishing an osmotic pressure between them. The physiological membrane may be **semipermeable,** which may permit diffusion of the solvent but generally not the solute; or the membrane may have **selective permeability,** under which condition certain substances may traverse the membrane while other substances of equal or smaller molecular dimension will be blocked by it. A selective membrane achieves its discrimination by a complex surface mechanism involving ionic exchange and other electropotential properties inherent in the chemistry of its composition.

In discussing diffusion, it was mentioned that, if a permeable membrane separates water from a salt solution, within a short period of time the salt diffuses through the membrane and the concentration on both sides becomes identical. Thus, there results a balance. But if the membrane is a selective semipermeable one so that water molecules will pass but salt molecules cannot, then a very different result is seen. Figure 1-6 shows that the water will pass into the salt solution, but since there cannot be a simultaneous transfer of salt into the water solution, the column of salt solution rises because the volume progressively increases. It requires energy to support a column of fluid, since fluid possesses weight. So long as water molecules continue to enter the salt solution, the column will rise. However, as it does so it becomes progressively heavier. A point

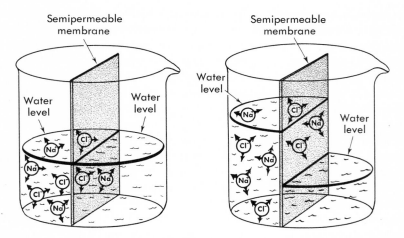

FIG. 1-6   Osmosis. The semipermeable membrane, in this case, will permit the water to pass but not the salt. Accordingly, water moves into the salt solution until the difference in height of the two columns balances the force of water movement.

will ultimately be reached at which the weight of the column of fluid balances the force driving the water molecules into the salt compartment. Then the net transfer of water will cease. In other words, the height of the salt solution above the water compartment is an index of the osmotic force or pressure. An example of this force is encountered when red blood cells are placed in a hypotonic (low-salt) solution. In this case, they swell and eventually rupture. This is so because the cell membrane is semipermeable. Therefore, the water molecules from the hypotonic (less concentrated) salt solution move into the red blood cell and continue to do so until the red cell can no longer withstand the force and bursts.

In brief, whenever a semipermeable membrane separates two solutions one of which contains a substance which cannot pass, then fluid from the other compartment will cross the membrane. This movement process is termed osmosis. A force associated with unequal solvent diffusion gives rise to an unequal pressure across the membrane, and this differential is called **osmotic pressure.**

ACTIVE TRANSPORT

Perhaps the most poorly understood process by which substances traverse a membrane is by means of active transport. Active transport requires energy. It has already been pointed out that responding to electrical field forces acting upon its molecular and ionic constituents, a substance will pass through a permeable membrane by diffusion. It has also been noted that gross external forces may drive molecules through such a membrane. This is filtration. But in active transport, the cell, admittedly by a poorly understood mechanism, moves solutes in the opposite direction, that is, "uphill" against either a concentration gradient or an electrical gradient, or both. It will be seen in subsequent sections that active transport is utilized by many organ systems.

PINOCYTOSIS

There has long been evidence that molecules, too large to pass through openings in the cell membrane, nonetheless get into and out of the cell. Electron microscopy has disclosed one possible method. Large particles come into contact with the cell wall after which an invagination occurs. The particles enter this invagination. Next, the invagination becomes pinched off so as to become a vesicle within the cell. Finally, the wall of the vesicle disappears leaving the particles within the cytoplasm of the cell. Large particles move out of the cell in a similar, but reverse sequence. This process is termed **reverse pinocytosis** or **emeiocytosis** (Fig. 1-7).

EXCITABILITY

Excitability, or, as it is often called, **irritability,** refers to the response of all living cells and organisms to sudden and significant change in their environment. If the lowly ameba is touched with a sharp object, it will usually retreat. Likewise, if a man were to step on a nail, he would rapidly withdraw his foot. In both illustrations there has been a response. Beyond question the reaction in the second instance is more complex, but fundamentally it is an example of excitability.

If the definition of the term excitability is analyzed, it will be found to

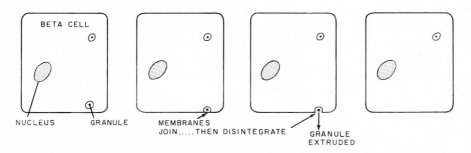

FIG. 1-7   Emeiocytosis. Molecules, too large to diffuse through the cell membrane, may be extruded as shown.

contain two essential elements: (1) a *change in the environment* and (2) a *response*. For the former, the word **stimulus** may be substituted. This is perhaps the most used term in all of physiology. One speaks, for example, of the response of the nervous system, the heart, and the digestive glands to various stimuli. Physiology is the study not only of the basic functions but of the response of those systems to stimuli. Yet, though the word is so commonly used, a precise definition is impossible. It will suffice to be familiar with the various types of stimuli and to recognize that a stimulus is a change in the immediate environment of a living system.

TYPES OF STIMULI

A change in any of many physical or chemical factors of the environment results in a response by the organism. Thus it is recognized that there are (1) **mechanical,** (2) **thermal,** (3) **electrical,** (4) **chemical,** and (5) **osmotic** stimuli. This list is not complete, but it does include the more important ones. The response to mechanical stimuli such as pressure, impact, and traction is too obvious to require illustration. Similarly, one is familiar with the typical reactions to change in temperature. Chemical, osmotic, and electrical stimuli, however, are not so well known. These will become clearer in subsequent discussions.

In physiology, one grades stimuli according to the response of the part being excited. Thus the terms **threshold, minimal,** or **liminal** have come into common usage. A threshold or minimal stimulus is one just strong enough to provoke a response. Minimal and liminal are generally used interchangeably. A **subliminal** stimulus is one too weak to produce a response. As the strength of a stimulus is increased, a point is ultimately reached beyond which no augmentation of reaction is noted. At this point, the stimulus is said to be **maximal.**

SPECIFIC ENERGY

The doctrine of specific energy states that the response is always the same no matter what type of stimulus is used. For example, a nerve may be activated mechanically, chemically, or electrically. In each instance an impulse is conveyed by that nerve in exactly the same way. The most striking illustration points out that if the optic nerve could be attached to the ear and the auditory nerve to the eye, the subject would see thunder and hear lightning! A more common example is the well-known phenomenon of "seeing stars" when the individual receives a vigorous blow about the head. In this instance the mechanical stimulus causes impulses to be conveyed by the optic nerve so that light is momentarily perceived. The eye normally responds to light, but mechanical stimuli evoke the same response.

It should be pointed out that there are reactions which do not adhere to this concept of specific energy. This is found in relatively undifferentiated cells, such as an ameba. In response to mechanical stimulation, the ameba will retreat, but if it is stimulated with a receptive object such as food, it will surround and engulf it. It can be appreciated that this is a rather specialized instance. For the most part, especially in the higher organisms, the doctrine of specific energy is valid.

CHARACTERISTICS OF EXCITABILITY

As the various systems are studied, it will be learned that there are many common response characteristics. These include the **latent period, refractory periods, summation,** and **adaptation.** All these will be discussed in subsequent chapters.

ANESTHESIA

Only mere mention can be given here of the important phenomenon of anesthesia which is, in reality, the antithesis of excitability. Various agents are commonly used in medicine to raise the threshold of tissues so that they will not respond to stimuli. Thus a **general anesthetic agent** may be given which causes the individual to lose consciousness, or the part to be operated on may be made less responsive by a **local anesthetic agent.** The precise mechanism by which anesthetic substances function is still open to question. Before this question can be answered, more knowledge of excitability must be acquired. At the present time, there are several theories purporting to explain excitability, but none is completely satisfactory.

ENZYMATIC ACTION

No matter what aspect of physiology is under consideration, the ultimate explanation lies within the myriad chemical reactions which proceed within the cell. Very few of these basic processes have been defined, but there are good reasons to believe that perhaps all of them are governed by substances known as **catalysts.** When the catalyst is of biological origin, it is termed an **enzyme.** It has been said that enzymes are a reflection of nature's impatience! About 1000 different enzymes have been estimated to be functional in a single cell.

TYPES OF ENZYMES

Enzymes are generally classified according to the reaction which they potentiate. The substance in the reaction influenced in this way is termed the **substrate.** It is now the custom to label the enzyme by adding *-ase* to the name of the substrate. Thus enzymes that influence fats (lipids) are called **lipases, amylases** act on carbohydrates, **phosphatases** split phosphate from organic combinations, and **cholinesterase** hydrolyzes acetylcholine. It can be seen that according to this classification there is an enzyme for every substrate. Consequently, the same enzyme may possess many names. It is for this reason that there is now a tendency to label these substances according to their chemical structure. However, they are all proteins, and the precise functional structure of most of them remains unknown.

FACTORS WHICH INFLUENCE ENZYMATIC ACTION

The **temperature, degree of acidity, concentration of substrate** and **enzyme,** and the **presence of other chemical substances** all modify enzymatic activity. Generally speaking, an elevation in temperature accelerates the action of the enzyme. It has been shown that a rise of 10°C hastens the reaction two- or threefold. It is characteristic of enzymes that there is an optimal acidity for maximal reactivity. Thus, when the digestive enzymes are studied, it will be found that the stomach enzymes function at a strikingly different pH than do those in the intestine. The fact that many chemical compounds influence enzymatic action is of vital concern in medicine because it is through various drugs that many of the bodily processes may be controlled or modified.

CHARACTERISTICS OF ENZYMATIC ACTION

It is generally true that enzymatic activity is restricted to a specific substrate. Thus lipase will hasten the digestion of fats but exerts no influence on the breakdown of protein or carbohydrate. This property is referred to as **enzyme specificity.** The second important quality is the **reversibility** of action. That is to say, if a reaction may proceed in either direction, then the enzyme which influences that reaction will speed it in both directions. Again using lipase as an example, it is found that in the intestinal tract it hastens the conversion of fat into fatty acid and glycerol. But in the tissues when there is a good supply of fatty acids and glycerol, lipase assists in the formation of fat.

SUMMARY

Homeostasis refers to the constancy of the internal environment. Dynamic processes, termed **homeostatic mechanisms,** maintain the equilibrium state. The discovery of the precise **sequence of events** by which this end result is attained is the goal of physiological research.

All living material is a source of **electrical activity.** In most instances, however, it is of such small magnitude that it must be ampified in order to be visualized and studied.

The cell membrane is **semipermeable.** Substances pass through it by (1) **diffusion,** (2) **filtration,** (3) **osmosis,** (4) **active transport,** or (5) **pinocytosis.** Diffusion depends on inherent ionic and molecular movement. Filtration requires an external force such as gravity or hydrostatic pressure. If the membrane is impermeable to a substance, fluid will flow across this barrier so as to dilute that material. This process is called osmosis. The force so produced is termed **osmotic pressure.** Cell membranes are generally capable of moving solutes against concentration and electrical gradients. This process is termed **active transport,** and energy is required. In pinocytosis, large molecules are engulfed by the cell by the formation of vesicles which then separate from the cell membrane and disappear, leaving the particle within the cell.

All living tissues respond to changes in their environment. Such changes are termed **stimuli** and the response, **excitability.** There are (1) **mechanical,** (2) **thermal,** (3) **electrical,** (4) **chemical,** and (5) **osmotic** stimuli. If the stimulus is just strong enough to evoke a response, it is termed **minimal, liminal,** or **threshold;** if weaker, **subminimal** or **subliminal.** The doctrine of specific energy states that the response is always the same no matter what type of stimulus is used. An **anesthetic agent** is a substance which raises the threshold of tissues so they will not be activated.

A biological **catalyst** is termed an **enzyme.** The substance upon which the enzyme functions is known as the **substrate.** Enzymes are generally named after the specific substrate with *-ase* added. **Temperature, degree of acidity, concentration of substrate** and **enzyme,** and the **presence of other chemical compounds** all influence enzymatic activity. Enzymes generally only modify specific reactions. This characteristic is termed **enzyme specificity.** If the reaction can proceed in both directions, the enzyme will hasten both processes. This is called **reversibility** of action.

QUESTIONS

1. What does the word homeostasis mean?
2. What is meant by sequence of events?
3. What is a semipermeable membrane?
4. Describe the various processes by which substances pass through a semipermeable membrane.
5. What is the doctrine of specific energy?
6. What is an enzyme?

SUGGESTED READING

Cooley, D. G., "Enzymes: Chemical Keys to Health and Disease," *Today's Health,* **39:**#12, 42–43, 66–70, December 1961.

Edelman, I. S., "Transport Through Biological Membranes," *Ann. Rev. Physiol.,* **23:** 37–70, 1961.

Engel, G. L., "A Unified Concept of Health and Disease," *Persp. Biol. Med.,* **3:**#4, 459–485, Summer 1960.

Frieden, E., "The Enzyme-substrate Complex," *Sci. American,* **201:**#2, 119–125, August 1959.

Herrman, H., and Tootle, M. L., "Specific and General Aspects of the Development of Enzymes and Metabolic Pathways," *Physiol. Rev.,* **44:**#2, 289–371, April 1964.

Wroblewski, F., "Enzymes in Medical Diagnosis," *Sci. American,* **205:**#2, 99–107, August 1961.

Cells and Tissues

THE BASIC UNIT OF ALL LIVING ORGANISMS is the **cell.** Some forms, such as the ameba, consist of but a single cell. In the more complex forms, there are millions of these units of various types. And in these complex organisms the cells are arranged into aggregates known as **tissues.** In view of the fact that the anatomical design and function of the various organs of the body are determined by the specific cells and tissues, it is well to survey these basic units at this time.

CELLS

CELL STRUCTURE

Most cells are far too small to be seen with the unaided eye. Under the microscope they appear, for the most part, as more or less spherical masses. This shape, however, in many tissues is quite varied. A few cells, notably those of motor nerves, are very large indeed. For example, one of these cells may extend all the way from the brain down into the spinal cord, a distance of 3 or 4 ft. Muscle cells are also large enough to be easily seen. But, on the other hand, the red blood cells or the cellular units of the skin are microscopic in size. For example, 3,000 red blood cells placed end to end would extend only about an inch.

Protoplasm The term **protoplasm** is extremely difficult to define. It is generally described as living matter, but such a definition really conveys very little. If a finger is scraped lightly so as to remove the most superficial layers of skin but not deeply enough to cause bleeding, the exposed raw area will be seen to be clear and viscid, somewhat resembling the white of an egg. This is protoplasm. It is the stuff of which all living tissue is formed. To examine protoplasm in detail it is best to study one of the unicellular animal forms such as the ameba.

19

Protoplasm upon analysis is revealed to contain the basic elements **carbon, hydrogen, oxygen,** and **nitrogen.** These substances predominate. All the other elements such as **calcium, potassium,** and **sulfur** collectively do not make up more than 3 or 4 per cent of the protoplasm. All these elements are common; they are found in abundant amounts throughout the earth. It is safe to conclude, therefore, that the various materials which constitute protoplasm do not give it the characteristic which we designate as life; rather it is the pattern in which these basic elements are arranged.

Protoplasm is mostly water. The percentage of water varies from tissue to tissue. Bone, for example, contains very little water, whereas fat and blood possess considerable quantities. In addition to water, the basic elements combine to form many other substances, ranging from simple inorganic compounds, like table salt, to the very complex protein molecules.

Returning once again to the simple ameba, it is found that in the protoplasm of this unicellular animal there are present practically all the substances which normally exist in the most complicated of living forms—**man.** In other words, protoplasm is the basic building material. Before the complexities peculiar to the multicellular animal are tackled, the student should be thoroughly familiar with the composition of this basic building substance.

It will be learned later that the inorganic compounds play a great role in the physiology of man. It is interesting to note that the concentration of inorganic salts in protoplasm is remarkably similar to their concentration in sea water. To speculate on this observation would take one far afield. It suffices to recognize, first, that the concentration of inorganic salts in most protoplasm is about 0.9 per cent and, secondly, that this concentration remains constant despite widely varying environmental conditions.

There are many organic compounds in protoplasm. The more important ones may be classified under three headings: (1) **carbohydrates,** (2) **proteins,** and (3) **fats.** The carbohydrates range from the simple sugars, such as glucose and fructose, up to the very complex molecules like glycogen. Proteins are made up of amino acids. There are many different amino acids; they are distinct in that their structural formulas vary in one way or another. Over 30 amino acids have been identified. Since these are the building blocks, it is clear that the number of proteins which can be created is very great. It is as though a builder had 30 basic materials with which to work. The student can readily visualize the many different structures he could erect with this variety. As will be seen when digestion is considered, these protein molecules are invaluable to man; they are used in many ways. Finally, fat is a compound composed of glycerol in combination with several, usually three, fatty acids. Numerous fatty acids have been identified, indicating that there are distinct types of fats just as there are different proteins, but the variety of fats is not nearly so great.

In short, protoplasm presents the picture of a colorless, viscous, slimy substance made up chiefly of water in combination with the various elements woven together into inorganic as well as organic substances. These materials and their interrelationships endow protoplasm with its fundamental property which we call life.

Cell Membrane If the ameba is cut with a sharp knife, the thick protoplasm will be seen, under a microscope, to escape. This indicates that the protoplasmic mass must be normally contained by a very thin envelope (Fig. 2-1). This envelope, the cell membrane, consists of a double layer of fat molecules organized between two layers of protein. It is an extremely thin structure. The cell membrane permits many substances to pass through, while at the same time it bars others. It is therefore termed a **selectively permeable** membrane—permeable to some substances while impassable to others. Thus, in the simple animal forms, foodstuffs are permitted to enter the cell and waste products are allowed to emigrate. But large, vital protein molecules are jealously held within the cell.

Nucleus Most cells contain a small mass different in consistency from the rest of the protoplasm. This mass is termed the **nucleus** (Fig. 2-1). The protoplasm of the nucleus is termed **nucleoplasm.** All the remainder of the protoplasm in the cell is called **cytoplasm.**

It is commonly held that all living cells possess nuclei. Conversely, if the cell is without a nucleus it is thought not to be living. Whether or not this conclusion is wholly accurate remains debatable. For example, it will be seen that the mature red blood cell does not possess a nucleus. Yet, one would hesitate to state that this important cell is not living. The nucleus is surrounded by its own membrane, the so-called **nuclear membrane.** It too is selectively permeable and serves (1) to contain the nuclear material and (2) to control the traffic of substances in and out of the nucleus.

The function of the nucleus is still being intensively investigated, but some definite facts have been established. It is known, for example, that in most, if not all, cells, the nucleus is the "heart" of the cell and so is essential for the continued survival of the entire cell. Thus, if an ameba is divided, the part containing the nucleus will undergo repair and survive. The other half will disintegrate. It has also been shown that the characteristic of growth is dependent upon the presence of the nucleus.

The most important constituent of the nucleus is **nucleic acid.** Two

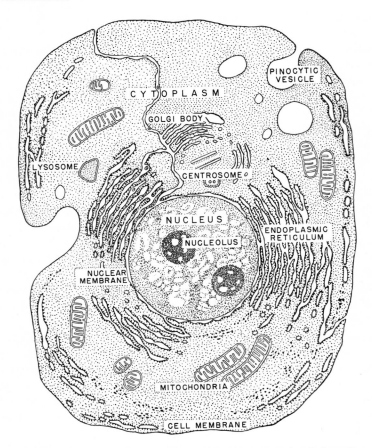

FIG. 2-1   Diagram of a typical cell. This representation is based upon electron microscopic studies. The dots that line the endoplasmic reticulum are ribosomes. (Reproduced, with permission, from J. Brachet, *Sci. American,* **205:**51, September 1961.)

types of nucleic acid have been identified: (1) **deoxyribonucleic acid (DNA)** and (2) **ribonucleic acid (RNA).** DNA is found, specifically, in the chromatin filaments. RNA, on the other hand, is located not only within the nucleus, but also in the cytoplasm of the cell. These substances are considered to be so important because it is now known that they are responsible for, and essential to, the reproduction of amino acids, the basic building blocks of all living matter. DNA controls the formation of RNA, and then RNA acts as the model for the arrangement of some 20, or more, amino acids in a specific order in protein molecules.

It is this amino acid arrangement which determines the characteristics of the resulting peptides and proteins.

Within the nucleus is a comparatively large, rounded body termed the **nucleolus.** The high concentration of RNA in the nucleolus suggests that this structure plays an important role in protein synthesis.

The **chromosomes** are essential nuclear structures. When the cell is not actively dividing, the chromosomes do not appear as discrete structures but rather as a mass of material called **chromatin.** During cell division the chromatin becomes organized into a specific number of easily identifiable chromosomes. Each chromosome has a definite number and distribution of **genes.** Genes are, in reality, DNA. The genes determine the hereditary characteristics.

Mitochondria   The **mitochondria** (Fig. 2-1) are large structures enveloped by a double membrane. Each membrane is composed of a layer of protein molecules lined by a double layer of lipid molecules. The inner membrane sends branches into the substance of the mitochondria and thus divides them into many compartments. Mitochondria are thought to play an important role in cellular metabolism of oxygen, carbohydrates, fatty acids, and amino acids. Thus they are often referred to as the "principal power plants of the cell."

Endoplasmic Reticulum   The **endoplasmic reticulum** consists of a network of internal membranes which form a series of small canals through the cytoplasm. These canals lead substances through the cell from the cell membrane to the nuclear membrane. Closely associated with the membranes are tiny granules termed **microsomes.** Because they contain a very high concentration of RNA, they are often referred to as **ribosomes.** Ribosomes are probably essential for protein synthesis.

Golgi Body   The **Golgi body,** or **Golgi apparatus,** as it is also known, is made up of a series of smooth membranes continuous with the endoplasmic reticulum. Enzymes have been found to be concentrated along the surface of these membranes. In some way, the Golgi body is thought to contribute to the formation of secretory products, or at least to the liberation of such products from the cell. The suggestion has been made that the Golgi body is an intracellular pump that regulates the movement of fluids in the cell and the expulsion of secretory products from the cell.

Lysosomes   The large spherical structures seen in the cytoplasm (Fig. 2-1) are termed **lysosomes.** As the term suggests, lysosomes are important to the intracellular mechanisms involved in the breaking down of large molecules. The lysosomes contain digestive enzymes that catabolize proteins, fats, and nuclei acids.

DIVISION OF CELLS

In the process of growth and development of any tissue, the component cells may grow in size, divide into additional cells, or undergo a combination of both. Cells divide by either **mitosis** or **amitosis.** When a cell divides amitotically, there is a cleavage of the nucleus without change in its structure, followed by the division of the cytoplasm. In other words, there is a simple splitting of the cell. In mitosis, there is differentiation and halving of the chromosomes before the cytoplasmic fission. There are complicated nuclear alterations which occur in a continuous series of changes, but which are usually divided into (1) the **prophase,** (2) the **metaphase,** (3) the **anaphase,** and (4) the **telophase** (Fig. 2-2).

Prophase   The first activity in a cell about to undergo mitotic division is observed about the **centrioles.** Radiating fibers termed **astral rays** appear. Now the centrioles begin to move away from each other and ultimately reach opposite sides of the cell. During the prophase the chromosomes appear as distinct, separate entities. Upon close observation they are seen to be paired, each member of the pair being named a **chromatid.** At the end of the prophase, the nuclear membrane disappears.

Metaphase   This is a very short period during which the chromosomes become aligned in an orderly fashion. It will be observed in Fig. 2-2 that the arrangement is such that half the **chromatids** face one centriole while their partners face the other one. They are in a position to separate.

Anaphase   The chromatids then separate, half migrating toward one centriole, the other half heading for the other one. As they move to opposite poles they assume a V shape, with the point of the V facing the centrioles.

Telophase   The chromatids reach the opposite centrioles during this period, and are once again properly called chromosomes. At this time the cell membrane is seen to form a constriction which ultimately divides the cell into two distinct units. Also during this phase a nuclear membrane forms around each chromosomal mass. Simultaneously, the individual centrioles return to their original positions. The daughter cells grow rapidly and are soon ready to divide anew.

The time required for the completion of mitotic division varies with the cell, the temperature, and probably the presence or absence of specific enzymes and hormones. The reported times for this process range from 30 minutes to several hours.

The important factor in mitotic division is the retention of the original number of chromosomes in each cell. It will be recalled that as soon as the chromosomes become differentiated at the beginning of the process

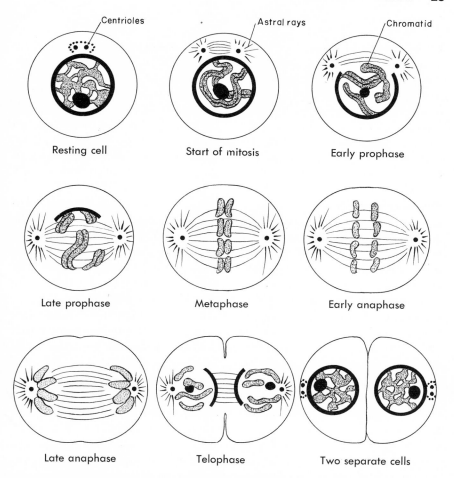

FIG. 2-2   Mitosis. The sequence of intracellular events which take place during cell division are diagrammatically depicted. (See text for explanation.)

they divide longitudinally so as to present a pair of chromatids. Accordingly, if the cell begins with, as in man, 46 chromosomes, each cell resulting from mitotic division will also contain 46 chromosomes.

THE TISSUES

A group of similar cells united into a mass or structure is termed a **tissue.** The very same cells may arrange themselves in one way and yield a specific tissue. Another type of cell aggregate may make up a different kind of tissue. In short, because of the variety of cell types and the manner in which they can be grouped together, the wide selection of tissues characteristic of the more complex organism such as man is made available. Although, strictly speaking, a tissue is a collection of like cells, the term is employed rather loosely; thus tissues may be classified in several ways. For example, they may be grouped upon the basis of the origin of the cells. Accordingly there are **endodermal, mesodermal,** and **ectodermal** tissues. On the other hand, it is more convenient to consider them as **epithelial, connective, muscular,** and **nervous** tissues. Only epithelial and connective tissues are reviewed here. Muscular and nervous tissues are discussed in more appropriate chapters.

EPITHELIAL TISSUES

Epithelial tissue covers the surface of the body, and it also lines the body cavities. This type of tissue consists of one or more layers of cells with scarcely any intercellular substance so that the cells form a practically unbroken sheet or membrane. As a consequence of their position, it is largely through the epithelial cells that the organism comes into relation with the external world. They serve, as in the **epidermis** or **skin,** to enclose and protect the other parts of the body. Through their substance, and largely by their activity, the body absorbs its nutriment and excretes its waste products. They are also the active elements of glands which elaborate the secretions. From this brief survey, it can be seen that epithelial tissue is a highly important substance.

Types of Epithelial Tissue   These tissues, as already suggested, may be classified according to their embryological origin. Thus, **mesothelium** spreads over the walls of the thoracic and abdominal cavities, **endothelium** lines the blood vessels and heart, and **ectothelium** covers the surface of the body. It is more common, and also more useful, however, to classify epithelium according to the shape of the predominating cells. There is thus **squamous, cuboidal,** and **columnar** epithelium. In all types, if the cells are arranged in a single layer it is called **simple,** and **stratified** when there is more than one layer of cells. Thus, for example, there may be simple or stratified squamous epithelium or simple columnar epithelium.

Figure 2-3 portrays various types of epithelia. As the name suggests, the squamous type contains flat cells arranged irregularly in a mosaic pattern. Simple squamous epithelium lines the inner surface of the lungs. It is also found in the lens of the eye and in the inner ear. Stratified squamous epithelium is far more common. It forms the external layer of the skin and lines the mouth, pharynx, esophagus, vagina, and anal canal.

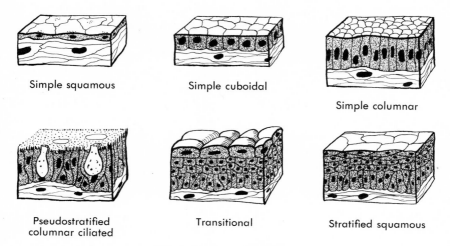

Simple squamous   Simple cuboidal   Simple columnar

Pseudostratified columnar ciliated   Transitional   Stratified squamous

FIG. 2-3   Types of epithelia.

Cuboidal epithelium is seen in Fig. 2-3 to consist of cube-shaped cells arranged in a very regular pattern. It is most commonly found lining small ducts and tubules.

There are many variations of columnar epithelium, but in all, the cells are taller than they are wide. Some of these cells possess hairlike projections called **cilia**. These fine hairs move in waves and thus cause the surface secretions to flow. This is an important mechanism. Such tissue is found in the trachea and bronchi. The simple columnar epithelium is found widely distributed in the digestive tract where it functions to secrete fluids and absorb digested foodstuffs.

Glands   Throughout the body there are masses of epithelial cells which have become specialized into secreting organs which are termed glands. Generally speaking, there are two types of glands: (1) **endocrine** and (2) **exocrine**. An endocrine gland does not have a duct, and for this reason it is also referred to as a **ductless gland.** It is a discrete organ which elaborates a specific substance directly into the blood stream for transportation to other parts of the body. These glands will be considered in the section devoted to endocrinology. The exocrine or **duct glands** have, as the term indicates, a duct which conveys the secretions from the secreting cells to a specific part of the body, usually very close to the gland, since most ducts are quite short.

Exocrine glands are depicted in Fig. 2-4. It can be seen that they are classified according to the configuration of the mass of secretory cells. If the mass is round, the gland is termed **alveolar;** if tubelike, **tubular.** On

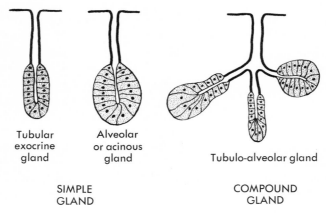

Tubular
exocrine
gland

Alveolar
or acinous
gland

Tubulo-alveolar gland

SIMPLE
GLAND

COMPOUND
GLAND

FIG. 2-4   Types of exocrine glands.

the other hand, if the duct is unbranched, the gland is said to be **simple** in contradistinction to the **compound** type in which the duct branches.

CONNECTIVE TISSUE

Connective tissue, as the term indicates, serves as a binding substance. It forms the framework of the various organs and connects them to other structures throughout the body. This type of tissue is easy to distinguish from epithelium because of the great abundance of intercellular substance. It will be recalled that epithelium consists of rows of cells placed one against the other, with little or no substance in between. Figure 2-5, on the other hand, shows that in connective tissue the intercellular mate-

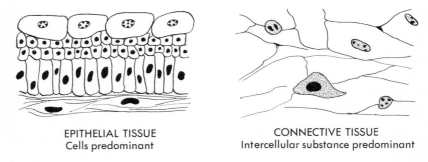

EPITHELIAL TISSUE
Cells predominant

CONNECTIVE TISSUE
Intercellular substance predominant

FIG. 2-5   Comparison of epithelial and connective tissue. Note how the cells predominate in the epithelial tissue but are few and far between in connective tissue.

rial dominates the entire structure. The cells are few and scattered. As a matter of fact, it is this character of the intercellular substance which is used to classify connective tissue.

Types of Connective Tissue   The cells which make up connective tissue, except in cartilage and bone, are called **fibroblasts.** In developing tissue they are quite numerous, but later they become less apparent and are almost obscured by the abundant intercellular substance. At this stage, **adipose, areolar, fibrous, cartilaginous,** and **bone** tissues may be identified.

Adipose tissue is fat. Each cell becomes filled with fat which pushes the cytoplasm off to one side (Fig. 2-6). The intercellular substance in this case consists of but a few fibers weaving in and about the fat-laden cells. Fat is widely distributed throughout the body, not uniformly but rather in a characteristic pattern which varies with the sex of the individual and the hormonal pattern. Fat serves a protective function, and it also is an excellent source of energy. However, the excessive accumulation of fat is deleterious.

Areolar connective tissue is the most common type. The term *areolar* means "space" and thus describes the characteristic spaces between the interlacing network of elastic fibers which make up the intercellular material (Fig. 2-7). This is the type of tissue which is found widely distributed around the organs. It serves to protect and support them. If such an organ is gently pulled out of its normal position, the strands of areolar tissue will be easily seen. The great spaces between the fibers permit the accumulation of fluid. When fluid accumulation becomes abnormal, the condition is termed **edema.**

Ligaments, tendons, and fasciae are excellent examples of **fibrous** connective tissue. The fibers are very dense, wide, and strong. The cells are

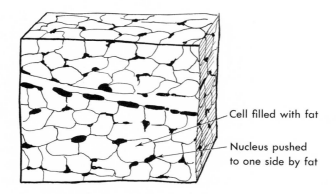

Cell filled with fat

Nucleus pushed to one side by fat

FIG. 2-6   Adipose tissue.

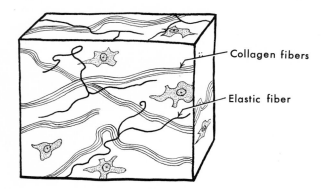

FIG. 2-7 Areolar tissue.

aligned between these tough strands. Because of the character of the fibers, this tissue possesses a glistening white appearance. Perhaps it is well at this time to emphasize that **tendons** attach muscles to bones, **ligaments** bind bones together at joints, and **fasciae** hold bundles of muscles together.

Cartilage, as shown in Fig. 2-8, is a smooth mass of intercellular substance in which the connective-tissue cells are embedded. Ordinarily, individual fibers cannot be discerned. They appear, rather, as a continuous, fused, homogeneous material. Cartilage is found in many structures throughout the body, where it plays an important supporting role. It also appears between bones to act as a cushion.

Bone is one of the hardest of all the tissues. It owes this quality to the presence of inorganic salts, primarily calcium phosphate, within the inter-

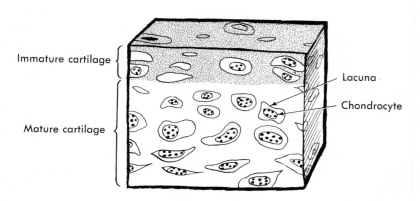

FIG. 2-8 Cartilage.

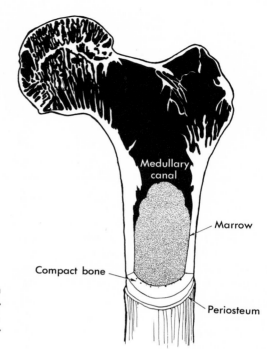

Medullary canal

Marrow

Compact bone

Periosteum

FIG. 2-9 Bone. A section has been cut away to disclose the medullary canal containing the marrow. The marrow is an important center for blood cell formation.

cellular substance. Bone is living tissue, though at first inspection one may be led to doubt this fact. It has the property of metabolism. It is constantly assimilating substances and converting them to new bone and, at the same time, tearing down and discarding old bone. If a long bone is cut longitudinally, it will be found to contain a **medullary canal** filled with **bone marrow** (Fig. 2-9). In the center of the canal the marrow is generally yellow, while at the ends of the bone it appears red. The **red marrow** is an important factory for many of the blood cells. The bones, except at the ends where they are in articulation with other bones, are covered by a fibrous membrane called the **periosteum.** This membrane is considered to be essential for the repair of the underlying bone following injury. If the bone is fractured, cells known as **osteoblasts,** which are found on the inner layer of the periosteum, function in a way that results in new bone being deposited between the severed ends.

The formation of bone is a very complex process, but an equally interesting one. In the very young embryo the skeleton is represented by cartilage and fibrous membranes. When the embryo is approximately eight weeks old, bone begins to develop in these two tissues. In other words, there are two sources of bone processes: (1) **endochondral** and (2) **intramembranous.**

Most of the bones of the body are formed from cartilage, that is, by **endochondral ossification.** The cartilage resembles a model of the future bone, in that it has the same general shape and proportions. These cartilaginous models are covered by fibrous connective tissue called **perichondrium.** The shaft or central part of each bone is called the **diaphysis.** Each end is termed the **epiphysis** (Fig. 2-10). In the perichondrium, there are fibroblasts which become **osteoblasts.** As the term indicates, the osteoblasts are responsible for the formation of bone. When they become active, a ring of bone is deposited around the diaphysis. The perichondrium is now properly called the **periosteum,** that is, it surrounds bone. While this is going on, blood vessels enter and spread throughout the cartilage which continues to grow while bone is being deposited. Eventually the cartilage, which is now surrounded by bone, disintegrates and bone takes its place, leaving only the central marrow. It can be seen in Fig. 2-10 that at this point there is a well-defined cartilaginous disk which separates the epiphysis from the diaphysis. Ultimately blood vessels enter the epiphysis and bone is laid down, extending from within out. Finally, at about the twentieth year of life, the cartilaginous disks which separate

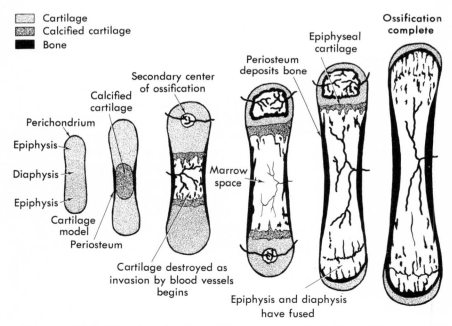

FIG. 2-10   Development of bone. (See text for explanation.)

the epiphysis from the diaphysis disappear and bone development is complete. After this time the bones are incapable of increasing in length; thus growth of the individual is complete.

Most of the bones of the face and cranium form by **intramembranous ossification.** There is no cartilaginous model. Instead, cells of the membranes send out strands to form a framework. Calcium salts then are deposited in this stroma to form bone. The membrane now becomes the periosteum. When the bone is complete, it is found to consist of an outer layer of very compact bone surrounding an inner core of bone of a more spongy nature.

Throughout life there is a constant "turnover" of bone. That is to say, new bone is deposited and old bone is reabsorbed constantly. There are two types of cells associated with this process: (1) **osteoblasts** and (2) **osteoclasts.** It is generally stated that osteoblasts are responsible for the formation of new bone, whereas osteoclasts bring about bone reabsorption. It is of considerable importance to realize that the new formation of bone, although it proceeds constantly throughout life, does so at slower and slower rates. It is for this reason that bones that have been fractured heal so much faster in young individuals than they do in older people.

CHARACTERISTICS OF LIVING TISSUES

It was mentioned earlier in this chapter that the chemical elements and their interrelationships give to protoplasm its fundamental property called **life.** Still it is very difficult to define exactly what is meant by the term. The best that can be done is to set out the more important characteristics of things recognized as possessing life.

If an ameba and a bit of pudding are placed side by side and studied with a microscope, the two are seen to possess some common properties. Chemical analysis would reveal the presence of many of the same elements. Yet the ameba is living and the pudding is not. What is the difference?

MOVEMENT

Perhaps the most obvious difference between the two is the capacity of the ameba to move. Unless some external force impinges upon the pudding it remains immobile, while the ameba manages to change shape and actually to travel from one point to another. Thus it is safe to conclude that one of the outstanding characteristics of living matter is the ability to move, although this is more generally true of animals than it is of plants.

GROWTH

If the mass of pudding and the ameba are observed over a period of time, it will be found that the ameba becomes larger whereas the pudding does not. This property of growth is common to all living forms, both animal and plant.

REPRODUCTION

Now if the observation is continued for an even longer interval, the examiner will find that instead of a single ameba there are two or more. In other words, this simple form of life has reproduced itself; it has multiplied. But in the meantime, the mass of pudding has remained unchanged, or perhaps disintegrated. Plants also possess this power of reproduction.

METABOLISM

Finally, if more elaborate techniques are used, it can be shown that the lowly ameba has the capacity of **metabolism.** This term *metabolism* literally means "to change," and by this process substances are changed from one form to another. For example, when one eats a steak, the animal protein is first broken down into the basic building blocks, the amino acids. The amino acids are absorbed by the intestinal tract and enter the blood stream. Then by a series of complex reactions, by the process of metabolism, these amino acids are built into a variety of substances. The steak is no longer recognizable. It has been modified; it has been metabolized. The single-celled ameba also possesses this property of metabolism. If a small piece of pudding is placed close to an ameba, the ameba will surround it, engulf the particle, and actually cause it to pass into the protoplasm which makes up the cell. And then, in short order, the pudding seems to vanish. It has been magically changed so that it is no longer distinguishable from the rest of the protoplasm. Plants also possess this property. Thus, the lawn is watered, and in due course the water is taken up by the roots and converted into the characteristic protoplasm of that grass. So it may be concluded that metabolism is another characteristic of living things.

Metabolism consists of (1) **anabolism** and (2) **catabolism.** Anabolism means to change into a higher or more complex form. For example, when the simple amino acids are converted into complex protein molecules, the process is spoken of as anabolism. Conversely, catabolism means to break down or to reduce to simpler forms. To use the protein example again, man is capable of converting complex protein molecules into simpler substances which are then further reduced to provide energy.

In short, the outstanding characteristics of living matter are (1) the **ability to move,** (2) the **capacity to reproduce,** (3) the **phenomenon of growth,** and (4) the **power of metabolism.**

SUMMARY

The basic unit of all living organisms is the **cell.** Cells are organized into masses known as **tissues.**

All cells contain **protoplasm,** the substance which possesses the characteristics of what is termed **life.** These include (1) **movement,** (2) **reproduction,** (3) **growth,** and (4) **metabolism.** The protoplasm of the cell exclusive of the nucleus is called **cytoplasm.** Protoplasm contains (1) **carbohydrates,** (2) **proteins,** (3) **fats,** (4) **inorganic constituents,** and (5) **water.** A selectively permeable **cell membrane** surrounds the cell. The **nucleus** contains the nucleic acids, **deoxyribonucleic acid (DNA)** and **ribonucleic acid (RNA).** DNA controls the formation of RNA which then serves as the model for the arrangement of amino acids in protein molecules. Other important cell constituents are the **Golgi body, mitochondria, lysosomes,** and the **endoplasmic reticulum.**

Cells divide either by **mitosis** or **amitosis.** In mitotic division, the chromatin strands form elongated **chromosomes** which bear the genes. The chromosomes split into **chromatids** which separate, half migrating to each new cell. Four distinct stages of mitosis are described. They are (1) **prophase,** (2) **metaphase,** (3) **anaphase,** and (4) **telophase.**

All tissues stem from **endoderm, mesoderm,** or **ectoderm** and may be so classified. It is more useful, however, to consider them as **epithelial, connective, muscular,** and **nervous** tissues. Epithelial tissue covers the surface of the body and lines its cavities and blood vessels. This type of tissue consists of one or more layers of cells with scarcely any intercellular substance in contrast to connective tissue which has an abundance of intercellular material. If there is but one layer of cells, the tissue is called **simple,** and **stratified** when there is more than one layer. Depending upon the cell shape, epithelium is classified as **squamous, cuboidal,** and **columnar.** Connective tissue varies in relation to its intercellular matrix. Thus there are **adipose, areolar, fibrous,** and **cartilaginous** connective tissue, as well as **bone.**

Ligaments, tendons, and **fasciae** are examples of fibrous connective tissue. Tendons attach muscles to bones, ligaments bind bones together at joints, and fasciae hold bundles of muscles together and in place. Long bones have a **medullary canal** filled with **bone marrow.** The bone is covered with **periosteum,** the underlayer of which contains **osteoblasts** essential to bone formation and repair.

QUESTIONS

1. What characteristics distinguish living from nonliving things?
2. What is cytoplasm?
3. What are the functions of DNA and RNA?
4. Describe the various steps of mitotic cell division.
5. How do the various types of tissues differ from each other?
6. Differentiate between ligaments and tendons.

SUGGESTED READING

Brachet, J., "The Living Cell," *Sci. American,* **205:**#3, 51–61, September 1961.

Gersh, I., and Catchpole, H. R., "The Nature of Ground Substance of Connective Tissue," *Persp. Biol. Med.,* **3:**#2, 282–319, Winter 1960.

Mazia, D., "How Cells Divide," *Sci. American,* **205:**#3, 101–120, September 1961.

Mommaerts, W. F. H. M., "The Muscle Cell and its Functional Architecture," *Am. J. Med.,* **35:**#5, 606–610, November 1963.

Slack, H. G. B., "Some Notes on the Composition and Metabolism of Connective Tissue," *Am. J. Med.,* **26:**#1, 113–124, January 1959.

Solomon, A. K., "Pores in the Cell Membrane," *Sci. American,* **203:**#6, 146–156, December 1960.

Physiology of Muscle

3

IT HAS BEEN EMPHASIZED that one of the characteristics of life, at least in so far as animal life is concerned, is the ability to change position. The unicellular forms move by altering their shape. Higher, more complicated organisms, however, depend upon **muscles** for movement. A muscle is tissue composed of bundles of contractile fibers. Because this tissue is so widespread throughout the body, it is well to consider the physiology of muscle in this orientation section.

There are three types of muscles: (1) **skeletal,** (2) **smooth,** and (3) **cardiac.** Since they differ both structurally and functionally, the histology and physiology of each type is discussed separately in this chapter.

Cardiac muscle, as the name implies, is found only in the heart. Skeletal muscle, on the other hand, has a much wider distribution. It is attached to the bones of the skeleton, making possible bodily movement. Smooth muscle is in many of the internal organs. For example, the urinary bladder and the stomach walls are largely made up of smooth-muscle tissue. These fibers also compose the iris of the eye and are found in the walls of some of the blood vessels.

SKELETAL MUSCLE

HISTOLOGY OF SKELETAL MUSCLE

Figure 3-1 depicts skeletal-muscle fibers. This type of muscle is also referred to as **striated** muscle, because of the characteristic crossbars, or striations, which are readily seen on microscopic examination. The individual muscle fiber is the structural and functional unit of the muscle. In Fig. 3-1 it can be seen that the fiber is relatively long and contains one or more nuclei. It is enveloped by a tubular sheath referred to as the **sarcolemma.** Groups of such fibers are held together in bundles by con-

37

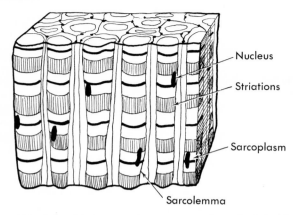

FIG. 3-1   Diagrammatic representation of skeletal muscle.

nective tissue. These bundles are termed **fasciculi.** A whole muscle consists of many fasciculi all bound together by more connective tissue.

With the electron microscope, the characteristic cross-striations may be analyzed in detail. It has become the practice to identify the various parts by letters (Fig. 3-2). The darkest area is termed the **A band.** The lighter area is the **I band.** The A band also has a light area which is labelled the **H band.** The very dark **Z line** is seen to traverse the I band. The entire region between two Z lines is called a **sarcomere.**

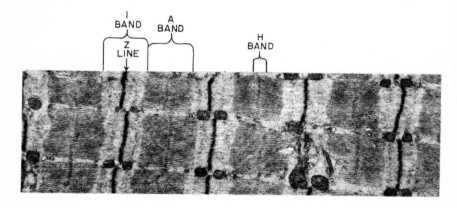

FIG. 3-2   Electron micrograph of skeletal muscle. A dense Z line is seen to bisect the center of each pale I band. A sarcomere is that portion of a myofibril bounded by two successive Z lines. In the center of each sarcomere is a dense A band which is bisected by an H zone. (Reproduced, with permission, from H. M. Price, *Amer. J. Med.,* **35:**589-605, 1963.)

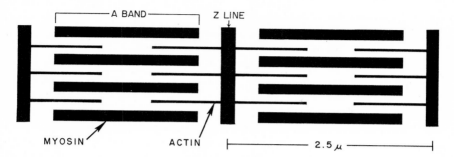

FIG. 3-3 Arrangement of myosin and actin. The actin filaments are attached to the cross membranes which are the Z lines seen in the electron micrograph. During contraction the actin and myosin filaments slide over one another, bringing the Z lines closer together.

The proteins **myosin** and **actin** are important constituents of muscle fibers. These proteins are arranged as filaments within the fiber as seen in Fig. 3-3. The Z lines are believed to be fine membranes to which the actin filaments are attached. The myosin filaments are much thicker than the actin filaments.

PHYSIOLOGY OF SKELETAL MUSCLE

During contraction the Z lines approach each other. This and other evidence has given rise to the concept that the myosin and actin filaments slide over one another. The exact mechanism responsible for this sliding action is still not certain.

Energy The energy required for the myosin and actin filaments to slide over one another and thus shorten the fiber, almost certainly comes from the hydrolysis of **adenosine triphosphate (ATP).** This is a highly important substance which contains so-called high-energy phosphate bonds. When these bonds are hydrolyzed—that is, broken—the energy is released. In some way, as yet unknown, this energy causes the myosin and actin filaments to slide over one another. ATP is considered to be the immediate source of energy for this response.

As ATP is hydrolyzed to release energy, it is just as quickly resynthesized; therefore, the total amount of ATP in the muscle at any time does not change significantly. Hence, there is a reversible reaction between ATP and ADP **(adenosine diphosphate).** The formation of ADP from ATP liberates energy as already emphasized, but the reverse reaction requires energy. It is supplied by the hydrolysis of **phosphocreatine.** Thus:

$$\text{Phosphocreatine} + \text{ADP} \rightleftharpoons \text{ATP} + \text{creatine}$$

Just as ATP must be regenerated for continued muscle action, so must phosphocreatine be re-formed. Here again energy is required, and this time it is supplied by ATP. In short, both the energy of contraction and the energy for the reconversion of phosphocreatine stem from ATP. Clearly, synthesis of ATP requires a source of energy other than the phosphocreatine reaction. This source is the reaction by which **glycogen** is converted to **lactic acid.**

To reconvert lactic acid to glycogen requires oxygen. The energy for this reconversion comes from, still again, ATP; but if oxygen is not available, the entire sequence grinds to a stop. Specifically, the oxygen is used to oxidize lactic acid to CO_2. Then, as shown in Fig. 3-4, ADP is converted to ATP which supplies the energy for the formation of glycogen from lactic acid as well as providing the energy for muscle contraction and the formation of phosphocreatine.

These interreactions become clearer upon careful examination of Fig. 3-4. It is seen that the only reaction that ATP does not participate

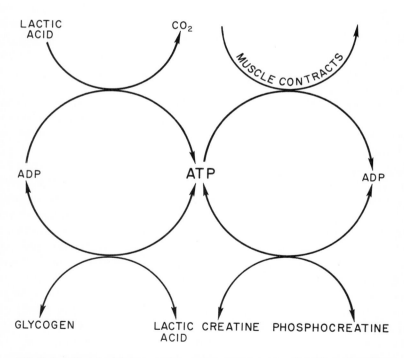

FIG. 3-4   Chemical interreactions essential to contraction. Note that ATP supplies the energy for every chemical reaction except the conversion of lactic acid to CO_2. This requires oxygen.

in is the conversion of lactic acid to carbon dioxide. This is the oxidative reaction requiring oxygen. If sufficient oxygen can be supplied, then all the other reactions can take place with the energy being supplied by ATP.

OXYGEN DEBT

In the schema just presented it was emphasized that only one of the reactions requires oxygen. The major source of energy is ATP; thus, so long as there is a store of ATP there is energy for contraction and because the conversion of ATP to ADP does not require oxygen muscle contraction can occur in the absence of oxygen, that is, **anaerobically.** Ultimately, however, the ATP will be depleted unless there is oxygen for the oxidation of lactic acid which supplies energy for the reconversion of ATP. Thus, in the presence of an adequate oxygen supply muscle contraction can continue for prolonged periods. On the other hand, during vigorous exercise, even though the supply of oxygen to the muscles increases tremendously, the demand is not satisfied. As a result, ATP is decreased and lactic acid accumulates. This explains the well known fact that even after one stops exercising he continues to breathe deeply and rapidly for sometime thereafter. It is during this post-exercise period that the accumulated lactic acid is oxidized and ATP re-formed. In other words, during vigorous exercise the muscles "live" beyond their means; they incur an oxygen debt. This debt is paid back later, during the recovery period. The exact magnitude of the debt may be calculated by determining the oxygen consumption immediately following exercise until the rate of consumption reaches the resting level. The excess oxygen utilization over and above this basal level is the oxygen debt (Fig. 3-5).

Steady State   During exercise it is impossible to detect any significant difference in the concentration of oxygen or carbon dioxide in the arterial blood. Yet, during exercise great quantities of oxygen are used by the muscles and even more carbon dioxide is produced. In other words, despite greatly altered activity, the status of the internal environment as represented by the arterial blood, remains constant; the homeostatic state is maintained. But in order to maintain this constancy, widespread adjustments are necessary. It should be clearly understood, even at this early stage, that the concentration of any substance in the blood simply represents a balance between intake or production on the one hand, and utilization, or loss, on the other. Thus, though during exercise more oxygen is taken out of the blood, at the same time more is entering. The mechanism may be compared to one's bank account. One may suddenly double his expenditures, but if his deposits are also doubled, the bank balance will remain unchanged, that is, steady. If exercise is not too

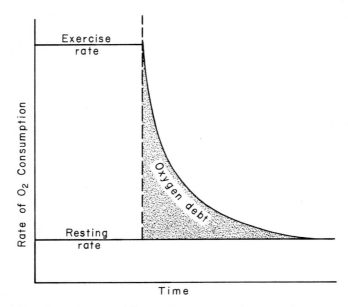

FIG. 3-5 Oxygen debt. During exercise the rate of O_2 consumption is much greater than at rest. After exercise terminates, the increased utilization continues. The difference between the actual consumption after termination of exercise and the resting rate is the oxygen debt.

severe, the oxygen demands can be met, the carbon dioxide removed, and the lactic acid oxidized as fast as it forms. The individual is, accordingly, said to be in a steady state.

Isotonic and Isometric Contraction   Contraction does not always involve an actual shortening of the fibers and movement of the bones to which the muscle is attached. This is apparent when one pushes against an immovable wall. Nothing moves; yet a great amount of energy is expended. This is an example of **isometric contraction. Iso** means "the same"; **metric** refers to "length." Isometric, then, means that the length remains the same. In this type of contraction there is no change in length of the muscle, but there is a sharp augmentation of tension. In **isotonic contraction,** on the other hand, the tension remains constant while the length of the fiber shortens. It should be realized that in either case the term contraction is properly used, and in both instances energy is utilized.

Heat Production   In isometric contraction all of the energy expended is recorded as heat. On the other hand, during isotonic contraction at least 25 per cent of the energy expenditure appears as mechanical work.

The rate of heat production during and after contraction of a muscle varies. Two general phases of heat production have been described: (1) the **initial heat** and (2) the **recovery heat.** Careful evaluation discloses that there is a burst of heat when a muscle contracts and another, but smaller emanation, when it relaxes.

Resting Potential   In Chap. 1 it was mentioned that electrical activity is associated with the activity of cells. This is certainly true of muscle cells. If one electrode is placed on the surface of the cell and the other within it, a current flows. The potential difference between the two electrodes is called the **resting potential,** or **membrane potential.** The latter term comes from the fact that the cell membrane is essential for the existence of the potential difference. The membrane is said to be **polarized.** Loss of the potential difference is termed **depolarization.** In the absence of oxygen, depolarization occurs. This indicates that the potential depends upon metabolic processes.

The ionic imbalance between the inside and the outside of the cell accounts for the resting potential. The concentration of potassium within the cell is greater than it is in the external environment, that is, in the plasma or the interstitial fluid which surrounds the cell. In contradistinction, sodium is more concentrated on the outside (Table 3-1). It can be seen from the average figures given for muscle that the inside of the cell has considerable potassium, but very low sodium and chloride. The deficit of inorganic anions is compensated for by organic anions.

**TABLE 3-1   Intra- and Extracellular Ions
(Average Values for Mammalian Muscle Cells)**

Ion	Intracellular, mEq/liter	Extracellular, mEq/liter
Potassium	155	4
Sodium	12	145
Chloride	5	105

The relative rate of diffusion of an ion through a membrane is spoken of as **conductance.** The conductance of potassium by the resting membrane is far greater than it is for sodium. Likewise, the chloride ion moves through the membrane with great ease. The cell membrane is virtually impermeable to the organic anions.

Just why the conductance of potassium is some 50 times greater than that of sodium is not completely understood. To be sure, the hydrated sodium ion is larger than the fully hydrated potassium ion, but this is probably not the only explanation of the significant difference in movement of the two ions through the membrane.

Table 3-1 shows the remarkable ionic imbalance between the inside and outside of the cell. First, consider the potassium ion. According to the concentration gradient, K+ should diffuse rapidly out of the cells. But as it does so, there is greater and greater negativity within the cell. Thus, as the K+ diffuses out, the concentration gradient causing it to exit decreases whereas at the same time the electrical gradient, which opposes movement in the outward direction, increases. Quickly, then, a balance of forces is reached and movement of the K+ ion ceases. More precisely, when these two opposing forces are equal, there is still movement of the ions, but now the rate of inward movement (influx) and the rate of outward movement (efflux) are equal. There is thus no net change of ion.

In the case of Na+, the same situation exists, but the forces are in the opposite direction. The concentration gradient drives sodium into the cell, but this creates an electrical gradient in the opposite direction. The same is true of Cl−.

The important point is that the electrical gradient, for each ion, depends upon the concentration gradient, that is, the ratio of the concentration of that ion on the two sides of the membrane. This is only true, however, if the membrane neither impedes the diffusion of the ion, or enhances it by active transport. It has been demonstrated that living membranes are quite capable of both impeding and enhancing transport.

If the concentration gradients were the sole determinants of the electrical gradient, then it could be calculated, using the concentrations given in Table 3-1, that each ion would have the following potential difference:

K	−96 mv
Na	+66 mv
Cl	−81 mv

Actual measurements show the inside of the cell to be negative to the outside. Accordingly, the electrical gradient will be outward for negative ions and inward for positive ions. For K+ the concentration gradient is outward and the electrical gradient is inward. For Na+, however, both the concentration gradient and the electrical gradient are inward. Yet, quite clearly there is far more Na+ outside the cell than inside. This fact has long been known, and it was at first assumed that the cell membrane must be impermeable to Na+. Radioisotope studies proved conclusively that the Na+ can pass through the cell membrane. In fact, there is relatively rapid influx and efflux, but because the efflux is so much more rapid, the Na+ imbalance is maintained. To put it another way, Na+ enters the cell, but it is just as quickly forced out. This discovery gave rise to the concept of the **sodium pump.** Just how the sodium pump operates is not known, but energy expenditure by the cell is required.

Accurate determination of the actual resting cell potential and the concentrations of K+ on both sides of the membrane discloses that the calculated potential for K+ based on the concentrations is generally higher than the actual determined potential. To put it another way, there is more potassium in the cell than one would expect on the basis of concentration and electrical gradients. This has been interpreted to mean that there is also a pump moving K+ into the cell. Whether or not there is a single pump which moves K+ and Na+ simultaneously, or whether there are two independent mechanisms, is not known. Recent evidence suggests that for every three Na+ pumped out there are two K+ transported into the cell. The important point is that by virtue of the active transport of Na+ and K+, ionic imbalance is maintained and, as a result, there is a resting potential.

In addition to the pumping activity for the ions, the permeability of the membrane to Na+ and K+ is a controlling factor in establishing the resting potential. If the permeability for Na+ increases, the resting potential decreases because of the inward movement of the ion. Conversely, if the permeability for K+ increases, then the membrane potential increases as the potassium ion diffuses more freely out of the cell. In the final analysis, the potential depends upon the concentration gradients established by active transport and the diffusion of these ions down their concentration gradients.

The actual resting potential varies from tissue to tissue and species to species. In nerve cells it is on the order of −60 to −70 mv. In muscle, especially mammalian muscle, it is generally somewhat higher, ranging up to about −90 mv.

Action Potential   So long as the cell is resting, in the case of a muscle cell, not contracting, the resting potential will remain constant. But when the muscle is stimulated to contract, then very striking changes occur in the potential difference across the cell membrane (Fig. 3-6). It is seen that there is a very rapid change in potential from the resting level up to zero and then to perhaps +20 or +30 mv. That is, there is a reversal of polarity in that the inside is now positive to the outside. This reversal is called the **overshoot.** With almost equal suddenness the potential then returns to the resting level and, in most cases, beyond. Ultimately it returns to exactly the resting level. All of these alterations together make up the **action potential.** The sharp rise and fall constitute the **spike**

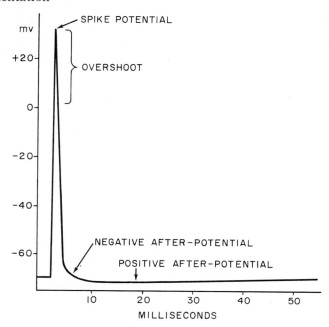

FIG. 3-6   Action potential. When the muscle is stimulated, the potential rapidly becomes positive and then negative again, forming the spike potential. All of the change, until the resting potential is reestablished, is termed the action potential.

potential. It will be noted (Fig. 3-6) that there is a short part of the action potential, just before it reaches the resting level, which is termed the **negative after-potential.** The part of the curve that falls below the resting level is termed the **positive after-potential.**

All of the changes that occur during the action potential are explicable on the basis of movement of K^+ and Na^+. When the cell is activated, its permeability for Na^+ is increased. The rapid influx of sodium causes the potential to become positive. If Na^+ diffused freely down its concentration gradient, it would create a potential of about $+66$ mv. However, the overshoot does not generally reach this value for two reasons: (1) the rapid influx of Na^+ does not persist; the influx slowing and the rate of efflux increasing, and (2) there is increased diffusion of K^+ out of the cell which creates a more negative potential. The initial inrush of Na^+ causes the rise in the spike potential. The slowing of Na^+ influx, increase in Na^+ efflux, and increase in K^+ efflux causes the fall in the spike potential. Because the sodium concentrations are reestablished before the K+ that has left the cell can be pumped back in, the potential becomes more negative than it is while the cell is at rest. Finally, the K+ is restored to the cell, and the resting potential is reestablished.

Excitation   Skeletal muscle may be excited by direct stimulation. It rarely contracts spontaneously. In the intact organism, all excitation is under the control of the nervous system. Just how the nerve fibers that innervate the muscle cause it to contract is not completely understood. It is known that when the nerve is active it liberates a chemical substance called **acetylcholine** at the junction of the nerve and muscle fibers. Acetylcholine has the ability to increase the permeability of the cell membrane for sodium ions. As a result, Na+ influx increases and sets into operation the sequence of events which depolarize the cell. In other words, the acetylcholine generates the action potential.

The most important unanswered question is how the depolarization of the muscle cell evokes contraction. The Z line is thought to play a role. It has been suggested that the Z line may liberate a substance which initiates the contractile process, but the evidence for this idea is scanty. All that is fairly certain is that following depolarization of the muscle, ATP provides energy for the reaction of actin and myosin, they slide over one another, and the muscle shortens.

Electromyography   The study of action potentials emanating from muscle is termed electromyography. The record of these action potentials is termed the **electromyogram (EMG)**. Electromyography is used clinically for many purposes including the analysis of a muscle following disruption of its innervation.

Response to Single Stimulation   Under controlled laboratory conditions, it is possible to analyze the response of a muscle to stimulation. Figure 3-7 shows a typical response to a single stimulation. It will be noted that a measurable period of time elapses after stimulation and before the muscle actually begins to contract. This brief interval is called the **latent period.** The true latent period is probably due to the time necessary for the chemical reactions of contraction to get under way. In man, the latent period may be considerable. This is not surprising when one realizes that bony levers are heavy and there is much inertia to overcome.

The recorded wave obtained in response to a single stimulus can be seen to be symmetrical (Fig. 3-7). The height of the wave is a measure of the **magnitude of the response.** And finally it will be noted that the wave is divided into a **contraction** and a **relaxation phase.**

The latent period, the magnitude of response, and the contraction and relaxation phases are all modified by many factors. For example, a partially fatigued muscle responds far differently from that of a rested

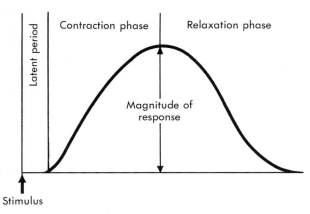

FIG. 3-7 Response of skeletal muscle to a single stimulus. Before the muscle contracts, there is after the stimulus a measurable period of time of a few milliseconds, called the latent period.

muscle. Changes in temperature and in acidity are also important determinants.

All-or-none Response It will be recalled that a muscle is made up of many fibers bound together by connective tissue. If a whole muscle is stimulated, it would be found that the magnitude of response increases with stronger and stronger stimuli. If only one muscle fiber is tested, however, this relationship does not obtain. When a very weak stimulus is applied, there is no response. Such a stimulus is called **subliminal** or **subminimal.** Then, as the stimulus is strengthened, a point is at last reached at which the muscle does respond. This is the **liminal, threshold,** or **minimal** stimulus. But now, as the stimulus is further increased, no change in magnitude of response takes place. In other words, a single muscle fiber either desponds maximally or it does not respond at all. This physiological property of skeletal-muscle fibers has been appropriately termed the **all-or-none response.**

This concept may seem at variance with human operations. It is well known that the force of contraction may be altered quite markedly. The answer lies in the fact that each muscle fiber obeys the all-or-none law but that *different fibers possess different thresholds.* Thus, if a very weak stimulus is applied to a muscle, only those fibers endowed with very low thresholds will be activated. As the strength of the stimulus is increased, more and more fibers are brought into play. This phenomenon is known as **recruitment** (Fig. 3-8). Obviously, the more fibers that are active, the greater will be the force of contraction of the whole muscle.

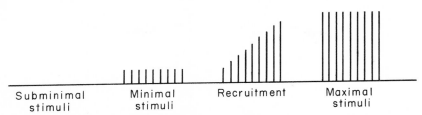

FIG. 3-8 Response of skeletal muscle to stimuli of increasing strength. A subminimal stimulus causes no response; a minimal stimulus, a minimal response. Then, as the strength increases, the response progressively increases due to recruitment. A maximal stimulus activates all the fibers so that increasing the strength beyond this level has no additional effect.

There is an apparent contradiction to the all-or-none law which should be reconciled. If a single muscle fiber is stimulated at a moderate rate, it will be found that the magnitude of response of the first few contractions steadily increases in a staircaselike manner. This ascending effect is called **treppe,** from the German word which means "staircase." But with repeated stimulation a landing or plateau is attained, and after that the response to each stimulus is exactly the same. Actually, the all-or-none law in its complete form states that single muscle fibers will respond at full capacity or not at all *as long as conditions are maintained constant.* When a muscle begins to contract after a period of rest, there are definite temperature and acidity changes. Just as soon as these conditions reach a constant state, the response of the muscle fiber is truly all-or-none.

Of singular importance in determining the magnitude of response is the **initial length** of the muscle fiber. Over a wide range the greater the initial length of the fiber, the more forceful is its contraction. Again, this observation in no way violates the all-or-none principle, because the law emphasizes the fact that conditions must be truly constant if it is to hold.

Man unknowingly makes good use of this physiological property of initial length of the muscle fiber. Greater weights can be lifted, for example, when the biceps muscles are extended (stretched) than when they are flexed. But it will be seen in Fig. 3-9 that there is a critical point beyond which the efficiency of the muscle diminishes.

Response to Repetitive Stimulation Thus far, only the response of a muscle to a single stimulus has been considered. It was seen that after a variable latent period the muscle shortens, reaches a definite magnitude, and then relaxes. Other important physiological attributes of skeletal muscle are disclosed by repetitive stimulation. If a muscle is stimulated a second time and if that second shock quickly follows the first stimulus, there is no additional response. The muscle fails to respond to a second

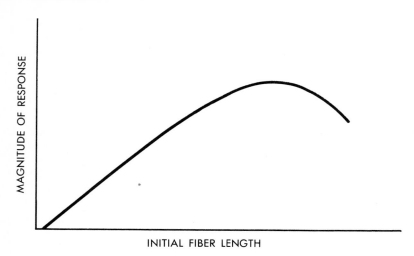

FIG. 3-9   Influence of initial length. The greater the length of the muscle fiber before contraction, the greater the magnitude of contraction up to a critical point. Beyond that point the magnitude diminishes.

stimulus. It is truly unresponsive, that is, **refractory.** The muscle now is said to be in the **absolute refractory state.** If the second shock is applied a fraction of a second later, that is, during the contraction phase, it is possible to elicit a second response from the muscle, provided a stronger-than-threshold stimulus is used. During this brief interval following the absolute refractory period, the muscle is still somewhat reluctant to respond, but if vigorously stimulated it will react. During this period the muscle is said to be in the **relative refractory state.** Finally, if the second stimulus is introduced at a still later time, it is possible to bring about a second contraction even using the threshold stimulus. The sensitivity of the muscle has, in fact, returned to normal.

Figure 3-10 demonstrates that the magnitude of contraction is increased by introducing a second stimulus during the contraction phase which results from the first stimulus. The second wave has been added to the first. The addition of contraction waves is known as **summation** of contractions. The phenomenon of summation might seem to violate the all-or-none law. This is not true. The all-or-none law states unequivocally that it is applicable only so long as conditions are kept constant. It has been learned that the length of the fiber at the time of stimulation determines the magnitude of response. Clearly, when the muscle is excited during the contraction phase, its length is less than it was at complete

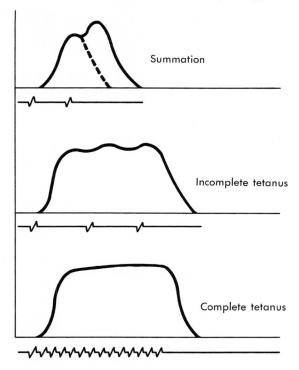

Summation

Incomplete tetanus

Complete tetanus

FIG. 3-10 Summation and tetanus. In the upper drawing it is seen that a second stimulus introduced during the contraction phase causes a second contraction that reaches a greater amplitude than the initial contraction. If the frequency of stimuli is great enough, the muscle will not have time to relax, thus contraction will be sustained (tetanus).

rest. It will be noted that the magnitude of the second response is really smaller than that of the first, but the total response is greater because the two contractions are added together.

The maximal response of a muscle may be elicited by employing a volley of stimuli so timed as to prevent the muscle from ever reaching the relaxation phase. Figure 3-10 shows that, if the rate of stimulation is fast enough, the muscle contracts maximally and remains in that state as long as the stimuli continue, or until the muscle fatigues. This smooth, sustained, maximal contraction is termed **tetanus.** Tetanus may be **complete** or **incomplete.** These are relative terms. If the resulting wave is straight and smooth, then the muscle is in complete tetanus. If the stimuli are so spaced as to allow the muscle some small degree of respite between the individual contractions, an undulating wave is produced. This is a demonstration of incomplete tetanus.

From this discussion of the physiological properties of muscle it should be clear that man uses his muscles to produce their greatest work when the fibers are at their optimal length, when the stimulus applied to them is maximal (to excite all the fibers simultaneously), and when the frequency of stimuli is high.

Muscle Tonus   It must be borne in mind that, although the maximal muscular response is obtained when all the component fibers act in concert, a weaker but still sustained contraction is possible when groups of muscle fibers contract asynchronously. In man, at least during the waking hours, the muscles have at least some of their units contracted. Assume that only 10 per cent of the muscle fibers are active. Then the muscle will be partially contracted. The muscle will feel firm; it will resist being stretched. The muscle, in this state, is said to display tonus. Tonus means tension; a muscle with tonus exerts a force, resists stretch. Muscle tonus may be defined as **involuntary resistance to passive stretch.**

As has been stated, in normal man all muscles exhibit tonus. This condition is maintained without significant fatigue because there is a system of rotation. At any one moment some of the fibers are in a state of contraction; others are relaxed and rested so as to take up their work in the next moment. A division of labor is indeed fortunate, for without it, standing erect would be extremely difficult, if not impossible.

In the clinic, the physician routinely examines the tonus of the muscles. This is because in so doing he can learn a great deal about many diseases. For example, there are numerous conditions in which the muscles become completely devoid of tonus. The muscles appear soft and flabby and do not resist being stretched. The muscles in such a state (and this is found in infantile paralysis) are described as being **atonic.** At the other extreme are those muscles which are tightly contracted. The muscles (and this may occur in persons suffering with a stroke) are said to be **hypertonic.**

Muscle Fatigue   Fatigue is a common experience. If a muscle is worked for a long period of time, a point is reached at which it is truly impossible for the muscle to continue to perform. From what has already been said about the chemistry of muscular contraction, it should be apparent that, if the primary constituents are utilized more rapidly than they are resynthesized, contraction must ultimately cease. At this point there will be a shortage of the organic phosphate compounds and of glycogen and an abundance of lactic acid. Until the basic substances can be replenished, the muscle must remain in a completely exhausted state.

ABNORMALITIES OF SKELETAL MUSCLE

Paralysis   Probably one of the most frequently encountered muscle abnormalities is **paralysis.** The term is derived from a Greek stem meaning "disable." Paralysis, by definition, *is a nervous affliction characterized by a loss of motor function.* Paralysis, then, may be defined as a loss of voluntary movement.

Growth and Waste   One of the earliest observations a child makes is that the more he uses a muscle, the larger it grows. Adolescents delight in flexing their biceps for general approbation. The fact is that muscle enlarges in proportion to the work load. Actually, there is no increase in the number of individual fibers. The total enlargement is simply due to the growth of each muscle fiber. This phenomenon of growth in relation to work is not restricted to muscle; it is common to many different organ systems. Any enlargement of living tissue in response to increased activity is termed **hypertrophy.** It is also possible for a tissue to enlarge as a result of an increase in the **number,** not size, of the cells. This is referred to as **hyperplasia.** Such is the case in tumors.

Decreased activity inevitably leads to wasting. The size of individual cell diminishes. The reduction in size of a tissue is referred to as **atrophy.** If a perfectly normal arm, for example, is immobilized in a plaster cast, all the muscles waste, somewhat, because of the lack of use of those muscles.

Fibrillation   After denervation of a muscle, asynchronous contractions of individual fibers occur. Such fibrillations are thought to be caused by acetylcholine circulating in the blood. If this is true, it means that the normally innervated muscle is not sensitive to the small quantities of circulating acetylcholine and in some way the muscle becomes more sensitive following denervation.

REGENERATION OF SKELETAL MUSCLE

Skeletal muscle apparently possesses the ability to regenerate. It has been shown that for two days following injury to the muscle there are no signs of regeneration. Following this period, however, there is considerable activity observable at the site of damage. Microscopic examination of the area reveals new protoplasmic shoots moving from the uninjured muscle into the traumatized region. Ultimately, new muscle fibers form.

SMOOTH MUSCLE

HISTOLOGY OF SMOOTH MUSCLE

Figure 3-11 depicts typical **smooth-muscle fibers.** It will be noted that they differ from skeletal muscle in that they do not have cross striations and that each cell possesses only one nucleus. The fibers are bound together by connective tissue to make up the walls of the blood vessels, the respiratory passages, the alimentary canal, and the genitourinary tract. Smooth muscle is also found in the skin, in the eye, and in glands.

Skeletal muscle is innervated by the so-called **somatic nervous system** and can be contracted voluntarily. Smooth muscle, in contradistinction, is innervated by the **autonomic nervous system.** Generally speaking, smooth muscle cannot be caused to contract by the will.

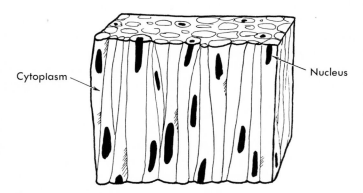

Cytoplasm

Nucleus

FIG. 3-11   Diagrammatic representation of smooth muscle. Note the single nucleus and lack of striations.

Although smooth muscle has long been differentiated from skeletal muscle by the absence of striations, under the electron microscope striations can often be discerned. Thus, although there is undeniably a difference in arrangement, myosin and actin filaments are undoubtedly present and are responsible for the muscle shortening.

PHYSIOLOGY OF SMOOTH MUSCLE

Infinitely less is known about smooth-muscle physiology than about the properties of skeletal muscle. This is largely because the smooth-muscle behavior of various organs is erratic. Even smooth-muscle tissue taken from the same organ refuses to react in a consistent manner. As one frustrated observer remarked, "Smooth muscle accommodates itself rather than the investigator!"

Contraction   The contraction of smooth muscle differs markedly from that of skeletal muscle. The response is measurably slower, and following a single stimulus the contraction may persist for several seconds. Most surprising is the fact that smooth muscle often contracts quite spontaneously. Even if the muscle is completely denervated, it may continue to shorten and relax rhythmically.

Action Potentials   The action potential associated with contraction of smooth muscle varies from moment to moment in the same muscle and from muscle to muscle. In some smooth muscles the action potential resembles that of skeletal muscle in that there is rapid repolarization. In others, the action potential is completely different. In addition, the resting potential also varies greatly. In some cases it is only about -30 mv, whereas at other times it is as great as -75 mv. Quite often a progressive change in the resting potential is noted between contractions. In Fig. 3-12 it is seen that after repolarization there is a slow depolarization which is culminated by the onset of the action potential. This preliminary slow depolarization is termed the **prepotential.**

Tonus   Smooth muscle exhibits tonus, but tension can persist even in the completely denervated organ. It should be recalled that when skeletal

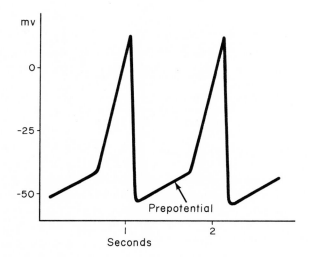

FIG. 3-12 Smooth muscle action potentials. Note that the duration of the action potential in smooth muscle is considerably longer than it is in skeletal muscle. Also, in some instances, as shown here, there is a prepotential, that is, a slow rise until the typical spike occurs.

muscle is denervated it becomes paralyzed and, in that state, ceases to function and atrophies. But smooth muscle does not waste. It continues to contract and does, in fact, maintain its tonus. To add to the confusion, the tonus of smooth muscle varies markedly. In the urinary bladder, for example, the tension remains relatively constant regardless of the quantity of urine present. This can only mean that, even though the smooth muscle of the bladder wall is greatly stretched by the accumulating urine, it progressively relaxes to accommodate the greater volume and at the same time maintains a constant tension. This is an inherent property of smooth muscle. In short, tonus is intrinsic to smooth muscle while the tonus of skeletal muscle is dependent on its innervation.

Accommodation Smooth muscle exhibits the property of changing length if stretched. In other words, instead of resisting the stretch by contracting (tonus) it may relax and lengthen. For example, in the bladder, as more and more urine accumulates, the smooth muscle wall relaxes sufficiently so that the pressure within the bladder remains practically unchanged. This ability of smooth muscle to relax in response to stretch is termed accommodation, or **plasticity.** Thus, in the bladder, a larger volume is accommodated with little change in intravesicular pressure. The same is generally true in other structures composed of smooth muscle.

REGENERATION OF SMOOTH MUSCLE

Very little is known concerning the ability of smooth muscle to regenerate. Nonetheless, the impression persists that new muscle fibers may form in sites of injury.

CARDIAC MUSCLE

HISTOLOGY OF CARDIAC MUSCLE

Skeletal-muscle fibers are distinct, and clearly delineated by a fibrous sheath called the **sarcolemma.** The fibers of the cardiac muscle, in contradistinction, appear to fuse into one another. The limits are vague, and the numerous nuclei seem to bear no relationship to individual fibers. For this reason, cardiac muscle has been described as a **syncytium,** a term derived from the prefix *syn-*, meaning "together," and *cytium,* referring to "cells." Syncytium means then that the cells are truly together. Electron microscopy, however, fails to support this classic description. Under the electron microscope practically all of the fibers are seen to be surrounded by a membrane and are seemingly well insulated from contiguous ones. It remains a fact, nonetheless, that even though cardiac muscle may not be a syncytium, it contracts as one would expect a syncytial muscle to contract, as will be described below. One explanation is that the **inter-calated** discs are responsible for conducting the action potential from one fiber to another. Intercalated discs are thickened and tortuous membranes which usually cross cardiac muscle in a stepwise manner. As a result of such conduction, activity of one cardiac muscle fiber would cause the firing of all of them.

PHYSIOLOGY OF CARDIAC MUSCLE

All-or-none Law   It will be recalled that, if the individual skeletal-muscle fibers are stimulated, they react maximally or not at all. They thus obey the so-called **all-or-none law.** Cardiac muscle also abides by this law, but it is not necessary to separate individual fibers. The entire muscle either reacts to a stimulus maximally or does not respond at all. Graded stimuli do not produce graded responses of cardiac muscle. So long as conditions are maintained constant, the cardiac muscle obeys this law.

Action Potentials   The action potentials associated with the contraction of cardiac muscle differ considerably from those of skeletal muscle (Fig. 3-13). The inside of mammalian cardiac muscle is negative (about −80 mv) to the outside. During activation there is the typical rapid up-

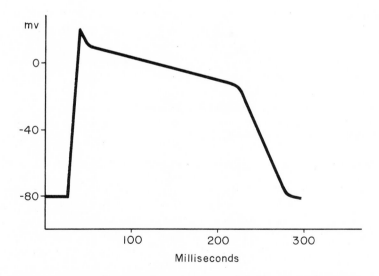

FIG. 3-13   Cardiac muscle action potential. The most character-istic aspect is the very long period of repolarization. Because repolarization is so prolonged, the absolute refractory period extends throughout the entire contraction phase.

swing of the spike, an overshoot, and then the process of repolarization begins. But it is noted that instead of lasting only a millisecond or two, in cardiac muscle it lasts at least 200 msec. When the contraction of cardiac muscle and the action potential are recorded simultaneously, it is seen that the muscle finishes its contraction phase and is well into the relaxation phase before repolarization is complete. Why repolarization of cardiac muscle differs so strikingly from skeletal muscle is not known.

Refractory Periods   The refractory periods in cardiac muscle persist much longer than they do in skeletal muscle. In cardiac muscle the absolute refractory period lasts throughout the entire contraction phase. This is important because while cardiac muscle is contracting it cannot be made to respond a second time. Accordingly, summation and tetanus cannot occur. If the heart were to go into complete tetanus, its pumping action would cease and death would follow.

Inherent Rhythmicity   If skeletal muscle is denervated, it is paralyzed. It cannot be contracted spontaneously. Cardiac muscle is not under the control of the will, and although it is regulated by its innervation, it will continue to contract rhythmically when denervated. Cardiac muscle has an inherent rhythmicity. The rhythm may be altered by changing the temperature or other environmental factors. The mechanism responsible for this inherent rhythmicity is not understood.

Energy of Contraction   Apparently the same chemical transformations occur in both skeletal and cardiac muscle to supply the energy of contraction. Thus the heart produces lactic acid and utilizes oxygen by these reactions. Under normal conditions, the rest period of the heart after each beat is long enough to permit complete recovery of the original essential compounds. This allows the heart to beat steadily for years. But in some diseased conditions, the heart rate becomes so rapid, the rest periods so abbreviated, that there is not adequate time for the resynthesis of the basic compounds. As a result, the heart tires and ceases to beat.

REGENERATION OF CARDIAC MUSCLE

Cardiac muscle has the ability to hypertrophy, that is, to increase the size of the fibers. However, there is no evidence that new fibers can be formed. In addition, it is well known that when cardiac muscle is injured, scarring, consisting of connective tissue, occurs. Thus, it is generally held that cardiac tissue, unlike skeletal and probably smooth muscle, is not capable of regeneration. This inability is of practical concern in cases of coronary occlusion. In such instances blood cannot flow through the blocked vessel to the heart muscle, and therefore the area supplied is deprived of oxygen and dies. This region of the heart can no longer contract. Connective tissue takes the place of the dead heart muscle and forms a scar. If the region is relatively large, the remaining functional heart muscle may prove inadequate to pump sufficient blood for survival.

SUMMARY

Histologically three type of muscles are recognized: (1) **skeletal,** (2) **smooth,** and (3) **cardiac.** The individual fiber in skeletal muscle is a separate unit enveloped in a sheath called the **sarcolemma.** Such fibers make up **fasciculi,** and many fasciculi are united by connective tissue.

The energy of contraction is supplied by a series of chemical reactions. The prime conversion is the breakdown of **adenosine triphosphate. Phosphocreatine** supplies the energy for resynthesis of adenosine triphosphate. **Glycogen** is converted to lactic acid in order to re-form phosphocreatine. Oxygen oxidizes lactic acid to furnish the energy for the reconversion of the remaining lactic acid to glycogen. Through these reactions, muscle proteins, **myosin** and **actin** slide over one another, which shortens the muscle. Since the basic conversions can proceed anaerobically, an **oxygen debt** may accrue.

Muscle may undergo **isotonic** or **isometric** contraction. Before a muscle responds to a stimulus, there is a measurable delay, called the **latent period.** The actual response consists of the **contraction** and **relaxation phases.** A muscle fiber either responds maximally or does not react at all. This **all-or-none law** pertains in skeletal-muscle fibers so long as all conditions are maintained constant. In cardiac muscle, the entire muscle obeys this rule. In a whole skeletal muscle, gradations of response are made possible by **recruitment.**

Both skeletal and cardiac muscle exhibit **absolute** and **relative refractory periods,** but in the heart these phases are much longer. For this reason, cardiac muscle cannot display **tetanus.**

Tonus is the involuntary resistance to passive stretch. If the muscle is flabby and does not respond to stretch, it is termed **atonic.** A **hypertonic** muscle overreacts. If a skeletal muscle cannot be moved voluntarily, it is said to be **paralyzed.** Great use of a muscle results in **hypertrophy,** disuse in **atrophy.**

Little is known concerning the properties of smooth muscle. This type of tissue is normally innervated by the **autonomic nervous system,** but it is capable of response even after the nerves are cut. The contraction of smooth muscle is much slower than that of skeletal fibers. Smooth muscle also displays tonus, but this state does not depend upon the integrity of its nerve supply as it does in skeletal muscles.

The potential difference between the inside and outside of a cell is termed the **resting potential.** Because it depends upon the characteristics of the cell membrane, it is also referred to as the **membrane potential.** Cellular metabolic processes maintain ionic imbalance between the two sides of the membrane. Sodium is actively extruded from the cell, and potassium is actively transported into the cell. The resulting ionic imbalance creates the resting potential. When the cell becomes active, a series of changes occur in this potential. The sum total of all the changes is referred to as the **action potential.** It is made up of the **spike potential,** the **negative after-potential,** and the **positive after-potential.**

QUESTIONS

1. How are the three types of muscles differentiated?
2. Outline the basic chemical reactions responsible for muscle contraction.
3. Explain the difference between isotonic and isometric contraction.
4. What does the term relative refractory period mean?
5. Explain the genesis of the resting potential.
6. Why does tetanus of cardiac muscle rarely if ever occur?
7. What is an action potential?

SUGGESTED READING

Hatcholsky, A., and Lifson, S., "Muscle as a Machine," *Sci. American,* **190:**#3, 72–74, March 1954.

Huxley, A. F., "Muscle," *Ann. Rev. Physiol.,* **26:** 131–152, 1964.

Lehninger, A. L., "How Cells Transform Energy," *Sci. American,* **205:**#3, 63–73, September 1961.

Price, H. M., "The Skeletal Muscle Fiber in the Light of Electron Microscopic Studies," *Am. J. Med.,* **35:**#5, 589–605, November 1963.

Sacks, J., "The Role of Adenosine Triphosphate in Muscular Contraction, *Persp. Biol Med.,* **7:**#3, 285–295, Spring 1964.

Stumpf, P. K., "ATP," *Sci. American,* **188:**#4, 85–92, April 1953.

Nervous System

Perception

4

THE NERVOUS SYSTEM is considered early in this study of the human organism because so many bodily functions are influenced by nervous activity. It is composed of two major components: (1) the **central nervous system** and (2) the **peripheral nervous system.** The former includes the **brain** and the **spinal cord.** The latter embraces the **cranial nerves,** the **spinal nerves,** and the **autonomic nervous system.**

All our knowledge depends on **perception.** Perception is defined as *knowledge through the senses of the existence and properties of matter and the external world.* Without perception there can be no knowledge, no great scientific discoveries, no cataclysmic inventions. Of fundamental import to perception are the senses. Normally we use more than one sense to gain knowledge of the external world. For example, even with the eyes closed, one can fondle an object and learn much about its properties. It is possible to tell if it is round or flat, long or short, hot or cold. One can ascertain whether it is of metal, stone, wood, or rubber. And from such information it is possible to identify or describe the object with amazing accuracy. Of course, we ordinarily keep our eyes open, and when we handle such an object we not only feel it but see it as well. We may tap it and from the sound produced learn something of its composition. The point is that we can gain information through several senses simultaneously. Through the constellations of our senses, the steady growth of knowledge becomes possible.

The senses, however, are not utilized exclusively for the acquisition of knowledge. They serve for protection, for pleasures, and for the integration of bodily functions.

The object of this chapter is to discuss the basic mechanisms by which perception is made possible. The special senses, such as vision and audition, will be considered later. Our interest at this point is to learn how a simple stimulus such as heat is recognized by the individual as being

63

heat, how a sharp blow is correctly labeled pain, how, even with our eyes closed, we know the position of each limb.

RECEPTORS

We all know that sound, in the form of electrical impulses, may be transmitted by telephone wires. But it should also be clear that in order to have electrical impulses there must be some mechanism for **transforming** sound waves into electrical impulses. In the telephone, the receiver carries out this transformation. In man, impulses are transmitted by nerves, but, as in the telephone, in order to have electrical impulses there must be some mechanism for transforming the various types of stimuli into impulses. The **receptors** carry out this transformation. A receptor, by definition, is *specialized nervous tissue sensitive to a specific change in the environment*. The change in the environment constitutes the adequate stimulus. For example, if a finger is placed in hot water, the change in the temperature (from the room air temperature to the temperature of the hot water) activates an appropriate receptor in the skin of the finger. The individual is able to perceive warmth.

A moment's reflection will convince the reader that there must be more than one type of receptor in the body. This is so because we can perceive not only warmth, but pain and cold, touch and pressure. Actually there are receptors for all these modalities of sensation.

ANATOMICAL CONSIDERATIONS

The receptor has just been defined as specialized nervous tissue sensitive to a specific change in the environment. The body is replete with receptors. Some of them lie close to the body surface and accordingly serve to perceive changes in the external environment. These are appropriately called **exteroceptors.** Others are strategically placed throughout the internal linings of the body and are thus admirably suited to report changes in the internal environment. These are logically referred to as **interoceptors.**

It will be emphasized that each receptor reacts to a specific type of stimulus. For example, a receptor designed to respond to changes in temperature will not normally be activated by pressure. Likewise, visual receptors cannot be excited by sound. Clearly, then, there must be a different type of receptor for each type of stimulus. There are receptors for pain, touch, cold, warmth, and pressure as well as receptors associated with the special senses of vision, gustation, audition, and olfaction.

Figure 4-1 shows a section of the skin containing some types of receptors. It will be noted that there are clear morphological differences.

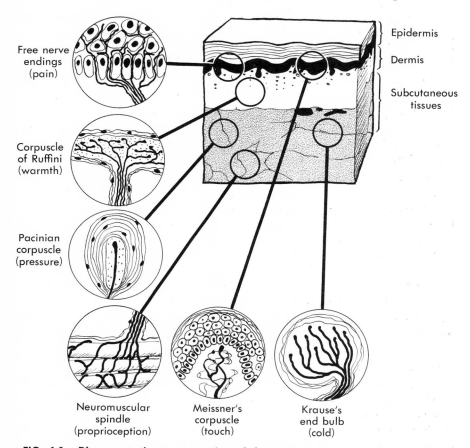

Free nerve
endings
(pain)

Epidermis

Dermis

Subcutaneous
tissues

Corpuscle
of Ruffini
(warmth)

Pacinian
corpuscle
(pressure)

Neuromuscular
spindle
(proprioception)

Meissner's
corpuscle
(touch)

Krause's
end bulb
(cold)

**FIG. 4-1   Diagrammatic representation of the exteroceptors in the skin and sub-
cutaneous tissue.**

There are receptors sensitive to cold, warmth, pressure, touch, and pain.
In addition, there is an important group which is sensitive to changes in
movement, position, and tension. These receptors have been termed
proprioceptors. In subsequent chapters the vital role that proprioceptors
play in the coordination of bodily function will become clear.

PHYSIOLOGICAL CONSIDERATIONS

Mechanism of Response   A transducer is an instrument that converts
one form of energy to another form. Receptors are biological transducers.
They convert the energy of the adequate stimulus into an electrical impulse that activates its associated neuron. The electrical impulse pro-

duced by the receptor is termed the **receptor potential,** or the **generator potential.** The magnitude of the receptor potential varies with the intensity of the stimulus. If the potential does not exceed 10 to 15 mv, the neuron is usually not activated.

It is thought that the adequate stimulus brings about an increase in permeability in the receptor. In the case of the Pacinian corpuscle, the permeability changes and the receptor potential occur in the central core of the receptor. This is probably true of other receptors as well. Most likely it is the surrounding structure of the receptor which permits it to respond to a particular type of stimulus and only to that type.

Specificity   It has already been stated that a receptor reacts to a change in the environment and only to that particular change for which it is designed. Thus, the first important physiological property of the receptor is specificity. That is, each receptor reacts specifically to a particular type of stimulus. However, under abnormal conditions it is possible to fire some receptors with other stimuli. For example, if one receives a blow on the eye, he often reports "seeing stars." The blow actually stimulates the receptors for vision, and the individual perceives light. But within the normal physiological sphere of changes a stimulus activates only a specific receptor.

Adaptation   The second physiological property of the receptor is **adaptation.** It is common experience that receptors adapt to a change in the environment. The individual, for example, is aware of the warmth of a fluid, but if the hand is kept immersed for a period of time, the feeling of warmth disappears. Likewise, if the water temperature is slowly increased, the individual will not perceive any temperature change until the fluid becomes quite hot. Two important conclusions may be formed from these observations. First, a receptor adapts to a stimulus. Second, in order to stimulate a receptor, the rate of change in the environment must be faster than the rate of adaptation.

But not all types of receptors adapt as readily or to the same degree. For example, touch receptors adapt very rapidly; pain receptors adapt hardly at all. Therefore, a few minutes after an individual dresses in the morning, he is no longer conscious of his clothes. However, if a pin were to lodge in one of the seams, adaptation would not occur and he would search until the painful stimulus was removed.

Rate of Firing   It should be recalled that below a specific intensity of stimulation the receptor does not respond. When the receptor does react, it produces a burst of activity. Within limits, the rate at which the receptor fires has been shown to be a function of the intensity of stimulation. The stronger the stimulus, the greater the rate of firing. This relationship between stimulation and rate of firing is the third important physiological property of receptors.

Different receptors have individual thresholds. Changes in threshold and rate of firing account for man's ability to sense changes in stimulus intensity. Let us consider the appreciation of changes in temperature. In any area of the skin there is a mass of warmth receptors. These receptors have varying thresholds, so that some of them are easily stimulated whereas others require a much greater change in temperature to be activated. In other words, a stimulus of low intensity (lower temperature) will activate only those receptors which possess the lowest threshold. As the intensity of stimulation increases (rising temperature), more and more receptors will be activated. Logically, the more receptors firing, the greater will be the number of impulses reaching the brain per unit time. The brain then interprets this greater rate of firing as an increase in the intensity of stimulation. Thus, if the hand is immersed in several beakers of water one after the other, it is easy for the subject to perceive the differences and arrange the beakers according to the temperature of the water. The hottest water fires the greatest number of warmth receptors; the tepid water activates only those warmth receptors with very low thresholds.

It has been emphasized that the greater the intensity of stimulation, the greater will be the rate at which the receptor responds. It is thus

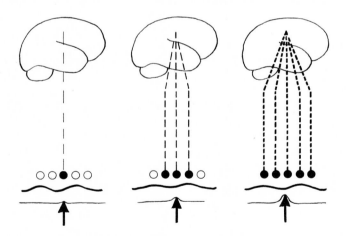

FIG. 4-2   Perception of changes in intensity of stimuli. As the intensity increases, more receptors become active and each receptor fires more rapidly. As a result of both changes, a greater number of impulses per unit time reaches the cerebral cortex.

possible for a receptor to be fired only once per minute or to be excited hundreds of times per minute. It will be recalled that the brain interprets an increase in rate of the impulses as an increase in the intensity of stimulation. The same result is obtained whether that increase is brought about by one receptor firing more rapidly or more receptors firing simultaneously.

In brief, then, changes in intensity of stimulation are appreciated by either or both of two mechanisms: (1) change in the number of receptors which are firing and (2) change in the rate of firing of each receptor (Fig. 4-2).

THE NEURON

The receptor, in response to a change in the environment, excites its associated neuron. It is the neuron which then propagates the resulting impulse along its length.

ANATOMICAL CONSIDERATIONS

Again before proceeding it is advisable to introduce and define a few terms. The student should have clearly in mind the difference between a neuron and a nerve. The **neuron** is the structural and functional unit of the nervous system. A **nerve** is a cord made up of thousands of neurons and held together by a connective-tissue sheath. A **tract** is a pathway of neuron processes in the central nervous system.

Multipolar Neuron   Anatomically, a neuron may consist of a **cell body,** of one long process known as the **axon** or **axis cylinder,** and of one or more shorter branches called **dendrites** (see Fig. 4-3). Such neurons are known as **multipolar** neurons.

Unipolar Neuron   Other neurons possess only one process or pole. This process divides close to the cell body. One branch, the **peripheral process,** conveys impulses from the periphery toward the cell body. The other branch, the **central process,** conducts the impulse toward the spinal cord or brain stem. These are termed **unipolar** neurons.

PHYSIOLOGICAL PROPERTIES

Conduction   The outstanding characteristic of the neuron is its ability to conduct an impulse. However, a neuron does not initiate the impulse. The impulse is initiated by the receptor. It is the activity of the receptor that fires the neuron. Once the neuron is activated, it rapidly conducts the impulse throughout its length.

Neurons may be stimulated in many ways. As has been emphasized, the normal mode of stimulation is through receptor activity. But neurons

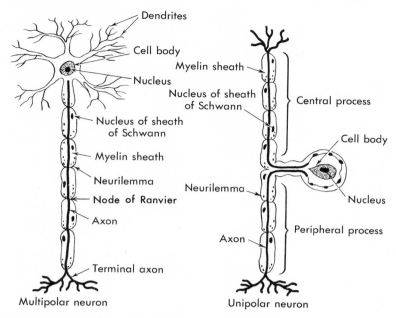

FIG. 4-3 Multipolar and unipolar neurons. The unipolar neuron has only an axon, no dendrites.

may also be excited mechanically, electrically, or chemically. It is well known that a sharp blow on the elbow will give rise to a tingling sensation in the fingers. In this instance the mechanical effect of the blow excites the neuron which normally conveys impulses from the fingers. Experimentally, the exposed nerves may be stimulated with electric current, with chemical agents, and by mechanical means. Nonetheless, it should be borne in mind that under normal circumstances the impulse is initiated by receptor activity.

It will be learned later that some impulses are not fired by receptors. These are so-called **motor** impulses, which are conducted by motor or efferent fibers. It is therefore necessary, at this point, to differentiate carefully between **afferent** and **efferent neurons.**

An **afferent neuron** conducts impulses toward the central nervous system (spinal cord and brain). The term afferent is derived from the Latin *ad,* meaning "toward," and *fero,* meaning "to bear."

An **efferent neuron** is a fiber which conducts impulses away from the central nervous system. These make up motor nerves. The term efferent is derived from *effero* meaning "to bring out," that is, to bring the impulse out of the central nervous system (Fig. 4-4).

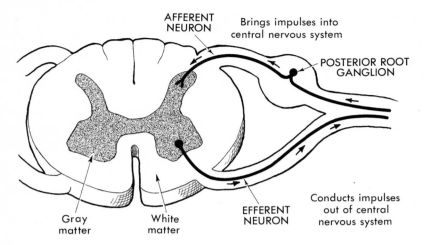

AFFERENT NEURON

Brings impulses into central nervous system

POSTERIOR ROOT GANGLION

Gray matter

White matter

EFFERENT NEURON

Conducts impulses out of central nervous system

FIG. 4-4 Afferent and efferent neurons. The afferent neurons conduct sensory impulses to the central nervous system; efferent neurons conduct motor impulses away.

For the present, we are concerned only with sensory systems, pathways which conduct impulses from the various parts of the body to the spinal cord and brain stem and then to the areas in the brain which are responsible for appreciation of these impulses and the sensations they represent.

The first and foremost physiological attribute of a neuron, then, is its capacity to conduct the impulse initiated by the receptor which, in turn, has been fired by a change in the environment. It has been stressed that the neuron is normally fired by the activity of the receptor. However, in order for the impulse to reach the brain, it must traverse a **chain** of neurons. Each neuron in this chain must excite the succeeding neuron. Thus we see that sensory neurons are fired in two ways: (1) by the activity of the receptor and (2) by the activity of the preceding neuron in the chain.

Mechanism of Conduction   A neuron, just like a muscle fiber, is negative inside in relation to the outside. The resting potential of mammalian neurons is about −70 mv. When the neuron is activated, there is an action potential that is very similar to that of skeletal muscle. As explained in detail in Chap. 3, in order to initiate an action potential there must be sufficient alteration of the membrane so as to permit the influx of Na^+. If this alteration is adequate, a sequence is set into motion which produces a brief reversal in the membrane polarity. The outside of the cell becomes negative in relation to the inside. But the entire length of the neuron does not participate in these changes simultaneously. The alterations first occur at the point of stimulation. In that area the outside of the membrane becomes negative while contiguous areas of the membrane are still positive (Fig. 4-5). The positive charges are therefore attracted to the negative ones. The area of negative charges is said to be a **sink** into which the positive charges flow. The removal of positive charges in this way reduces the potential difference of the two sides of the membrane at that point. That is to say, the resting potential at that point becomes less negative; therefore, the permeability increases and sodium quickly moves in. This part of the membrane now undergoes polarity reversal and the outside becomes negative. This sequence is rapidly repeated step by step along the entire length of the neuron. Accordingly, there results a progressive series of action potentials along the nerve from the point of stimulation. The action potentials so generated constitute the **impulse.**

The above is believed to explain impulse propagation along an unmyelinated neuron, but if there is myelin (Fig. 4-3) the situation is somewhat different. The myelin acts as an insulator, but this insulation is broken at the **nodes of Ranvier.** Accordingly, the positive charges flow from one node over the myelin to the next node when that node becomes negative. Because the charges leap from node to node to node, this form

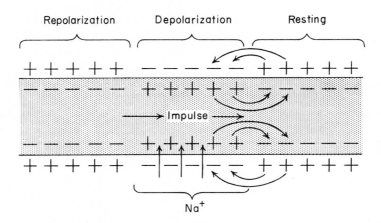

FIG. 4-5 **Impulse conduction. The first part of the neuron to the left has already been depolarized and repolarized. The impulse is now midway along the fiber. Here the polarity has been reversed. As a result positive ions from the outside of the resting area flow into the negative area. At the same time positive ions from the inside of the active area flow into the resting area. These flows activate the resting segment.**

of conduction is termed **saltatory** conduction, saltatory meaning dancing or leaping.

All-or-none Law The recording of action potentials is a very helpful experimental procedure. When a neuron is not conducting an impulse, there is no electrical activity. Therefore, by this technique it is possible to ascertain whether or not there is activity in the fiber. Using this procedure it is easy to demonstrate another important physiological property of the neuron, namely, that it obeys the **all-or-none law.** Every neuron has a specific threshold. Stimulation of an intensity below this threshold fails to fire the neuron. But increasing the intensity greatly in excess of the threshold does not give a greater response than a stimulus which is barely liminal. In other words, if the amplitude of the spike potential is measured following activation with a liminal stimulus and then with a more intense stimulation, it will be the same. To state the all-or-none law in still another way it may be said that a neuron reacts either maximally or not at all.

Rate of Conduction The **rate** at which neurons conduct an impulse varies from neuron to neuron. Using the cathode-ray oscillograph, it can be noted that when the recording electrodes are placed close to the point of stimulation only a single spike potential is recorded. However, if the electrodes are attached at a distance from the point of stimulation, the recorded picture reveals several distinct spikes. This is due to the fact that a nerve is made up of many fibers. Not all the fibers conduct at the same rate. Consequently, when the recording electrodes are placed at a distance from the point of stimulation, several spike potentials are observed because some impulses reach the electrodes before others.

This phenomenon can probably best be illustrated at an auto race (Fig. 4-6). When the gun is fired, all the cars start. This may be likened in our case to the simultaneous firing of all the neurons in the nerve. Actually, from the very start of the race some of the cars are moving faster than others. But if one were to observe the cars at the 50-yard mark, they would all appear to be bunched together despite the fact that some are traveling faster than others. This can be likened to the recording of a simple wave form close to the point of stimulation. If, however, the cars are observed at the end of the first lap, it will be noted that they are now spread out because of different speeds over a period of time. This is to be compared to the complex wave obtained when recordings are taken at a point distant to the place of stimulation.

The largest neurons in man are capable of conducting impulses at a velocity of up to 150 meters per second. Sensory fibers are generally smaller and conduct more slowly. The very small sensory neurons have a velocity as low as 2 meters per second. In brief, it may be said that the

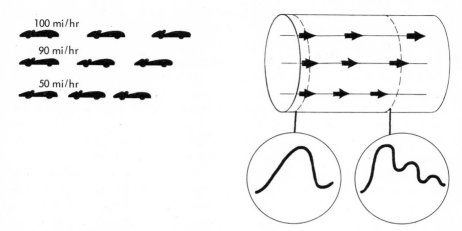

FIG. 4-6 **Different rates of conduction in a mixed nerve. Because the neurons conduct at different rates, the impulses arrive at the recording electrodes at different time intervals, thereby producing a complex action potential.**

larger the diameter of the neuron (1) the higher will be the rate of conduction, (2) the lower will be the threshold of intensity necessary to fire the fiber, and (3) the greater will be the amplitude and duration of the spike potential. Conversely, the smallest fibers require an intense stimulus and conduct very slowly, and the amplitude and duration of the spike are relatively reduced.

Refractory Periods It is a physiological fact that immediately following the activation of a neuron it is impossible to make that neuron conduct another impulse. The neuron, in a sense, must rest for a period of time. It is true that this period is extremely short, amounting to only a few thousandths of a second. Nonetheless, during this brief interval the neuron is refractive. This refractiveness is another important physiological property of the neuron.

For a very short period of time it is absolutely impossible to cause the neuron to conduct an impulse. This period is appropriately called the **absolute refractory period.** Immediately following this interval the neuron regains its ability to conduct; the sensitivity slowly returns to normal. During this period it is possible to cause the neuron to transmit an impulse, but a **stronger-than-minimal** stimulus is required. This phase is logically called the **relative refractory period.**

The absolute refractory period occurs throughout the rising phase of the spike potential and for about a third of the descending limb. This phase is immediately followed by the relative refractory period which persists until the negative after-potential (Fig. 3-6). During the negative after-potential the cell is actually easier to stimulate than at any other time. During the positive after-potential, however, it is again relatively refractory. All of these changes in level of excitability are explicable on the basis of movement of sodium and potassium ions.

Frequency of Response   The absolute refractory period limits the number of impulses propagated per unit time, that is, the frequency of response. If a neuron has an absolute refractory period of 0.4 millisecond, then the maximum impulse frequency cannot exceed 2,500 per second because $(0.4 \times 10^{-3}$ second$) \times (2.5 \times 10^3$ per second$) = 1$.

Degeneration and Regeneration   Most of the tissues of the living body are endowed with regenerative properties. For example, if an area of skin is lost, over a variable period of time the skin returns to normal. Similarly, if an axon is severed from its cell body, regeneration occurs, although it is not so rapid nor so complete as replacement of skin. The ability of nervous tissue to regenerate is, of course, an important physiological property.

It was shown many years ago by Waller that when an axon of a peripheral neuron is cut, the part separated from the cell body degenerates. This phenomenon has since been referred to as **Wallerian degeneration.** Not only does the severed segment of axon die, but the part still attached to the cell body also displays marked alterations. These changes are called **retrograde degeneration.** Ultimately, however, the axon still attached to the cell body begins to regenerate. If steps are taken to encourage it to grow toward its other completely degenerated peripheral segment, effective function may be restored.

Many of the surgical techniques currently used are based on an appreciation of the property of degeneration and regeneration of neurons. For example, it is now feasible to cross-suture the regenerating end of one nerve with the degenerated segment of another. In this way it is possible to "order" a nerve to grow into a locale foreign to it and to innervate muscles which that nerve has never innervated before.

THE SYNAPSE

The neuron conducts the impulse which has been initiated by the receptor. It will be seen shortly that the pathways over which the impulse must pass are made up of a chain of neurons. Each link in the chain leads the impulse on to the next neuron. The anatomical gap between two neurons is called a **synapse.** The word synapse means "a binding together." The synapse, then, is the part of the nervous system which binds together two or more neurons.

ANATOMICAL CONSIDERATIONS

Anatomical Gap Actually, there is no protoplasmic continuity at the synapse. This is convincingly demonstrated when the axon of the primary neuron in a chain is severed from its cell body. As noted previously, this axon now degenerates. Histological studies reveal that the process of degeneration occurs up to the synapse. The secondary neuron with which it is in synaptic union is spared. It is clear, therefore, that a true anatomical gap exists at the synapse.

Convergence and Divergence In some instances, there may be more than two neurons in synaptic junction. There is excellent anatomical and physiological evidence to demonstrate that several neurons may converge on one secondary neuron. This arrangement is termed **convergence.** On the other hand, it has been noted that in some parts of the nervous system the axon of one neuron branches and each branch activates a separate secondary neuron. This arrangement is spoken of as **divergence.** The physiological significance of convergence and divergence will be made clear later.

PHYSIOLOGICAL CONSIDERATIONS

Mechanism of Synaptic Transmission Painstaking investigation disclosed that a compound, **acetylcholine,** is highly concentrated at the synapse. Acetylcholine is capable of firing neurons, probably because it increases the permeability and thus initiates Na^+ influx. Accordingly, when the impulse reaches the end of the axon, acetylcholine is liberated and this substance activates the secondary neuron. It transmits the impulse, so to speak, across the synapse.

There is another substance present at the synapse. It is acetylcholinesterase, which quickly inactivates acetylcholine, thus preventing acetylcholine from stimulating the secondary neuron repeatedly. In short, the enzyme must inactivate acetylcholine during the refractory period of the secondary neuron; otherwise, it will be fired a second time (Fig. 4-7). As a matter of fact, this inactivation occurs in less than about 50 microseconds, which is much shorter than the refractory period.

Synaptic Delay By the use of the cathode-ray oscillograph, it is possible to measure the rate of conduction in a neuron with considerable accuracy. By employing this technique and taking into consideration the fiber size, it has been possible to demonstrate that there is a measurable delay in conduction when the impulse traverses the synapse. This synaptic delay is usually less than 1 millisecond in duration.

The explanation for synaptic delay is still not adequate. It has been claimed that the delay is due to the time required for the liberation of

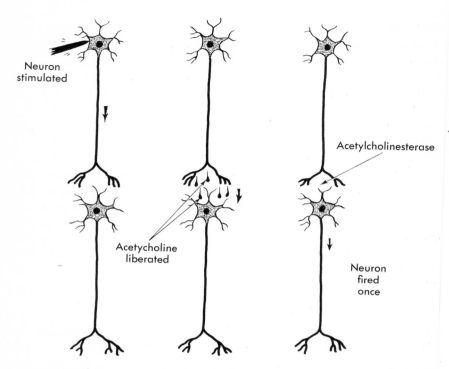

FIG. 4-7 Synaptic transmission. The upper neuron liberates acetylcholine at the synapse. The acetylcholine activates the lower neuron. Acetylcholinesterase inactivates acetylcholine before the postsynaptic neuron can be fired a second time.

acetylcholine at the end of the first axon plus the time required for it to fire the secondary neuron. Recently a simpler explanation has been offered. The axon, as it approaches the synapse, arborizes into many terminal branches. Each twig, of course, is smaller than the undivided axon. In other words, the impulse which has been traversing a fiber of relatively large diameter now is being led through several strands of much smaller size. In view of the fact that the rate of conduction bears a direct relationship to the fiber caliber, the branching of the axon into smaller units may, in itself, account for the delay at the synapse.

One-way Conduction   A neuron will conduct an impulse in either direction. In a chain of neurons, however, it has been shown that the impulse courses in only one direction, that is, from the dendrites to the cell body to the axon. *One-way conduction, then, must be due to the synapse.* This concept can be verified by attaching recording electrodes to two neurons in synaptic association. If one is stimulated and then the other, it will be seen that only in one instance does the impulse cross the synapse and that is in the direction already described. Thus, it can be concluded that the characteristic one-way conduction in the nervous system is due to the presence of a synapse. Again, this property of the synapse may be due to the fact that acetylcholine can be liberated by the axon at the synapse but not by the cell body or dendritic process.

Summation   There are two ways in which neurons are stimulated in the sensory pathways: (1) by the receptor or (2) by the action of the preceding fiber in a chain of neurons. Often, the action of the preceding neuron is inadequate in itself to fire the following fiber. In other words, the impulse coursing through the first fiber is subminimal with respect to the second fiber. However, it is possible for two or more such subminimal impulses acting in concert to be strong enough to fire the secondary fiber. This teamwork, this adding together or summing up of subminimal stimuli, is called **summation** (Fig. 4-8).

Quite often two or more neurons converge on one secondary fiber (convergence). If the impulses arriving over two such neurons are sub-

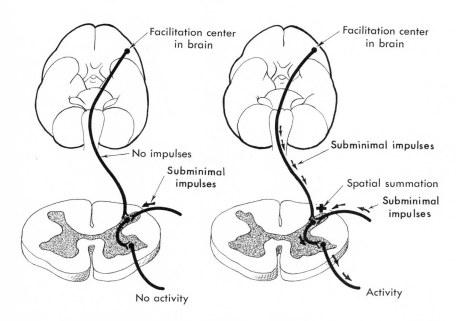

FIG. 4-8   Facilitation. Two neurons converge upon a common postsynaptic neuron. The influence of both summate, thus effectively firing the postsynaptic neuron.

minimal and impinge on the succeeding fiber at the same time, they may collectively prove adequate to fire the second fiber. Since the impulses in this case arrive over two fibers separated by space, this type of summation has been termed **spatial summation.**

A subminimal stimulus does not fire the secondary, or postsynaptic neuron, but it does, nonetheless, produce a change in that neuron characterized by a small decrease in the negativity of the resting potential. This alteration is called the **excitatory postsynaptic potential (EPSP).** During the EPSP, which lasts only a few milliseconds, the postsynaptic neuron can be more easily depolarized. If, during this time while the EPSP persists, a second impulse arrives, the neuron may fire. Here again, additive factors combine to produce activation of the secondary neuron. Because the impulses are separated by time, this type of addition is termed **temporal summation.**

Facilitation It is highly probable that there are many presynaptic neurons which are incapable, by themselves, of activating postsynaptic neurons. Help is needed. This help is provided in the form of another presynaptic neuron which also does not fire the postsynaptic neuron but does evoke sufficient local alteration in membrane permeability, of which the first presynaptic neuron takes advantage. This aid is termed facilitation. Facilitation, then, depends upon spatial summation.

Inhibition It has been known for many years that synaptic transmission may be inhibited by the activity of specific presynaptic neurons. Apparently such neurons alter the membrane permeability of the postsynaptic neuron in such a way as to raise the threshold of excitation. Actual measurements of the membrane potential show that in response to the firing of an inhibitory presynaptic neuron there is hyperpolarization, that is, the membrane potential becomes more negative than it is at rest. This change is termed the **inhibitory postsynaptic potential (IPSP).** It has been postulated that there is an inhibitory transmitter substance liberated by certain presynaptic neurons. This substance is thought capable of hyperpolarizing the membrane of the postsynaptic neuron. These inhibitory neurons are believed to be short-axon neurons which liberate the as yet unidentified inhibitory substance.

MAJOR SENSORY PATHWAYS

Thus far it has been learned that the receptor reacts in response to a specific change in the environment. As a result of receptor activity, an afferent neuron is caused to conduct the impulse to the central nervous system. After the impulse reaches the spinal cord or brain stem, it may be conveyed by specific sensory pathways to higher centers for awareness.

On gross examination, the spinal cord may be observed to be divided into **white matter** and **gray matter** (see Fig. 4-4). The white matter is composed of nerve tracts. The gray matter consists primarily of nerve cell bodies. These cell bodies may give rise to axons which then leave the cord to innervate muscles. Therefore, these fibers are referred to as **motor** neurons. Other cell bodies give rise to axons which course only a short distance and serve to connect two neurons within the spinal cord. These are termed **internuncial** or **interconnecting** neurons. Finally, some of the cell bodies give rise to long axons which ascend the length of the spinal cord to synapse with neurons destined for higher brain centers. These axons conduct the modalities of sensation which we have been considering.

POSTERIOR COLUMNS

Figure 4-9 shows representative sections through the central nervous system at various levels. It will be noted that some of the afferent neurons enter the spinal cord and immediately turn upward to ascend on the same side to the medulla oblongata. These neurons make up a group of tracts known as the **posterior columns** because of their position in the back part of the cord.

The posterior columns convey sensations of touch, pressure, and proprioception. If the posterior columns are destroyed, these sensory modalities will be lost on the *afflicted* side. Touch and pressure are also transmitted in part by other pathways. Hence, destruction of the posterior columns does not completely impair the ability to appreciate touch and pressure. There is, however, a serious loss of proprioception. Proprioception controls ability to appreciate changes in position and muscle tension. The individual in this case is unable to regulate the **direction, force, rate,** and **extent** of voluntary movements. Consequently there is a loss of the usual high integration and smoothness of muscular activity. In the chapter on coordination, the mechanisms responsible for bringing about the almost incredible degree of smoothness and grace of muscular move-move will be considered. Suffice it here to say that knowledge of the direction, force, rate, and extent of movement is fundamental to graceful activity. Destruction of the posterior columns impairs this ability. A dysfunction of this type is called **ataxia.** The word ataxia is derived from *taxis,* meaning "order." The prefix a- implies the lack of. Therefore the term ataxia indicates the lack of coordination.

Clinically, this disorder is exemplified by well-advanced cases of syphilis. As a result of degenerative changes in the posterior columns, the individual cannot perceive the direction, force, rate, and extent of movement. Because proprioception has been lost, the victim must utilize his

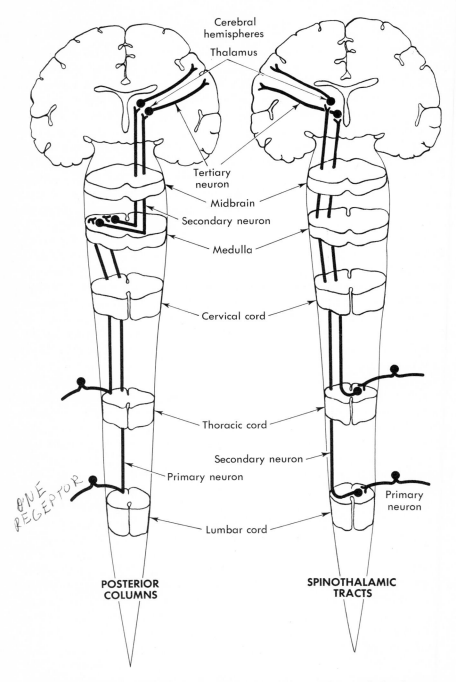

Cerebral
hemispheres

Thalamus

Tertiary
neuron

Midbrain

Secondary neuron

Medulla

Cervical cord

Thoracic cord

Secondary neuron

Primary neuron

Primary
neuron

Lumbar cord

ONE
RECEPTOR

**POSTERIOR
COLUMNS**

**SPINOTHALAMIC
TRACTS**

FIG. 4-9 Sensory pathways. The posterior columns and spinothalamic tracts
are the major pathways which conduct sensory impulses from the trunk and
extremities.

other senses to tell him about his position. Unless such individuals watch their feet, they stagger along as if they were drunk, raising each leg unnecessarily high and then slapping it down. By examining these patients we come to appreciate the highly complicated and delicately integrated proprioceptive mechanism which allows the normal individual to execute the walking act efficiently.

An examination of Fig. 4-9 will also indicate that the neurons which constitute the posterior columns end in the medulla. In other words, the very same neuron which has been fired by a receptor in the peripheral part of the body has conducted the impulse to the spinal cord and throughout the entire length of the cord to end in the medulla. Thus we see that a neuron may be several feet long. In the medulla the impulse is transmitted across a synapse to activate a secondary neuron in the chain of this sensory pathway. The axons of these neurons cross the medulla to the opposite side, turn up, and ascend in a tract known as the **medial lemniscus.** This secondary neuron ends in the **thalamus.** The thalamus is the great sensory relay station. All modalities of sensation from all parts of the body are funneled into the thalamus which, in turn, relays the impulse to the cerebral cortex. In brief, the sensory pathway for the conduction of touch, pressure, and proprioception is a three-neuron chain.

SPINOTHALAMIC TRACTS

The perception of pain and temperature requires the transmission of appropriate impulses over an entirely different pathway from that employed for the perception of touch, pressure, and proprioception. The afferent neurons which are activated by the receptors specific for pain and temperature transmit the impulse into the spinal cord through the dorsal roots. Unlike touch, pressure, and proprioception, these fibers end in the dorsal horn of the gray matter (Fig. 4-9). Thus, in contradistinction to the initial neuron for touch, pressure, and proprioception, the primary neuron for pain and temperature is relatively short.

The axon of the secondary neuron arises from a cell body situated in the nucleus of the dorsal horn of the gray matter. This axon crosses the spinal cord at the same level and then turns upward on the opposite side to ascend through the spinal cord and medulla directly to the thalamus.

The secondary fibers of the tract transmitting impulses of pain and temperature end in the thalamus. From this point, neurons are projected to the cerebral cortex for appreciation. The transmission of impulses of pain and temperature also traverses a three-neuron chain.

Thus, for normal perception, two major pathways are involved: (1) the posterior columns which convey impulses of touch, pressure, and proprioception and (2) the lateral spinothalamic tracts for the conduction of impulses of pain and temperature.

THE CEREBRAL CORTEX

Cerebral and **cerebrum** have reference to "the brain." **Cortex** literally means "bark," that is the outer covering of a tree. As applied to the brain, the word signifies the outer covering of that structure, specifically of the cerebral hemispheres. The major sensory tracts which traverse the spinal cord and brain stem to end in the cerebral cortex have been described. In subsequent chapters other pathways and other important structures which make up the brain will be considered. At this point, our interest will be focused on the outer covering or cortex of the brain—that is, the **cerebral cortex.**

A study of comparative anatomy discloses the greater complexity of the brain in the higher forms. In man the brain reaches its greatest development. And it will be seen that this maturation, especially of the cerebral cortex, accounts for the superior intelligence and ability which characterize man. All the other organ systems of the body, circulatory, respiratory, alimentary, and so forth, may be studied in lower animals and the knowledge so gained transferred to man without important modifications. But only in the nervous system, in the cerebral cortex of that nervous system, is a striking difference noted between man and the lower forms of animal life. Man's extraordinary capacity to remember and to utilize past experience in the light of new situations is a function of the cerebral cortex. Man's great dexterity is dependent on the integrity of the cerebral cortex. In short, we must turn our attention to the cerebral cortex in order to understand the obvious differences between man and the rest of the animal kingdom.

ANATOMICAL CONSIDERATIONS

Cerebral Convolutions   The convolutions (folds) of the human cerebral cortex are characteristic (Fig. 4-10). It is a fact that the complexity of the convolutions increases in the higher forms. These folds are caused by the surface of the cortex growing more rapidly than the underlying structures. As a result, the surface rolls and folds upon itself. The bulge is called a **gyrus.** The crease or fissure between two gyri is known as a **sulcus.**

Cerebral Lobes   Taking into consideration the gyri and sulci, neuroanatomists have recognized four major **lobes** in the cerebral cortex. They are the **frontal, parietal, occipital,** and **temporal lobes** (Fig. 4-10).

Cerebral Areas   It will be noted that the subdivisions or **areas** are designated by numbers (Fig. 4-11). At the turn of the century, workers in neuroanatomy observed definite differences in the cell structure of various parts of the brain. They began to designate different areas according to

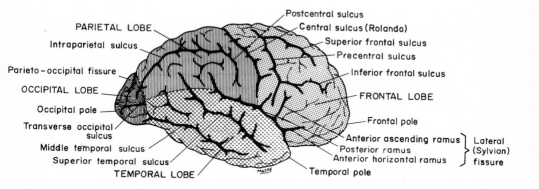

FIG. 4-10 Lobes of the cerebral cortex. (From E. L. House and B. Pansky, "A Functional Approach to Neuroanatomy," McGraw-Hill, 1960. Used by permission.)

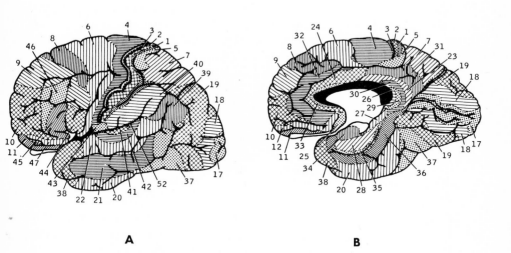

FIG. 4-11 Areas of the cerebral cortex. A. Lateral view. B. Medial view. (From E. L. House and B. Pansky, "A Functional Approach to Neuroanatomy," McGraw-Hill, 1960. Used by permission.)

this cell architecture. As a result, charts have been prepared with many areas of the cerebral cortex numbered. None of these charts is complete. In recent years the tendency has been to examine these areas more on a functional than on an anatomical basis. But the numbers utilized by the earlier investigators persist and are used to identify the various areas.

Sensory Areas   The tertiary neurons in the chains of fibers which transmit sensory impulses connect the thalamus and the cerebral cortex. These fibers terminate in the **postcentral gyrus** of the cerebral cortex. These areas have been designated by the numerals **3, 1,** and **2** (Fig. 4-11). More posteriorly lie areas **5** and **7**, which are also concerned with the appreciation of sensation. Two groups of areas as a whole (areas 3, 1, 2, and 5, 7) make up the general sensory part of the cerebral cortex.

PHYSIOLOGICAL CONSIDERATIONS

Sensory Areas   If the entire sensory cortex is removed from both cerebral hemispheres, the individual is unable to appreciate any sensation. On the other hand, if the sensory areas are cut away from only one hemisphere, then sensation is lost only on the opposite side of the body. The reason for this becomes clear if it is recalled that both major sensory pathways cross before they terminate in the cerebral cortex.

As has just been mentioned, complete ablation of the sensory cortex on both sides in man destroys sensory appreciation. However, in the primates it is possible to show some retention of sensory appreciation even after such a drastic procedure. Lower animals demonstrate even greater sensory retention. It is probable that subcortical areas and the thalamus are utilized in the lower forms for sensory reception, whereas this function has been almost exclusively reserved for the sensory cortex in man.

Two-point Sensibility   If two points are set close together and then pressed against the skin, the individual will report a double stimulation. However, if the points are brought even closer together, the subject then reports only one sensation. There is thus a critical distance by which two points must be separated in order for the subject to be able to discriminate two distinct stimuli. This critical distance is termed the **two-point threshold.** It varies markedly for different areas of the body. Figure 4-12 shows that both the fingertips and the lips possess very great two-point sensibility. These areas can appreciate two distinct stimuli even when they are very close together. On the other hand, the back of the neck is relatively insensitive and can discriminate two distinct stimuli only when they are widely separated. The two-point threshold depends on the closeness of the receptors and the density of the sensory innervation. In order to recognize two point discretely, at least two receptors must be stimu-

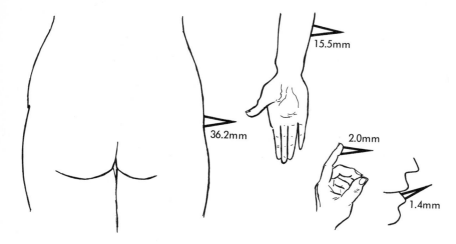

FIG. 4-12 Two-point sensibility. The distance two points must be separated to be appreciated as two points varies markedly on different parts of the body.

lated. Thus it is found that areas like the tongue are densely supplied with receptors and sensory neurons.

Sensory Localization   If the skin of the arm is pricked, the subject knows the point of stimulation. He is able to localize the stimulus. This ability to localize a point of stimulation is independent of the sense of vision. Even with the eyes closed, most individuals can localize a point of stimulation almost anywhere on the body with surprising accuracy.

Localization depends upon the **point-to-point representation** of sensory neurons upon the cerebral cortex. The sensory neurons from each part of the body maintain topographic integrity throughout the sensory tracts and then are projected onto a specific area of the sensory cortex. Through the learning process, the individual comes to associate stimuli with particular parts of the body.

The importance of the learning process is underlined by the fact that an individual has great difficulty in accurately localizing stimuli which emanate from the internal areas of the body. For example, pain produced by an inflamed appendix is usually referred to the surface of the body. Pain does not ordinarily arise from internal structures, and it is impossible to observe these organs. Accordingly, when stimuli do originate internally, they are customarily referred to another site which is on the body surface. Herein is the basis of **referred pain.**

Referred pain is an everyday experience. For example, a patient suffering with sinus trouble will insist that his teeth hurt even though examination reveals that the dentition is perfectly sound. Conversely, a patient may present himself to a physician with neck pain when in reality the stimuli are arising in decayed teeth. The complete explanation of referred pain has not yet been written. It is unquestionably in part the result of the learning process. But an equally important aspect is the fact that many primary neurons in the sensory system converge upon the same secondary fiber. Accordingly, neurons from the appendix and those from the anterior abdominal wall enter the cord and then impinge on the same secondary ascending neuron. As a result, an attack of appendicitis will usually cause the patient to complain of pain in his right side.

It was mentioned earlier that if the elbow is struck the fingers will seem to tingle. This is due to the fact that no matter where a neuron is stimulated along its course the individual refers the stimulus to the usual site of activation, namely, the receptor. This explanation lies at the basis of **phantom pain.** Phantom pain is most dramatically observed in amputees. Not infrequently, especially soon after a limb has been lost, the patient complains of sensation, usually pain, as emanating from the fingers or toes of the amputated limb. The stimulus, of course, is at the point of amputation but is referred to the once-present receptor of that neuron in the extremity.

Stereognosis   A blind person, needless to say, can gain considerable knowledge of his environment by the use of the other senses. Although these senses are not so highly developed in the normal individual, with the eyes closed it is still possible to identify objects with surprising accuracy by utilizing the various other sensory modalities. The ability to recognize objects without visual assistance is termed **stereognosis.** The word is derived from *stereos,* meaning "solid," and *gnosis,* implying "knowledge." Literally, then, it means only the appreciation of form by touch. Actually its connotation is much broader. In common clinical parlance, the term implies the ability to recognize many properties (size, shape, texture, temperature, etc.) of an object. The loss of this ability is called **astereognosis.** For example, if a central-nervous-system lesion interrupts the transmission of impulses over the posterior columns, there will be a loss of proprioception. Some tactile sensation would persist (because of the intact ventral spinothalamic tracts), but with the eyes closed it would be impossible to identify the size, the shape, and possibly the texture of an object.

SUMMARY

A **receptor** is specialized nervous tissue sensitive to a specific change in the environment. **Exteroceptors** react to alterations in the external environment. **Interoceptors** respond to changes in the internal milieu. Receptors attuned to a change in movement, position, or tension are known as **proprioceptors.**

A receptor requires a stimulus of adequate intensity before it will respond. As the intensity of stimulation increases above threshold, the **rate** at which the receptor fires also increases. The individual perceives varying intensities of stimuli by two mechanisms: (1) a change in the number of receptors being fired and (2) a variation in the rate of firing of each receptor. The brain interprets an increase in the rate of impulses as an increase in intensity of stimulation. Receptors **adapt** to a constant stimulus. Not all receptors, however, possess the same rate of adaptation. Touch receptors adjust quite readily; pain receptors adapt hardly at all.

Neurons which carry impulses to the central nervous system are called **afferent neurons.** Those which convey impulses away from the central nervous system are termed **efferent neurons.** The larger the diameter of the neuron, the faster will be the rate of conduction, the lower will be the threshold of intensity necessary to fire the fiber, and the greater will be the amplitude and duration of the spike potential. Immediately following the transmission of an impulse, the neuron cannot be made to conduct a second impulse. If a neuron is cut, the segment severed from the cell body degenerates. This process is called **Wallerian degeneration.** The part still attached to the cell body first shows **retrograde degeneration** but ultimately regenerates.

The anatomical gap between two neurons is termed the **synapse.** If several fibers impinge on one secondary neuron, the arrangement is referred to as **convergence.** Conversely, when one terminal axon arborizes and each branch is in synaptic union with a separate secondary neuron, the relationship is termed **divergence.** When the impulse arrives at the end of most axons, **acetylcholine** is liberated which activates the second neuron. Acetylcholine is inactivated by **acetylcholinesterase,** thus preventing repetitive firing of the secondary fiber. When the impulse arrives at the synapse, there is a measurable delay in its transmission called **synaptic delay.** A synapse will conduct an impulse in only one direction. The impulse conveyed by one neuron may prove inadequate to fire its succeeding fiber. However, two or more such subminimal impulses may summate to provide an adequate stimulus. This mechanism is referred to as **summation.** Facilitation depends upon the establishment of the **EPSP;** inhibition upon the **IPSP.**

The **posterior columns** mediate proprioception, touch, and pressure. The **spinothalamic tract** is the important pathway for impulses of pain and temperature.

The chains of neurons transmitting impulses of sensation terminate in the **postcentral gyrus** (areas **3, 1, 2, 5,** and **7**) of the **parietal lobe** of the cerebral cortex. This area of the brain is termed the **sensory cortex.** Removal of the sensory cortex on one side causes loss of sensation on the opposite side of the body.

There is a **point-to-point** relationship between all parts of the body and the cerebral cortex. As a result the individual is able to localize stimuli accurately. However, since the learning process and the visual sense play a role in sensory localization, pain from internal regions may be referred to the external surface. By the same token, whenever a nerve is irritated along its course, the subject interprets the pain as arising in the receptor for that nerve. These observations constitute the basis of **referred** and **phantom pain.** The ability to identify an object without using vision is termed **stereognosis.** It depends on the integrity of the extravisual senses. Loss of this ability is called **astereognosis.**

QUESTIONS

1. What is the difference between a receptor and a neuron?
2. Explain the mechanism responsible for the conduction of the impulse.
3. How does the impulse cross the synapse?
4. By what major pathways are impulses conducted to the cerebral cortex?
5. How does one perceive whether a stimulus is weak or strong?
6. What is meant by the term stereognosis?

SUGGESTED READING

Cooley, D. G., "Cells that Communicate. Part 2. How Nerve Cells Work," *Today's Health,* 41:#6, 39–41, 62–66, June 1963.

Davis, H., "Some Principles of Sensory Receptor Action," *Physiol. Rev.,* 41:#2, 391–416, April 1961.

Hagbarth, K. E., "Lower Somatic Functions of the Nervous System," *Ann. Rev. Physiol.,* 26: 249–270, 1964.

Johns, R. J., "The Electrical and Mechanical Events of Neuromuscular Transmission," *Am. J. Med.,* 35:#5, 611–621, November 1963.

Melzack, R., "The Perception of Pain," *Sci. American,* 204:#2, 41–49, February 1961.

Miller, W. H., Ratliff, F., and Hartline, H. K., "How Cells Receive Stimuli," *Sci. American,* 205:#3, 222–238, September 1961.

Movement

5

IN MAN THERE ARE TWO BASIC TYPES OF MOVEMENT: (1) reflex movement and (2) voluntary movement. For example, when one taps the tendon of the leg just below the knee, the limb shoots out. Much the same movement is carried out when kicking a football. But the first reaction is a reflex, the second voluntary. Specifically, a reflex is defined as an involuntary response to a stimulus. It is an automatic action dependent upon the functional integrity of the nervous system. The individual may be aware of the movement, he may even be able to inhibit it, but when the movement occurs it does so purely involuntarily and without conscious assistance. Although we shall, in this chapter, consider only reflex movement, it should be understood that a reflex may involve a gland instead of a muscle. The gland may respond involuntarily to a stumulus. As a matter of fact, that is the usual mode of glandular response. For example, when a foreign object strikes the eye, tears are secreted. The foreign object stimulates the reflex mechanism, resulting in lacrimation. Ordinarily, it is quite impossible to cause a gland to secrete voluntarily.

In this chapter, both reflex and voluntary movement will be studied.

ANATOMICAL RELATIONSHIPS

ARTICULATIONS

Figure 5-1 shows a human **skeleton.** It consists of about 200 bones in articulation with one another. Articulation is derived from a Latin stem which means a "connection." Quite appropriately, then, the connections between the various bones of the body are referred to as articulations.

LIGAMENTS

If the classroom skeleton is examined carefully, it will be noted that the bones are held together by nails and wires. In the living form, however,

89

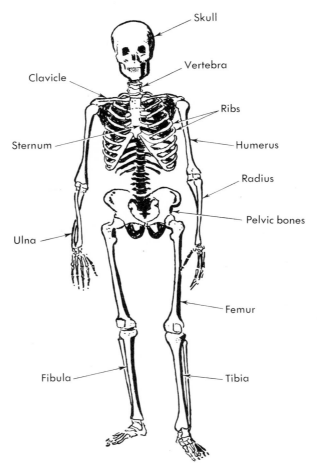

FIG. 5-1   The human skeleton.

the bones are bound together by tough, relatively inelastic connective tissue. Tissues designed to bind bones together are termed **ligaments.** The term ligament implies a band or bandage. In a sense, the ligaments serve as bandages which hold the bones in articulation.

The student can convincingly demonstrate to his own satisfaction that some articulations are freely movable, others are somewhat less mobile, and some cannot normally be moved at all (Fig. 5-2). For example, one's arm can be moved in almost any direction. The shoulder joint, or articulation, then, is an excellent instance of a freely movable joint. On the other hand, the knee joint is not nearly so mobile. The excursions of

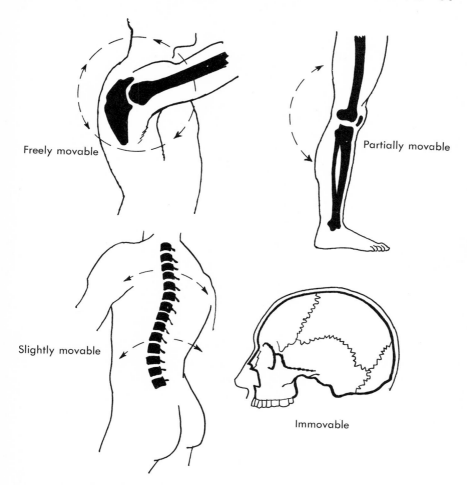

Freely movable

Partially movable

Slightly movable

Immovable

FIG. 5-2   Degrees of movement permitted by different types of articulations.

the lower limb are definitely limited to a forward and backward hinge action. An example of an even more restricted articulation may be found in an examination of the spinal column. Here we see that the movements between the individual vertebrae are extremely limited. Finally, the skull is composed of several bones held tightly together and completely immovable. Thus we find that, though movement is dependent on muscular activity, the type of articulation with which the muscle must contend is a major factor in determining the type and degree of possible movement.

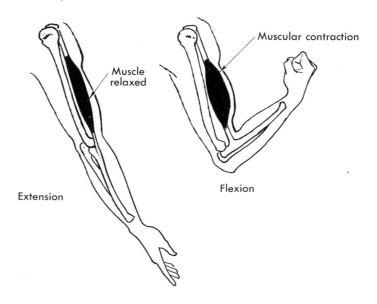

FIG. 5-3   Movement of bony levers.

Figure 5-3 demonstrates grossly how a typical muscle is attached to the skeleton. It should be noted that the muscle stretches between two bones. These bones are hinged at their articulation. Therefore, when the muscle contracts and shortens, the bones are caused to move. If one bone is held fixed by other muscles, then only one of the bones will change position.

TENDONS

Muscular tissue does not connect directly to the bone. Even on gross inspection a difference between the muscle tissue and that which connects with the bones can be noted. Tissues which join muscles to bones are called **tendons.** The term is derived from the Greek stem meaning "stretch" and refers to a tough, inelastic band of tissue which bridges the space or stretches from the end of the muscle to its point of fixation on the bone. A tendon appears white and opaque, and it is truly tough and inelastic. The tendon as a whole consists of many individual fibers coursing lengthwise. The muscle fibers become intimately interwoven with the tendon fibers, thus forming a powerful connection capable of withstanding great forces. At its other end, the tendon is intermingled with the substance of the bone. Of the three, muscle, tendon, and bone, the tendon proves the toughest, and the connection between the tendon and muscle stronger than that between the tendon and bone. Abnormal stresses which accompany an automobile accident or a fall may break bones or rupture muscle fibers, but the tendon is rarely damaged. Not uncommonly, the tendon may be ripped away from the bone, but separation of tendon and muscle is most infrequent.

ANATOMY OF REFLEX MOVEMENT

The anatomy of most reflex patterns is extremely complex. All reflexes possess a basic design, however. This consists of an **afferent limb** which is sensory in nature; that is, it conducts the impulse from the periphery toward the central nervous system. It also includes an **efferent limb** which transmits the impulse from the central nervous system out toward the periphery. In addition to these basic constituents, there is ample evidence to suggest that all reflexes, even the most simple, are influenced normally by the higher brain centers. Thus, it may be said that the pathways from these higher brain centers constitute the third basic component of the reflex pattern.

AFFERENT LIMB

The afferent limb of the reflex arc consists of the receptor and its sensory pathway.

Receptors   The discussion of the receptors (Chap. 4) should now be reviewed. A reflex may be elicited in response to variations in temperature, changes in pressure, alterations in position, or any other environmental disturbance adequate to stimulate the receptor mechanism.

One group of receptors which plays an extremely important role in reflex activity is sensitive to changes in the position of the body. These end organs are termed **proprioceptors.** This term has a rather fascinating derivation and connotation. *Proprius* means "one's own," and *capere* means "to take." A proprioceptor, then, permits awareness of oneself; it initiates impulses which give the individual knowledge of the position of his extremities, of the tension in muscles and tendons. The proprioceptors not only provide us with such information but also serve to initiate impulses which participate in important reflex adjustments.

Sensory Pathways   The pathways by which impulses pass from the receptors to the sensory cortex for perception have been studied in Chap. 4. It was noted then that these pathways embrace three components. The first link connects the receptor with the central nervous system. The second link carries the impulse to the thalamus. The third link connects the thalamus and the sensory cortex. Complex reflex activity may involve all three components, but the more fundamental, simpler reflex patterns utilize only the first link.

Figure 5-4 demonstrates the anatomy of some simple reflex patterns. In the first instance (upper left), the sensory fiber terminates in the ventral horn of the spinal cord in synaptic union with the efferent limb. In the second illustration (upper right), the afferent limb is seen to end soon after it enters the cord. Then a short fiber conveys the impulse to the efferent limb. The remaining diagrams simply portray variations of this basic theme.

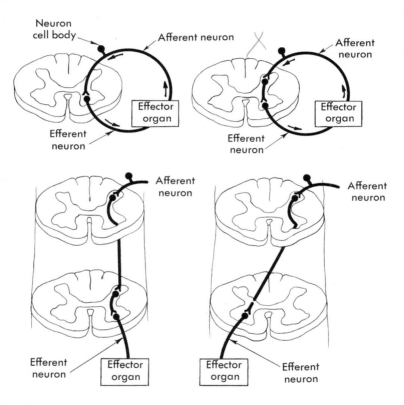

FIG. 5-4 **Diagrammatic representation of the anatomy of simple re-flexes. In the upper drawings it is assumed that the receptor lies in the effector organ, for example, a muscle. On the left the afferent fiber directly impinges upon the efferent neuron. On the right there is an internuncial neuron interposed between them. In the lower drawings the receptor and effector organ are separated; thus the impulse may involve several different levels of the cord. It may be restricted to one side of the cord, or cross over to the other.**

EFFERENT LIMB

The efferent limb of a reflex consists of a **motor pathway** and an **effector organ,** which may be either muscle or gland.

Motor Pathways A motor pathway conducts impulses destined for control of muscle or glandular activity. The simplest motor system consists of two links, one which begins in the motor areas of the cerebral cortex and transmits the impulse to lower centers in the brain stem or spinal cord and the other which then conveys the impulse from the central nervous system to the effector organ, that is, the muscle or gland. Reflex activity may involve both links of the motor system, but the basic and more simple reflexes usually employ only the second component.

Figure 5-4 draws attention to several simple reflex patterns. It will be noted that in most cases the cell body of the motor fiber resides in the anterior or ventral horn. The fiber then leaves the spinal cord and courses toward the effector organ. The pattern in the brain stem is essentially the same. In cases involving the autonomic nervous system, the motor fiber arises from a cell body which dwells in the lateral horn.

Effector Organs The effector organ effects, or brings about, the reflex action. This activity may be one of muscular contraction or glandular activity. In Fig. 5-4 it may be seen that in some cases the receptor which initiated the reflex lies within the effector organ. This arrangement is the basis of important self-regulatory mechanisms. For example, if a muscle is stretched, the proprioceptor within the muscle is activated, and as a result, there is reflex shortening of that muscle which serves to oppose the stretching force. In other cases, the receptor is far removed from the effector organ. This arrangement serves well to coordinate bodily function.

PATHWAYS FROM HIGHER CENTERS

The reflex impulse is transmitted from the afferent to the efferent limb across one or more synapses, depending on the complexity of the reflex. But synaptic transmission is influenced by the activity of higher cerebral centers. This activity is conveyed by pathways which descend the brain stem and spinal cord to influence the synapse between the afferent and efferent limbs (Fig. 5-5). Some of these pathways are also utilized for impulses which originate volitionally. Other nerve routes serve no other function than to control reflex activity.

It is true that under abnormal conditions the basic reflexes continue to function even after the influence of the higher centers has been eliminated. For example, if a man's spinal cord is completely severed, let us say in the midthoracic region, reflex movement may still be elicited. Such a person cannot move his leg voluntarily, but if the leg is tapped

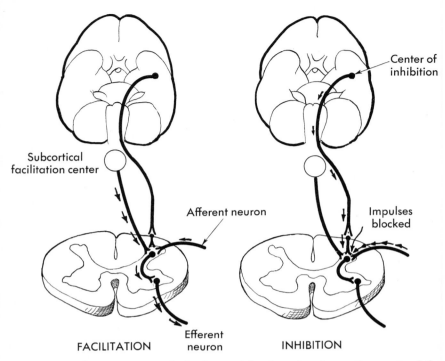

FIG. 5-5   Higher-center control of reflex activity. Impulses from other parts of the nervous system may either facilitate or inhibit the reflex.

below the knee, the typical reflex kick can be observed. This must mean that, even though the influence of higher centers can no longer be exerted because of spinal-cord transection, reflex action does remain functional. But there is excellent evidence to indicate that in the normal living man even the most simple reflexes are constantly under the guidance of these higher centers.

In summary the anatomical components of the basic reflex are (1) a receptor, (2) a sensory fiber, (3) a synapse, (4) a motor fiber, (5) an effector organ, and (6) a nerve fiber from higher brain centers which influences the synapse between the afferent and efferent limbs.

PHYSIOLOGY OF REFLEX MOVEMENT

There are fundamental principles which govern all reflex action. In order to appreciate the role played by reflex movement in the total physiology of man, it is first necessary to comprehend fully the basic principles. Accordingly, these primary physiological characteristics of reflex action will be considered, and then specific reflexes will be discussed to illustrate the part they play in the physiology of man.

BASIC PRINCIPLES

Reaction Time   One often hears, in popular parlance, references to quick and slow reflexes. Athletes insist that as they grow older their "reflexes" slow down. They mean, of course, their reaction time. For example, the shortstop sees the batter swing, hears the bat connect with the ball, and notices the direction the ball takes. If it is destined for his area, he must move rapidly in order to effect the catch. Outstanding players seemingly make these adjustments simultaneously with the crack of the bat. The sandlotter takes a discernible time to get under way. Perhaps a more personal illustration is that of the need for rapid reaction times in automobile driving, avoiding being caught in a subway door, or escaping the wheels of an enthusiastic cyclist. These are all examples of reaction time.

It will be recalled that a reflex is an *involuntary* response to a stimulus. This implies, of course, that no thought is involved in the process. When the ball is hit, the shortstop cannot pause to meditate and then plan his movements; the pedestrian cannot leisurely reflect on the onrushing bicycle. One must and does react promptly with no thought. One subconsciously or involuntarily executes an act. In all fairness it must be admitted that these situations are far more complex than the simple reflex action studied under laboratory conditions. These examples require training and experience. The important point to remember is that there is a demonstrable delay between the time of stimulation and time of reaction and that this interval can and does vary.

Clearly, reaction time differs from person to person, but there is a minimal irreducible reaction time. In the previous chapter it was emphasized that the passage of an impulse along a nerve fiber depends upon numerous factors. It was also noted that it requires a measurable interval for the impulse to cross the synapse as well as the neuromuscular junction. It also takes time for muscle to contract after it has received the stimulus. Since even the simplest reflex involves all these components, the reflex reaction time or **reflex latent period,** as it is sometimes termed, must be the addition of all the component latent periods. In the complicated reflex responses in man already discussed there are, of course, the various psychological factors to be elaborated upon subsequently.

Reciprocal Innervation   It can be easily demonstrated that all muscular movement involves reciprocal activity of two or more sets of muscles. For example, when one flexes his biceps, he must simultaneously relax the triceps. If this coordination did not exist, there could be no movement, for one muscle group would oppose another muscle set, and the arm would remain rigid and immobile. In later chapters the exquisite co-ordination required for all activity will be considered. Suffice it here to say that, even in the simplest movements, when one group of muscles contracts, another group must simultaneously relax. Since all skeletal-muscle activity is in response to nervous stimulation, it follows that this simultaneous contraction and relaxation demand **reciprocal innervation** of the opposing muscle groups. It is safe to conclude that no reflex re-sponse is ever quite so simple as the usual laboratory exercises would lead one to believe. Concurrently with the passage of impulses to the con-tracting muscle, there must be inhibition of impulses to the antagonistic muscle groups. For example, if one inadvertently touches a hot grill, one's arm is quickly withdrawn. This is a reflex act; it is truly involuntary and automatic. Visualize the basic components. Not only must there be a receptor, an afferent limb, a synapse, an efferent limb, and the muscle which actually contracts, but there must also be another efferent limb which innervates the antagonistic muscles. At the same time that impulses are bombarding the contracting muscle, there is inhibition of the oppos-ing muscles. This *pari passu* stimulation and inhibition of antagonistic muscle groups is termed **reciprocal innervation.**

Facilitation The general statement has been made that in man it is highly unlikely that any reflex normally proceeds in the absence of higher-center influence. What then is the nature of this influence?

Figure 5-5 portrays diagrammatically one possibility as to how the higher centers modify the reflex act. It is believed that the impulses con-veyed by the afferent limb of a reflex arc are subminimal, at least as they relate to excitation of the efferent limb. In other words, the impulses reach the synapse but fail to fire the efferent neuron. However, at the same time impulses are thought to arrive at the synapse from higher centers. These impulses are also subminimal, but when summated with the subminimal impulses arriving over the afferent limb, threshold strength is achieved and the efferent neuron is activated. Put somewhat differently, it is thought that the subminimal impulses from the higher centers, although they in themselves fail to activate the efferent limb, do create an excitatory postsynaptic potential (EPSP), which lowers the threshold of excitability of the efferent neuron and allows it to be excited by the subminimal impulses coming in over the afferent neuron. This is the concept of **spatial summation** and the basis of **facilitation.**

The degree of facilitation may vary considerably. For example, it is well known that if one is emotionally upset a slight noise will cause one to jump, whereas under normal circumstances the same sound would pass unnoticed. In the laboratory it has been shown that the stimulation of various areas of the brain definitely influences reflex activity. Finally, in man, immediately after the spinal cord has been severed, as in an automobile accident, all reflex responses are lost. From the available evidence, one must conclude that the simplest reflexes in the normal man are facilitated to varying degrees by higher-center activity.

Inhibition   Just as reflexes may be facilitated or aided, they may be inhibited or impeded. In the discussion of reciprocal innervation it was stated that when one muscle group is activated the antagonistic group must be inhibited.

Inhibition is a function of the central nervous system. Actual inhibitory nerve pathways have been identified coursing through the length of the spinal cord. There is reasonable evidence to indicate that all reflexes are incessantly being bombarded by facilitatory and inhibitory impulses. Reflex action then must reflect the balance between the two, and it seems clear that the balance may vary widely, thereby strongly activating or blocking the reflex response.

Just as facilitation is caused by a chemical substance that lowers the threshold of the postsynaptic neuron, so is inhibition thought to be caused by a chemical substance that raises the threshold of the postsynaptic neuron. The postsynaptic neuron, in both cases, is the motor fiber that innervates the muscle. In the case of inhibition there is a short internuncial neuron interposed between the neuron from higher centers and the motor fiber (Fig. 5-5). It is this short internuncial neuron that liberates an as yet unidentified substance which causes the inhibitory **postsynaptic potential (IPSP)** in the motor fiber. As a result its threshold is raised and impulses which ordinarily would activate it, now fail to do so. In other words, it has been inhibited.

Spinal Shock   If, in living man, the spinal cord is severed, let us say in the midthoracic region, all reflex responses below the level of transection are temporarily lost for a period of time. The individual is said to be in **spinal shock.** At one time it was thought that this clinical picture was due to radiation of the injury causing inhibition of the reflex. This explanation is not tenable, however, because after a period of time reflex activity returns. Interestingly enough, if the cord is transected a second time just below the original site, reflex movement does not again disappear. The more likely explanation is that there is normally a preponderance of facilitatory impulses coursing down through the spinal cord. When the cord is cut, these impulses no longer reach the reflex synapse; consequently, synaptic transmission cannot occur, and there is no response. This theory may be satisfactory as far as it goes, but the fact remains that after a period of time reflex activity *does* return. If the loss of reflexes is due to the removal of facilitatory impulses, how do we explain the recovery? As yet, there is no satisfactory answer to this question.

The lower the animal in the phylogenetic scale, the shorter the duration of spinal shock. In the frog, for example, it is possible to destroy the brain completely, and yet the animal survives. More than that, after a delay of only a few minutes the frog squats in the normal position, and if its hindquarters are stimulated it will respond with its characteristic jump. In cats and dogs, spinal shock lasts for about two to three days, whereas in man it persists for a week or more.

TYPES OF REFLEX MOVEMENT

Reflexes may generally be classified under two or three headings, although there are some unique reflex patterns which cannot be so categorized in any of the usual categories. We shall consider primarily the stretch reflexes, the flexor reflexes, and the supporting reflexes. The righting and visceral reflexes will be deferred to more appropriate chapters.

Stretch Reflexes   These are extremely important mechanisms. In living man, if a muscle is stretched it usually responds by contracting. In a sense, it withstands or opposes the stretching force. This is an invaluable response, because without it man could not maintain the upright position. If he begins to sway or to fall, one or more muscle groups will be stretched (Fig. 5-6). Reflexly, the muscle will contract and thereby prevent the individual from toppling.

It should be apparent that the adequate stimulus for the so-called stretch reflex is stretching. The receptors activated by stretch are the proprioceptors which reside within the muscle and tendon. Thus when the muscle is stretched, the proprioceptor is activated and the afferent fiber is fired and conducts the impulse to the central nervous system. The impulse is facilitated across the synapse firing the efferent neuron which then conducts the impulse back to the muscle which was stretched. As a result, that very same muscle shortens and thus prevents itself from being significantly elongated.

This mechanism may be best illustrated by the classic **knee-jerk** (Fig. 5-7). One can readily demonstrate that if the relaxed leg is tapped just below the kneecap, the limb will swing forward. What happens is simply that one taps the tendon of the quadriceps muscle, thus stretching that muscle. The proprioceptors in the quadriceps muscle are fired, and according to the mechanism just outlined, that very same muscle shortens, and the lower limb swings out.

It should be emphasized that the main function of these stretch reflexes is to oppose gravity. For that reason they are often termed **antigravity reflexes.** If it were not for these reflexes, one would be required to make

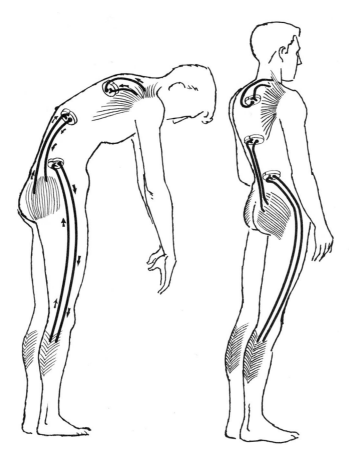

FIG. 5-6 The stretch reflex. This highly diagrammatic drawing shows that several groups of muscles are stretched when
man leans forward. In the stretched muscles are proprioceptors which initiate impulses which are carried to the cord.
As a result motor neurons are activated, the stretched muscles contract, and the individual is returned to the upright
position. Very slight stretching suffices; thus the amount of
leaning in any direction required to initiate the reflex is
almost imperceptible.

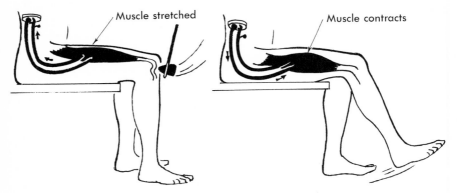

FIG. 5-7   The knee-jerk. Another example of a stretch reflex. Tapping the tendon of the quadriceps muscle stretches that muscle and, as a result of the reflex, the muscle contracts, causing extension of the leg.

a constant conscious or voluntary effort to keep the mouth closed, to maintain the body upright. It is common experience, of course, that one need not do these acts volitionally. The stretch reflexes serve that purpose. The force of gravity stretches the muscles initiating the reflex, and as a result, the muscles stiffen and maintain the upright position against the force of gravity.

The subject of **muscle tone** has already been discussed. Muscle tone is *the involuntary resistance to passive stretch*. It should be reemphasized at this point that the stretch reflex determines muscle tone. If the muscle is completely denervated, only the inherent elasticity of the muscle will oppose stretch. On the other hand, in the normal muscle the stretch reflex is initiated and the stretching process is resisted. The muscle in this case is said to possess tone. Obviously, if the reflex is hyperactive, the slightest stretch will evoke a disproportionately vigorous contraction. This muscle then is termed **hypertonic.** It should be evident that muscle tone may be altered by several factors. If the afferent or efferent limb of the reflex arc is cut, tone will be lost. If the nervous pathways from higher centers are severed, as in spinal-cord damage, for the period of spinal shock the muscle will be **atonic.** Lesions in various areas of the brain may modify either facilitation or inhibition and thus produce either increased or decreased tone. It is for these reasons that the clinician tests the reflexes and in this way appraises the muscle tone. Many clinical conditions are characterized by marked alterations in muscle tone. Accordingly, an accurate evaluation is an important diagnostic measure.

One condition which is worthy of brief consideration is so-called **decerebrate rigidity.** If the brain stem is cut just above the centers·which control respiration and circulation, a remarkable postural alteration occurs. The legs are held straight and rigid, the arms are also extended, the back is arched, the head is held high, and the jaws are tightly clamped. The mouth can be forced open only with great effort, the legs resist bending, and the trunk is curved backward. All the extensor muscles are strongly contracted, and any further stretching simple reinforces the already exaggerated contraction. This condition is believed to result from removal of inhibitory centers, which leaves the basic reflex mechanism overfacilitated, so to speak. *In short, the stretch reflexes function primarily to oppose gravity and determine muscle tone.*

Flexor Reflexes   If one inadvertently touches a hot stove, the arm is withdrawn. When one accidentally steps on a nail, the leg is lifted. If one bites down on a hard object, the mouth reflexly opens. These are everyday examples of the flexor reflexes. In all these instances the flexor muscles are involved, that is, muscle groups which are opposed to the extensor muscles utilized by the stretch reflexes.

The primary function of the flexor reflex is protection. The basic pattern is one of withdrawal from a painful or noxious stimulus. As in all reflexes, there must be a receptor. In these cases the receptor is called a **nociceptor,** derived from *nocere,* meaning "to injure." It logically follows that the nociceptor is *specialized nervous tissue sensitive to injurious stimuli.*

The flexor reflexes are somewhat more complicated than the stretch reflexes in that they usually involve more muscle groups. A stretch reflex is often operative in a single muscle. For example, the quadriceps muscle plays the major role in the knee-jerk. But it is obvious that, when one steps on a nail, one does not simply elevate a toe or flex the ankle. The entire limb is withdrawn. The efferent limb of this reflex clearly must involve several fibers passing to the numerous muscles which act to withdraw the entire lower extremity. Conceivably there may be only one afferent limb; and this pathway, by the anatomical arrangement known as **divergence** (page 75), activates the several efferent fibers.

The flexor reflexes, like the stretch reflexes, are under higher-center control. During the period of spinal shock these reflexes are also inactive. This evidence, along with other experiments, suggests that the flexor reflexes may be facilitated or inhibited.

Supporting Reflexes   Although it is true that the extensor muscles play the major role in supporting man against the force of gravity, the importance of the flexor musculature should not be overlooked. In the standing position the joints are fixed, thus converting the lower extremities into rigid pillars. In order to make possible such rigidity, both the flexor and extensor muscle groups must be partially contracted.

To avoid confusion at this point, some reiteration is necessary. Although we regard the stretch reflexes as involving, for the most part, the extensor muscles, it is a fact that the flexor muscles also contain proprioceptors. Hence, when they are stretched, the muscle will respond by shortening. On the other hand, these very same muscles contract in response to painful stimuli. The muscle is one and the same; the reflex pathways are distinct and serve distinctive purposes. Thus we see that the stretch-reflex component of the flexor muscles is essential in maintaining the limbs as rigid pillars which support the body against gravity. While upright, if the knee flexes the extensor muscles will be stretched and be caused to contract. On the other hand, if the knee threatens to bend in the other direction (overextend), the flexor muscles are stretched and caused to shorten. The net result is that the knee joint is held immobile and the individual remains upright.

All these reflexes not only function to support the individual but also aid in walking. As one foot is brought down and weight shifted to it, the extensor muscles are stretched and react accordingly. Moving forward still more, there is a tendency for overextension. Now the stretch reflexes in the flexor muscles are called into action, and the leg is fixed. The individual then lifts the leg, actively inhibiting the reflex action and at the same time removing the effective stimulus for the reflex, namely, stretch. The cycle is ready to begin again. It can be seen that it is rhythmical, coordinated, smooth, and quite graceful. This simple illustration serves to emphasize the status of the basic reflex mechanisms in the total physiological pattern of human operations.

ANATOMY OF VOLUNTARY MOVEMENT

The essential components of voluntary movement are (1) a primary motor fiber which arises from a cell body in the cerebral cortex, (2) a secondary fiber which leaves the brain stem or spinal cord and courses to the muscle, and (3) the skeletal muscle.

MOTOR AREAS

It has already been learned that a part of the human cerebral cortex is devoted to the appreciation of sensory stimuli. Other areas are concerned with the initiation of voluntary movement (Fig. 4-11). These are called the **motor areas.** If this region of the brain is stimulated, specific muscles are caused to contract. Such observations have been repeatedly verified in the human as well as in lower animal forms. In many brain operations, only a local anesthetic agent is used. Thus the patient is fully conscious but is simply freed of the pain of surgery. Under these conditions, stimulation of the motor areas brings about movement of different parts of the body depending on the region stimulated. Also, if this area on both sides of the brain is destroyed, then there results complete motor paralysis. Reflex movement will still be possible, but the individual will be incapable of voluntary activity. Thus it seems clear that the motor areas of the cerebral cortex are singularly responsible for the initiation of voluntary movement.

Area 4   It will be recalled that the cerebral hemispheres are divided into four lobes: (1) parietal lobe, (2) the occipital lobe, (3) the frontal lobe, and (4) the temporal lobe. It has been noted that the areas which are concerned with awareness of stimuli reside in the parietal lobe. These are designated as areas 3, 1, 2, 5, and 7. The motor regions, on the other hand, are located in the frontal lobe and are known as areas 4 and 6 (Fig. 4-11).

Area 4 lies just in front of the central fissure. This area is characterized by the presence of very large pyramidal-shaped cells. These are the **cells of Betz** and give rise to the primary motor fibers which descend through the brain stem and spinal cord. But in addition to these major tracts, area 4 also delivers fibers to subcortical nuclei. From our knowledge of these connections, it is clear that area 4 is equipped not only to initiate motor activity but also to carry out motion in a highly integrated manner.

Area 6   Area 6, also referred to as the **premotor area,** lies just in front of area 4. The very large Betz cells which characterize area 4 are not present in area 6. There are, however, small pyramidal cells. These cells give rise to fibers which connect area 6 with subcortical nuclei as well as with the cerebellum.

MOTOR PATHWAYS

Corticospinal Tracts   Figure 5-8 shows that from the Betz cells in area 4 long fibers arise which descend through the brain stem and into the spinal cord. These fibers collectively constitute the so-called **pyramidal tracts** or **corticospinal tracts.** It will be observed that most of these axons cross or decussate in the brain stem just before they descend into the spinal cord. In other words, impulses originating on one side of the brain activate muscles on the opposite side of the body. It follows, therefore, that paralysis of the muscles on one side of the body may be associated with a lesion in the cerebral cortex of the opposite side. This is the situation when man is afflicted with a "stroke." Usually there is a blood clot or hemorrhage on one side of the brain, causing paralysis of the opposite half of the body.

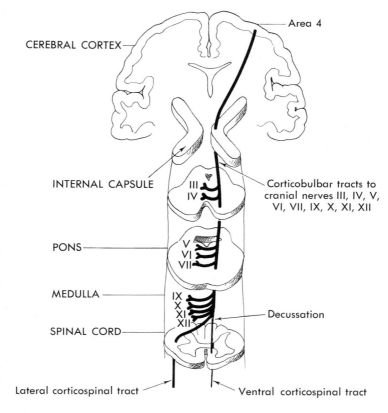

FIG. 5-8 Pyramidal tracts. Cells in area 4 give rise to neurons which descend to end in the brain stem to form the corticobulbar tracts. Others descend into the cord as the corticospinal tracts. Note that the corticobulbar and the lateral corticospinal neurons cross to the opposite side before terminating.

In the spinal cord, these fibers terminate at various levels in association with cells lying in the anterior- or ventral-horn substance. Some of the neurons which arise from the Betz cells of area 4 end in the brain stem. Figure 5-8 demonstrates that these primary neurons also cross. Thus the end result is the same as for the body; that is, the point-to-point relationship between the motor areas and all parts of the face, head, and body is crossed.

Extrapyramidal Tracts   From area 6 and other motor nuclei arise fibers which also descend into the brain stem and spinal cord (Fig. 5-9). These pathways are not so discrete, direct, or well delimited as the pyramidal

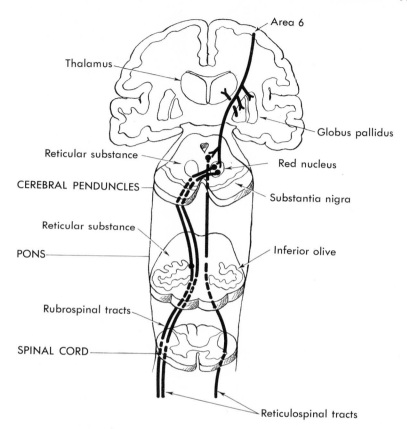

Area 6

Thalamus

Globus pallidus

Reticular substance

Red nucleus

CEREBRAL PENDUNCLES

Substantia nigra

Reticular substance

Inferior olive

PONS

Rubrospinal tracts

SPINAL CORD

Reticulospinal tracts

FIG. 5-9   Extrapyramidal tracts. Cell bodies in area 6 and in many subcortical nuclei give rise to descending neurons which collectively make up the complex extrapyramidal tracts.

tracts. The impulses conveyed by these tracts play an important role in the coordination of muscular movement. They are believed to be crossed just like the pyramidal pathways.

Association Pathways   There are many tracts which interconnect the primary motor areas which are essential to smooth, coordinated, purposeful muscular movement. These fibers convey the constant traffic of impulses which pass between the motor areas and practically all other parts of the brain. Thus muscular activity is not only coordinated but synchronized in the light of the position and status of the body at all times. As will be seen in subsequent chapters, these association routes are of the utmost importance.

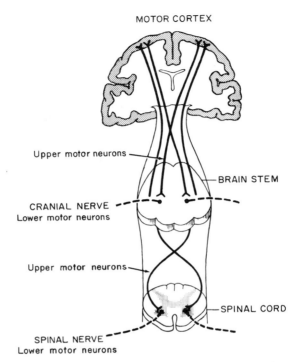

MOTOR CORTEX

Upper motor neurons

BRAIN STEM

CRANIAL NERVE
Lower motor neurons

Upper motor neurons

SPINAL CORD

SPINAL NERVE
Lower motor neurons

FIG. 5-10 Upper and lower motor neurons. The final common pathway, that is, the neuron that actually innervates the muscle, is the lower motor neuron. All other motor fibers are upper motor neurons.

Motor Neurons   It has been emphasized that the motor pathways involve a two-neuron chain. The fiber which arises in the motor cortex and ends either in the brain stem or in the spinal cord is termed the **upper motor neuron.** The neuron which originates in the brain stem or spinal cord and then courses out to the periphery to innervate muscle is called the **lower motor neuron** (Fig 5-10).

PHYSIOLOGY OF VOLUNTARY MOVEMENT

The particular function of the individual components which make up the motor system has been clarified by various procedures. By means of these techniques it has been found that area 4 is fundamentally concerned with discrete movement. It is important in the contraction of specific and individual muscles. Area 6, on the other hand, seems to control movement patterns involving groups of muscles. Finally, the subcortical nuclei and all the extrapyramidal pathways are essential to the coordination of voluntary movement.

DISCRETE MOVEMENT

If area 4 is stimulated in man, it is found that specific muscles may be caused to contract. From these studies it is clear that there is a point-to-point relationship between area 4 and all the muscles of the body. It is also evident that some areas of the body have a much larger cortical representation than do others.

Point-to-point Relationship Figure 5-11 demonstrates that each area of the body is represented on the motor cortex. It will be noted that this point-to-point relationship is inverted. When the top of area 4 is stimulated, the muscles of the hip contract. When the lower sections of area 4 are stimulated, the facial muscles move. In other words, there are Betz cells in the upper regions of area 4 which give rise to nerve fibers which traverse the brain and pass through the cord to the lowest segments. Here they transmit impulses to the lower motor neurons which then course to the muscles of the extremities. On the other hand, Betz cells from more inferior portions in area 4 project fibers only as far as the brain stem. From here the lower motor neurons convey the impulse to the muscles of the head.

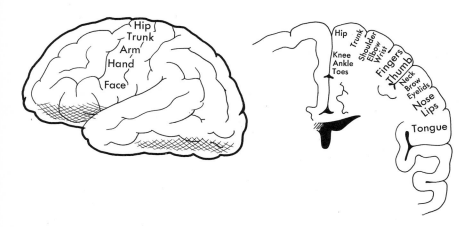

FIG. 5-11 Representation of the body in the motor cortex. There is a specific region of the motor cortex for each part of the body. Note that the order is reversed. Also observe that some parts of the body have larger representation than do others.

Cortical Representation   Figure 5-11 also demonstrates the unequal cortical representation of the various parts of the body. It will be readily seen
that the tongue and fingers have a relatively large representation, whereas
the body trunk has a very small area relegated to it. It has been shown
that the larger the cortical allocation, the greater the mobility and flexibility of the part. This is easy to understand, because a larger cortical
representation means that there are many Betz cells sending fibers to
specific muscles such as those of the tongue, lips, and fingers, as compared
to the muscles of the back and thigh.

When a nerve fiber reaches a muscle, it divides into several branches,
and each branch then innervates a single muscle fiber. Thus, a large part
of the muscle in innervated by one neuron. On the other hand, several
neurons may arborize very little, and yet the same amount of muscle
tissue may be innervated in this instance as in the former. The difference
is that in the second case there are more neurons, greater cortical representation, and consequently greater dexterity of the muscle. In the first
instance, the entire muscle area must contract as a unit, whereas in the
second case it is possible to contract small segments of the muscle. This
relationship between neurons and muscle fibers is sometimes referred to
as the **innervation ratio.** One can thus say that the greater the innervation ratio (neuron-to-muscle fiber relationship), the greater and more
precise and delicate the movement.

Decortication   The removal of the cerebral cortex is termed decortication. This can be done in experimental animals without fatal results. In
man, a condition comparable in some ways to decortication is seen in
cases of massive hemorrhage involving the internal capsule. In lower
animals, decortication does not cause paralysis. The motor deficit becomes progressively more severe in higher forms. Yet even in primates
some movement is still possible following recovery from the operation.
But this is a very gross movement completely devoid of any influence
of learning or conditioning. In addition, there is a degree of rigidity.
Decorticate rigidity is not as marked as decerebrate rigidity. Movement,
although stiff and difficult, is often possible.

In experimental animals, the **placing** and **hopping** reactions are dis-
rupted by decortication. In the placing reaction an animal will lift its
legs and place them on the surface, say of a table, when the animal's leg
are touched to the edge of the table. In the hopping response the legs
are quickly moved to support the animal when it is pushed sideways.
These reactions depend, to a great extent, upon the integrity of the
cerebral cortex. Thus, these reactions are used to evaluate cortical integrity in experimental animals.

COORDINATED MOVEMENT

BASAL GANGLIA

The basal ganglia, also called subcortical nuclei, are extremely important centers of coordination. The basal ganglia include the **caudate, putamen, and globus pallidus** nuclei. The putamen and globus pallidus together are referred to as the **lenticular nucleus.** The caudate and lenticular nuclei together with the internal capsule which separates them constitute the **corpus striatum.**

The clue to the function of the basal ganglia is provided by experiments in which the various nuclei are stimulated. If no movement is taking place, stimulation of the basal ganglia is usually without demonstrable effect. However, if movement is first elicited, for example, by stimulating the motor cortex, then activation of the basal ganglia promptly inhibits that movement. From this and other lines of evidence, it is generally believed that the major function of the basal ganglia is inhibition. The general activation or facilitation resulting from cortical activation can thus be appropriately inhibited by the basal ganglia and thereby bring about orderly, smooth, purposeful, and coordinated movement. To put it another way, movement is initiated by the motor cortex, but this "raw" movement clearly needs refinement. Such seems to be the role of the basal ganglia.

ABNORMALITIES OF VOLUNTARY MOVEMENT

During an earlier consideration of skeletal muscle, some of the locomotion abnormalities were mentioned. These disorders are due to a pathologic condition within the muscle itself. There are, however, many other conditions in which muscular activity is deranged but in which the difficulty lies within the nervous system and is manifest only in abnormalities of voluntary movement.

PARALYSIS

Paralysis is the most common abnormality of voluntary movement. Paralysis means the loss of voluntary movement. It is important to bear in mind that in many types of paralysis reflex movement of the part may still be elicited even though that same region cannot be moved volitionally. For example, following damage to the middle of the spinal cord, a man may be unable to move his leg even though it is still possible to evoke the knee-jerk.

Generally speaking, there are two types of paralysis: (1) **flaccid paralysis** and (2) **spastic paralysis.**

Flaccid Paralysis   It will be recalled that the tonus of a muscle depends on the activity of the stretch reflex. If the reflex arc is interrupted, the muscle will become flaccid. If the reflex chain is unduly inhibited, flaccidity will follow. On the other hand, if the reflex is abnormally facilitated (that is, if it is hyperactive), the muscle will be highly sensitive to stretch and will accordingly be spastic.

From these basic facts it is possible to surmise under what conditions the flaccid type of paralysis will be observed. The most common cases, of course, involve damage to the lower motor neuron. The lower motor neuron not only serves as the efferent limb of the reflex arc but also functions as the secondary neuron in the voluntary motor chain. It is for this reason that the lower motor neuron is often termed the **final common pathway.**

If the lower motor neuron is severed, it is obvious that the part cannot be moved either voluntarily or by reflex action. This is true because there is no route for the impulse to reach the muscle, and skeletal muscle normally responds only to nervous stimulation. One can still cause the muscle to contract by artificial means, such as direct electrical or mechanical excitation, but in so far as the individual is concerned there is unquestionably loss of volitional movement. There is, in short, paralysis. But in addition there is no longer any response to stretch, because the efferent limb of the stretch reflex has been interrupted. The muscle cannot, therefore, resist stretch, and it appears soft and flabby. It will be flaccid. This muscular state is logically termed **flaccid paralysis.**

It has been emphasized that muscle tonus reflects the status of the stretch reflex. Theoretically, then, it may be supposed that even with the lower motor neuron intact a flaccid type of paralysis could be found if the lesion were to involve an important facilitatory center leaving an inhibitory dominance. This theory has been substantiated under experimental conditions. If area 4, and only area 4, is destroyed without harming area 6, then a flaccid paralysis follows. Likewise, if the pyramidal pathways are cut carefully so as to leave all other nerve tracts undamaged, flaccid paralysis ensues. It seems clear that area 4, in addition to being the primary motor area, is also an important facilitatory center. When it is destroyed or its influence censored, inhibition dominates the stretch reflex and flaccidity occurs. In clinical cases, this type of paralysis is rarely seen in the absence of lower-motor-neuron damage, probably because the lesions are seldom so selective. Extrapyramidal areas and tracts are usually also involved, and the type of paralysis is spastic. Thus, when the clinician detects a flaccid paralysis, he usually suspects a lower-motor-neuron lesion.

Spastic Paralysis   From the basic mechanisms thus far considered, it should be clear that in order to demonstrate a spastic type of paralysis there should be damage to the voluntary motor system but at the same time the stretch-reflex mechanism must remain intact. Hence, the lesion must involve higher brain centers or the upper-motor-neuron pathways.

If the hypothesis is correct that reflex action is controlled by higher centers and that reflex activity at any one moment reflects the balance between facilitation and inhibition, then it must follow that for unknown reasons lesions involving the higher centers and pathways interfere more with inhibition than with facilitation. Almost invariably such injuries result in spastic paralysis, a condition in which the stretch reflex is indeed highly facilitated so that the muscle is firm, hypersensitive, and strongly resistant to stretch. These are the clinical findings in a case of "stroke" where hemorrhage has occurred within the brain.

In this type of paralysis there is loss of voluntary movement, but the part can still be easily moved by reflex action. If the spinal cord is cut, for example, the individual cannot willfully move his leg. But in response to a sharp tap below the knee, the leg will shoot out vigorously and the muscle will be firm and hard.

For all practical purposes, then, a flaccid paralysis in man suggests a lower-motor-neuron lesion; a spastic paralysis indicates abnormality at higher levels.

TREMORS

The term **tremor** means "shaking." There are many conditions in which a person will tremble or exhibit a tremor. Trembling is a conspicuous finding in some psychological states. This type of tremor is usually transient and not associated with any organic changes in the central nervous system. Thus an individual may tremble when he is frightened. On the other hand, there are conditions in which nervous-system lesions give rise to tremors. Some tremors persist only during the waking hours. There is the characteristic rhythmic muscular contraction and relaxation which is beyond the individual's capacity to control or inhibit. In other cases, the tremor appears only when fine muscular movements are executed. This latter type is termed as **intention** or **terminal tremor.**

Nonintention Tremors   The nonintention tremor may wax and wane. In a condition known as **parkinsonism,** for example, there are periods when the patient is almost without tremor while at other times the disorder is so intense as to shake the entire body. The term nonintention tremor is used to distinguish it from the intention or terminal tremor which occurs only when the person attempts a delicate, controlled muscular gesture.

As yet there is no satisfactory explanation for the former type. The movement is indeed involuntary and cannot be controlled. In many such clinical cases, autopsy has disclosed lesions in one or more of the sub-cortical motor nuclei. It is believed that these nuclei are inhibitory centers. It may well be that the motor areas of the cerebral cortex fire continuously and under normal conditions this incessant barrage is in-hibited or contained by the subcortical nuclei until voluntary movement is desired. However, when there is damage to these nuclei, some of the impulses from the motor areas break through the funnel down to the final common pathway, producing rhythmic, involuntary, purposeless muscular contractions, that is, a tremor. It is interesting to observe that in many such conditions there is also some degree of spastic paralysis. This added evidence supports the contention that inhibitory nuclei are deranged. However, at present the mechanism by which the tremor is pro-duced is still obscure. All that can be said is that the difficulty apparently resides in higher centers, possibly in most instances in the subcortical motor nuclei.

Intention Tremor In adult man, complex muscular acts are executed with such ease, with so little conscious attention, that we often fail to appreciate just how complicated the act is and what superlative degree of synchrony is required. This fact is dramatically illustrated, however, when a patient with a nervous-system lesion which destroys this superb degree of coordination is observed. The patient's hand begins to shake, to tremble more and more as the movement becomes finer and finer. When such a person attempts to feed himself, his hand will be quite steady until it begins to approach the lips. Then it will begin to shake, and as he comes closer and attempts to guide the fork into his mouth the tremor will become very pronounced. The tremor may become so severe that the fork cannot be introduced into the mouth. The difficulty lies in the loss of coordination which makes it possible to guide the hand with smoothness and accuracy. This type of tremor is usually due to cerebellar dysfunction. The great role of the cerebellum in coordination will be considered in Chap. 9.

SUMMARY

The bones of the skeleton are in **articulation** with one another. They are held together by **ligaments**. Some articulations are freely movable, others less so, and some totally immobile. Skeletal muscle moves the bones of the body and is connected to the bones by **tendons**.

A **reflex** is an involuntary response to a stimulus. The simplest reflex involves a **receptor,** an **afferent limb,** a **synapse,** an **efferent limb,** an **effector organ,** and the pathways which impinge upon it from higher brain centers. The reflex **latent period** includes the time required for transmission of the impulse over the pathways plus the delay in the synapse and neuromuscular junction. In addition, training apparently can alter this period.

Impulses arriving at the synapse between the afferent and efferent limbs from higher centers may **facilitate** or **inhibit** the transmission of the impulse across the synapse. Following spinal-cord section in man, all reflex action below the lesion is lost. This condition is called **spinal shock.** The loss of reflex response is thought to be due to the removal of the dominant facilitatory influence.

The effective stimulus of the **stretch reflex** is stretch, which eventuates in muscular contraction. The main purpose of this mechanism in skeletal muscles is to oppose gravity. The stretch reflex determines **muscle tonus.** In **decerebrate rigidity,** there is an exaggeration of the stretch reflexes so that all extensor muscles are in a hypertonic state. The **flexor reflexes** serve to protect man. Injurious circumstances excite the **nociceptors,** and as a result, the part is withdrawn to a safe position. The **supporting reflexes** involve both the extensor and flexor muscle groups and serve to keep man erect as well as to aid in locomotion.

Voluntary movement is initiated by **areas 4** and **6** in the frontal lobe of the cerebral cortex. Area 4 is the primary motor area. It is characterized by the presence of very large pyramidal cells called **Betz cells** which give rise to **upper motor neurons.** The axons of these neurons descend into the brain stem and spinal cord. The **lower motor neurons** arise from cells residing in the brain stem and spinal cord and conduct the impulses to the muscles. The upper motor neurons arising in area 4 descend in the **pyramidal tracts.** All other upper motor neurons originating in area 6, or the subcortical nuclei, form collectively the **extrapyramidal tracts.**

There is a point-to-point relationship between the motor area and all the muscles of the body. The greater the **innervation ratio,** the broader the cortical representation, the more specific, the more delicate, the act. Area 4 is responsible for the discrete activity of individual muscles. Area 6 is concerned with movement patterns. The **basal ganglia** (subcortical nuclei) serve to integrate muscular movement. They play, for the most part, an inhibitory role.

Interference with any part of the motor system results in **paralysis.** If the lesion is in the lower motor neuron, the paralysis is **flaccid.** If the disorder involves the upper motor neuron or higher centers, the paralysis is usually **spastic.**

QUESTIONS

1. What is a reflex?
2. How do stretch and flexor reflexes differ?
3. How are reflexes inhibited?
4. What is the function of area 6 of the cerebral cortex?
5. What type of paralysis is produced by severing the final common pathway? Why?
6. What is the difference between flaccid and spastic paralysis?

SUGGESTED READING

Brodal, A., "Spasticity—Anatomical Aspects," *Acta Neurol. Scand.,* **38:** Suppl. #3, 9–40, 1962.

Brumlik, J., "On the Nature of Normal Tremor," *Neurology,* **12:**#3, 159–179, March 1962.

Day, M. A., "Postural Reflex Pattern," *Nursing Res.,* **13:**#2, 139–147, Spring 1964.

Jansen, J. K. S., "Spasticity—Functional Aspects," *Acta Neurol. Scand.,* **38:** Suppl. #3, 41–51, 1962.

Lundberg, A., and Voorhoeve, P., "Effects from the Pyramidal Tract on Spinal Reflex Arcs," *Acta Physiol. Scand.,* **56:** 201–219, November–December 1962.

Mettler, F. A., and Stern, A., "On the Pathophysiology of Athetosis," *J. Nervous Mental Disease,* **135:**#2, 138–146, August 1962.

Vision

6

THE BASIC components of the nervous system have been considered in previous chapters. The nervous system consists essentially of a mechanism for perceiving changes in the environment and another system for reacting to that environment. Part of the motor member is under voluntary control. Another segment, the autonomic system, operates outside the voluntary sphere of influence. In subsequent chapters an attempt will be made to demonstrate the incredible degree of coordination which is required for the nervous system to operate as an integrated and purposeful whole. But first there are highly developed and important special systems which must be considered such as vision, audition, olfaction, and gustation. These are sensory functions, but they differ in many respects from the simple appreciation of pain and temperature, and of touch and pressure.

Vision is the most important of all the senses. Blind people can and do learn to depend upon the other senses to a remarkable degree, but for the loss of vision there is never anything approaching complete compensation. We rely upon vision for protection, for equilibration, for coordination, for creation, and for pleasure.

Fundamentally, the sense of vision is similar to all other sensory modalities in that there are receptors (sensitive to light, in this instance), there is an afferent pathway which conveys the impulses to the cerebral cortex, and there is an area of the cerebrum necessary for the appreciation of light. In addition, the afferent limb unites by synaptic union with diverse efferent limbs for reflex responses to vision. But vision is far more complex than the relatively primitive modalities of pain and temperature. In order to understand fully the means by which man sees, it is necessary to consider the physics, anatomy, physiology, biochemistry, and psychology of vision.

PHYSICS OF VISION

PROPERTIES OF LIGHT

Light Wave   Light is a form of radiant energy which travels in waves at the rate of about 300,000 kilometers per second. The length of each wave varies from 3.85 to 7.60 ten-thousandths of a millimeter. This is obviously an inconvenient way of expressing the wavelength of light. Light wavelengths are sometimes measured in **angstroms** or, as is now more common, in **millimicrons**. A millimicron is, as the term indicates, 1/1,000 of 0.001 mm. Put more simply, a millimicron is equal to 1/1,000,000 mm. A millimicron is usually designated by the symbol $m\mu$. The wavelengths of light which can be perceived by the human eye may then be said to range from about 385 to 760 $m\mu$ (3,850 to 7,600 angstroms since 1 angstrom = 0.1 $m\mu$).

Refraction   The word refraction means "to bend" or "turn aside." This is precisely what occurs when a ray of light passes from one medium into another of different refractive index. If the light penetrates a transparent medium at a right angle, there is no bending. But, as shown in Fig. 6-1, when rays of light pass at an angle from air into a medium of different refractive index, the beam is bent. The bending results from the fact that the velocity of light is determined by the optical density of the medium it traverses. The more dense the medium, the slower is the speed of light through it. It can be seen, therefore, that if rays of light are projected through air into a dense medium at an angle, the rays on one side of the beam will still be in the less dense medium for a fraction of a second after the rays on the other side have already entered. In observing a beam of light passing from its source into air (one medium), thence into water (a second medium of greater optical density), and emerging again into air, at any instant during the observation we view the components of the beam at different velocities. An apparent change in the direction of the beam occurs at each interface between mediums of different optical density. The angle that the beam makes with a perpendicular line extended from the surface of the denser medium is the angle of refraction. The **index of refraction** is the ratio of the velocity of light in air to the velocity of light in the denser medium. It will be noted that when the light strikes the surface it is bent toward a line drawn perpendicular to the surface. On the other hand, when the light emerges from the glass into the air medium, it is bent away from this perpendicular axis. The two angles are identical; thus the rays of light entering and emerging are truly parallel.

The general law of refraction may be summarized as follows. Light, in passing from a rarer medium (air) to a denser medium (glass), is refracted

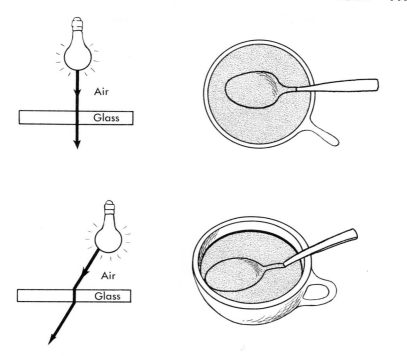

FIG. 6-1 Refraction of light. Whenever light passes from one medium into another medium of different density it is bent if the rays strike the new medium at an angle.

toward the perpendicular; when light is caused to pass from a denser medium into a rarer medium, it is bent *away* from the perpendicular.

LENSES

A **lens** is a transparent substance which causes light to converge or diverge. Artificial lenses are usually made of glass and possess two surfaces. The two surfaces may be convex or concave, or one may be convex and the other concave. It is also possible to have one surface straight and the other either convex or concave.

Convex Lens By referring to Fig. 6-2, one can see that the passage of light through a lens follows the general rules of refraction. This is true whatever the type of lens. In the case of a biconvex lens, the parallel rays are bent on entering the lens and bent again, in the same direction, as they emerge. If the ray of light strikes the center of the lens, it passes through without being refracted. This is true because the ray of light at that point is already perpendicular to the surface of the lens. On the other hand, the rays striking the lens at every other point are oblique in relation to the lens surface. For example, consider the uppermost ray. It can be seen that as the ray of light enters the denser medium it is bent down, that is, deflected toward the perpendicular. When this same ray emerges into the rarer medium, it is also bent down, but this time away from the perpendicular. The lowermost ray follows the same principles of refraction and is bent up both upon entering and upon emerging from the denser medium. The net result of a biconvex lens, then, is to cause the parallel rays to **converge**. The light rays converge to meet at a point. This point is termed the **principal focus** of the lens.

Strictly speaking, light rays are rarely parallel. But when the light source is at a considerable distance from the lens, for all practical purposes the rays of light may be considered parallel. If the light source is close to the lens, the rays will diverge as they approach the lens. From Fig. 6-2 it can be gathered that the closer the source of light to the lens, the farther back will be the point of focus. Accordingly, it is proper to speak of the focal point of parallel rays as the principal focus, whereas the focal point of diverging rays of light is known as the **conjugate focus**.

Concave Lens   Employing the same basic principle of refraction, it is simple to determine the manner in which light passes through a biconcave lens. Figure 6-2 demonstrates that rays of light are dispersed by such a lens. The rays of light which strike the top of the lens are bent up on entering and in the same direction as they emerge. The rays striking the bottom of the lens pass in the opposite direction. Thus the emerging rays diverge and no focus is attained.

Diopter   The power of a lens to refract light depends upon two factors: (1) the substance used and (2) the curvature of the lens. For example, the higher the refractive index, the greater will be the refraction. In actual practice, however, most lenses have the same density. Thus variations in refraction are achieved by altering the curvature of the surfaces. Figure 6-3 demonstrates that the greater the curvature, the greater will be the refraction.

The ability of a lens to bend light, that is, its strength, is measured according to its **focal distance**. The focal distance is the number of centimeters the principal focus lies from the center of the lens. An arbitrary distance of 100 cm has been taken to represent the unit of measure of lens strength. This unit has been termed the **diopter**. The term diopter is derived from two Greek stems and means "to see through." In a sense, the term implies the ability to see through the lens, or its power to bring parallel rays into focus. A lens which focuses parallel rays of light at a point 100 cm away has a strength of 1 diopter. If the lens is more convex

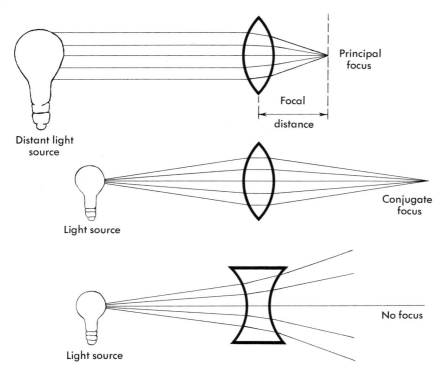

FIG. 6-2   Convex and concave lenses. A convex lens brings rays of light to a focus; a concave lens does not.

and focuses parallel rays at a point only 20 cm away, it has a strength of 5 diopters (100/20).

One might suspect from the definition of a diopter that only the strength of a biconvex lens can be so indicated. This is, however, not the case. If a biconcave lens is placed between a convex lens and the principal focus, the focal point will be caused to recede. Thus convex lenses are arbitrarily designated as plus and concave lenses as minus. The strength of a concave lens may be determined by ascertaining the angle of refraction of parallel rays and then extrapolating them back to a virtual focal point on the same side of the lens as the source of light. The distance from the center of the lens to the focal point is then measured. Again 100 cm is taken as 1 diopter, in this case −1 diopter. Thus if the focal distance is 50 cm, the concave lens would have a power of −2 diopter (Fig. 6-3).

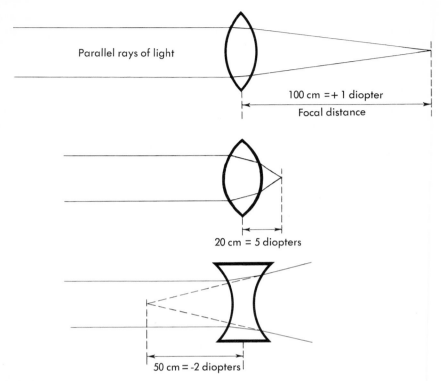

FIG. 6-3 Determination of lens power. A lens that brings parallel rays of light to a focus at a focal distance of 100 cm has a power of +1 diopter.

ANATOMY OF VISION

The anatomical structures essential to vision are (1) the **eye,** (2) the **visual pathways,** and (3) the **visual areas** of the cerebral cortex.

THE EYE

The Eyeball   Figure 6-4 shows a cross-sectional diagram of the eyeball. The outer layer consists of a tough, resistant material. It is termed the **sclera,** which means "hard." The sclera gives shape and substance to the eyeball. The most anterior or forward continuation of the sclera is transparent. This area is referred to as the **cornea,** which connotes the horny nature of this tissue. It, too, is a tough, resistant material and thus not only permits the passage of light but effectively protects the eye. On the inside of the posterior or back two-thirds of the eyeball is the **retina.** Retina means "a net," and that quite accurately describes the network of highly specialized nerve cells and their processes. There are about 130,000,000 such cells in each eye. These cells are the receptors sensitive to light. The image is focused on this layer. Consequently, the receptors are activated and the impulses transmitted via the optic pathways to appropriate centers in the cerebral cortex. The processes from all the nerve cells which reside in the retina gather together to make up the **optic nerve.** The retina consists of two types of visual cells: (1) the **rods** and (2) the **cones.** These cells differ not only anatomically but physiologically as well.

Between the retina and the sclera is a layer of tissue called the **choroid,** which means "skinlike," because this layer resembles the corium or true skin. The choroid layer, like the true skin, is extremely vascular. Its prime function is to supply blood to the other layers of the eyeball, especially the retina. Anteriorly, at the front of the eye, the choroid is modified and continues as the **ciliary muscles.** These muscles support and modify the shape of the lens.

The lens is a transparent, colorless body, consisting of a more or less semisolid substance enveloped by a very thin capsule. It can be seen from Fig. 6-4 that the human lens is biconvex although the anterior and posterior surfaces do not have identical curvatures. Thus it serves to converge rays of light and focus them on the retina. Just in front of the lens is a thin muscular layer called the **iris.** Iris is derived from the term meaning "rainbow" and probably refers to the fact that it is this structure which gives color to the eye. It has an opening at the center through which light may pass. This circular aperture is termed the **pupil.**

Examination of Fig. 6-4 reveals two spaces, one between the cornea and

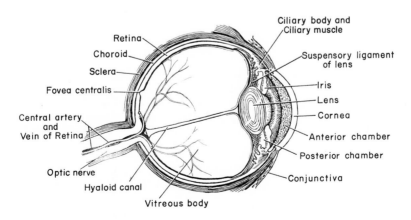

FIG. 6-4   Diagrammatic representation of the anatomy of the eye.

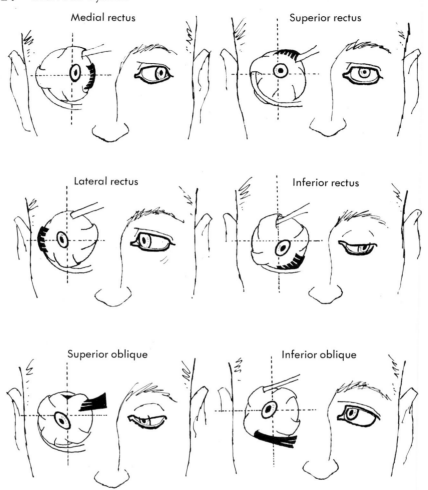

FIG. 6-5 Action of the extrinsic eye muscles. The actions of the recti muscles are easy to understand. The obliques are more complicated. The superior oblique attaches to the superior surface of the eyeball in such a way that it rotates the eyeball down and laterally. The inferior oblique is so attached to the inferior surface that contraction pulls the eyeball upward, but also laterally.

the lens and the other between the lens and retina. The more anterior space contains **aqueous humor,** while the posterior space is filled with a more viscid **vitreous humor.**

Extrinsic Eye Muscles　In man, the two eyes move together and possess considerable range of action. This movement is a function of the six muscles which are attached to each eyeball (Fig. 6-5). These extrinsic muscles are true skeletal muscles which are innervated by three of the cranial nerves.

There are 12 cranial nerves in all, and these are usually designated by their numbers. Some of these nerves have a purely sensory role, others contain only motor fibers, while the remaining ones possess both motor and sensory components. The cranial nerves which innervate the extrinsic eye muscles are purely motor in function. These are cranial nerves **III (oculomotor), IV (trochlear),** and **VI (abducens).**

Figure 6-5 illustrates the arrangement of the six extrinsic eye muscles. In a general way it can be noted that they are so distributed as to permit extremely varied movements of the eyeball. The innervation and action of each of these muscles are summarized in Table 6-1.

TABLE 6-1   The Extrinsic Eye Muscles

Eye Muscle	Cranial Nerve	Movement
Superior rectus	III	Up and in
Inferior rectus	III	Down and in
Medial rectus	III	In
Lateral rectus	VI	Out
Superior oblique	IV	Down and out
Inferior oblique	III	Up and out

It should be noted that the same muscle on either side moves the eye in opposite directions. For example, the lateral rectus will move the right eyeball to the right and the left eyeball to the left. Yet these muscles are both innervated by nerve VI. Normally both eyes will move either to the left or to the right. If movement is to the right, there must be contraction of the right lateral rectus and the left medial rectus. In other words, impulses must traverse cranial nerve VI on the right and cranial nerve III on the left. It should therefore be evident that movement of both eyes, so-called **conjugate movement,** which involves all the eye muscles, requires coordination at higher brain levels.

VISUAL PATHWAYS

The cell bodies which give rise to the primary fibers of the visual pathways reside in the retina. The processes from these cell bodies sweep across the internal surface of the retina to be gathered at a depressed point on the retina called the **optic disk.** It can be seen in Fig. 6-6 that fibers emerge from the eyeball as the **optic nerve** (see Fig. 6-4). It is important to note that the neurons which innervate the medial half of each retina cross at the **optic chiasm.** On the other hand, the fibers which

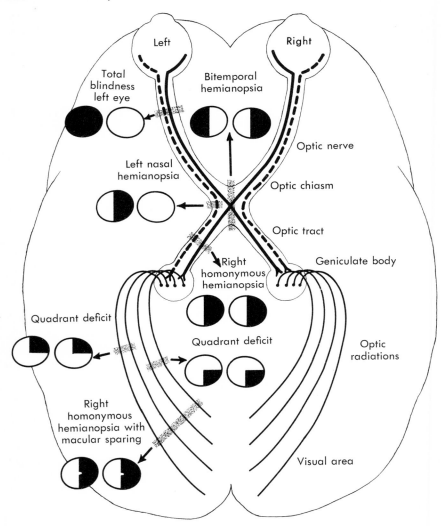

FIG. 6-6 **The optic pathways. Note that neurons that innervate the lateral halves of the retinas do not cross. The shaded bars indicate lesions. The deficit in the visual field for each lesion is shown.**

supply the lateral half of the retina do not cross but continue back on the same side. The two discrete pathways beyond the chiasm are known as the **optic tracts.** Most of these primary neurons terminate in a part of the brain called the **lateral geniculate bodies.** From these bodies arise the secondary neurons which collectively form the **optic radiations.** The secondary link in the optic chain is appropriately designated because the fibers are seen to fan out or radiate as they sweep around the temporal lobe to end in the occipital lobe of the cerebral cortex. The visual pathways, then, consist of a two-neuron chain.

VISUAL AREAS OF THE CEREBRAL CORTEX

The areas of the cerebral cortex essential for vision and the coordination of vision with other bodily functions are designated as **areas 17, 18, and 19** (see Fig. 4-11).

Area 17 is the primary visual area. Bilateral removal of this portion of the human occipital cortex results in total blindness. In lower animals it is possible to destroy area 17 and yet the organism retains some appreciation of light. In man, however, all visual responsibility has apparently been shifted to the cerebral cortex. Areas 18 and 19, on the other hand, may be destroyed without loss of vision, although the individual suffers marked impairment in the integration of vision with other activities. Areas 18 and 19 are known as **association areas.** They house cell bodies and pathways which integrate that which is seen with that which is done. For example, the presumably simple task of reaching for a glass is, in reality, a highly complex act. It can be readily understood that what we see must be coordinated with voluntary movement. The visual association areas, areas 18 and 19, serve man in this way.

PHYSIOLOGY OF VISION

Figure 6-7 is designed to illustrate the striking similarities between a camera and the human eye. They function in much the same manner. In the camera, the image is cast on the sensitive film by the lens. In the eye, the image falls on the sensitive retina. In the camera, there is a mecha-

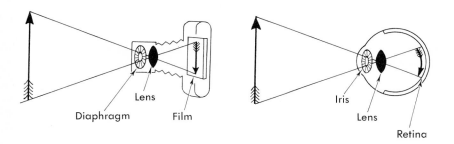

FIG. 6-7 Comparison of the eye with a camera. To focus a camera the focal distance is changed; to focus the eye the curvature of the lens is changed.

nism for bringing the image into sharp focus; the eye is also so equipped. In the camera, there is a diaphragm to regulate the amount of light which enters the lens. In the eye, the iris assumes this function. Finally, the image is inverted in both. The student who is familiar with simple photographic technique should have little difficulty in understanding the physiology of vision.

FORMATION OF THE IMAGE

Accommodation It should be recalled that the lens is biconvex. From our consideration of refraction we know that light rays, in passing through a biconvex lens, are caused to converge at the focal point. This is the point at which the image is sharpest. In other words, if a camera with a ground-glass back is used, it will be found that by shifting the lens back and forth the image passes in and out of focus. When the lens is held at a distance from the glass equal to the focal distance of that lens, the image appears sharp. The same rule applies to the eye. But in the human eye the distance between the lens and the retina cannot be varied. To effect a sharp image, the curvature of the lens must change. The alteration in lens curvature in order to focus the image sharply is termed **accommodation.** When an object is held close to the eye, the light rays diverge as they approach the eye. The radius of the curvature of the lens must be decreased so as to bend those rays more acutely in order to bring them to their focal point upon the retina. Conversely, when the object is at some distance, the rays are practically parallel. In this case they require little bending. Hence the lens is now flatter than in the previous example.

The curvature of the lens is controlled by the ciliary muscles. The eyeball contains fluid (vitreous and aqueous humors) under pressure. This intraocular pressure tends to hold the eyeball round and firm. The lens which is attached at its periphery to the suspensory ligaments is held taut and relatively flat (large radius of curvature) by intraocular pressure. When the ciliary muscles contract, the choroid layer is drawn forward. This releases the tension on the suspensory ligaments. The lens, because of its inherent elasticity, springs together and bulges. Thus the lens becomes more round and has a lesser radius of curvature.

It can be seen that when the ciliary muscle is at rest the intraocular pressure holds the lens stretched, with a relatively flat surface. In this position parallel light rays are brought to focus, in the normal eye, upon the retina. As the object is brought closer, the rays diverge and must be refracted or bent more. To do this, the lens must become rounder. The ciliary muscles contract, tension on the lens is reduced, and the lens, by its inherent elasticity, now assumes a rounder contour. Thus once again the light rays are focused on the retina. A point must obviously be reached a which the ciliary muscles are completely contracted and the lens is as round as it can possibly become. If the object is brought still closer, the eye will be unable to focus it sharply. This critical point is appropriately termed the **near point.** The normal human eye sees objects clearly from a near point of about 6 in. to infinity.

A knowledge of this mechanism reveals why the eye is at rest when viewing objects at a distance. Reading, on the other hand, requires the ciliary muscles to remain in a constant state of contraction. This may contribute to the fatigue which accompanies close work.

Corresponding Points In man, it is not only necessary that the object be focused for clear vision but the image must fall in both eyes on similar areas so that one sees a single image instead of two. A reexamination of Fig. 6-7 will underscore the fact that fibers from the medial half of one retina cross and then course to the cerebral cortex accompanied by fibers from the lateral half of the other retina. An object to the right of an individual, for example, will be focused on the inner half of the right retina and the outer half of the left retina. Neurons from these areas then transmit the image to the same area of the cerebral cortex, in this case area 17 in the left occipital cortex. In other words, there are points on each retina which correspond to points on the other retina so that the image is viewed as one. These are termed **corresponding points.**

The Blind Spot If the right eye is closed and Fig. 6-8 held about 8 in. from the left eye which is then focused on the cross, the circle may be seen. But if the figure is moved a little closer or farther away, a point will be reached where the circle disappears. This effectively demonstrates that there is a spot on the retina which is not sensitive to light. It is termed the **blind spot.** This is the place on the retina where the neurons

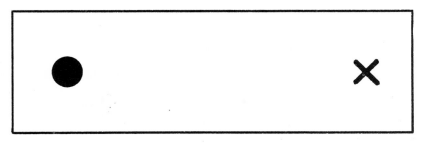

FIG. 6-8 The blind spot. To demonstrate that an area of the retina is insensitive to light, close the right eye and focus the left eye on the cross. Move the page closer or farther away until a position is found at which the spot cannot be seen.

turn through to form the optic nerve (Fig. 6-4). At this point there are no receptors; accordingly, there is no vision.

Visual Acuity In order to see an object clearly, the object must be focused on the retina. But there are still other factors which determine visual acuity. They are (1) the size of the object and (2) the distance of the object from the eye. If two small marks are inscribed very close together on a piece of paper, they will appear as two distinct marks when the paper is held fairly close to the eye. However, at a distance they will be seen to fuse into one mark. In order for two objects to be differentiated as distinct entities, it is necessary for the resulting image of these objects to cover two or more retinal receptors. In actual practice, visual acuity is tested with standard charts known as **Snellen charts** (Fig. 6-9). The standard distance from the chart to the eye is arbitrarily set at 20 ft. At this distance, letters of a certain size can be identified with the normal eye. That line of letters is labeled 20. If, while standing 20 ft from the chart the subject can read the line marked 20, then his visual acuity is normal and is said to be 20/20. On the other hand, if he can only read a line with larger letters, say one marked 30 (which normal vision could read at 30 ft) then his visual acuity it 20/30, and so forth.

VISUAL REFLEXES

When a distant object is brought progressively closer to the eye, three important changes in the visual mechanism take place: (1) accommodation, (2) convergence, and (3) constriction of the pupil. Accommodation is designed to focus the image sharply on the retina. Convergence assures the image of striking corresponding points. Constriction of the pupil decreases the amount of light which enters the eye. All these are essential to visual acuity. They are all involuntary; hence they are reflex mechanisms.

Accommodation Reflex Not all the components of the accommodation reflex have as yet been clarified. It is clear that the optic nerve forms the afferent limb and that the parasympathetic component of cranial nerve III (oculomotor) makes up the efferent limb, but the central connections remain obscure. It seems logical that the effective stimulus to evoke changes in the lens is an unclear image, that is, one which is out of focus. Accordingly, the impulses so elicited must be transmitted to the visual cortex and then back to the **tectal region** of the brain where the cell bodies of the involuntary motor fibers are situated. These fibers are part of the oculomotor nerve. Destruction of cranial nerve III, then, not only would partially paralyze extrinsic eye movement but also would prevent accommodation due to interruption of the motor supply to the ciliary muscles.

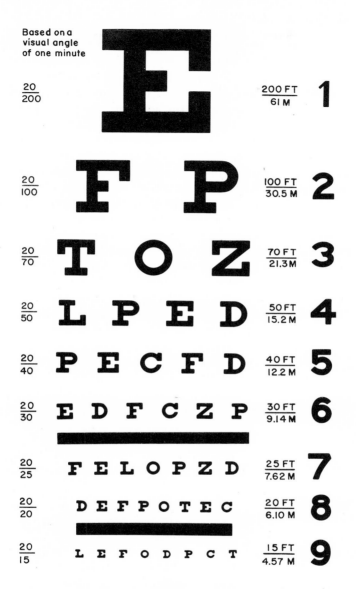

FIG. 6-9 A Snellen chart. Snellen charts are used to evaluate visual acuity. The subject stands 20 ft from the chart. This figure 20 is the numerator. The number of the line that can be clearly seen at this distance is the denominator. Normal vision would be 20/20.

Convergence Reflex Here again the afferent limb is the optic nerve, but now the efferent limb consists of the motor fibers of cranial nerves III, IV, and VI, which supply the extrinsic eye muscles. If the eyes did not converge as the object was brought forward, the image would not strike corresponding points. Apparently the formation of a double image is the effective stimulus which is transmitted to higher centers via the optic pathways and then back to the tectal region for activation of the nerves supplying the extrinsic eye muscles. As a result, the eyes turn synchronously, thus maintaining the image on corresponding points in each retina. Of course, in order to turn the eyes inward (Fig. 6-10), the lateral recti muscles must relax. These, it should be recalled, are innervated by cranial nerve VI (abducens). It is also necessary that there be relaxation of the superior oblique muscles, indicating that cranial nerves IV (trochlear) are also implicated. In other words, the convergence reflex is extremely complex, involving superb reciprocal innervation and a high degree of coordination of all its components.

Light Reflexes Visual acuity requires optimal illumination. Within a considerable range, the eye possesses its own mechanism for controlling the amount of light which strikes the retina. On a bright and sunny day the pupil appears extremely small, whereas at dusk it is usually relatively large. Changes in pupillary size are a function of the iris. The larger the pupil, the greater will be the quantity of light admitted into the eyeball.

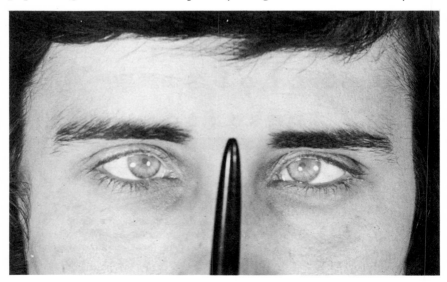

FIG. 6-10 Convergence reflex. As an object is brought closer to the eyes, the eyes reflexly turn inwards.

The smooth muscles which make up the iris are innervated by both divisions of the autonomic nervous system (Chap. 8). The intensity of the light which strikes the retina is the effective stimulus for initiating the light reflexes. If the light proves too strong for optimal visual acuity, impulses are fired via appropriate nervous pathways. As a result, the pupil constricts, thereby decreasing the amount of light which enters the eye. Conversely, a decrease in illumination, through a comparable reflex mechanism, causes the pupils to enlarge. If a light is directed into only one eye, *both* pupils will rapidly constrict. This is termed the **consensual light reflex** (Fig. 6-11). One must conclude from this observation that there exists an intimate connection between the two eyes.

In summary, it should be evident that a series of complicated reflexes

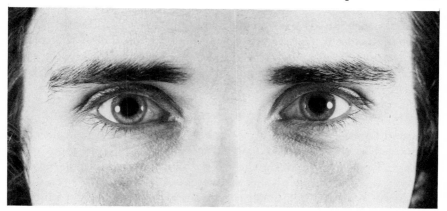

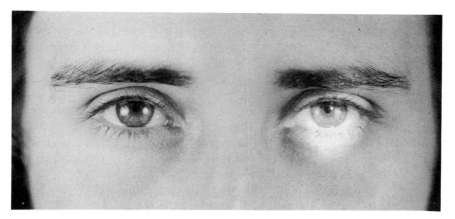

FIG. 6-11   Light reflex. As shown above, the pupils are large (dilated) before light stimulation. As shown below, a bright light focused on the left pupil causes both pupils to constrict (consensual light reflex).

brings the object into focus on corresponding points of the two retinas under optimal illumination. When the student ceases to gaze out of the window and turns his attention to this text, there are simultaneous *accommodation of the lenses, convergence of the eyeballs, and pupillary constriction.*

Protective Reflexes If the cornea is touched, the eyelids immediately close. This is a reflex mechanism of a protective nature. Thus, when the cornea is irritated, as by a foreign object blown into the eye, receptors fire impulses to the brain stem where they are transmitted across a synapse to motor neurons which effect the closing of the eyelids and the warding off of the foreign body.

In association with each eye there are **lacrimal glands** which, upon stimulation, produce a fluid in the form of tears. Tears are copiously produced when any foreign body comes in contact with the cornea. Lacrimation, too, is a protective reflex. Thus we see that if the corneal reflex is unsuccessful in blocking the ingress of a foreign body, the lacrimal reflex swings into action, supplying fluid to flush out the noxious agent.

VISION UNDER HIGH AND LOW INTENSITIES OF LIGHT

Rods and Cones It has already been mentioned that the light receptors are located in the retina. Actually, there are two different types of receptors: (1) the **rods** and (2) the **cones.** These structures not only are histologically distinct but also serve different functions. It has been shown that the cones are utilized under conditions of relatively bright illumination, whereas man relies upon the rods for vision in dim light. This arrangement allows the eye to function under a tremendous range of light intensities. It has already been noted that the iris regulates the quantity of light which strikes the retina, but obviously this mechanism has definite limitations. Under conditions of very low illumination, the pupil is maximally dilated. At this point the highly sensitive rods take over to increase the range of vision.

The greatest concentration of cones is found at the center of the retina. As the periphery is approached, the percentage of cones sharply decreases while the rod population becomes more dense, until a point is reached at which the retina consists only of rods. Thus in bright daylight we can examine an object best if we look directly at it; but at night, or under other conditions of very low light intensities, we can see objects better by looking to one side of them, thus permitting the object to fall on the rod-laden periphery of the retina.

Rhodopsin and Iodopsin Biochemists engaged in the study of vision demonstrated as long ago as 1878 that a chemical substance found in the retina plays a role in the adaptation of the eye to conditions of low illumination. The eye is capable of making several adjustments. In passing from the glaring sunlight into a darkened theater, the pupil rapidly dilates to admit the maximum available light. At the same time, the image is focused on the rods which are vastly more sensitive than the cones. Finally, a series of chemical changes takes place which increases the sensitivity of the rods even more. Extensive research now indicates that **rhodopsin** is the substance which is essential for the conversion of radiant energy of light into nerve impulses, that is, into electrical impulses which can be conveyed by the optic pathways. Bright light causes rhodopsin (or **visual purple,** as it is also called) to bleach. Under these conditions the rods are relatively inactive and the eye depends chiefly upon the cones. When the light intensity is once again reduced, rhodopsin is re-formed and the rods assume their appropriate role. The time required for the resynthesis of rhodopsin accounts for the time delay required to adapt the eye to night vision. It explains why, when an individual enters a darkened theater, he can see very little at first but after a few minutes is able to distinguish considerable detail.

The sequence of events of the rhodopsin cycle is now known. Figure 6-12 shows that light causes rhodopsin to be converted to **lumirhodopsin** which is then rapidly converted to **metarhodopsin.** Next metarhodopsin breaks down to **scotopsin** and **retinene.** These two substances are capable of slowly combining to re-form rhodopsin, thus completing the cycle. But it is important to note that retinene is in equilibrium with vitamin A. If there is too little vitamin A, retinene is converted to the vitamin and thus is not available for rhodopsin formation. For this reason individuals with vitamin A deficiency have difficulty seeing under conditions of low illumination.

For a long while this photochemical theory of vision was weakened by

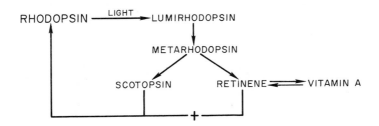

FIG. 6-12   The rhodopsin cycle. Rhodopsin is formed from sco-topsin and retinene. Vitamin A is essential for an adequate supply of retinene. Light causes the breakdown of rhodopsin.

the inability to demonstrate a comparable chemical substance in the cones. Recently, however, such an agent has been found. It is a violet pigment and is, accordingly, called **iodopsin.** This substance, it is thought, converts the radiant light energy into nerve impulses emanating from the cones.

COLOR VISION

The normal eye can appreciate and differentiate various colors. The mechanism which makes this possible is still not completely understood. A comprehensive consideration of color vision requires cutting a broad pathway through the physics, biochemistry, and psychology of vision, which is clearly beyond the scope of this text.

Mechanism of Color Vision We know that white light is made up of light of various wavelengths. When this light is broken down into its component parts, light of various colors is obtained. One of the leading theories of color vision assumes that the retina contains receptors which are sensitive to specific colors. This theory states that the three basic psychological and physiological colors of blue, red, and green stimulate specific receptors, and impulses are then transmitted to the visual cortex. Here, depending on the number of receptors being fired, mixing is done. As a result, we can appreciate the entire range of the color spectrum.

The cones are primarily concerned with color appreciation. As the light gradually decreases in intensity, we lose our color sense. At twilight all objects appear as varying intensities of gray. The rods apparently do not permit color vision.

Colorblindness Approximately 5 to 6 per cent of Americans cannot differentiate colors in the entire range. Careful testing reveals that they may not perceive one or even two of the basic colors. According to the above theory of color vision, it seems probable that such individuals suffer a congenital lack of one or more of the specific receptors required for color appreciation. Color vision is tested by the use of **Ishihara's plates.** They consist of dots of various colors with numbers formed by dots of specific colors. Individuals who are colorblind cannot identify the numbers.

The phenomenon of colorblindness has had a rather exciting history. Early in the Second World War it was felt that air-force personnel were seriously handicapped if they were colorblind. Later it was learned that these individuals are extremely well suited as observers in the detection of camouflage. This is so because camouflage is usually designed to mislead normal vision. Thus it was learned that these people can often detect the most well-executed camouflage techniques.

ABNORMALITIES OF VISION

Normal vision is a highly complex function involving many essential components. If any one of its constituents is impaired, there may be an abnormality of vision. The more common disturbances concern the eye itself, the visual pathways, and the visual cortex.

REFRACTIVE ERRORS

Myopia   Many people can see objects clearly only when held close to the eyes. They are therefore **nearsighted.** Everything in the distance is blurred. They have a tendency to squint, and the term **myopia,** which means "to half close the eyes," describes this condition.

Figure 6-13 demonstrates that the difficulty in many of these cases is that the eyeball is abnormally long. As a result, the focal point lies in front of the retina. The eye has no way in which it can accommodate itself to this condition. Only when objects are brought close to the eye and the light rays have diverged will they then be focused on the retina. Such individuals, in order to see distant objects, must wear glasses with **biconcave** lenses. Figure 6-13 illustrates how a concave lens causes parallel rays to diverge, thus permitting the lens of the myopic eye to focus them upon the distant retina.

Hyperopia   The reverse of myopia is also frequently encountered. In these cases the eyeball is shorter than normal. Consequently the individual must accommodate even when he looks at distant objects. As the object is brought closer, greater accommodation is required. In such cases the near point will be farther away than in a normal person.

The term **hyperopia** means "beyond the eye." If the lens did not accommodate, even for parallel rays of light, the image would, theoreti-

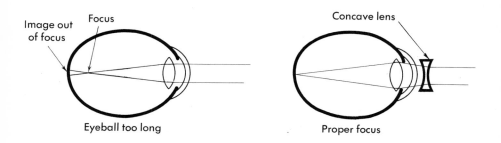

FIG. 6-13   Myopia. To compensate for the elongated eyeball, a concave lens is required.

cally, be focused behind the eyeball (Fig. 6-14). The important observation to note in these cases is that the lens must accommodate at all times. In other words, the ciliary muscle is always in a state of partial contraction. It can relax only when the eyes are closed. In the normal eye (**emmetropia**), distant objects are viewed with the ciliary muscle completely relaxed, but in the hyperopic eye this is not the case. The degree of contraction, of course, depends on just how short the eyeball is. Most young people, however, possess enough accommodation so that they can get along quite successfully without glasses. When they read, their eyes are maximally accommodated, and sometimes they report fatigue more readily than do others. There is a difference of opinion among experts as to whether or not glasses should be worn in mild cases of hyperopia. If the eyeball is so short that the individual cannot do close work, glasses are definitely indicated.

It is important to emphasize that there are other causes of both myopia and hyperopia than the length of the eyeball. For example, the eyeball may be of normal dimensions, but the curvature of the lens may be such that the image does not come to focus upon the retina.

Presbyopia The term **presbyopia** means "old eye." As one ages, various changes occur. There is a gradual loss of the ability to accommodate. Presumably the lens loses some of its elasticity, so that when the ciliary muscle pulls the choroid forward the lens does not become so round as it formerly did. As a result, the light rays cannot be bent as sharply. Thus there is a progressive recession of the near point with advancing age. Everyone is familiar with older people who must hold small print at arm's length in order to read it. The hyperopic eye, it will be recalled, must accommodate at all times, and for close work maximum accommodation is required. As the lens hardens with age, such changes are no longer possible. The individual may still see distant objects clearly, but for all

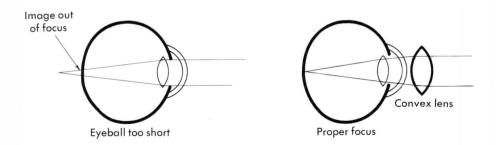

Image out
of focus

Eyeball too short

Convex lens

Proper focus

FIG. 6-14 Hyperopia. To compensate for the short eyeball, a convex lens is required.

close work glasses with biconvex lenses are essential. When the aging processes finally cause almost a complete loss of the power of accommodation, glasses are required in any case, and ones with two types of lenses are usually preferred. The person then looks through the top of the lens for distant objects and the lower part (which is a different lens) for close work. These glasses are called **bifocals.**

The near point, that is, the minimum distance from the eye that an object can be clearly seen, is a good measure of the ability of the eye to accommodate. In children and young adults the near point is less than 10 cm. Usually, between 40 and 50 years of age the near point recedes rapidly and by the time man is about 60 the near point is over 80 cm (Fig. 6-15).

Astigmatism   Thus far we have discussed lenses as being parts of a perfect sphere. The lens of the eye does not usually attain this perfection and in many cases is far from it. Consequently, different parts of the lens or cornea vary in refractive power. Therefore, when an individual looks at an object, some areas of it will be in focus whereas other parts will not be. The term **astigmatism** means "without a point." In other words, there is no point upon which the eye can focus all its rays (Fig. 6-16). Everyone has a degree of astigmatism, but it is usually so slight as not to inter-

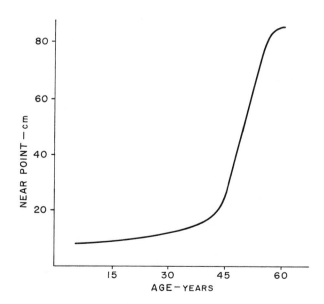

FIG. 6-15   Presbyopia. With age the power of accommodation decreases so that the near point recedes.

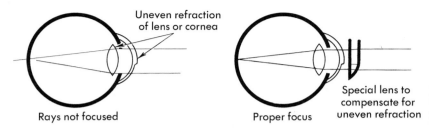

Uneven refraction of lens or cornea

Rays not focused

Proper focus

Special lens to compensate for uneven refraction

FIG. 6-16   Astigmatism. To compensate for uneven refraction of the lens or cornea, special lenses are required.

fere with work, or be noticeable. However, if the condition is severe, it proves very annoying and may promote fatigue and chronic headaches. Astigmatism is corrected by specially ground lenses which compensate for the inequalities of refraction.

LESIONS IN THE VISUAL PATHWAYS

A review of the visual pathways will make it obvious that a lesion which interrupts these tracts, or a part of them, will cause visual deficits. Figure 6-7 summarizes the more common locations where such lesions occur. In each case there is partial or half-blindness, termed **hemianopsia**. In designating the hemianopsia, we refer to the visual field and not the afflicted retinal area. For example, if the left optic tract is destroyed, no impulses will be received from the left half of the left retina or from the left half of the right retina. As a result, the individual will be half-blind and will see nothing to his right. He is said to have a **right homonymous hemianopsia**. The term homonymous refers to the fact that both right fields are involved. Hemianopsia means half-blindness. A careful study of Fig. 6-6 will disclose the anatomical basis of the various types of disorders due to lesions of the visual pathways, along with the proper designation of each.

LESIONS IN THE VISUAL CORTEX

Area 17   Complete destruction of area 17 on both sides results in total blindness. Figure 6-6 shows that if this area is destroyed on only one side there is homonymous hemianopsia, as is to be expected, but the central area of the blinded visual field is spared. The explanation for this observation is not yet certain, but it seems probable that some of the fibers which come from the central part of the retina cross over before they reach the visual cortex so that there is actually a dual cortical representation for this central retinal region. Thus, destruction of only one side of the visual cortex leaves central vision relatively unaffected.

Areas 18 and 19 It is believed that these areas serve to coordinate visual sensation with other bodily functions. However, since it is extremely difficult to remove them without interfering with area 17 or the optic radiations to area 17, the precise function of areas 18 and 19 cannot be stated. Patients who have tumors involving these areas have been studied. Such neoplasms are frequently associated with visual hallucinations. These people report seeing objects, usually highly developed patterns, which do not in fact exist. There may also be an inability to interpret the written word. The patient can see the word but can no longer translate its meaning. Yet in speech he will use the word in good context. In addition, there may be impairment of coordination between vision and muscular activity. Fortunately, such disorders in the visual cortex are not common.

SUMMARY

Light is a form of radiant energy which travels in waves. When it passes from one medium to another of different density, it is bent. This bending phenomenon is called **refraction**. Convex lenses converge light to a point termed the **principal focus**. Concave lenses diverge parallel light rays, and no image is formed. The strength of a lens is expressed in **diopters**. A lens which focuses parallel rays of light at a distance of 100 cm has a strength of 1 diopter.

In the eye, light is focused by the **lens** on the **retina** which consists of light-sensitive receptors. These cells are of two kinds: (1) the **rods** and (2) the **cones**. They give rise to fibers which are gathered together to form the **optic nerve**. In front of the lens is the **iris,** which controls the amount of light which enters the eye. The lens is elastic and held stretched by intraocular pressure. Contraction of the **ciliary muscle** opposes this pressure and allows the lens to bulge, become rounder, and thus exert greater refraction, or bending of light rays.

The lens focuses the light rays on the retina. Near objects cause the rays of light to diverge; thus the lens must bend them more to bring them to a focal point. This is called **accommodation**. A reflex mechanism controls the ciliary muscle. In order to see one image with both eyes, that image must fall on **corresponding points** on the two retinas. This is accomplished by having the eyes converge as the object is brought closer. **Convergence** is also a reflex mechanism. The third reflex evoked by bringing an object closer is **constriction** of the pupil. The iris responds to changing intensities of light. The eye is protected by the **corneal reflex** and the **lacrimal mechanism.**

The cones are not as sensitive as are the rods and are utilized under conditions of bright illumination. In low intensities of light the highly sensitive rods make vision possible. The transformation of the radiant energy of light into nerve impulses in the rods is believed to be the function of **rhodopsin. Iodopsin** is said to serve this role for the cones. The cones are essential to color vision. The rods can discern only varying intensities of gray. It is believed that there are receptors sensitive to three basic colors—red, green, and blue. The mixing of these colors to result in the perception of all hues is thought to occur in the visual cortex. Some individuals cannot perceive one or perhaps two of the basic colors. They are said to be **colorblind.** This condition may be due to a congenital lack of the proper color receptors in the retina.

Myopia is a condition characterized by an elongated eyeball which causes the image to be focused in front of the retina. In **hyperopia,** the eyeball is too short, and constant accommodation is required to focus the image on the retina. **Presbyopia** is an abnormality of old age in which the lens hardens and the range of accommodation is decreased so that the near point recedes. **Astigmatism** is a condition of unequal refraction by the lens or cornea so that part of the image is in focus while other parts are blurred.

Disturbances involving areas 18 and 19 may produce visual hallucinations, loss of coordination, or failure to interpret the written word.

QUESTIONS

1. Make a drawing showing how convex and concave lenses bend rays of light.
2. How does the normal eye keep the object in focus as it moves closer to the eye?
3. What protective reflexes does the eye possess?
4. Describe the changes which occur in the eye under conditions of low illumination.
5. Discuss one theory of color vision.
6. What is the difference between myopia and hyperopia?

SUGGESTED READING

Brown, P. K., and Wald, G., "Visual Pigments in Single Rods and Cones of the Human Retina," *Science,* 144:#3614, 45–52, April 3, 1964.

"Cranial Nerve Examination," *Spectrum,* 6:#15, 416–417, September 1, 1958.

Crescitelli, F., "Physiology of Vision," *Ann. Rev. Physiol.,* 22: 525–578, 1960.

Hubel, D. H., "The Visual Cortex of the Brain," *Sci. American,* 209:#5, 54–62, November 1963.

Land, E. H., "The Retinex," *Am. Scientist,* 52: 247–264, 1964.

Rushton, W. A. H., "Visual Pigments in Man," *Sci. American,* 207:#6, 120–132, November 1962.

Audition, Olfaction, Gustation

7

VISION IS BY FAR THE MOST IMPORTANT OF THE SPECIAL SENSES. It is for this reason that so much space has been devoted to its analysis. The other special senses of audition, gustation, and olfaction have progressively less importance, in that order. Audition ranks perhaps almost with vision, but certainly in man, olfactory acuity has been allowed to atrophy. Lower animal forms are far more dependent upon an acute sense of smell than we are. In fact, in many cases, actual survival hinges upon the animal's ability to find food and to avoid his enemies. A keen sense of smell is important to the animal for these purposes. Modern man, however, need not resort to these methods. In fact, it is the rare person today who can ascertain by sniffing whether or not food is fresh. It is approximately true that we use our olfactory ability fundamentally and almost exclusively for pleasure—to enjoy exotic perfumes, to savor the fragrance of the rose, and to augment our sense of taste.

Gustatory acuity, in contradistinction to olfaction, has at least by some men been developed to a fine art. The lower creatures and even our ancestors ate according to their caloric needs. They took what they could get; there was very little opportunity to select or reject purely by gustatory sensations. Today, despite economic limitations, the ingestion of food is highly selective. This selectivity in some cases has been developed to a remarkable degree. The sense of taste serves more than the simple function of pleasure, for it is also truly protective. In a series of ingenious experiments it has been shown conclusively that animals and young children will select a diet, if given a random choice, which coincides astonishingly with their physiological needs. However, before the child grows very old, other more compelling forces govern his selection of food. Thus, in the adult at least, the importance of gustatory function is not very great. In short, it seems fair to conclude that gustation and olfaction serve primarily to make man's life more pleasurable.

Audition unquestionably also adds to the enjoyment of life, but it must also be considered to be a very vital sense. A person who cannot hear can speak only after arduous training, and then speech is never normal. Audition, like vision, is important for protection because this sense informs one of the environment, of impending danger.

AUDITION

PROPERTIES OF SOUND

Sound is produced by vibrations of air. Sound waves travel through air at approximately 336 meters (1,100 ft) per second. If this figure is compared with the speed of light waves (about 300,000 kilometers per second), it becomes clear why we often hear the noise produced by something we see only after a considerable time interval. For example, we see the lightning before we hear the thunder.

Sound has three important properties: (1) **pitch,** (2) **intensity,** and (3) **timbre.** The pitch is a function of the number of vibrations per second. Figure 7-1 shows some typical sound waves. The greater the number of vibrations, the higher the pitch. For example, middle C has a frequency of 256 cycles per second. The number of vibrations per second is called

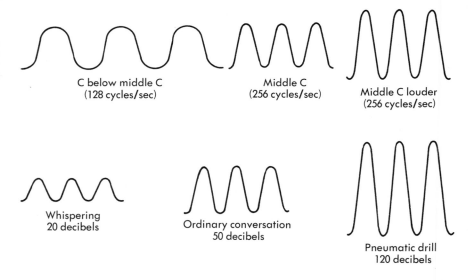

C below middle C
(128 cycles/sec)

Middle C
(256 cycles/sec)

Middle C louder
(256 cycles/sec)

Whispering
20 decibels

Ordinary conversation
50 decibels

Pneumatic drill
120 decibels

FIG. 7-1 Sound waves. The frequency of the waves determines the pitch; the amplitude, the intensity.

the **frequency.** The human ear can discriminate frequencies as low as 20 and as high as 20,000, though, of course, this ability varies from person to person.

Intensity of sound is varied by changing the amplitude of the wave. The greater the wave amplitude, and therefore the intensity of the sound, the louder will it seem to the listener. It has been found convenient to express sound intensity in **decibels.** A decibel is only a relative measure and is based on a logarithmic scale. An arbitrary intensity has been selected as a reference point. A sound which has an intensity about 26 per cent greater is said to be 1 decibel more intense or louder. A whisper at approximately 4 ft has a decibel rating of about 20, normal conversation at 12 ft is 50 decibels, while a pneumatic drill produces sound of about 120 decibels. Above this critical level, sound is not only heard but felt as well. At higher intensities, sound may be painful and even damaging.

A decibel, as the term indicates, is one-tenth of a bel. A bel is defined as an increase in sound intensity of 10 times. Thus, if the normal hearing range is from 20 to 120 decibels, on the bel scale this would be 2 to 12. Because each bel equals a tenfold increase, a change from 2 to 12 equals 10^{10}, or a 10-billionfold increase in intensity. This calculation strikingly illustrates the range to which the ear can respond.

There is, finally, the third property of sound, which is called its quality or timbre. Even though middle C always has the same frequency and can be produced with the same intensity, for example, on both the tuba and the zither, one can readily differentiate between the two instruments. This is because the sound has a different quality due to the presence of overtones.

When a string, a reed, the human voice, or any other vibrating body is analyzed, it is found to oscillate not only as a whole but also in parts. This can best be illustrated in a vibrating violin string. When the string is set in motion by the bow, it vibrates as a whole and then divides itself into segments which oscillate at their own frequencies, which are inversely related to their length. For example, if the string is bowed so that 256 cycles per second are produced, we hear middle C. At the same time, each half of the string vibrates at twice that frequency (512 cycles per second), so that we also hear C above middle C. Middle C is called the **fundamental tone,** and C above middle C is called a **partial tone** or an **overtone.** Likewise, each half of each half (one-fourth of the whole string) vibrates at 1,024 cycles per second. This produces a second overtone. Theoretically, at least, there are as many overtones as there are segments of the string, although all these overtones cannot be discerned by the normal human ear. For practical purposes, they fuse into one full, rich tone.

The richness or quality or timbre of a tone differs from one instrument to another. The only way to distinguish pitches of equal intensity is by the constellation of overtones. With training, one soon learns to identify any particular instrument.

ANATOMY OF AUDITION

The ear functions to gather and concentrate sound waves onto an area containing receptors sensitive to sound vibrations. Anatomically, the ear may be considered as consisting of three parts: (1) the **external ear,** (2) the **middle ear,** and (3) the **inner ear.**

External Ear   In man, the external part of the ear has more of an esthetic than a functional value. This part of the ear is called the **pinna** (meaning "wing") or better the **auricle,** which is derived from the Latin signifying ear. In many of the lower animals, the auricle serves the very useful function of capturing the sound waves. A dog, for example, can perk up its ears and move them so as to serve this purpose. But in man the auricle is relatively immobile, and it has been shown that in the absence of this appendage there is minimal hearing loss.

From the auricle there is a tube leading to the eardrum. This tube is termed the **external auditory meatus.** Meatus means "passage." The eardrum is called the **tympanic membrane** (Fig. 7-2).

Middle Ear   The middle ear is a cavity which lies beyond the tympanic membrane in the temporal bone. It is lined with a mucous membrane and contains three small bones in articulation with one another. These are termed the **auditory ossicles.** Figure 7-2 shows that the ossicles serve to connect the eardrum with the membrane in the oval window. In order, the ossicles are named the **malleus** (hammer), the **incus** (anvil), and the **stapes** (stirrup). The middle ear is not a closed chamber. It communicates with the oral cavity by means of the **eustachian tube,** which extends from the floor of the middle ear to the pharynx (Fig. 7-2). This tube must remain patent in order to maintain equal pressure on either side of the tympanic membrane.

Inner Ear   The inner ear lies behind the oval window and is composed of a winding cavity within the temporal bone. This tortuous tube is coiled like a snail and accordingly is labeled the **cochlea.** Figure 7-2 includes a cross section of the cochlea. The cavity is seen to be divided into three compartments. All three compartments are filled with fluid. Fibers of **cranial nerve VIII,** also known as the **auditory nerve,** course along the **basilar membrane** to innervate the highly important **organ of Corti.** This organ, in conjunction with the basilar membrane, is essential for the reception of sound. Close examination of the basilar membrane reveals that

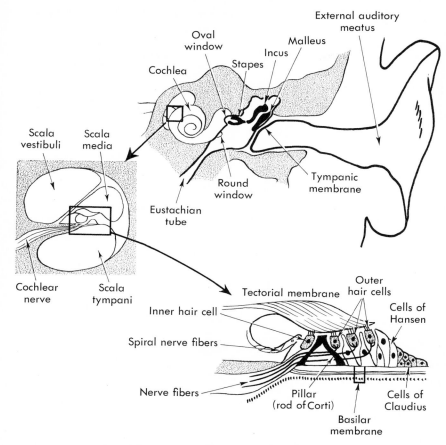

FIG. 7-2 Diagrammatic representation of the anatomy of the ear. In the upper drawing the external, middle, and inner ears are shown. To the left, the cross section of the cochlea is depicted. In the lower drawing are seen the details of the organ of Corti.

it is made up of progressively shorter fibers arranged much as in a harp. This design is thought to lie at the basis of pitch appreciation. The hair cells rest on these fibers and are innervated by the neurons of the auditory nerve.

Figure 7-3 illustrates the auditory pathways. It will be noted that this is a multineuron chain. The primary fiber arises in the cell bodies lying in the **spiral ganglion** in the inner ear; the central processes of these neurons end in the **cochlear nuclei** in the brain stem. Figure 7-3 shows

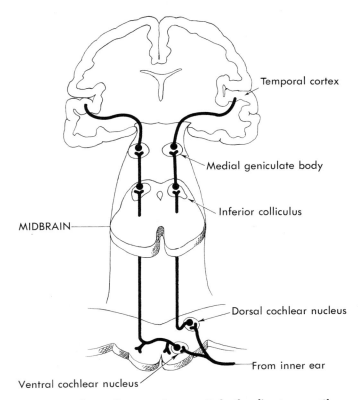

Temporal cortex

Medial geniculate body

Inferior colliculus

MIDBRAIN

Dorsal cochlear nucleus

From inner ear

Ventral cochlear nucleus

FIG. 7-3 The auditory pathways. Only the direct connections are drawn. In actuality there is extensive crossing of fibers and many more links.

only the simplest, most direct pathways to the cerebral cortex. But in addition there are many more complex routes. The impulse may be conducted by as many as five neurons before reaching the auditory area in the temporal lobe.

In man the specific area of the temporal lobe to be considered the primary acoustic area is still in doubt. The large region designated as area 22 is definitely involved, but there is some evidence, in animals at least, that the smaller areas, 41 and 42, constitute the primary acoustic area (Fig. 4-11). It is interesting that ablation of the temporal lobes does not cause complete deafness, although there is marked hearing deficiency. In man, tumors involving the temporal lobes are associated with auditory disturbances, speech defects, and vertigo.

It is important to realize that the auditory fibers have an orderly distribution in the organ of Corti and a point-to-point projection onto the cerebral cortex. This is believed to be the anatomical basis for pitch discrimination.

PHYSIOLOGY OF AUDITION

Transmission of Sound Waves It has already been pointed out that the auricle plays a surprisingly insignificant role in the transmission of sound waves into the middle ear. Sound waves are transmitted through the external auditory meatus to beat against the tympanic membrane. As a result, the tympanic membrane is caused to vibrate in harmony with the frequency of the sound waves. The tympanic membrane is, in reality, a very effective diaphragm. It responds accurately to all frequencies, and its movements stop almost instantly upon cessation of sound.

The vibrations of the tympanic membrane in response to sound waves cause the auditory ossicles to move with it. The handle of the malleus is embedded in the tympanic membrane, and its head is articulated with the incus. Therefore, as the membrane moves, the motion is transmitted through the head of the hammer onto the anvil and finally onto the stapes, which is fixed to the membrane of the oval window. This membrane now moves in harmony with the eardrum.

It should be recalled that the inner ear is filled with fluid. Thus, as the oval membrane vibrates, waves are created in this fluid. These waves will now be carried to the basilar membrane and exert their effects upon fibers of varying length. The movement of these fibers stimulates the hair cells of the organ of Corti. The motion of the fluid, then, is the effective stimulus for the sound receptors made up of the basilar-membrane fibers and the hair cells of the organ of Corti. Consequently, nerve impulses are fired along the auditory pathways to the temporal cortex for the appreciation of sound.

Under normal conditions, sound waves pass through the external auditory meatus and strike the eardrum, causing it to vibrate. This energy is then amplified and transmitted by the ossicles to the fluid of the inner ear and, in turn, the hair cells in the organ of Corti are caused to move and initiate auditory impulses. Actually, some of the sound energy is simultaneously conveyed to the inner ear via the bony tissues around the ear. Under normal circumstances, however, the amount of energy transmitted in this way does not contribute significantly to the appreciation of sound. But the physician utilizes bone conduction to ascertain whether there is hearing loss and precisely what part of the hearing system is deranged.

The examiner customarily strikes a tuning fork and places it on the bony prominence just behind the ear. He instructs the patient to motion when he can no longer hear the sound. Then the tuning fork is brought next to the external ear. Under normal conditions, the sound produced by the tuning fork can be heard twice as long by air conduction as by bone conduction. If there is obstruction in the external auditory meatus (excessive wax, for example), if the eardrum cannot vibrate, or if the ossicles are rigid for one of several reasons, air conduction will be impaired. In these cases the subject will hear the sound via bone conduction and not through air conduction. This is so because the bony tissues bypass the external and middle ear and transmit the sound directly to the inner ear.

Localization of Sound   A person with normal hearing can localize the direction from which sound waves are emanating. The essential factor is the difference in arrival time of the sound at the two ears. Even though the sound may originate to the right, for example, it is heard by both ears, but the waves arrive at the right ear slightly before they impinge upon the left ear. Consequently, the listener interprets the sound as coming from the right. Another factor which aids in localization is the difference in the intensity of the sound. The sound which strikes the right ear, in this example, will be slightly louder than that which arrives at the left ear.

This explanation for sound localization obviously applies only to *discontinuous* sound. If the sound is *continuous,* the ears will be stimulated constantly, ruling out the differences in arrival time. The factor of intensity still plays a role, but this clue alone is inadequate to localize accurately the sound source. In the case of continuous sound of less than about 800 cycles per sound, the waves will impinge upon the two ears in different phases. This permits localization. But when the frequency is increased, the phase difference is not great enough to provide an adequate clue. As a result, the individual believes the sound to be coming from all sides at once. This is well known to the combat soldier as he listens to the scream of the shell above him.

Intensity Discrimination   One concept of man's appreciation of variations in intensity of sound is easy to understand. It is similar to the estimation of intensity of any of the other sensory modalities. The louder the sound, the greater will be the amplitude of the sound waves. As a result, the waves transmitted to the basilar membrane and organ of Corti will also have a greater amplitude. Consequently, each receptor fires more rapidly, and more receptors are activated. The net result is to deliver more impulses per unit time to the auditory cortex. This is recognized as an increase in intensity.

Pitch Discrimination   The mechanism by which man discriminates pitch is complex. Basic to this ability is the anatomy of the basilar membrane.

The basilar membrane is about 0.04 millimeter wide close to the oval window. It then progressively widens until it is close to 0.5 millimeter at the other end. In addition, it also becomes progressively less stiff. There is a difference in stiffness from one end to the other of at least one hundredfold. The frequency of vibrations in any system is: (1) directly proportional to the stiffness (elastic coefficiency), and (2) inversely proportional to the inertia. The short, stiff fibers (close to the oval window) will respond to waves of high frequency; the larger, less stiff fibers at the other end respond to low frequencies. The current concept, instead of visualizing only a specific area of the basilar membrane as responding, concludes that there is a traveling wave of displacement. This wave increases in amplitude as it moves from the oval window apically. It reaches a maximum at the point of the membrane which resonates with the frequency of the driving waves. The amplitude then falls off rapidly (Fig. 7-4). The peak amplitude of the wave varies with the frequency of the sound. It is thought to be the maximal displacement of the portion of the basilar membrane influenced by the greatest amplitude of this traveling wave that provides the clue for pitch discrimination. Because a specific pitch activates a definite place on the basilar membrane more than it activates any other part of the membrane, this concept of pitch discrimination is termed the **place theory.** In other words, one localizes the place on the basilar membrane which is being most actively stimulated just as he localizes an area of the skin that is stimulated. There is a point-to-point representation between the membrane and the cerebral cortex which makes such localization possible.

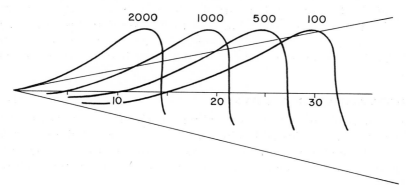

FIG. 7-4 The place theory of pitch discrimination. The basilar membrane widens progressively with the narrowest portion lying closest to the oval window. Sound waves build to a peak and then suddenly decrease. There is a specific peak for each pitch. The upper numbers are frequency in cycles per second; lower numbers represent distance from oval window in millimeters.

This explanation, however, is probably not the entire story. The number of impulses conducted by the auditory neurons per unit time varies with the frequency of the sound up to a maximum of about 4,000 cycles per second. It is thought that for all pitches below this figure the number of impulses conducted per unit time provides an important clue for pitch discrimination. This is the **volley,** or **periodicity** principle. Current thinking on this problem embraces both the place and the volley concepts into what is termed the **duplex theory.** In summary, frequencies below 4,000 cycles per second are primarily discriminated according to the rate of impulse propagation per unit time. The place theory provides the explanation for pitch discrimination of frequencies above 4,000 cycles per second.

If the volley theory is valid, then our explanation for intensity discrimination needs modification, because it has long been assumed that frequency of impulses arriving in the temporal cortex was concerned only with discrimination of intensity. According to the volley theory, frequency gives the essential clue as to pitch. To reconcile this problem it has been suggested that there are high-threshold receptors which are only activated when the sound becomes intense. It is then assumed that it is the activity of these neurons and not the frequency of the impulses that permits us to discriminate various intensities. Clearly, the entire field of audition needs further investigation.

One frequently hears the remark, "He has an ear for music," or perhaps, "He has absolute pitch." What is really meant is that the individual can listen to a pitch, let us say middle C, and immediately be able to identify it as middle C. The ramifications of this problem are truly many and beyond the scope of this text. Suffice it to say here that this ability may appear early in life, that it can be acquired to some degree with training, and that it is not an all-or-none affair. All individuals possess it to some degree.

ABNORMALITIES OF AUDITION

Disturbances of any part of the auditory mechanism may eventuate in partial or complete deafness. This may be caused by a failure of transmission of sound waves, it may be associated with occlusion of the eustachian tube, or there may be an interruption of the central auditory pathways.

Transmission Deafness   Any object in the external auditory meatus, such as wax or a foreign body, will buffer the transmission of the sound waves and may also dampen the tympanic membrane, resulting in hearing loss. This condition is usually transient, and normal hearing is resumed just as soon as the external ear is cleaned.

Acute otitis media is a condition in which there is, as the term indicates, an inflammation of the middle ear. It is often associated with the common cold, influenza, and other upper-respiratory disorders. The inflammatory process spreads from the pharynx up the eustachian tube to involve the structures in the middle ear. As a result, this cavity may become filled with fluid. The accumulation of fluid increases the pressure within the middle ear, causing the eardrum to bulge outward. This not only impairs hearing but is painful and may eventuate in a ruptured eardrum and the pouring out of a purulent exudate, popularly referred to as a "running ear."

Ordinarily the inflammation is mild and does not progress to the point where fluid accumulates. In some cases the eardrum is surgically incised to allow the exudate to escape. In these instances the eardrum heals rapidly without any subsequent hearing deficit. But should the condition become chronic, there may develop fibrous adhesions of the auditory ossicles. As a result, these little bones move less freely and hearing will be impaired.

The internal ear, as well as the middle ear, may become involved in inflammatory processes. If this occurs, there is interference with the transmission of the sound waves through the fluid of the cochlea, as well as damage to the sensitive hair cells of the organ of Corti. A few cases of partial deafness have been reported in which a tumor growth within the cochlea has blocked sound-wave transmission. Finally, there are instances of a congenital defect in the formation of the inner ear resulting in varying degrees of deafness.

Central Deafness A review of the anatomy of the auditory pathways will convince the student that a unilateral lesion can cause hearing loss only if it involves the auditory nerve close to the ear before crossing of the nerve fibers takes place. Unilateral lesions anywhere else are not so serious, because there is such great fiber crossing that each ear is represented on both sensory cortices. For the same reason, there is very little acoustic loss when there is destruction of the auditory cortex on one side. But if the lesion involves the auditory nerve before the fibers decussate, unilateral hearing impairment will ensue.

Occlusion of the Eustachian Tube It has been stressed that the function of the eustachian tube is to permit the pressure on either side of the tympanic membrane to be equalized. Everyone is now familiar with the fact that when descending in an airplane one must swallow periodically in order to relieve the pressure within the ear. If this maneuver fails, the pressure may cause pain and the eardrum may even rupture. When one swallows, the pharyngeal end of the eustachian tube is caused to open. Since the pressure within the pharynx is now greater than it is in the

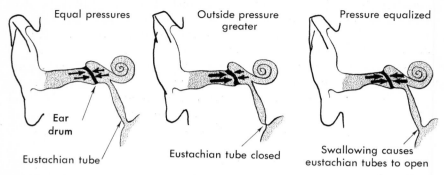

Equal pressures

Outside pressure greater

Pressure equalized

Ear drum

Eustachian tube

Eustachian tube closed

Swallowing causes eustachian tubes to open

FIG. 7-5   Function of the eustachian tube. Air moves through the eustachian tube, thus equalizing the pressure on the two sides of the tympanic membrane.

middle ear, air rushes into the middle ear, and once again the pressure on either side of the membrane is equal (Fig. 7-5). While ascending in an airplane, no conscious effort need be made to keep the pressures equal; when the pressure in the middle ear builds up, it finally becomes great enough to force the eustachian tube open, permitting equalization. Under normal circumstances one experiences no difficuty in ascending or descending, but it is easy to understand that, should the individual suffer with a cold which has resulted in a blocking of the eustachian tube, equalization may not occur and the eardrum may be forced in one or the other direction and result in pain and possible rupture.

Aside from air travel, occlusion of the eustachian tube can prove serious. In severe inflammatory conditions, not only may the tube be blocked but the inflammatory process may migrate into the middle ear as well. This may lead to fluid accumulation which cannot be relieved because the occluded eustachian tube does not allow drainage. In such cases the tympanic membrane may rupture.

TESTS OF AUDITION

There are two hearing tests which are commonly used. One estimates sound transmission; the other measures auditory acuity.

Sound Transmission   If a tuning fork is made to vibrate and then pressed against the forehead, the normal person will localize the sound as being directly in front of him. If there is blockage of sound-wave transmission through the middle ear on one side, the patient will report the sound as coming from the impaired side. If the experiment is conducted in a completely soundproof room, this result will not follow The explanation lies in the fact that, in most cases, there are other sounds as well as those emanating from the tuning fork. The patient does not detect these extraneous sounds with the defective ear. With that ear he recognizes only the tuning-fork vibrations, because these sound waves are being transmitted to the internal ear by bone conduction. The normal ear hears both the extrinsic sounds and the tuning fork by bone conduction, but the patient evaluates the vibrations of the tuning fork as being louder on the defective side and reports the sound as originating from that direction.

A more satisfactory test of failure of middle-ear transmission is to evaluate each ear separately. The tuning fork is struck and then held on the bony prominence just behind the ear. Sound is heard because of bone conduction. After the sound is no longer heard, the tuning fork is placed just in front of the external auditory meatus. If there is sound-wave-transmission interference, it will not be heard, whereas the normal ear will perceive the vibrations. The normal ear can hear the sound after bone transmission has ceased.

Auditory Sensitivity   The hearing threshold or auditory sensitivity may best be ascertained by the use of the **audiometer.** This is an instrument which produces sounds of varying pitches at different intensities. The subject wears a set of earphones, and the instrument is set to emit a specific pitch. Then the intensity is slowly increased until the subject reports that he hears the sound. The entire range of audible pitches is then tested and plotted. The record so obtained is called an **audiogram.** These are compared with normal audiographic patterns, and the degree of auditory impairment may be easily determined.

GUSTATION

ANATOMY OF GUSTATION

Taste Buds   Taste is a chemical sense. The effective stimulus to initiate gustatory sensation is a change in the chemical environment. There are chemical receptors which are sensitive to such changes. These chemoreceptors are called **taste buds.** Careful testing has revealed that there must be at least four different types of taste buds. This is so because man can easily distinguish among substances that are (1) **sweet,** (2) **salty,** (3) **bitter,** and (4) **acid** or **sour.** The anatomists have yet to describe morphological differences in the taste buds. But whether or not such anatomical variations are ever discerned, the fact remains that the taste buds are capable of discriminating among these four gustatory sensations.

The taste buds are found on the tongue, floor of the mouth, palate, pharynx, tonsils, and epiglottis. They are so widely distributed that food entering the mouth, no matter how casually, should give rise to gustatory sensations.

Taste buds are goblet-shaped modified epithelial cells. They have a small pore opening to the mucosal surface. In man they measure about 70 microns in length and close to 40 microns in diameter. It has been estimated that there are approximately 10,000 taste buds. This number remains fairly constant until about age 45, after which it decreases.

Gustatory Pathways Figure 7-6 portrays the gustatory pathways. It will be observed that three cranial nerves participate. Afferent fibers from the taste buds course in cranial nerves VII, IX, and X. These nerves are also termed, respectively, the **facial,** the **glossopharyngeal,** and the **vagus.** It can be seen that these afferent fibers enter the medulla oblongata where they end in association with secondary fibers. The secondary fibers cross

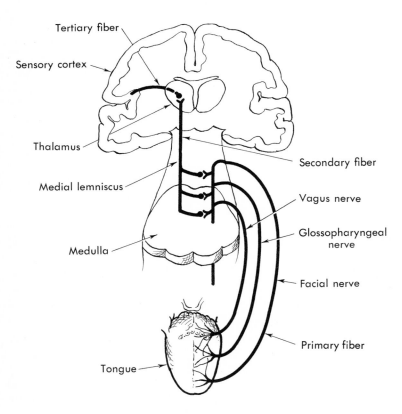

FIG. 7-6 The taste pathways.

the brain stem and then ascend in the medial lemniscus to the thalamus. From the thalamus, tertiary fibers are projected to the sensory cortex in the parietal lobe.

PHYSIOLOGY OF GUSTATION

Taste Perception   The taste buds are chemoreceptors, so-called because they respond to a change in the chemical environment. The taste buds are stimulated by fluids introduced into the mouth, or by solids that are dissolved in the saliva after entering the oral cavity.

Dry solids are not effective. Just how the solution stimulates these receptors is not understood. It has been postulated that specific solutions can cause an alteration in permeability and thereby initiate the action potential. Another hypothesis suggests that the charge on the small hairs of the taste bud is altered by the solution sufficiently to discharge the cell. The adaptation of taste receptors to stimuli is very rapid. The four basic tastes are sweet, sour, salty, and bitter. It is possible to map the taste buds (Fig. 7-7). Gourmets unknowingly recognize this anatomical fact and take pains to concentrate different foods in specific parts of the mouth. Some foods will be sipped slowly, a solid substance will be rolled about on the tip of the tongue, and other foods will be tossed into the back of the mouth for finer appreciation.

FIG. 7-7   Localization of the taste receptors on the tongue.

It is common experience that we can easily differentiate among far more than the four basic tastes. This ability depends upon two factors: (1) utilizing more than one type of taste bud in a blend, so to speak, and (2) deriving clues from activation of extragustatory receptors such as those of temperature, pressure, pain, and olfaction. For example, if an individual were to chew a piece of raw potato he could distinguish it from a morsel of raw carrot or an apple. Yet it is clear that none of these foods can be described as truly acid or sour, bitter, or sweet. The texture of the substance, its moisture content, the temperature, the relative proportion of the various types of taste buds stimulated, and finally the sense of smell all contribute. All this information is funneled into the sensory cortex, and in the light of past experience, a mental image is created.

The precise role that olfaction plays in gustation is often difficult to evaluate. Everyone knows that when he has a cold his gustatory appreciation and discrimination are diminished. This and other evidence lead to the incontrovertible conclusion that clues obtained through the olfactory system play an important role in gustation.

It is possible to perceive taste even though there in nothing in the mouth. For example, the presence of some substances in the blood stream gives rise to a sensation of taste. This is thought to be due to the compounds reaching the taste buds via the circulating blood. There are numerous drugs which fall into this category. For example, if vitamin B_1 (thiamine) is injected into a vein, the patient may report within a few seconds a nutty or fruity taste.

Gustatory Sensitivity   If a substance is diluted extensively, a point will be reached at which it can no longer be identified. The threshold dilution of different substances varies widely. For example, quinine, even in one part in over a million can still be reported as bitter. However, if sugar is dissolved and diluted over about one part in 200, the sensation of sweetness is lost. Actually, very little difference has been noted among normal subjects in the gustatory thresholds. There can be no question, however, but that some people can identify foods with greater ease and accuracy than can others. This ability is almost exclusively the result of training, although a part of it may certainly be explicable on the basis of greater receptor sensitivity.

It is easy to demonstrate that the taste of a substance depends upon contrast. For example, coffee consumed after a very sweet dessert does not taste nearly so sweet as the same coffee does in the morning when nothing else has preceded it. Again, the individual who has taken pains to develop his gustatory sensibilities takes cognizance of this fact and avoids the commingling of various foodstuffs. For example, the true lover of wines never touches his salad until he has finished the wine. Salad dressing usually contains a high vinegar concentration which can impart to the wine a disastrous flavor.

OLFACTION

ANATOMY OF OLFACTION

Olfactory Receptors   Figure 7-8 shows schematically the arrangement of the odor receptors in the olfactory epithelium. Herein lies a distinctive characteristic. In every case considered so far, the receptor was found to be innervated by an afferent neuron which transmitted the impulse toward the central nervous system. In other words, there is one cell for reception and another cell belonging to the neuron. Close examination of Fig. 7-8 reveals only one cell. This one cell serves the dual role of initiating the impulse for olfaction and then transmitting it to higher brain centers.

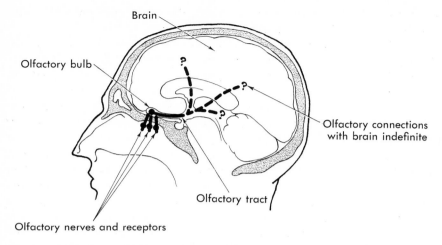

FIG. 7-8 The olfactory pathways. The olfactory tract has many connections with various parts of the brain but not all are believed to be concerned with olfaction.

Olfactory Pathways The axons of the cell which serves both as a receptor and as a neuron enter the cranial vault through the **cribriform plate** of the ethmoid bone. These axons are called the **olfactory nerves,** also referred to as **cranial nerves I.** These primary neurons end in the **olfactory bulb.** From the olfactory bulb arise the secondary neurons, which course along the undersurface of the frontal lobe of the brain, forming the **olfactory tract.** From this point on, our anatomical knowledge is uncertain. Many olfactory pathways and connections have been described, but the reports are not in harmony and the fact remains that olfactory impairment can be demonstrated only after interruption of the olfactory nerves or tracts. Lesions placed in various parts of the cerebral cortex as well as in subcortical nuclei have consistently failed to influence olfaction significantly. Thus, for the present, the anatomical apparatus for the perception of odors must remain undescribed.

PHYSIOLOGY OF OLFACTION

Odor Perception The olfactory receptors are considered to be chemoreceptors similar to the taste buds. In order for substances to be tasted, they must be in solution. Perfectly dry salt placed upon the tongue does not excite a salty sensation. But once it is dissolved in fluid, it is capable of chemically activating the taste buds. Likewise there are reasons to believe that in order for a substance to stimulate the olfactory receptors it must be in the form of a vapor and that the vapor must enter the fluid which constantly bathes the olfactory epithelium.

In order to detect an odor the vapor must reach the olfactory receptors. These receptors reside in the upper portions of the nasal cavities. Air passing in and out during ordinary respiration does not pass over them. Thus, many investigators insist that in order to smell a substance it is necessary to sniff so as to bring the vapor-laden air into contact with these receptors. It is admitted, however, that without sniffing, the vapor will ultimately reach the sensitive cells by diffusion. Although these concepts are no doubt fundamentally valid, they leave much to be desired. It is certainly common experience that as soon as one walks into a kitchen where shrimp are being boiled, or drives by a paper mill or a garbage dump, the sense of smell is rapidly awakened. One need not sniff, and it is doubtful if the diffusion process, being characteristically slow, is adequate to account for the ability to detect these pungent odors so rapidly.

However the olfactory receptors are stimulated, they fire impulses via the olfactory pathways, undoubtedly to some area of the sensory cerebral cortex for awareness. Odor, just as other sensory modalities, may be perceived as varying degrees of intensity, and the mechanism is probably the same. But once again the subject of discrimination confronts the physiologist, a problem that has been seen to be perplexing in all the special senses. For color discrimination it has been assumed that the retina contains three different types of receptors, each one sensitive to a specific color. The visual cortex could then mix these colors to allow perception of the entire color spectrum. For pitch discrimination the theory has been advanced that sounds of different wavelengths activate specific parts of the basilar membrane. In this case the auditory area of the cerebral cortex localizes the active receptors on the basilar membrane, and pitch may accordingly be discriminated. But what about odor? We can certainly differentiate a rose from limburger cheese. It is a simple matter to identify wet paint, alcohol, and a host of other substances. It is inconceivable that there are specific receptors for each particular odor. It has therefore been suggested that there are certain basic odors. There would then be receptors which are relatively more responsive to one of those odors than to any of the others. These primary odors are said to be, **camphoraceous, musky, floral, pepperminty, ethereal, pungent,** and **putrid;** seven in all.

In order for a substance to be perceived by the olfactory mechanism it must be volatile, it must be at least slightly soluble in water, and it must be soluble in lipids. In addition, according to this so-called **stereochemical** theory of odor, each of the seven primary substances has a specific molecular shape. There are assumed to be seven different types of olfactory receptors, each of which will accept a molecule of appropriate configuration "just as a socket takes a plug." Such receptors have not been identified, but action potential studies have shown that different odors do selectively activate specific receptors and not others. In some way the odor-producing substance must alter the permeability of the olfactory receptors so as to generate the action potential, but how this is accomplished is not known. The stereochemical theory may provide the necessary clue.

Olfactory Sensitivity As with all other modalities of sensation, the concentration of the odoriferous substance must reach a critical level before it is detected. That concentration or threshold varies with the substance. Some chemicals may be detected in extremely small concentrations. In comparing the sense of taste and of smell, it has been found that olfaction is many thousands of times more sensitive than gustation.

As was pointed out in the introduction to this chapter, the sense of smell in man is, in comparison with that in lower animal forms, very poor. Animals must rely upon their sense of smell for protection and food, and it also plays a significant role in sexual activities. In man, olfaction contributes immeasurably to the enjoyment of food and in some cases prevents the eating of spoiled foods, but for the most part we do not depend upon this sense. We use it fundamentally for pleasure and stimulation. Just how important olfaction is to man's sexual activities cannot be determined. Certainly the manufacturers of perfume believe it to be of inestimable importance, but meaningful statistics on this subject are rather difficult to obtain.

Olfactory Tests Ingenious but simple equipment has been developed for testing the sense of smell. The most widely used **olfactometer** consists of two tubes, glass or plastic, one of which slides within the other (Fig. 7-9). The outer tube is lined with an odorous material. When the inner tube is completely within the other and the small end is placed in the nostril, there will be no olfactory sensation. But as the inner tube is withdrawn, more of the odorous material will be exposed. This tube is graded, and thus the olfactory acuity may be ascertained. The gradations are in arbitrary units sometimes referred to as **olfacties.**

SUMMARY

Sound travels in waves. The **frequency** of the waves determines the **pitch.** The **amplitude** of the waves indicates the **intensity** of the sound. There is a third property, **timbre** or the quality or richness of the sound. The human ear can appreciate frequencies from about 20 to 20,000 cycles per second. The intensity of sound is expressed in **decibels.** Sounds louder than about 120 decibels are felt as well as heard, and if louder may cause damage to the ear.

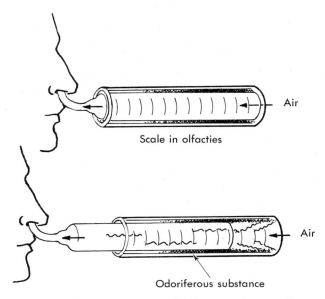

Scale in olfacties

Air

Odoriferous substance

Air

FIG. 7-9 Olfactometer. An odoriferous substance lines the outer barrel. The more the inner barrel is withdrawn, the more of the substance is exposed to the incoming air stream.

The ear is divided into the **external ear**, the **middle ear**, and the **internal ear**. The esthetic external part of the ear is termed the **pinna** or **auricle**. The **external auditory meatus** is the tube which leads to the **tympanic membrane**. The three bony ossicles, the **malleus, incus,** and **stapes,** connect the tympanic membrane to the **oval window**. The middle ear is connected to the outside via the **eustachian tube**. The inner ear is composed of a winding tube termed the **cochlea**. The cochlea is divided into three cavities which are all filled with fluid. The **organ of Corti** is in contact with the **basilar membrane,** which is composed of fibers of varying length arranged in harplike fashion. **Cranial nerve VIII** or the **auditory nerve** innervates the hair cells of the organ of Corti. The central process of these neurons ends in the brain stem. Secondary fibers cross and ascend on the same side to the **medial geniculate body**. Tertiary fibers then course from here to the temporal lobe of the cerebral cortex.

The most tenable theory of pitch discrimination, the **place theory,** postulates that sounds of different pitches activate a particular area of the basilar membrane more than any other part. Since there is a point-to-point relationship between the basilar membrane and the cerebral cortex, the localization of the part stimulated indicates the pitch. Intensity discrimination is probably, at least in part, a function of how much of the basilar membrane is activated and how frequently each receptor fires.

The **taste buds** are the receptors for gustation. They are chemoreceptors sensitive to the chemical environment. In order for them to be stimulated, the substance must be in solution. There are apparently four types of taste buds, those which give rise to the sensations of (1) **sweet,** (2) **salty,** (3) **bitter,** and (4) **sour.** The taste buds are distributed, in varying concentrations, throughout the oral cavity. Afferent fibers from these receptors course in the **facial, glossopharyngeal,** and **vagus** nerves. The primary fibers enter the medulla oblongata. Secondary fibers cross the brain stem and ascend, to end in the thalamus. Tertiary fibers are then projected to the sensory cortex of the parietal lobe.

Taste discrimination depends upon the relative stimulation of the four basic types of receptors plus clues from other senses, such as olfaction, temperature, pressure, touch, and even pain. The sensory cortex interprets these clues in the light of previous experience.

The olfactory receptors are found in the upper regions of the nasal passages. The cells play the dual role of reception and transmission. The primary axons make up the **olfactory nerves.** They traverse the **cribriform plate** to end in the **olfactory bulb.** Fibers which make up the **olfactory tract** arise here. The central connections essential to olfaction are uncertain.

In order for a substance to be smelled, the vapor must dissolve in the fluid which bathes the olfactory epithelium. The stereochemical theory purports to explain the ability to discriminate among odors. Olfactory acuity may be tested by the use of the **olfactometer.** Such an instrument measures olfaction in arbitrary units termed **olfacties.**

QUESTIONS

1. How can an individual tell one pitch from another?
2. How are the sound waves transmitted from the outer to the inner ear?
3. How is sound intensity discriminated?
4. By what means can we identify various foods?
5. What part of the brain is essential for the appreciation of taste?
6. Explain the stereochemical theory of olfactory discrimination.

SUGGESTED READING

Amoore, J. E., Johnston, J. W., Jr., and Rubin, M., "The Stereochemical Theory of Odor," *Sci. American,* **210:**#2, 42–49, February 1964.

Godwin, R. W., "Clinical Testing for Sound Localization," *Ann. Otol., Rhinol. & Laryngol.,* **70:**#4, 976–996, December 1961.

Harbert, F., Wagner, S., and Young, I. M., "The Quantitative Measurement of Taste Function," *Arch Otolaryngol.*, **75**:#2, 138–143, February 1962.

Hawkins, J. E., Jr., "Hearing," *Ann. Rev. Physiol.*, **26**: 453–480, 1964.

Hodgson, E. S., "Taste Receptors," *Sci. American*, **204**:#5, 135–144, May 1961.

Pfaffmann, C., "Taste, its Sensory and Motivating Properties," *Am. Scientist*, **52**: 187–206, 1964.

Rosenzweig, M. R., "Auditory Localization," *Sci. American*, **205**:#4, 132–142, October 1961.

Autonomic Nervous System

THUS FAR WE HAVE CONSIDERED perception and movement pertaining to the external regions of the body. Within the body there are, of course, vital organs collectively called the **viscera.** Stimulation of the viscera in some cases can be perceived. For example, excessive distention of the urinary bladder is recognizable, as is acute cardiac pain. In some instances the viscera prove completely insensitive. It is possible to anesthetize the body wall with a local anesthetic agent, open the abdominal cavity, and then manipulate the viscera without pain to the patient. The viscera contain glands which secrete; in many cases, this secretion is under nervous control. The viscera also contain smooth muscle which contracts; its contraction is usually governed by the nervous system.

There is a member of the nervous system which has not yet been discussed. This component is termed the **autonomic nervous system.** The autonomic nervous system, by definition, is *that part of the nervous system which innervates smooth muscle, cardiac muscle, and glands.* It is therefore a motor system. All perception emanating from the viscera involves pathways similar to the ones already discussed. Thus there are visceral afferent fibers which pass from the viscera to the central nervous system. The impulses then ascend the cord to the thalamus and are projected onto the sensory cortex. On the other hand, important visceral reflex arcs use the visceral afferent fibers to channel the impulse into the cord, but the efferent limb of the visceral reflex is the autonomic nervous system.

Visceral reflexes, like somatic reflexes, are under constant higher-center surveillance, but since the autonomic nervous system cannot be utilized as a final common pathway for voluntary movement, it is seldom possible volitionally to influence visceral reflexes. The system is, as the name implies, autonomous, that is, self-governing.

Before considering the autonomic nervous system in detail, a word of caution is needed. It is important to realize that the autonomic nervous system is not something apart from the nervous system as a whole. It is one part of the nervous mechanism and is, at all times, intimately integrated with all other components. An acute attack of appendicitis, for example, will give rise to pain. In addition, it may cause the legs to be drawn up to the abdomen. This illustrates the intimate interplay of a visceral afferent limb and a somatic efferent limb to produce a reflex. Simultaneously, there may be marked alterations in blood pressure. This reflex involves the same afferent visceral limb, but now in liaison with the visceral efferent limb of the autonomic nervous system. It should be obvious that numerous other illustrations could be cited to emphasize the fact that the autonomic nervous system is an integral constituent of the total nervous mechanism.

ANATOMY OF THE AUTONOMIC SYSTEM

The autonomic nervous system differs anatomically from the somatic motor mechanism. The chief difference lies in the fact that the autonomic fibers which originate in the spinal cord do not innervate muscle or gland. It may be seen that the fiber ends in synaptic union with a second neuron which does innervate a muscle or gland (Fig. 8-1). This is in direct

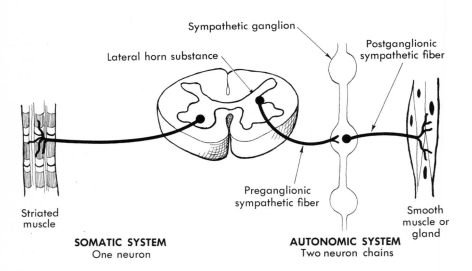

FIG. 8-1 Comparison of the somatic and autonomic nervous systems. Note that in the somatic system there is only one neuron; in the autonomic system there are always two.

contradistinction to the somatic fiber which, it will be recalled, connects the spinal cord directly with an effector organ. Thus, in considering the autonomic nervous system, we speak of **preganglionic** and **postganglionic fibers.** The preganglionic fiber terminates in the ganglion consisting of cell bodies which give rise to postganglionic fibers. These latter fibers innervate smooth muscles and glands.

The autonomic nervous system is composed of two parts: (1) the **sympathetic** and (2) the **parasympathetic** divisions (Fig. 8-2). These components differ both anatomically and physiologically. However, they are alike in that both contain preganglionic and postganglionic fibers.

SYMPATHETIC SYSTEM

Figure 8-2 reveals that anatomically the sympathetic fibers arise from the lateral-horn substance of the **thoracolumbar** segments of the spinal cord. These neurons then leave the spinal cord and course to one of the sympathetic chains of ganglia. The two sympathetic chains run parallel to the spinal cord. It can be noted that there is a nodular swelling, that is, a ganglion, at each spinal-cord segment. A **ganglion** consists of an aggregate of cell bodies. These cell bodies give rise to the postganglionic fibers which are then projected to the muscles and glands.

The preganglionic fiber which arises in one of the thoracolumbar segments may end in the sympathetic ganglion at that same segmental level. Or the fiber may pass through the ganglion at its own level and ascend or descend the sympathetic chain for a variable distance to terminate in another ganglion where it synapses with the cell body of a postganglionic fiber. Some of the preganglionic fibers may pass through the sympathetic ganglion and course out to other ganglia.

The postganglionic fibers usually leave the ganglia and embrace neighboring blood vessels. In this way they travel to all parts of the body in close association with vascular channels. Thus we see that even though the origin of sympathetic fibers is limited to the thoracolumbar section of the spinal cord, nonetheless this system wends its way to all parts of the body.

PARASYMPATHETIC SYSTEM

The origin of the parasympathetic fibers is much more diverse than is the case with the sympathetic system. The parasympathetic fibers originate from four major levels. In the spinal cord these neurons leave the **sacral segments** and are directed to the pelvic viscera (Fig. 8-3). Here the preganglionic parasympathetic fibers end. Very short postganglionic fibers then convey the impulse to the regional muscles and glands. Herein lies an important anatomical difference between the two divisions of the

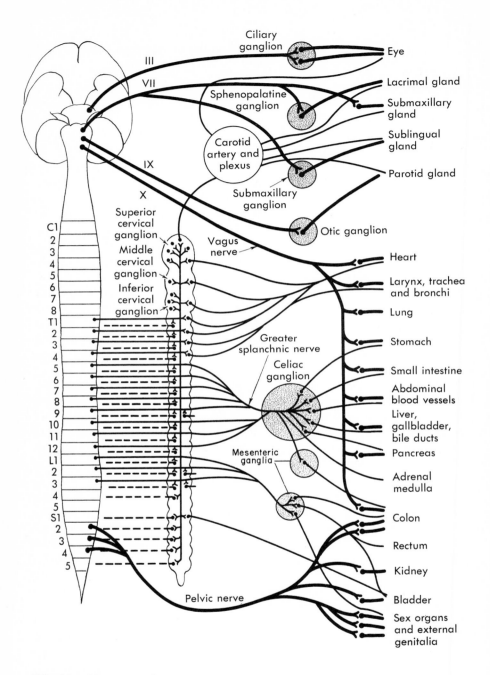

FIG. 8-2 Diagrammatic representation of the autonomic nervous system. Heavy lines are parasympathetic; light lines, sympathetic. The dotted lines represent postganglionic fibers that travel with the spinal nerves.

168

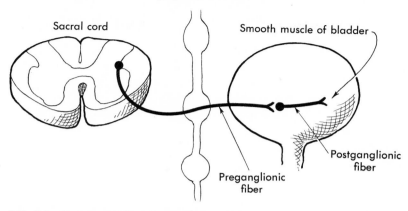

FIG. 8-3 Parasympathetic relationships. The preganglionic fiber extends from the central nervous system to the organ to be innervated, or to a special ganglion (Fig. 8-2). The postganglionic fiber is generally very short.

autonomic nervous system. The sympathetic system has an orderly chain of ganglia situated close to the spinal cord. The parasympathetic system does not. These parasympathetic preganglionic fibers are long and extend almost to the organ to be innervated. It is here that they synapse in ganglia. A second major outflow of parasympathetic fibers is located in the **brain stem.** These neurons are associated with cranial nerves VII, IX, and X (Fig. 8-2). Another source of parasympathetic neurons is found in the so-called **tectal region.** These fibers are associated with cranial nerve III and supply the eye (see Chap. 6). Finally, nuclei in the **hypothalamus** give rise to neurons which are properly classified as parasympathetic.

FUNCTION OF THE AUTONOMIC SYSTEM

It has been already emphatically underscored that perhaps the most important concept in the entire study of physiology is embraced by the word homeostasis. In discussing the steady state, it was noted that the increased demands of the actively contracting muscles are met so that the percentage composition of the blood remains constant. This is a superb example of homeostasis. But even though the term implies stasis, or a static situation, it is important to realize from the outset that the stasis is the end result; the mechanisms which make possible these constancies are indeed dynamic, movable, and exquisitely attuned to any forces which threaten to upset the desired balance. The autonomic nervous system plays an indispensable role in the maintenance of the constancy of the internal environment. It contributes, in short, to important homeostatic mechanisms.

SYMPATHETIC AND PARASYMPATHETIC INTERPLAY

The two divisions of the autonomic nervous system differ not only anatomically but in their functions as well. Most viscera, but not all, are innervated by both types of fibers. Stimulation of one division usually produces effects just opposite to those noted upon stimulation of the other member (see Table 8-1). This makes for a convenient and effective mechanism. The interplay between the divisions is analogous to a tug of war. The handkerchief tied to the middle of the rope does not move so long as the teams pull with equal force. Should the handkerchief move, increased activity on the part of the weakening team can bring the marker back to its original neutral position. This is precisely what occurs in man. If, because of a sudden forceful action of the parasympathetic system, the blood pressure should fall, the sympathetic system will, through complicated reflexes, oppose the fall and quickly restore the blood pressure to within normal limits. One reason for the antagonistic effects of the two autonomic divisions is the difference between the chemical substances secreted by the postganglionic fibers.

Adrenergic Fibers   Activation of a postganglionic neuron of the sympathetic nervous system causes an impulse to travel the length of the neuron. When the impulse reaches the end of the axon, a chemical substance is liberated. This compound is now known to be **norepinephrine.** Norepinephrine and epinephrine are hormones secreted by the adrenal glands, accordingly, neurons that liberate these substances are termed adrenergic. There is now general agreement that in most, if not all instances, the specific compound is norepinephrine.

Not all postganglionic sympathetic neurons are adrenergic. For example, those that innervate the sweat glands are cholinergic (see below). There are also cholinergic sympathetic fibers that innervate some of the blood vessels of skeletal muscle.

Examination of Table 8-1 will disclose that adrenergic fibers sometimes inhibit and in other organs they excite. For example, they dilate the coronary vessels but constrict the skin vessels; they excite the heart muscle but inhibit the gut muscle. There is, as yet, no satisfactory explanation for this difference. It has been postulated that there must be some substance in the effector cell which reacts with norepinephrine to produce a compound which is either excitatory or inhibitory. The nature of this substance, if it exists, is not known.

TABLE 8-1   Autonomic Nervous System Control

Part	Sympathetic Action	Parasympathetic Action
Heart	Rate increases Stronger contraction	Rate decreases Weaker contraction
Blood vessels		
Coronary	Dilatation	Constriction
Skeletal muscle	Constriction (adrenergic) Dilatation (cholinergic)	None
Skin	Constriction	None
Gut wall	Weaker contraction	Stronger contraction
Gut glands	Less secretion	Greater secretion
Gut sphincters	Contraction	Relaxation
Eye pupil	Enlargement	Made smaller
Ciliary muscle	Some relaxation	Contraction (accommodation)
Glands		
Sweat	Secretion (cholinergic)	None
Salivary	Slight secretion	Copious secretion
Lacrimal	None	Secretion
Gallbladder	Relaxation	Contraction
Urinary bladder	Relaxation (?)	Contraction
Male sexual organs	Ejaculation	Erection

Cholinergic Fibers   In so far as is known, all active postganglionic fibers of the parasympathetic division liberate acetylcholine when activated. Such fibers are termed **cholinergic.** Actually, the great majority of neurons in man are of the cholinergic type. It will be recalled that an essential element of synaptic transmission from one neuron to another involves the elaboration of acetylcholine by the presynaptic neuron. Likewise, it has already been mentioned that somatic motor fibers activate skeletal muscle at the neuromuscular junction through the liberation of this same substance. In the autonomic nervous system, all preganglionic fibers are cholinergic, as are the postganglionic neurons of the parasympathetic division. Thus, only the postganglionic fibers of the sympathetic component, with a few exceptions, are adrenergic.

VISCERAL REFLEXES

A complete study of visceral reflexes involves all of the physiology of man. When circulation is studied, it will be learned that heart action as well as blood pressure is controlled to a great extent by visceral reflexes. When we review respiration, it will be found that the breathing rate is dictated by visceral reflexes. The ingestion and digestion of foodstuffs evoke numerous visceral reflexes. These mechanisms will be analyzed in detail in more appropriate sections. For the present it is necessary to understand the anatomy and basic physiology of the visceral-reflex arc.

It has already been noted that the autonomic nervous system is a motor system. It is the motor system which makes up the efferent limb of visceral reflexes. Figure 8-4 shows a typical visceral reflex. This one controls the activity of the urinary bladder. The bladder wall is composed for the most part of smooth muscle. Within the muscle tissue are proprioceptors. As the urine collects, the bladder wall is stretched and the proprioceptors are activated. Consequently, impulses are carried by the visceral afferent fibers to the spinal cord. Here they synapse with fibers of the parasympathetic division of the autonomic nervous system. These fibers carry the impulse back to the very same smooth muscle of the bladder wall and cause it to contract. Hence, urine is expelled and the stretch is relieved. In brief, the anatomical configuration of

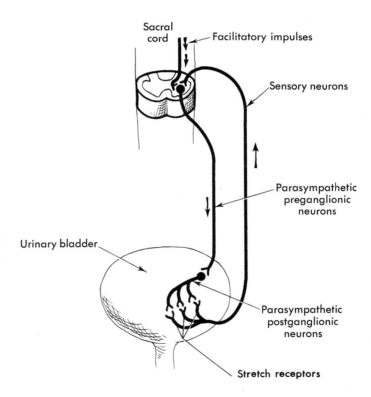

FIG. 8-4 A visceral reflex. In a visceral reflex the motor neuron is part of the autonomic nervous system.

the visceral and somatic reflexes is the same. The primary difference is that the autonomic nervous system makes up the efferent limb in a visceral reflex. As in the somatic system, visceral reflexes are facilitated or inhibited by higher-center censorship. Thus, following spinal-cord damage in man, visceral as well as somatic reflexes are lost. Obviously, the unfortunate individual in spinal shock is in a precarious state. The bladder then fills to an abnormal degree. There is no expulsion of fecal material. The blood pressure below the level of damage drops precipitously. After spinal shock fades, these reflexes reappear. They are then completely automatic, having been divorced from higher-center control. Thus when the rectum fills to a critical point, it automatically evacuates; when urine accumulates to a threshold degree, the bladder empties quite spontaneously.

It is unquestionably true that the effects of some of the visceral reflexes may be altered by the will. For example, it is quite possible to prevent voluntarily urination or defecation. But this inhibition is probably brought about more by somatic sphincter control than by inhibition of the visceral reflexes. For the most part, visceral reflexes cannot be altered by volition. Thus we note that it is impossible for the average person to vary his heart rate, raise his blood pressure, or dictate the flow of digestive juices.

In reviewing the somatic reflexes, it was noted that a variety of stimuli could evoke them. The same applies for the visceral mechanisms. In the urinary-bladder illustration, the effective stimulus was stretch. In the blood vessels, as we shall learn, there are receptors which respond only to pressure, others responsive only to changes in the chemical composition of the blood. Thus, through these highly specialized receptors, adjustments to a specific aspect of the internal environment may be made.

There are many so-called **mixed reflexes.** A change in the external milieu, acting through a somatic afferent limb, brings about alterations within the body through the autonomic efferent limb. For example, if on a hot and humid July afternoon one leaves an air-conditioned theater, marked physiological adjustments swing into action. Temperature receptors in the skin notify the central nervous system, and then through autonomic activity, widespread circulatory changes effect the shunting of blood from the internal areas to the surface of the body. Once again the superb rapport of autonomic fibers with all other parts of the nervous system is emphasized.

HYPOTHALAMUS

The most expeditious way to illustrate the homeostatic role of the autonomic nervous system is to examine the **hypothalamus.** Hypothalamus means "under the thalamus." This has reference to its position at the base of the brain. The hypothalamus consists of a family of nuclei which project fibers to all parts of the brain and into the spinal cord and which markedly influence autonomic function. In view of the fact that the two autonomic divisions have diametrically opposite effects, it is to be expected that there would be one great center of integration of these two systems. The hypothalamus serves this function. Although visceral reflexes are still operative after hypothalamic destruction, the experimental animal is far from normal. The major defect following hypothalamic destruction is the loss of rapid and effective adjustment to sudden environmental changes.

It is possible experimentally either to stimulate or to destroy specific nuclei in the hypothalamus. By this procedure it has been disclosed that some hypothalamic nuclei are concerned with sympathetic activity and others with parasympathetic function. In other words, these two great divisions have representation in the hypothalamus; it is here that higher-center coordination takes place.

There are other centers of autonomic-nervous-system integration. It will be seen that there are brain-stem centers which govern the circulatory and respiratory mechanisms. And the cerebral and cerebellar cortices are also concerned with autonomic functions. The hypothalamus plays a major role in many functions including temperature regulation, alimentation, sexual reactions, and water balance. Only temperature regulation will be discussed now. The other functions are more properly considered in later chapters.

Temperature Regulation   Even the layman knows that body temperature remains, or should remain, within a very narrow range. Under normal circumstances the internal temperature of man is about 98.6°F. Even the most uneducated people are surprised and become alarmed when body temperature varies as much as a degree or two. What is most remarkable is that body temperature remains so constant despite such wide variations in the external temperature.

The autonomic nervous system and the hypothalamus play a paramount part in maintaining body temperature. The hypothalamus may be likened to the **thermostat** of a modern heating plant. Most homes today have thermostats to regulate the production of heat. A thermostat consists of a mechanism which is sensitively attuned to deviations in the temperature.

When the temperature rises above a desired point, the thermostat, through its electrical circuit, shuts off the furnace. When the temperature falls, electrical impulses are fired through the circuit, which start the furnace. By this method the temperature of the house is kept within a narrow range. The hypothalamus functions as the human thermostat, and the nerve fibers of the autonomic nervous system supply the circuit which can start or stop the furnace and control the dampers.

Body heat is produced as a result of all the metabolic processes. Every metabolic process requires energy, and some of this energy is dissipated as heat. For example, when a muscle contracts, a measurable quantity of heat is produced. It is for this reason that people in bitter cold weather swing their arms and jump about. More subtle muscular activity is involved in the **shivering** act. This is an involuntary expression designed to increase heat production. Through all the basic metabolic processes, by shivering, and finally by voluntary muscular contraction, heat is made available to the body.

The heat which is so produced can be lost from the body at a greater or lesser rate. Heat is lost principally by **radiation** from the relatively large body surface to objects at lower-than-body temperature. There is also some loss through **convection** (a cold gust of wind) and **conduction** (standing barefooted on a cold bathroom floor). If the great mass of blood is brought close to the body surface, and the surface arterioles and capillaries are opened wide, a large radiation surface will be presented, thus enhancing heat loss. If the blood is shunted away from the skin surface to the interior, it is protected, and heat loss becomes minimal. Another route for heat loss available to man is through perspiration. When water evaporates, it utilizes and hence removes heat. The heat of evaporation can be graphically demonstrated by placing a highly volatile substance, such as ether, on the back of the hand. As the ether evaporates, the hand feels noticeably colder.

The rate of perspiration varies with the temperature, but even at low temperatures there is still some perspiration. This is called **insensible water loss.** It averages about 100 ml per day. During vigorous exercise, especially in a hot and humid environment, perspiration can exceed 100 ml per hour.

In summary, man is endowed with efficient mechanisms by which heat may be (1) produced, (2) conserved, or (3) lost. By the control of these factors, body temperature can be maintained surprisingly constant despite a wide range in the external temperature.

A simple example will illustrate how this system operates. Assume for the moment that you have been inadvertently locked in a large meat locker with the temperature below freezing. As soon as you enter the locker, cutaneous temperature receptors will be activated. Impulses will be fired into the spinal cord and to the sensory cortex for awareness of your dilemma as well as to the hypothalamus for action. Within a matter of seconds, perspiration will be cut to a minimum, shivering will be initiated, and by widespread circulatory changes blood will be shunted away from the skin surfaces. If these changes fail to protect the internal environment, the temperature of the blood itself will start to fall. This chilled blood bathes the hypothalamus. As a result, all the already mentioned mechanisms are reinforced. Should this still prove unequal to the task, you will begin to jump about, breathe deeply and rapidly, and wave your arms about, all of which increases heat production. The result is to increase heat production to a maximum and to reduce heat loss to a minimum. You have now done all in your power. If the conditions are too extreme, these mechanisms will be overwhelmed, body temperature will fall, and death will result.

In very hot weather, muscular contraction is kept at a minimum, there is no shivering, one takes it easy, and heat production is kept at low ebb. One sees the classic caricature in the tired old man half asleep under the apple tree who, when told that he has a fly on his nose, simply says, "Just let 'im alone, he's fall off with the first frost." In this case the hypothalamus has been apprised of the situation through information obtained from the cutaneous warmth receptors. Thus, messages are channeled through both divisions of the autonomic nervous system. The result is the shunting of blood to the surface and an increase in perspiration. Consequently, heat production is low and heat loss high; the body temperature remains constant.

The complete picture then shows that man has *two lines of defense*. (1) Small changes in temperature stimulate the temperature receptors in the skin, and impulses reach the hypothalamus via the sensory system. The hypothalamus, like the thermostat, alters heat production and loss so as to compensate for those external changes. For this purpose the autonomic nervous system is utilized. (2) If this system proves inadequate, the blood temperature drops and directly influences the hypothalamus to reinforce its efforts.

Under some circumstances the body temperature rises and is maintained at this new abnormal level. In such a case the person is said to have a **fever.** To exploit our analogy once again, we may say that in a fever state the thermostat has been set for a higher temperature. It is well known that when a fever is just developing the individual feels cold and may even shiver. The skin usually becomes pale. In other words, heat production is raised and heat loss cut down. Therefore, the body temperature rises and the patient is feverish. Conversely, when the fever "breaks," the individual sweats profusely. This returns the temperature to within the normal range. Infectious processes often affect the thermostat in just this way.

SUMMARY

The autonomic nervous system is that component of the nervous system which innervates smooth muscle, cardiac muscle, and glands. It contains only motor fibers. They constitute the efferent limbs of the visceral reflexes. Unlike somatic motor fibers, autonomic neurons synapse, in ganglia, before reaching the effector organ. There are, therefore, **preganglionic** and **postganglionic** neurons.

The autonomic nervous system is divided into **sympathetic** and **parasympathetic** divisions. Most preganglionic sympathetic neurons course to an orderly sympathetic chain of ganglia which lie close to and on either side of the spinal cord. Most postganglionic fibers arise in the ganglia and are projected to the organ to be innervated. There is no such orderly arrangement in the parasympathetic division. These fibers usually synapse close to the effector organ. Sympathetic neurons arise from the **thoracolumbar segments** of the spinal cord. Parasympathetic neurons originate from the **sacral segments,** from the **brain stem,** in the **tectal region,** and in the **hypothalamus.**

The autonomic nervous system is an important homeostatic mechanism. Its two divisions usually have antagonistic effects. The constancy of the internal environment is maintained by balancing these forces.

Fibers which when stimulated liberate norepinephrine are called **adrenergic.** Most postganglionic sympathetic fibers are of this type. Those which produce acetylcholine are termed **cholinergic.** These include all preganglionic fibers, parasympathetic postganglionic fibers, and a few postganglionic sympathetic neurons.

Visceral reflexes are similar to somatic reflexes, the major difference being that autonomic fibers make up the efferent limb. These reflex patterns are controlled by higher centers, but after a period of spinal shock they establish an inherent automaticity. A variety of internal stimuli such as stretch, pressure, temperature, and chemical composition of the blood evoke the visceral reflexes. Thus, the internal environment remains surprisingly constant.

The **hypothalamus** is the center of integration for the autonomic nervous system. It plays an essential role in (1) the digestive mechanisms, (2) temperature regulation, (3) sexual reactions, and (4) water balance.

QUESTIONS

1. How does the autonomic nervous system differ from the rest of the nervous system?

2. Describe the differences between the sympathetic and parasympathetic divisions.
3. Explain how sympathetic fibers excite some organs, but inhibit others.
4. What is a cholinergic fiber?
5. What is a visceral reflex?
6. Outline the mechanisms by which body temperature is maintained constant.

SUGGESTED READING

Benzinger, T. H., "The Human Thermostat," *Sci. American,* **204:**#1, 134–147, January 1961.

Bovard, E. W., "A Concept of Hypothalamic Functioning," *Persp. Biol & Med.,* **5:**#1, 52–60, Autumn 1961.

Carlson, L. D., "Temperature," *Ann. Rev. Physiol.,* 24: 85–108, 1962.

"Functions of the Hypothalamus," *Spectrum,* **6:**#15, 403–405, September 1, 1958.

Kuntz, A., "The Autonomic Nervous System," *Clin. Symposia,* **2:**#8, 277–283, October 1950.

Strom, G., "Visceral Functions of the Nervous Sytsem," *Ann. Rev. Physiol.,* **23:** 419–450, 1961.

Coordination

9

NO PART OF THE BODY FUNCTIONS INDEPENDENTLY. Simply flexing and extending one finger brings about widespread alterations throughout the body. Even with the movement of one digit there are measurable changes in respiration and circulation, while nervous impulses are distributed to practically all parts of the nervous system. That is why it is necessary, in order truly to understand the physiology of man, to integrate one's ever-growing knowledge. For teaching purposes, small units are considered as seeming independent wholes, but once each quantum is understood, it should be fitted into the constellation which is really the physiology of man. This integration is singularly important in the comprehension of the nervous system.

Thus far the basic components of the nervous system have been studied. The mechanisms for perception, for reflex and voluntary movement, and for the special senses have been analyzed. But clearly none of these mechanisms functions independently. The nervous system in normal man acts as an integrated whole; there is ever present exquisite coordination of all its components. Important areas of coordination are the **reticular formation** and the **cerebellum**. The mechanism within the **bony labyrinth** functions in collaboration with the cerebellum and will also be considered in this chapter.

RETICULAR FORMATION

The reticular formation is a mass of gray matter that extends from the caudal end of the brain stem on up to the thalamus. Pathways from the basal ganglia, the cerebellum, various brain stem nuclei, and the spinal cord feed impulses into the reticular formation. The reticular formation, on the other hand, initiates pathways that go to these various structures. The reticular formation, in essence, is a complex network of afferent and

179

efferent neurons. In the reticular formation there are vital centers for the regulation of circulation, respiration, and gastrointestinal activities. These functions will be considered in detail in later chapters. The activities of the reticular formation in coordinating movement are discussed here.

MOTOR FUNCTIONS

When the rostral part of the reticular formation is stimulated, both discrete and more generalized movements are elicited. This does not mean that this area initiates movement. It does suggest that the reticular formation participates in movement that is initiated at higher levels. More importantly, stimulation experiments disclose that certain parts of the reticular formation inhibit and other areas facilitate movement. Thus, the reticular formation probably coordinates at least the grosser types of movement which involve large groups of muscles.

RETICULAR ACTIVATING SYSTEM

All of the sensory pathways, as they traverse the brain stem, send collaterals into the reticular formation. This input undoubtedly is utilized by the reticular formation in its role of coordinating motor activitiy. It also forms the basis for the firing of the reticular formation into higher centers. There is a diffuse projection of impulses up to the thalamus, the basal ganglia, and to all parts of the cerebral cortex. As a result, these higher centers are activated. In the absence of this reticular function, wakefulness is not maintained. Clinically this is seen in cases involving damage to the mesencephalic portion of the reticular formation. In such cases, the patient remains in a coma and cannot be aroused. Apparently, under normal circumstances, all sensory activity is funneled into the reticular formation which then fires nonspecifically into higher centers to activate them.

CEREBELLUM

GROSS ANATOMY

Figure 9-1 illustrates the position of the cerebellum in relation to the other parts of the brain. This relatively large structure lies just behind the larger cerebral hemispheres. In lower animals, the cerebellum is small and comparatively inconspicuous. It becomes larger as one ascends the phylogenetic scale; in man, it is very prominent and highly important.

Upon detailed examination, the cerebellum is found to resemble the cerebral hemispheres in that it consists of a mantle of gray matter cover-

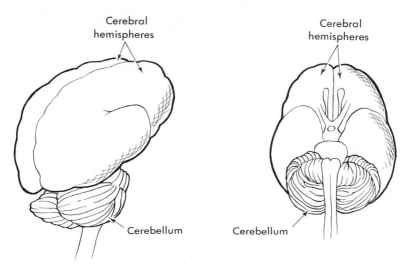

**FIG. 9-1   The cerebellum. Diagram shows the relationship of the cere-
bellum to the cerebral hemispheres and the brain stem.**

ing the internal white fibrous substance. And, like the cerebral cortex,
the cerebellum is divided into lobes by deep and distinct fissures. Figure
9-2 shows the boundaries of the three major lobes of the cerebellum.
They are (1) the **anterior lobe,** (2) the **posterior lobe,** and (3) the **flocculonodular lobe.** The cerebellum is often considered anatomically to consist
of (1) the **flocculonodular lobe,** (2) the **paleocerebellum,** and (3) the **neocerebellum.** Paleocerebellum implies an old part, that is, one that was
present very early in the development of the species. Neocerebellum, on
the other hand, is a term to describe an area that is newer. In view of the
fact that the following discussion concerns the specific lobes, it is well
to point out that the paleocerebellum is composed of the anterior lobe
and a small portion of the posterior lobe. The neocerebellum is com-
prised of the remainder of the posterior lobe.

CONNECTING PATHWAYS

There is good reason to believe that the cerebellum is connected by
afferent and efferent pathways with all other parts of the nervous system.
For example, it is possible to stimulate discrete parts of the cerebellum
and pick up action potentials in other areas of the brain. One must conclude from such experiments that there is a pathway over which the impulses have traveled from the cerebellum to the position of the recording
electrodes. In this way numerous important tracts have been identified

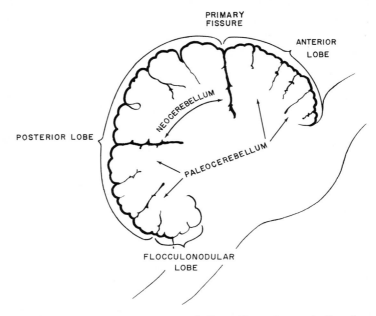

FIG. 9-2   Major lobes of the cerebellum. The paleocerebellum includes the anterior lobe and part of the posterior lobe.

(Fig. 9-3). Though only a few of the more important connections are shown, it is clear from the figure that the cerebellum is admirably situated to receive information from every part of the body and, at the same time, to influence all parts of the body. In short, anatomically the cerebellum is designed to coordinate sensory and motor functions.

PRINCIPLES OF MUSCLE COORDINATION

In discussing reciprocal innervation, it was emphasized that whenever one muscle contracts an opposing muscle must relax. That is true, but it is only part of the story. All muscular movement in man involves *four* distinct types of muscles. These are (1) the **prime movers,** (2) the **antagonists,** (3) the **synergists,** and (4) the **fixation muscles.**

The prime movers are the muscles which actually produce the desired movement. If a weight is to be lifted, the arm must flex at the elbow. This is brought about principally by contraction of the biceps muscle. Flexion at the elbow is opposed by the triceps and other muscles in that group. While the biceps is contracting, the triceps relaxes but not completely or all at once. A degree of tension is maintained which opposes

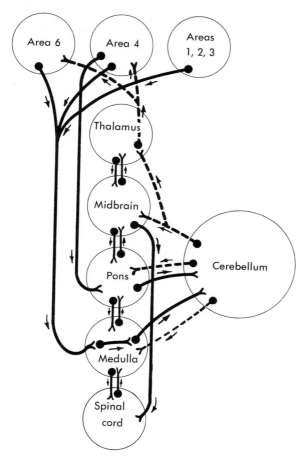

FIG. 9-3 Cerebellar connections. Only a few of the major pathways leading to and from the cerebellum are shown.

or antagonizes the flexion act. This is not so inefficient as it may appear upon first thought. The small amount of antagonistic tension steadies the joint and makes the movement smooth and controlled. Thus the muscles which oppose any movement are known as the antagonists. The roles of prime movers and antagonists may be switched. When the arm is extended, the triceps becomes the prime mover and the biceps assumes the role of antagonist.

The designation **synergist** means "to work together." Thus this term aptly applies to those muscle groups which work together with the prime mover and antagonists to produce the desired motion. These muscles are especially important in a freely moving articulation. To return to the weight-lifting example, it should be clear that the freely movable elbow joint must be supported in such a way that as the biceps contracts the forearm is brought up with little or no lateral motion. In order to accomplish this act, there must be contraction of the muscles which insert upon the lateral surfaces of the forearm. These latter muscles cooperate with the prime movers to bring about flexion and the elevation of the weight.

In addition to the muscle groups discussed, it is apparent that in order to produce movement of any sort there must be fixation of various parts of the body. In our illustration the forearm, the shoulder, the trunk, and the wrist must be rigid so that the contraction of the biceps can bring the forearm up with the weight. Muscles which fix a part so that bones in articulation with it can move are called fixation muscles.

One should be impressed with the fact that even the simplest movement is a highly complex process involving many muscles—some contract, others relax, and still others maintain a steady tension throughout the process. It follows that if movement is to be smooth and efficient there must be a higher center to coordinate the activity of these muscle groups. The major function of the cerebellum is to bring about this superb degree of coordination.

CEREBELLAR FUNCTION

For years attempts have been made to associate each part of the cerebellum with a specific function. With the exception of the flocculonodular lobe, these attempts have caused more confusion than enlightenment. Thus, the flocculonodular lobe function will first be discussed, and then the remainder of the cerebellum as a whole will be analyzed.

Flocculonodular Lobe   The flocculonodular lobe functions in connection with the vestibular mechanism in the bony labyrinth (see below). Accordingly, this lobe is essential to equilibration. The vestibular apparatus feeds information concerning the position of the head in space, and its rotation, into the flocculonodular lobe. This lobe, through its connections with descending motor pathways, is able to coordinate the information with movement and thus maintain equilibrium even during highly complex and violent movements. The importance of the lobe is emphasized when it is destroyed. Such individuals have difficulty standing erect; when they walk, they do so with their legs wide apart, that is, on a **broad base,** and still they tend to stagger or even to fall.

Anterior and Posterior Lobes   The anterior and posterior lobes of the cerebellum receive impulses from all the proprioceptors throughout the body. These receptors fire neurons that are very large and conduct impulses at rates up to 120 meters per second. The anterior and posterior lobes also receive impulses from the cerebral cortex each time they send out motor commands. These lobes have pathways over which impulses can be sent to the lower motor neurons or to the motor cortex (Fig. 9-3). Finally, there is an input from the visual and auditory receptors. In short, these lobes receive sensory and motor information, and they send out impulses to the motor cortex and to the lower motor neurons. It is, then, in a superb position to coordinate motor function in the light of sensory data; and that is exactly what it does. Each time the motor cortex sends out a stream of impulses to initiate movement, the cerebellum is immediately apprised of this activity. At that instant it has information of a visual, auditory, and proprioceptive nature. It can now modulate the motor command of the cortex by a direct action on the lower motor neurons. It can also influence subsequent motor activity by firing back to the motor cortex. In addition, as the movement proceeds, there is continuous feedback from vision, the proprioceptors, and perhaps audition. All of this information is utilized to adjust, refine, and perfect the movement.

ABNORMALITIES OF THE CEREBELLUM

We have already seen how lesions in various parts of the cerebellum result in disorders of equilibration, posture, and movement. In clinical practice, such discrete lesions are seldom seen; there is usually involvement of one or more lobes, so that the findings represent a combination of disturbances. A few of the more obvious clinical entities will be mentioned in order to illustrate the great function of coordination performed by the cerebellum.

Dysmetria The term **dysmetria** is derived from *dys-*, "difficult," and *metria*, "measure." The patient, then, has difficulty measuring the extent of his muscular movements. If the examiner holds his finger pointed to the patient and instructs him to touch it with his finger tip, the patient is unable to accomplish this simple task. He will point all about it, or past it.

Intention Tremor Dysmetria is usually accompanied by the so-called intention, or **terminal** tremor. Not only does the patient find it difficult to point precisely, but as the finger approaches the target it begins to shake. The tremor only occurs when there is great intention on hitting the mark, that is, at the end or termination of the act. For example, in eating, as the fork is brought closer and closer to the mouth, the hand shakes more and more.

Adiadochokinesis This frightening word, when reduced to its components, means "loss of successive movements." It thus aptly describes the deficiency noted in many patients with cerebellar damage. A normal person can pronate and supinate (in other words, rotate his wrist one way and then the other) with great rapidity. With cerebellar dysfunction this apparently simple exercise can be performed only very slowly and tediously. The movement requires alternating roles between the prime movers and the antagonists. One muscle group contracts while the other relaxes; then there is a sudden reversal. Apparently this can be accomplished only with the assistance of the cerebellum.

Decomposition of Movement   If a patient with extensive cerebellar damage is observed, it will be noted that he executes movements in robotlike fashion. Every movement is broken down into its individual units. There is decomposition of the usually smooth and efficient pattern. If the subject wishes to lift a glass from the table, he first brings the forearm up, then the entire arm is thrust forward, then the hand opens, and the arm moves forward once again until the hand comes in contact with the glass; then the fingers close about it. Each muscle must act independently. The striking feature is that there is no coordination.

Rebound Phenomenon   If a normal person pushes against the examiner's hand which is then slid away, the individual's arm will move forward just a few inches before he inhibits the motion. If the patient with cerebellar dysfunction is tested in the same way, his arm will jump forward unchecked. If the test is carried out with the patient's arm flexed and his fist pulling against the examiner's hand, as soon as the examiner lets go the patient's forearm rebounds with great force. Once again this test makes apparent the loss of muscular coordination which depends upon an intact cerebellum.

THE BONY LABYRINTH

By this time the student should be impressed with the fact that maintaining the upright position both while standing still and during locomotion requires the coordination of many mechanisms. This balance, or equilibration, is dependent upon (1) functional reflexes, (2) an uninterrupted flow of proprioceptive impulses to the cerebral and cerebellar cortices, (3) vision, (4) voluntary adjustments, and (5) impulses originating from the bony labyrinth. All except the last have been discussed. Now the anatomy and physiology of the bony labyrinth will be considered.

ANATOMY

Within the **temporal bone,** beyond the oval window, there are several winding cavities. We have already learned that one of these cavities contains the cochlea, a spiral structure essential to audition. The other chambers house the **utricle,** the **saccule,** and the **semicircular canals.**

SEMICIRCULAR CANALS

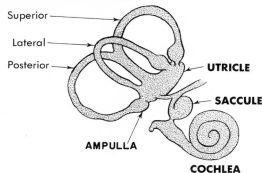

FIG. 9-4 Bony labyrinth apparatus. The cochlea is concerned with audition. The semicircular canals, the utricle, and probably the saccule are essential for equilibration.

Utricle and Saccule Figure 9-4 shows two membranous sacs. The smaller is the saccule, and the larger is the utricle. **Saccule** means "a small sac," while **utricle** is the diminutive of *uter* and refers to "a skin bag." The utricle, and probably the saccule as well, are concerned with balance, with awareness of position. Within each of these organs there is a sense organ composed of delicate hair cells covered by a gelatinous substance. This sense organ is termed the **macula** (Fig. 9-5). The utricle and saccule are in communication with one another and are filled with endolymph.

Semicircular Canals The remaining cavities within the temporal bone contain the three membranous semicircular canals. Figure 9-4 illustrates that these canals lie approximately at right angles to each other. In other words, there is a semicircular canal in each of the three planes. The canals have a swelling at one end known as the **ampulla**. The ampulla contains the receptors sensitive to a change in velocity. It is composed of sensory hair cells and is called the **crista** (Fig. 9-5). The semicircular canals are in communication with the utricle and saccule and are filled with the same endolymph.

Innervation Cranial nerve **VIII** supplies the utricle, saccule, and semicircular canals as well as the cochlea. This nerve, also known as the **auditory nerve,** has two major branches: (1) the **cochlear** division which innervates the organ of Corti and (2) the **vestibular** division which supplies the crista of the semicircular canals and the macula of the utricle and saccule. Because of this dual role of the auditory nerve, individuals who are congenitally deaf may also demonstrate equilibratory deficits.

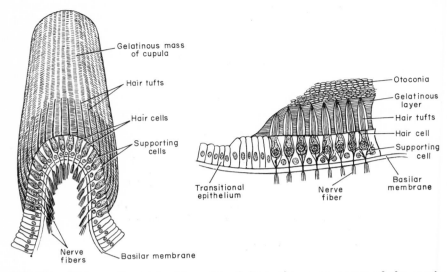

Gelatinous mass of cupula

Hair tufts

Hair cells

Supporting cells

Nerve fibers

Basilar membrane

Otoconia

Gelatinous layer

Hair tufts

Hair cell

Supporting cell

Basilar membrane

Transitional epithelium

Nerve fiber

FIG. 9-5 Crista and macula. The crista (left) is the sense organ of the semicircular canal. The macula (right) is the sense organ of the utricle and saccule. In both instances bending of the hair tufts initiates the impulse. (From E. L. House and B. Pansky, "A Functional Approach to Neuroanatomy," McGraw-Hill, 1960. Used by permission.)

Most of the neurons which innervate the equilibratory receptors pass to the medulla, where they end. Some continue on to the cerebellum. Secondary fibers are projected in several different directions. Some ascend to terminate in the nuclei of cranial nerves III, IV, and VI, thus forming the connections for reflex movements of the eyes in response to change in position. Other fibers descend the spinal cord to end in synaptic union with the anterior horn cells, thereby completing the circuit for reflex movement in response to positional change. Finally, some fibers undoubtedly wend their way, probably via the thalamus, to the sensory cortex so as to make one aware of position and changes in velocity.

FUNCTION

The bony labyrinth apparently serves a dual role: (1) *to initiate appropriate reactions to movement* and (2) *to aid the maintenance of the upright position.* The semicircular canals are sensitive to movement, while the utricle is fundamentally concerned with position.

Reaction to Movement The semicircular canals are arranged at right angles to each other, thus no matter in what plane the movement takes place, at least one pair of canals is involved. The canals are filled with endolymph which has inertia. Accordingly, when the canal is accelerating or decelerating there is movement of the fluid. It is similar to being thrown backwards in a car that starts off abruptly, or being thrown forward when it is stopped suddenly. As the endolymph moves forward or backward is bends the hair tufts. Whenever these tufts are bent, impulses are initiated which are conducted by the vestibular branch of the auditory nerve to the brain stem. As a result there are reflex movements of the eyes as well as changes in the autonomic nervous system, plus the usual dizziness or giddiness which is associated with rapid rotation. In addition, following the termination of rotation, the individual demonstrates characteristic errors in voluntary motion.

Nystagmus Impulses which arise in the semicircular canals are conducted by a two-neuron chain to the nuclei of cranial nerves III, IV, and VI. It will be recalled that these nerves innervate the extrinsic ocular muscles. This, then, is the anatomical background for the reflex movements of the eyes which accompany rotation.

If the subject is rotated to the right, it will be noted that during the acceleration phase there is a slow conjugate movement of the eyes to the left. This is then followed by a rapid jerk back to the right, another slow movement to the left, and so forth. This rhythmic oscillation of the eyeballs is termed **nystagmus**. The term is derived from the Greek and means "to nod," particularly "to nod as in sleep." The term probably has reference to the fact that as one falls sleeps, especially in the sitting position, one begins slowly to drop his head, then suddenly and quickly the head is raised, and the process is repeated. In a sense, then, the dozing act consists of a slow and a quick phase. Nystagmus is also composed of two components: (1) the slow phase and (2) the rapid phase. During acceleration the slow phase is in the opposite direction to the rotation. Nystagmus is classified according to the direction of the quick phase as well as the plane in which the eyes move. For example, in the illustration just cited, the quick phase is to the right and the eyes move in the horizontal plane. It is therefore referred to as a **right horizontal nystagmus.** Should the body be rotated with the head flexed so as to rest on one or the other shoulder, a vertical nystagmus will appear. Finally it is possible, by rotating the body with the head bent forward or backward, to produce a rotary nystagmus.

The slow phase of nystagmus is a reflex act. The eyes attempt to remain fixed upon an object so that as the head turns in one direction the eyes, remaining stationary, appear to be moving in the opposite direction. A limit is reached, and then by voluntary effort the eyes attempt to "catch up," thus leap back to the opposite side. This phenomenon can be readily substantiated by watching a passenger's eyes as he views the scenery from a rapidly moving train. The eyes will be seen to fix upon the passing telephone poles; then the eyes must periodically jump ahead to come to focus upon another one. In short, the slow phase of nystagmus is away from the direction of rotation; the quick phase is in the direction of movement.

If rotation is continued at a steady rate, nystagmus ceases. When rotation decelerates, the nystagmus once again occurs, but this time the quick phase is in the opposite direction. These facts underline the mechanism of semicircular-canal reaction, not to movement as movement per se, but rather to movement during acceleration and deceleration. It is change in velocity which activates these receptors, and not velocity as such. This is understandable when it is recalled that the crista is activated by being bent by the movement of the endolymph. The endolymph moves only during acceleration and deceleration.

Postrotary Errors of Movement   If a subject who has just been rotated in a chair attempts to stand up, he will invariably fall to one side. This is not a reflex act but an error in volitional movement. The subject's equilibratory mechanism has been disturbed by the rotation. As a result, when he stands erect he is under the impression that he is falling to one side when actually he is not. Consequently, he throws himself in the opposite direction in an attempt to compensate for the imagined movement.

It is precisely for this reason that pilots are instructed not to trust to the "seat of their pants" when flying, especially in combat maneuvers which involve rapid changes in direction and acceleration. The resulting disturbances to the equilibratory mechanisms may prove fatal unless the pilot relies on his instruments more than his sensations.

Reaction to Thermal Stimuli   If the external auditory meatus is irrigated with warm water, reactions similar to those just described take place. There follows nystagmus, autonomic-system alterations, and disturbances of equilibration. The mechanism of the reaction to heat is very similar to the response to movement. The heat applied to the external ear causes an increase in the temperature of the endolymph in the end of the semicircular canal lying nearer the outer ear. As a result, convection currents are initiated which bend the hairs of the crista and thus evoke the typical responses. Nystagmus in the opposite direction results from cold-water irrigations.

Reaction to Change in Position   It has been stressed that the semicircular canals respond only to acceleration and deceleration or, put another way, to a *change in velocity*. The utricle, on the other hand, is stimulated by any change in position of the body. The receptor is the macula. This consists of a mass of sensitive hair cells covered by a gelatinous substance. On this gelatinous material there are crystals composed of lime (Fig. 9-5). These lime crystals are called **otoconia.** The otoconia give weight to the hair cells, so that the entire mass is influenced by gravity and, accordingly, moves with any deviation of the body. This movement of the otoconia in the utricle and saccule initiates impulses which are conducted to the medulla and then down the spinal cord to synapse with the anterior horn cells. As a result, volitional and reflex movements are modified. In this way, a deviation of the body from the upright position will give rise to appropriate responses so as to oppose that particular movement.

INTEGRATION OF EQUILIBRATION

In most living forms, equilibration is so perfect that one pays little heed to it. A man 5 to 6 ft tall has no difficulty supporting himself upon a base of approximately 12 in. If a cat is dropped, it will invariably land on its feet. An athlete can hurl himself horizontally over a bar and land upright. Such illustrations are almost limitless. The common denominator in all of them is that the body is equipped with many mechanisms which, when properly integrated, serve to inform the individual of his position and simultaneously bring about appropriate reflex and voluntary acts so as to maintain the desired posture.

REVIEW OF BASIC MECHANISMS

Stretch Reflex   Muscles and tendons contain proprioceptors which are sensitive to a change in tension. Thus, when a muscle or tendon is stretched, there is an increase in tension. As a result, the proprioceptors fire impulses which are conducted by an afferent neuron to the spinal cord or brain stem. If there is appropriate facilitation at the synapse, the motor neuron will be activated, thereby causing a contraction of the stretched muscle. This is a fundamental reflex mechanism which requires no volitional assistance. It suffices to a degree to support the individual against gravity.

Bony Labyrinth   There are two important physiological structures in the bony labyrinth: (1) the **semicircular canals** and (2) the **utricle.** These systems are sensitive to a change in velocity as well as in position. It has been stressed that the proprioceptors are stimulated by a change in position, but this is true only if the muscles and tendons in which they reside are altered. For example, when a standing individual begins to sway to one side, the muscles on the opposite side will be stretched and the proprioceptors will be fired. Simultaneously the utricle will be activated. In this case the body is apprised of its position by two separate mechanisms, and they function synergistically to reinforce one another. On the other hand, the semicircular canals constitute, for all practical purposes, the only available means for detection of changes in velocity.

Cerebellum   The proprioceptors, the semicircular canals, and the utricle maintain ever-constant vigil over the body's position and movement. The information which they gather is utilized for reflex compensation, is fired into the sensory cortex, thus making the subject conscious of his position at all times, and is also directed to the cerebellum. The cerebellum, it will be recalled, is also kept continuously informed of plans for voluntary movement. In a sense, the cerebellum previews things to come. Therefore, before the movement is actually undertaken, necessary adjustments, in the light of position, muscle and tendon tension, and movement, are made. The cerebellum then conveys this integrated information back to the motor cortex which can now execute the planned movement with smoothness and efficiency.

Vision   The visual sense plays an important role in equilibration. It is true that with the eyes closed the normal person can maintain balance, but with the eyes open all the mechanisms thus far discussed are refined and reinforced. The importance of vision is underscored in conditions in which one or more of the other equilibratory mechanisms is impaired. For example, in **tabes dorsalis,** more commonly called **locomotor ataxia,** the posterior columns of the spinal cord are destroyed. As a result, there can be no transmission of proprioceptive impulses to the higher brain centers. If an individual so afflicted closes his eyes, he will sway backward and forward and from side to side. Such patients depend upon vision for much of their equilibration. Likewise interruption of the auditory nerve disconnects the bony labyrinth and, as a result, there is impairment of balance. But as long as vision is possible, these individuals can manage. Many such persons have drowned because, having dived into deep water, they cannot see the surface; they have no knowledge of their position and are as likely to swim down as up.

RIGHTING AND SUPPORTING REFLEXES

It has been mentioned that if a cat is held upside down and released it will whip about, land on its feet, and then support itself. This rapid act involves many reflexes. An analysis will serve to integrate the various equilibratory mechanisms.

Labyrinth—Neck Muscles   While the cat is suspended upside down, impulses from the utricle inform the animal of its position. It will be noted that even while being held the head is twisted in an attempt to regain the normal position. As soon as the animal is dropped, the head turns, thus causing stretch upon the opposing neck muscles. During rotation the semicircular canals are excited, and these impulses also serve to orient the animal.

Neck Muscles—Body Muscles   The turning of the head in response to labyrinthine stimuli causes stretch of the opposing neck muscles. Thus proprioceptive impulses not only cause these muscles to contract and pull the body around with the head but also set up reflexes which involve appropriate contraction of the trunk muscles as well, thereby completing the rotary act.

Visual Reflexes   If the animal is blindfolded and dropped, it still rights itself without difficulty. This does not mean, however, that the visual reflexes are not important for equilibration. For example, if an animal in which the labyrinth has been destroyed is dropped, it still rotates, but if it is blindfolded, it does not. The visual reflexes serve to reinforce the labyrinthine mechanism. The normal animal utilizes both.

Supporting Reflexes   The supporting reflexes have already been discussed but for the sake of integration are reintroduced here. While the animal is falling, it rotates so that it comes into contact with the ground on all fours. As soon as the toes touch, they are spread apart by the weight of the animal. This toe-spreading initiates widespread stretch-reflex contraction. Next the extensor muscles are stretched by the weight of the falling animal. These muscles now respond vigorously by contracting. At the same time the flexor muscles contract so as to prevent overextension, thus converting the limbs into rigid pillars to support the animal. This coordination between opposing muscle groups is purely reflex in nature, but the basic reflexes are controlled and modified by the cerebellum. Thus the animal spins about, falls upon its feet, is supported, and then prances off. The entire act requires but a fraction of a second and is performed with great ease and economy of motion.

All these mechanisms functioning together make it possible for man to engage in an endless variety of activities. Any equilibratory deficit manifests itself in such a seemingly simple act as walking, which we come to take for granted and to which we give little consideration. It should be evident that the complex abilities required to drive a car or fly an airplane, to participate in sports, and to carry out all the requirements of modern living would be impossible were it not for the highly synchronized equilibratory mechanisms.

SUMMARY

The **reticular formation** is a mass of gray matter that extends from the caudal end of the brain stem on up to the thalamus. It is a mass of cell bodies and neurons that functions to coordinate motor functions and essential visceral activities.

The **cerebellum** is a large cone-shaped structure which lies just behind the cerebral hemispheres. The cerebellum is connected by afferent and efferent pathways with all other parts of the nervous system. Propriocep-tive impulses from every muscle in the body flow into the cerebellum. Here they are coordinated with messages from the motor cortex and then fired back to the appropriate motor nuclei to effect smooth, coordinated, and purposeful movement.

The cerebellum is fundamentally concerned with posture, movement, and equilibration. These activities are underscored by lesions which pro-duce discrete deficiencies. Disturbances of the flocculonodular lobe are associated with a loss of equilibration, forcing the patient to walk on a broad base. Other cerebellar disorders result in **dysmetria, tremor, adiado-chokinesis, decomposition of movement,** and the **rebound phenomenon.**

There is a series of cavities in the temporal bone containing the **utricle,** the **saccule,** and the **semicircular canals.** The utricle is a spherical struc-ture containing a sense organ termed the **macula.** The macula is particu-larly sensitive to changes in position.

There are three semicircular canals arranged perpendicularly to one another. At one end they are enlarged into an **ampulla.** Within the ampulla is a tuft of hair called the **crista.** The semicircular canals are filled with **endolymph,** which, because of inertia, moves in the opposite direction to movement of the head. As a result of this movement, the hair cells are bent; this initiates impulses which inform the individual of a change in velocity. These impulses not only permit cognizance of this change but also bring about eye movements as well as muscular adjust-ments throughout the body.

As a result of change in velocity, the eyes move slowly in a direction opposite to the movement and then quickly snap back. This two-phase response is called **nystagmus.** Nystagmus is classified according to (1) the plane of movement and (2) the direction of the quick phase. During acceleration the quick phase is in the same direction as the movement. During deceleration it is opposite to the movement. The slow phase is a reflex act, the quick phase is a voluntary effort to catch up. During constant motion there is no nystagmus.

Man is endowed with several mechanisms available for equilibration. Normal activity demands fine integration of all of them. These mechanisms include proprioceptive impulses from muscles and tendons, stretch reflexes, impulses from the labyrinth, coordination by the cerebellum, visual adjustments, and voluntary movements in the light of sensory data.

QUESTIONS

1. What is the function of the reticular formation?
2. Describe the function of the cerebellum.
3. How do cerebellar disorders manifest themselves?
4. What is the function of the utricle?
5. Explain how the semicircular canals aid equilibrium.
6. How does man maintain the upright position?

SUGGESTED READING

Braitenberg, V., "Functional Interpretation of Cerebellar Histology," *Nature (London)*, **190**:#4775, 539–540, May 6, 1961.

Fernandez, C., and Lindsay, J. R., "Progress Report: the Vestibular System," *Arch. Otolaryngol.*, **75**:#3, 276–278, March 1962.

Foerster, D. W., "We Have More Than 5 Senses," *Today's Health*, **35**:#4, 36–37, 56–57, April 1957.

Kraus, R. N., "Disorientation in Flight. An Evaluation of the Etiological Factors," *Aerospace Med.*, **30**:#9, 664–673, September 1959.

Snider, R. S., "The Cerebellum," *Sci. American*, **199**:#2, 84–90, August 1958.

"The Determination of Cerebellar Disease," *Spectrum*, **6**:#20, 556–557, November 15, 1958.

10   Integrative Functions

FIGURE 4-11 shows that the regions of the cerebral cortex thus far studied occupy a relatively small portion of the hemispheres. By far the larger fraction is made up of areas which are concerned with the coordination of the basic mechanisms into a functional whole. These are the **association areas.**

Investigation of such regions in lower animals has not been too fruitful. Thus, what little is known has been culled from clinical cases in which there is evidence of disorder in the association areas. At best our knowledge is scanty, and until the association areas are better understood there can be no true comprehension of the physiology of the nervous system. All that can be presented here is a cursory outline of our knowledge of a few of these areas and how they relate to the physiology of man.

SPEECH

Speech is a complex mechanism which involves superb integration of sensorimotor functions and learning. There is perhaps no human activity which requires greater nervous-system coordination than speech. At one time an attempt was made to locate a speech center in a relatively small area of the cerebral cortex, but it is now known that much greater space is relegated to normal speech.

ANATOMY AND PHYSIOLOGY OF SPEECH

Production of Sound   In order to produce sound, and this is as true in a musical instrument as it is in the human vocal apparatus, three mechanisms must be available. There must be some force which sets a vibrating part in motion, there must be a vibrating object, and there is need of one or more resonators which serve to reinforce the vibrations. In the piano, for example, the force is represented by the hands which strike the keys, the strings are the vibrating bodies, and the sounding board serves

196

as a resonator. In man, the force is set off by the blast of air which is emitted from the lungs, the vibrating bodies are the true vocal cords. The pharynx, mouth, and nose collectively act as resonators.

In order to make possible a blast of air, the pressure within the lungs must be increased. This is accomplished by the simultaneous action of the muscles of the chest and abdomen. While lung pressure is being built up, the vocal cords are closed. As the air passes up through the larynx, the vocal cords are forced apart and caused to vibrate. The greater the pressure of the expelled air, the wider will be vibratory oscillations. It will be recalled that the amplitude of the sound wave signifies the intensity of the sound. In other words, the loudness of the voice is controlled by the muscles of the chest and abdomen.

The vocal cords are highly mobile structures and, as such, are capable of modifying their length, position, and degree of tension. In the production of high-pitched sound, the cords become long and very tense and are held closely together. With low tones, we find that the cords are relaxed and shortened.

The third and last important sound component is the resonator. In man, the resonating apparatus consists of the pharynx, mouth, nose, and possibly the paranasal sinuses. These areas contribute to the quality of the voice, reinforce the sound produced in the larynx, and make it possible for the individual to utter vowels and consonants. One has only to recall the change of one's voice during a cold or sore throat or following the loss of the teeth to appreciate the importance of these resonating chambers.

Higher Centers The muscular movement required to control respiration, to force air past the vocal cords, to vary pitch and timbre, and finally for articulation depends, fundamentally, upon the integrity of the primary motor area (area 4). Isolated movement of these muscles, however, would not even produce a sound, let alone speech. Obviously area 6 must also be implicated. For the coordination of all these muscles, the cerebellum is indispensable; in cerebellar disorders, speech dysfunction is often noted. But, in addition to these basic centers, large association areas are also needed. Figure 10-1 shows the areas of the cerebral cortex which are involved in speech. The frontal lobe is concerned with voluntary muscular movements which are necessary in speech. One important part of the frontal lobe has been designated as **area 44 or Broca's area**. Broca's area does not directly control the muscles of speech, for these muscles are influenced by area 4. Broca's area is essential for the synchronization of all these muscles. If Broca's area is bilaterally destroyed, there is no paralysis of the various muscles utilized in speech; each one can still be moved individually, but the subject cannot coordinate them so as to produce articulation. Area 44, then, is an association area essential to speech.

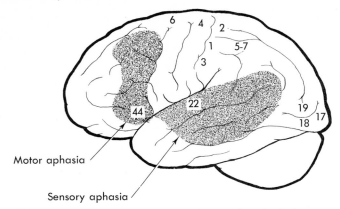

Motor aphasia

Sensory aphasia

FIG. 10-1 Aphasia. Lesions involving the shaded areas cause either motor or sensory aphasia.

ABNORMALITIES OF SPEECH

The term **aphasia** really means the complete loss of speech. However, the designation is generally applied more loosely so as to include any impairment of speaking. When aphasia is due to paralysis of the speech muscles, it is called **motor aphasia**. On the other hand, there may be a sensory deficit which makes speech impossible; this is known as **sensory aphasia**. Finally, difficulty may lie only in the coordination or intellectual sphere. This type of aphasia is termed **amnesic aphasia**.

Motor Aphasia If one is suffering with a lesion which interferes with the use of the muscles utilized for speech, there will be impairment. Thus we find that a "stroke" is frequently accompanied by paralysis of the speech muscles. Similarly, destructive lesions in the motor areas of the cerebral cortex result in motor aphasia. But aside from these cases, motor aphasia also develops as a result of lesions in area 44 (Fig. 10-1). In this case each muscle can be moved at will. Thus the aphasia cannot be due to paralysis. In addition, these subjects are also unable to write. This indicates that there is a loss in the ability to form words. Interestingly enough, even though the patient cannot declare himself with words, nonetheless emotional expression remains so that his face may indicate vividly what he is trying to say even though it is in pantomime. It is almost as though one were watching television without sound. The individual knows what he wishes to say, there may be no paralysis of any of the speech muscles, yet he cannot coordinate the muscular apparatus so as to produce speech.

Sensory Aphasia There is a large area on the cerebral cortex which extends from the temporal lobe back into the occipital region (Fig. 10-1).

This portion of the brain is presumably necessary for comprehension of the written and spoken word. The visual cortex is concerned with visual acuity, but simply because a person sees a word clearly does not mean that he understands the word. Comprehension involves training and memory, functions of the association areas. The same, of course, applies to the spoken word. Thus, in clinical practice, one encounters cases of **word blindness** or **word deafness** which upon examination are found to be caused by lesions involving these very large association areas. It should be evident that, if the individual does not understand words that he sees or hears, his speech will be very limited and he will be unable to carry on a conversation or to read aloud. Since the deficit is on the sensory side, the impairment is called sensory aphasia.

Amnesic Aphasia   This is a type of speech deficit which is often difficult to distinguish from motor or sensory aphasia. But upon careful testing it becomes clear that the patient can utter some words, indicating no motor impairment, and that he can understand the written and spoken word. But when he attempts to speak, he has great difficulty in finding his words even though they be very simple and common ones. If the examiner suggests or supplies the words, the patient will repeat it as though he had simply forgotten it and the clinician's prompting helped in recall. Because of this seeming forgetfulness, the disorder is termed **amnesic,** which means "to forget." As one might suspect, these cases are generally associated with widespread cortical damage.

INTELLIGENCE AND PERSONALITY

As yet our knowledge of the nervous system, and especially the cerebral cortex, is inadequate to permit a physiological analysis of intelligence. It is known that the more intelligent the animal, the larger and more highly developed is the cerebral cortex. But little can be added to that gross observation. Intelligence depends on the ability to observe, to comprehend, to retain, and to recall.

LEARNING AND MEMORY

The physiological basis of both learning and memory is probably the same. It is well known that information can be funneled into the central nervous system, that it can be understood, interpreted, stored, and then recalled. Some primitive types of learning and memory can be carried out at lower levels, but for the most part, the cerebral cortex would seem to be of primary importance. Attempts have been made to explain learning and memory in accord with the mechanism of an electronic computer in which data may be introduced into the circuits and so long as those circuits are maintained, the data is retained and can be recalled and utilized at any time. Thus, one visualizes neuronal circuits being activated during the learning process. This, however, is probably not the explanation, or certainly not the entire explanation. In the first place, it is known that experimental lesions and also various types of brain damage cause loss of memory for recent events but not for more distant occurrences. Secondly, if memory simply involved the activation of neuronal circuits, electroshock treatment would be expected to obliterate all memory by interfering with the propagation in these circuits. This does not occur except for memory of very recently learned information. Thus, it seems as though in the process of learning some more or less permanent alteration occurs in the cortex. There is some evidence that RNA plays a role. Perhaps the RNA of the neuron becomes altered in the learning process. Since RNA acts as the model, or template, for subsequent protein synthesis so long as no further alteration in this particular RNA occurs, the change will be permanent and self-regenerative.

The particular area of the cerebral cortex primarily concerned with learning and memory, indeed if there is such specialization, is not known. Some evidence implicates the temporal lobes, but this is far from conclusive.

EMOTIONAL RESPONSES

Many areas of the brain contribute to the emotional response. These areas include the **limbic system,** the **hypothalamus,** and the **prefrontal areas 9 to 13** (Fig. 4-11).

Limbic System and Hypothalamus   Much of what was formerly called the rhinencephalon is now known as the limbic system. It was Broca who first made this distinction. Rhinencephalon refers to the part of the brain that has to do with olfaction, but it is amply clear that not all of the rhinencephalon, certainly not in man, has this function. "Limbic," on the other hand, means border and in this sense designates its position, but not its function.

The limbic system consists of two rings of medially located cortex along with the amygdala, hippocampus, and septal nuclei. The limbic system sends efferent fibers to the thalamus via the mammillary bodies. There are afferent fibers from the thalamus back to the hippocampus. There are also circuits to and from the hypothalamus.

The limbic system, along with other parts of the central nervous system, but particularly the hypothalamus, is concerned with sexual behavior and with various emotions. Sexual behavior will be outlined in a later chapter.

That the hypothalamus and the limbic system play some role in emotion is shown when these areas are stimulated (Fig. 10-2). The animal may show fear, rage, or a combination of both. In contradistinction, lesions in these areas seem to leave the animal completely unruffled in the face of even highly provocative circumstances. Thus, if the stimulating electrodes are in the hypothalamus, the animal shows rage but is, apparently, unaware of this state. The animal has all of the outward signs including the usual associated autonomic changes, but it can be shown that inwardly rage is not being experienced. So the hypothalamus seems to be a coordinating center for the outward expression of rage, but the areas of the brain necessary for the inward appreciation of rage are not known. It does not seem to be the function of the limbic system. As a matter of fact, if electrodes are placed within the limbic system and the animal is free to close a switch that will stimulate the area, he soon finds the experience so pleasurable that he continues to stimulate for prolonged periods of time. It is hardly likely that the stimulus gives rise to a sensation of rage.

Prefrontal Areas   In the middle of the last century a man by the name of Phineas Gage had a crowbar blown through his head by an explosion. It entered the left eye and emerged from the center of the head. Not only was he not killed, but after getting over his astonishment, he was able to walk to a doctor's office. He then lived for 12 years, but with marked personality changes. Subsequent investigation revealed that the prefrontal areas had been destroyed without harming the motor centers. The case was widely studied and stimulated extensive research into the function of the prefrontal cortex.

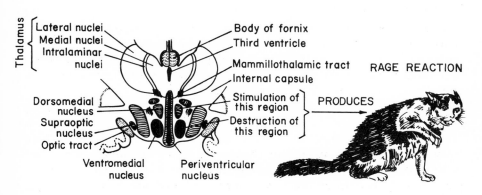

FIG. 10-2   **Production of rage. Stimulation of the dorsomedial nucleus, or destruction of the ventromedial nucleus, results in a rage reaction.** (From E. L. House, and B. Pansky, "A Functional Approach to Neuroanatomy," McGraw-Hill, 1960. Used by permission.)

In this day and age, when the individual is torn by such highly complex problems of love and hate, peace and war, freedom and subjugation, it is not surprising that the incidence of psychiatric disease has risen phenomenally. The interesting accident of Phineas Gage and the work it led to brought forth a great deal of information to suggest that the prefrontal areas are intimately concerned with the psychological operation of man. It was therefore reasoned that if this area of the cortex could be divorced from the rest of the brain this might be a form of therapy for some types of psychiatric disorders. This has ushered in the now well-popularized **prefrontal lobotomy.** The operation consists of undercutting the prefrontal areas so that the neurons which enter and leave at this point are separated from the prefrontal region. Individuals who have suffered with severe depressions have been found to become euphoric and amiable after this surgical procedure.

Prefrontal lobotomy does not seem to cause any loss of intelligence, but the patient responds to various situations without inhibition and with almost complete euphoria. There is usually loss of drive or ambition, and an individual who formerly could evaluate his environment and then act with good judgment now responds apparently without thinking, quite rapidly, and with little or no evaluation of the consequences of his act. These findings suggest that the prefrontal areas have an inhibitory influence over other areas of the brain. They seem to cause one to pause before responding, to evaluate all of the factors and consequences. These areas appear essential to careful planning. But in some cases, this inhibitory function is so exaggerated that the individual cannot reach a decision at all, is completely incapable of responding, and, as a result, becomes abnormally depressed.

Chemotherapy   There are numerous drugs which have a central nervous system effect. Some excite; others tranquilize. As these drugs have become better evaluated, the drastic operation of prefrontal lobotomy has been performed less frequently. There is general optimism that chemotherapy will one day permit exacting control of the emotions.

SLEEP

It should be pointed out that the changes which accompany sleep can be described, but the basic physiological mechanisms concerned with this pleasurable phenomenon are mostly in the realm of pure conjecture.

DESCRIPTION OF SLEEP

Soundness   The soundness of sleep has been measured in several different ways. One method is to generate noise of increasing intensity until the sleeping subject is aroused. The intensity of the noise is directly related to the soundness of sleep. This any student can attest to. Another procedure is to have the subject sleep on a bed which automatically records movement. It is then assumed that the amount of movement is inversely related to the soundness of sleep.

By means of these methods, it has been determined that a person quickly approaches maximal soundness. But Fig. 10-3 shows that this state of sound sleep it not maintained for long. It can be seen that there is a constant oscillation in the depth of sleep throughout the night. As a matter of fact, the curve indicates that several times the subject almost awakens. The usual and most satisfactory explanation for this waxing and waning in the depth of sleep is that the subject becomes uncomfortable in one position. This growing discomfort steadily lessens the depth of sleep until the sleeper does something about it, that is, assumes a new position. Equipment which records the sleeper's movements confirms this viewpoint.

Figure 10-3 also indicates that the fluctuations in the depth of sleep become more and more frequent as morning approaches. It can also be seen that the depth of sleep steadily lessens. In short, it can be concluded that the average individual quickly falls asleep and soon afterward reaches the maximum soundness. Throughout the remainder of the period there are marked variations in the depth of sleep, with a progressive over-all decrease in soundness.

An analysis of curves obtained in the above manner reveals that people vary widely in their sleeping pattern. Most individuals conform to the

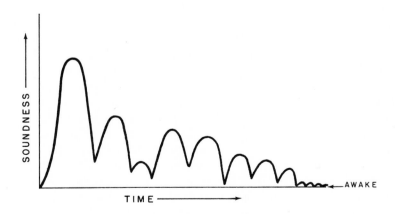

FIG. 10-3   Soundness of sleep. Sleep reaches maximum soundness soon after retiring. It then becomes progressively less sound during the night.

picture presented in Fig. 10-3, but others show a reversal of the curve in that they sleeply lightly at first, and only as morning approaches do they settle into a sound sleep. Such individuals find it extremely difficult to arouse themselves in the morning and never really collect their faculties until midafternoon. Whether these marked differences are due to habit or more fundamental physiological causes has not been resolved.

Requirements   Just how much sleep a person requires cannot be stated precisely. Sleep is a commodity difficult to measure objectively and to control adequately so as to produce reliable data. It seems clear that sleep requirements are greatest at birth and then progressively decrease throughout life. But here again there are wide individual variations depending upon one's activities, habits, and psychophysiological make-up.

Physiological Alterations   During the sleeping state, many changes in the so-called physiological values are noted. For example, the blood pressure decreases, the basal metabolic rate is lessened, the body temperature falls a fraction of a degree, urine formation is suppressed, and reflex activity is conspicuously reduced. However, it is interesting to note that perspiration is elaborated in surprisingly large amounts. It has been calculated that during the sleeping hours one perspires as much as one does during exercise.

MECHANISM OF SLEEP

Sleep has fascinated man throughout history. Yet today we seem to know little more about the mechanism than our ancestors did. But, with the degrees of interest it evokes, it is not surprising to learn that numerous theories have been proposed. None, however, is truly adequate.

Cortical Theories   In view of the fact that the cerebral cortex is essential for sensory appreciation and voluntary movement, and since both of these capacities are reduced during sleep, investigators have looked to the cerebral cortex for an explanation of the sleeping state. There is one current theory which postulates that sleep results from a decrease of impulses flowing to the cerebral cortex. According to this concept, the most important element is fatigue or inhibition at the neuromuscular junction and, as a result, a decrease in proprioceptive impulses. In addition, it is well known that sleep usually requires a reduction in light and sound which would also minimize the sensory barrage to the cortex. There should also be freedom from anxiety and other emotional states which would tend to excite the cortex. But all that this theory does is describe the conditions conducive to sleep. It contributes very little to the explanation of the mechanism of sleep.

Hypothalamus   Experimentally, it is possible to place lesions in the hypothalamus which cause sleep in animals. People suffering with abnormal somnolence may have a tumor in the hypothalamic region. These observations have pointed to the hypothalamus as a possible sleep center. This theory is supported by the many autonomic function changes which accompany sleep and which are coordinated by the hypothalamus. The impression to be gained from these studies is that there is in the hypothalamus a **waking** center, and when this center is inhibited or depressed sleep ensues. But this theory has now been discredited.

Reticular Formation and the Thalamus It has been established that a sensory input into the reticular formation causes activation of the thalamus and the cerebral cortex. In addition, it is possible to stimulate thalamic nuclei at low frequency and produce sleep. Higher frequencies cause arousal. On the basis of these observations it has been postulated that the thalamus has a basic, synchronous rhythm which is projected to the cortex to cause, or at least, to permit, sleep. When there is adequate sensory input, collaterals going to the reticular formation activate this area which, in turn, fires to higher centers and brings about arousal and wakefulness.

Again it would seem that in the absence of sufficient sensory input, sleep occurs. Though this theory does define some of the essential centers and pathways, it leaves many unanswered questions.

CEREBRAL CORTEX ELECTRICAL ACTIVITY

The development of suitable electronic equipment was quickly followed by the observation that the cerebral cortex gives rise to electrical activity. This electrical activity constitutes the so-called **brain waves.**

ELECTROENCEPHALOGRAPH

The very small voltage of the brain waves is amplified and recorded by an instrument called the electroencephalograph. Usually several electrodes are attached to the scalp and, after suitable amplification, the electrical activity of the brain is amplified to activate ink writers which form a record upon fast-moving paper.

ELECTROENCEPHALOGRAM

The record obtained by the use of the electroencephalograph is called the electroencephalogram or **EEG** (Fig. 10-4). At first glance it may seem as though the records would prove quite meaningless, but extensive investigation has revealed that there are typical wave forms. The waves are usually classified into three categories: (1) **alpha waves** which predominate have a frequency of from about 6 to 13 per second and the amplitude is approximately 50 microvolts; (2) **beta waves** with frequencies higher than

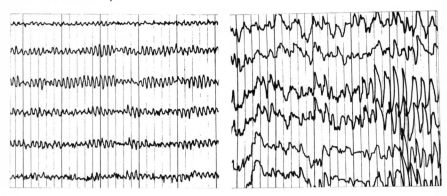

FIG. 10-4   Electroencephalograms. On the left is the normal pattern. On the right is the EEG taken during an epileptic attack.

13 per second and with low voltage; and (3) **delta waves** of high voltage but a frequency lower than 6 per second.

Brain waves vary during different activities. In sleep the frequency is very slow but the voltage increases. Intense mental activity is characterized by low-voltage, high-frequency waves.

The EEG has developed into a valuable tool for the neurologist. Epilepsy, for example, is a chronic disorder characterized by attacks of unconsciousness and convulsions. The EEG in such cases is distinctive (Fig. 10-4).

COMMISSURES

Thus far the brain has been considered as though it were a single, unpaired organ. Actually it consists, for the most part, of two halves bound together and bridged by the commissures. The commissures are bundles of nerve fibers which connect the two cerebral hemispheres. The largest, by far, is the **great cerebral commissure,** termed the **corpus callosum** (Fig. 10-5). Others are the **hippocampal commissure, habenular commissure, posterior commissure, anterior commissure,** and the **massa intermedia.** The **optic chiasm** should also be included.

Interestingly, these bridges may be cut and after recovery from the operation, the animal appears to function quite normally unless special testing is carried out. In man, the corpus callosum and other commissures are often surgically severed for relief of epileptic convulsions. Again, without special test procedures, it is impossible to note any change in the patient other than dramatic relief from the convulsions. With various testing methods, however, it has been demonstrated that the nerve fibers that make up the interhemispheral bridges serve to transmit information

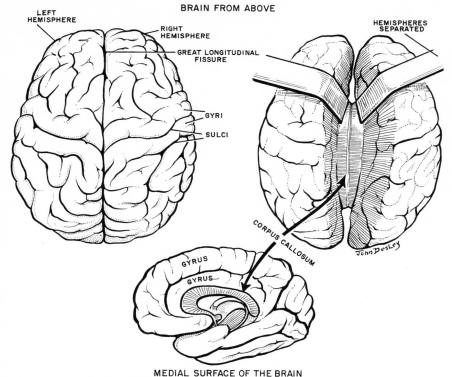

BRAIN FROM ABOVE

LEFT HEMISPHERE

RIGHT HEMISPHERE

HEMISPHERES SEPARATED

GREAT LONGITUDINAL FISSURE

GYRI

SULCI

CORPUS CALLOSUM

JohnDesLey

GYRUS

GYRUS

MEDIAL SURFACE OF THE BRAIN

FIG. 10-5 **Diagrammatic representation of the major commissure, the corpus callosum.**

from one half of the brain to the other. As already noted, the left half of the brain is primarily concerned with the right side of the body, and the right half with the left side. If the commissures are cut, the experimental animal can be taught to respond say with its left hand. The normal animal could then give the same response with the right hand; but following section of the commissures this is impossible. In short, the information learned by one side of the brain is normally available to the other side if the commissures are intact.

In man, one hemisphere is dominant. In the right-handed individual, it is the left hemisphere. By virtue of the intact commissures, the right hemisphere is subjugated. But if the left hemisphere is damaged, the right hemisphere can take over. If the commissures are cut, each half can function independently in the control of an opposite side of the body. It is as though there were two independent brains. Clearly, this could lead to interesting conflicts, and it has been suggested that such conflict between the two hemispheres may underlie certain mental illnesses.

SUMMARY

Speech is a complex, highly coordinated function. The integrity of areas 4, 6, 44, 22, 17, 18, and 19 is essential. Damage to these areas or to the large **association areas** causes **aphasia.**

Learning and **memory** are thought to depend upon alteration of the RNA of the cerebral neurons. **Emotional responses** involve the **limbic system,** the **hypothalamus,** and the **prefrontal areas** 9 to 13.

Sleep occurs when there is inadequate arousal input into the cerebral cortex. Arousal depends upon sensory input into the **reticular formation** which fires into the **thalamus** which in turn arouses the cerebral cortex. Why sleep is essential is not known.

The typical **electroencephalogram** (EEG) is composed of **alpha, beta,** and **delta waves.** Alpha waves have a frequency of 6 to 13 per second and an amplitude of about 50 microvolts; beta waves have a higher frequency but lower voltage; delta waves have a lower frequency but a higher voltage.

The **commissures** serve physically and functionally to connect the two halves of the cerebral hemisphere. When these connections are severed, the two halves function independently in their control of opposite sides of the body.

QUESTIONS

1. Outline the sequence of physiological events essential to speech.
2. Explain the various types of aphasia.
3. What is the function of the prefrontal areas?
4. Discuss the current concept of the mechanism of sleep.
5. What are brain waves?
6. Discuss the function of the commissures.

SUGGESTED READING

Cooley, D. G., "Cells that Communicate. Part 1. The Brain and its Pathways," *Today's Health,* 41:#5, 21–25, 78–80, May 1963.

Linde, S. M., "What Brain Waves Tell Your Doctor," *Today's Health,* 36:#1, 44–47, January 1958.

Ratcliff, J. D., "Our Wonderful Nervous System," *Today's Health,* 34:#5, 20–21, 50–51, May 1956.

Shapiro, A., "Observations on Some Periodic and Nonperiodic Phenomena in Normal Human Sleep," *Ann. N.Y. Acad. Sci.,* 98:#4, 1139–1143, October 30, 1962.

Soderberg, U., "Neurophysiological Aspects of Homeostasis," *Ann. Rev. Physiol.,* 26: 271–288, 1964.

PART
3

Circulatory System

Blood

11

BLOOD MAY BE LIKENED TO THE TRANSIT SYSTEM OF A CITY. If transportation were halted, the inhabitants would be deprived of many of the necessities of life, and survival would indeed become difficult. The analogy may be translated to the body. The individual cells are like the millions of people in a metropolis. The blood provides these cells with their necessities. When the circulation fails, the cells cannot survive; death ensues.

The blood is propelled through the vessels by the pumping action of the heart. The blood receives its essential oxygen supply through the intricate operation of the respiratory system. The blood constituents collect foodstuffs from the alimentary tract. Other vital substances are manufactured by specially designed cells and secreted into the circulating blood for delivery to other parts of the human city. Finally, undesirable materials are extracted from the blood by the kidneys, the skin, the lungs, and the liver. All these mechanisms will be considered in detail in subsequent chapters. First it is necessary to examine the blood itself.

COMPOSITION OF BLOOD

We are all acquainted with blood. Normally it appears brilliantly red, thick, opaque, and homogeneous. It is about five times more viscid than water and has a specific gravity of about 1.055.

Actually, blood is not homogeneous. If a thin film is placed under a microscope, its heterogeneous character becomes obvious. If blood is allowed to stand or if it is centrifuged, it separates into two distinct fractions. After centrifugation less than half the tube is packed with the so-called **formed elements,** consisting of **red blood cells, white blood cells,** and **platelets.** The upper fraction is a clear straw-colored fluid called the **plasma.**

211

RED BLOOD CELLS

The red blood cells, also referred to as **erythrocytes,** are shown in Fig. 11-1. They are biconcave disks. Erythrocytes are truly small, measuring less than 1/3,000 in. in diameter; hence, placed end to end, 3,000 of them would occupy only one inch. In addition, the red blood cells are very flexible and elastic. They travel through the blood vessels at great speed under pressure and, as confirmed by the slow-motion picture camera, are bent and twisted to a remarkable degree. The red cell contains a nucleus only during its early formative period. When it is functioning in the blood stream, the cell is without a nucleus.

Hematocrit   The term **hematocrit** really refers to the tube used to determine the ratio of plasma to the total formed elements, or to the red blood cells. In practice, however, hematocrit has come to mean the percentage, by volume, of the red blood cells in the whole blood. The hematocrit, **hematocrit reading,** or **hematocrit ratio,** as it is variously called, is determined by putting incoagulable blood in a Wintrobe tube, which is a small, narrow-bore calibrated tube. The tube is then centrifuged for 30 minutes at a speed that will produce a force of 1,500 gm. After centrifugation, the total volume of blood can be read as can the volume of red cells. From these values the percentage of red cells is calculated (Fig. 11-2).

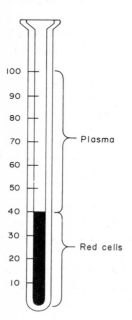

FIG. 11-2   **Hematocrit. After centrifugation the volume of packed red cells is normally 40 to 45 per cent of the total volume.**

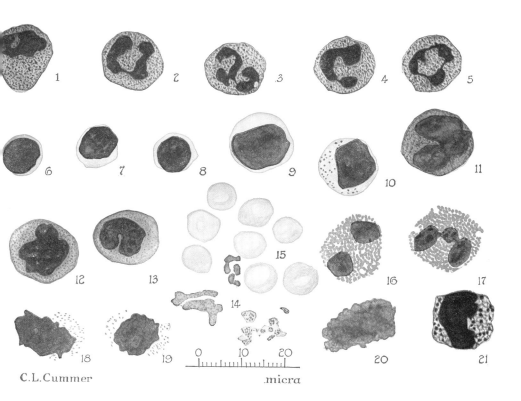

C.L.Cummer

.micra

FIG. 11-1   Types of cells found in normal blood. Colored by Wright's stain. All cells drawn with the same magnification; × 1150. Numbers 1–5, neutrophils; 6–8, lymphocytes; 9–13, monocytes; 14, platelets; 15, erythrocytes; 16, 17, eosinophils; 18–20, "basket cells" (degenerated leukocytes); 21, basophilic leukocyte. (Reproduced, with permission, from J. C. Finerty, and E. V. Cowdry, "A Textbook of Histology," 5th ed., Lea & Febiger, 1960.)

By the use of radioisotopically labelled plasma, it has been shown that by the above procedure about 4 per cent of the volume of the cells is trapped plasma. Accordingly, unless allowance is made for this, the hematocrit reading will be too high. Accordingly, it is the usual practice to multiply the hematocrit reading by the factor 0.96 to obtain the true value.

It should further be understood that the hematocrit value varies depending upon the part of the circulatory system from which blood is drawn. It is the general practice to draw venous blood from a subject. Because venous blood has a higher hematocrit than the average for all the blood in the circulation, in some procedures a special factor is employed to calculate the average hematocrit. However, in general practice this is not done, and the value is simply expressed as the venous hematocrit.

The venous hematocrit for men averages about 44 per cent; for women about 40 per cent.

Number of Red Blood Cells   In human blood there are approximately 5,000,000 red blood cells per cubic millimeter of blood. Since the total blood volume is about 5,000 ml and there are 1000 cubic millimeters in each milliliter, it can be calculated that there are approximately 25×10^{12} erythrocytes in the total circulation ($5 \times 10^6 \times 5 \times 10^3 \times 10^3$).

Red blood cells are counted by use of a **hemocytometer.** This is an instrument which permits the cells to be counted in a small but accurately measured volume of blood focused under a microscope. Then, by the use of appropriate factors, the number of cells per cubic millimeter of blood may be determined. There are now available electronic devices to count blood cells faster and more accurately.

Hemoglobin   The red cells are red because they contain a complex protein-iron pigment called **hemoglobin.** *Hemo* means "blood," and *globin* refers to the protein nature of the substance. It is the blood protein or pigment which gives to blood its characteristic red appearance. Hemoglobin readily unites with oxygen and, as will be learned when respiration is studied, this substance is essential for the transport of oxygen by the blood. When hemoglobin is carrying its full complement of oxygen, it is red. When it loses oxygen, it turns somewhat blue. This explains why arterial blood is bright red and venous blood has a blue tinge, or cast.

Normally, blood contains about 15 gm of hemoglobin per 100 ml of blood. Each gram of hemoglobin is capable of carrying 1.34 ml of oxygen. It can therefore be calculated that each 100 ml unit of blood can carry approximately 20 ml of oxygen (15×1.34).

The complex nature of hemoglobin is seen in Fig. 11-3. Of primary importance is the presence of iron (Fe) in the molecule. It is the iron that combines with oxygen. Accordingly, abnormalities involving iron metabolism strikingly alter the oxygen-carrying capacity of the blood. A decreased oxygen-carrying capacity of the blood is termed **anemia.**

Hemoglobin is produced by the erythrocyte while the cell is being formed in the bone marrow, and this production continues for many days after the red cell enters the circulation. Hemoglobin is synthesized from glycine and ketoglutaric acid. The final product is a relatively large molecule that has a molecular weight of 68,800.

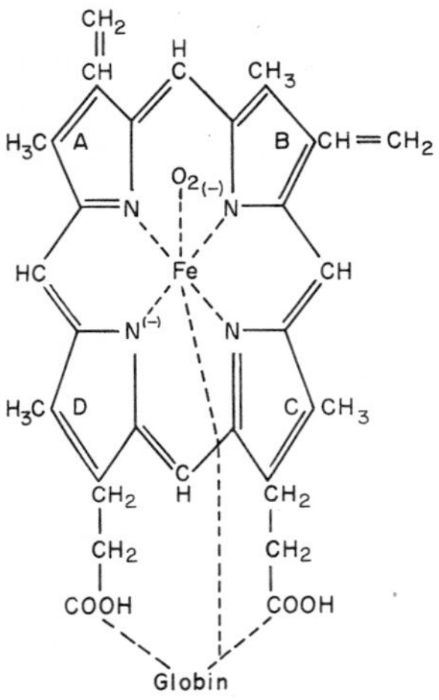

After the disintegration of the erythrocyte (see below), the hemoglobin is liberated and then undergoes a series of changes. The iron is set free. A small amount of this iron is excreted, but most of it is used again to be incorporated into new hemoglobin. The remainder of the hemoglobin molecule is converted to **biliverdin** and then to **bilirubin.** The liver removes these end products from the blood and secretes them into the gut in the bile. Bilirubin is excreted in the feces.

FIG. 11-3   Structure of hemoglobin.

Hemolysis   Erythrocytes, as has been pointed out, are very flexible and elastic, but they can be caused to rupture by abnormal stresses. For example, if the cells are placed in a hypotonic solution, fluid will pass through the semipermeable wall of the red cell because of the osmotic gradient between the fluid within and the fluid outside the cell. As a result, the cell will swell and ultimately rupture (Fig. 11-4). This rupture, or destruction, is termed **hemolysis,** which is derived from the stem *lysis,* meaning "to break down," and *hemo,* meaning "blood." On the other hand, if the cells are placed in a hypertonic solution, fluid will pass out of the cell, and the red cell will shrink and shrivel. This shrinkage is referred to as **crenation.** But apparently this process does not necessarily damage the erythrocytes, for when the cells are returned to their normal medium they may regain their usual appearance.

Red cells can also be damaged mechanically. When blood is drawn from a vein, if due care is not observed, some of the cells will be torn or broken, the hemoglobin will escape, and the plasma, instead of being straw-colored, will now display a red tinge.

Life of a Red Blood Cell   The erythrocyte develops in the red bone marrow. During the early stages it contains a nucleus, but this is usually

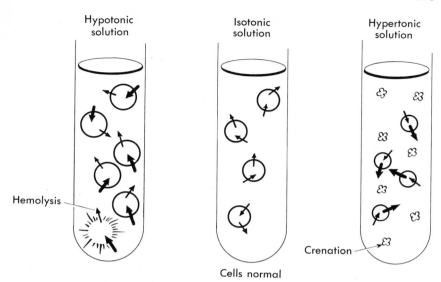

Hypotonic
solution

Isotonic
solution

Hypertonic
solution

Hemolysis

Cells normal

Crenation

FIG. 11-4   Hemolysis and crenation. Hypotonic solutions cause hemolysis; hypertonic solutions, crenation.

extruded before the cell enters the circulation. In the blood stream the red cells function for a period of time and then disintegrate, and the remains are removed from the blood by the liver and spleen.

The life span of the erythrocyte has been determined by the use of radioisotopes, usually radioactive iron which becomes a part of the hemoglobin molecule and thus "tags" the cell that carries it. By this method it is now known that the average life span of the red blood cells is about 120 days. It has further been calculated that approximately 2.5 million red cells are formed and destroyed each second. This seems to be an incredibly large number, but when it is compared with the total number of erythrocytes in the circulation, that is 25×10^{10}, it is seen that 2.5×10^6 is but a small fraction.

Under normal conditions, the number of circulating erythrocytes remains remarkably constant—so steady, in fact, that a red-bood-cell count is a routine clinical procedure. Any variation from the normal is usually indicative of a pathological condition. Obviously, if 2,500,000 red cells are destroyed every second, there must be an equal number put into the blood system to maintain the balance. We have seen that the bone marrow produces the cells, but there must be some mechanism to control the *rate* of erythrocyte production and the rate at which the cells are introduced into the circulation. The bone marrow is apparently controlled

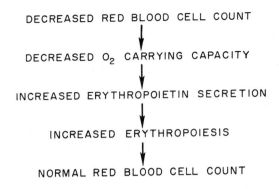

DECREASED RED BLOOD CELL COUNT

DECREASED O₂ CARRYING CAPACITY

INCREASED ERYTHROPOIETIN SECRETION

INCREASED ERYTHROPOIESIS

NORMAL RED BLOOD CELL COUNT

FIG 11-5 Regulation of the red blood cell count.

by the oxygen content of the blood. It is the hemoglobin in the red cells that carries the oxygen. Thus, if there is a shortage of red cells, the oxygen content of the blood will decrease. This stimulates the bone marrow, and more red cells are produced and introduced into the circulation.

Figure 11-5 demonstrates that this is a self-regulating homeostatic mechanism designed to maintain the constancy of the red-blood-cell count. It does not matter what causes a decrease in oxygen content. This is shown clearly in individuals who live at elevated altitudes, such as atop a high mountain. As a result of the lowered oxygen pressure, the blood contains less oxygen, the bone marrow is excited, and more red blood cells enter the blood stream. Since there was the normal quantity to begin with, such people, after a short residence at high altitude, display a red-cell concentration considerably above the average. A greater than normal number of red cells is termed **polycythemia.**

The formation of erythrocytes is termed **erythropoiesis.** The increased rate of production as a result of decreased oxygen carrying capacity of the blood is thought to be mediated by a substance called **erythropoietin** (Fig. 11-5). Erythropoietin is believed to be secreted by the kidneys. The exact mechanism by which anoxemia stimulates the production of erythropoietin is not known.

WHITE BLOOD CELLS

The white blood cells are also termed **leukocytes,** derived from *leuko,* meaning "white," and *cyte,* signifying a "cell." The normal white-blood-cell count is about 6,000 to 8,000 per cubic millimeter in comparison with 5,000,000 red cells.

Types of White Cells   There are various types of leukocytes which can be easily identified under the microscope. Examination of representative types of white cells shown in Fig. 11-1 reveals that they differ in the shape of the nucleus and in the character and staining qualities of the cytoplasm. The important types of white cells are (1) the **neutrophil,** (2) the **lymphocyte,** (3) the **monocyte,** (4) the **basophil,** and (5) the **eosinophil.**

The neutrophils make up about 60 to 70 per cent of the white cells, the lymphocytes about 20 to 30 per cent. The others are relatively scarce.

Life of a White Cell   It will be recalled that the red blood cells form in the red bone marrow. This marrow is also the site of origin of the neutrophils, eosinophils, and basophils. In fact, there is evidence to indicate that these white and red blood cells may develop from the same parent. The white cells, unlike the erythrocytes, continue to differentiate after they enter the blood stream. They retain their nuclei and are capable of further development. The red cells, without nuclei, can only eventually disintegrate.

The lymphocytes and the monocytes are formed in the spleen, lymph nodes, thymus, and tonsils.

In view of the fact that white cells are constantly being formed by the bone marrow and the lymphoid tissue, and since the white-blood-cell count remains constant, it is clear that there must also be a steady disintegration of leukocytes. The granulocytes are thought to have a life span of about 10 days, the lymphocytes 2 to 3 days. Little is known of the monocytes.

Function of the White Cells   By far the most important function of the white cells is to combat foreign substances that enter the body. The neutrophils are the major combatants. They are so small that they can readily leave the circulation by squeezing through the pores of the capillaries. This process is termed **diapedesis.** Not only are the neutrophils capable of quickly leaving the circulation in this manner, but they also have the power of independent locomotion. They move in the same manner that an ameba does. A part of the cell is protruded, becomes attached to a stationary object, and then the remainder of the cell pulls itself forward. Even more remarkable is the phenomenon of **chemotaxis.** This means that the cell becomes oriented toward, and moves toward, the site of the invading substance. The mechanism is not known, but it is believed that the invading foreign substance causes tissue damage and, as a result, a chemical called **leukotaxine** is liberated. In some manner leukotaxine attracts the neutrophil.

When the neutrophil reaches the foreign substance it engulfs it and makes it a part of its own cell. This process is termed **phagocytosis.** Once inside the cell intracellular enzymes go to work and effectively destroy or neutralize the substance. In the process the neutrophil itself may be destroyed. The harmless debris is then removed by the lymph nodes.

Finally, an invasion of foreign substances, such as bacteria, stimulate the production of neutrophils so that their number markedly increases **(neutrophilia)**. It is thought that the cells damaged by the invasion release not only leukotaxine which attracts the leukocytes, but also forms another substance which is responsible for increased leukocyte formation.

Monocytes and eosinophils function in a similar manner to the neutrophils, but it is thought that they may have specific functions, as yet undefined, in combating invasion. Basophils can carry out a similar function. In addition, there is evidence that they release **heparin** into the circulating blood. Heparin is a potent anticoagulant. This function of the monocytes may be essential to prevent intravascular clotting.

The lymphocytes are something of a mystery. Many roles have been assigned to them. It is known that they can be transformed into other types of cells and thus may serve as a ready source of such cells when the demand arises. There is growing evidence that the lymphocytes are involved in the development of allergy, but their precise role remains to be defined.

BLOOD PLATELETS

Platelets are very small structures which do not contain nuclei. The normal platelet count ranges from 250,000 to 500,000 with the average close to 300,000 per cubic millimeter of blood.

The platelets contain a precursor of **thromboplastin** and also large quantities of **serotonin.** Both of these substances are important in **hemostasis,** that is, the control of bleeding (see below).

Little is known about the life cycle of the platelets.

ABNORMALITIES OF THE FORMED ELEMENTS

A few of the more important abnormal conditions will be mentioned so as to illustrate the importance of the formed elements in the physiology of man.

Anemia   The term **anemia** means, literally, "a lack of blood." This is, of course, a misnomer. In most cases of anemia there is no true lack of blood. The term is used to describe any condition in which the oxygen-carrying capacity of the blood is reduced. This may be because of (1) a decrease in the number of circulating erythrocytes per unit volume of blood, (2) a decrease in the total number of red blood cells, as in hemorrhage, or (3) a reduction in the hemoglobin concentration of the blood with a normal red-blood-cell count.

In all these cases, the common denominator is a decrease in the available hemoglobin. Since this is the agent responsible for the transport of oxygen, it logically follows that in all such cases there will result a reduced oxygen-carrying capacity of the blood. Each molecule of hemoglobin may be thought of as a bus. If these buses are filled to capacity and if there is a decrease in the number of buses, the only way in which the usual number of people can be delivered to their destinations is by increasing the speed at which each bus circulates over its route. This is precisely what occurs in man when there is a decrease in the total number of hemoglobin molecules. In order for the normal number of molecules of oxygen to be delivered to their destinations, the circulatory velocity must be increased. Thus, all forms of anemia are characterized by an accelerated circulatory rate. The sequence of physiological events by which this increase is brought about will be analyzed in subsequent chapters.

If the basic principle of anemia is understood, namely, that it is a condition in which the oxygen-carrying capacity of the blood is decreased, then the student can readily understand the various *types* of anemia. For example, in some cases the bone marrow ceases to produce an adequate quantity of erythrocytes. It may be because of a defect in the bone marrow or an inadequate diet which fails to supply the bone marrow with the necessary building materials. This latter type is termed **nutritional anemia.** In other cases, the rate of destruction of the red cells may greatly exceed the rate of formation, even when the rate of formation is within normal limits. As a result there will be a progressive decrease in the red-cell count. One such type is **congenital hemolytic anemia.** Finally, **hemorrhagic anemia** is due simply to massive hemorrhage or loss of blood such as may occur following a severe injury.

Leukocytosis and Leukopenia It has already been pointed out that *leukocyte* refers to the "white blood cell." *Osis* signifies an increase, and *penia* denotes a "lack of." Thus, **leukocytosis** refers to an increase in the total number of circulating white cells, and **leukopenia** implies an abnormally low white count.

Leukocytosis is the more commonly observed. Practically all acute infectious processes evoke leukocytosis. Thus, even in the absence of any other findings, a high white-cell count causes the physician to suspect the presence of infection. There are conditions in which the leukocyte count soars to as high as 500,000 per cubic millimeter. This state is termed **leukemia,** which means "white blood." Leukemia is a fatal form of cancer. In this condition the white cells are formed very rapidly in the bone marrow, so rapidly that the embryonic red cells are literally "starved out." This, of course, leads to a severe anemia which predisposes to many other diseases which, in turn, may lead to death. In addition, the tremendous number of circulating white cells may actually plug up important blood vessels in the brain, heart, and kidney. This sequence of events may also create physiological inconsistencies which are incompatible with life. The cause of this type of "blood cancer" is poorly understood and poses the same problems as other types of malignant growths.

Leukopenia is often associated with many of the viral diseases such as measles, mumps, chickenpox, and infantile paralysis. In other words, acute infections due to a virus usually result in a decreased rather than an increased leukocyte count. The reasons for this state are still poorly understood.

PLASMA

The plasma is the fluid portion of the blood. Under normal conditions, it occupies over half of the total blood volume. This percentage varies within a small range, but under pathological conditions it may exceed its usual limits. Like all other values to be studied, the blood-plasma volume is controlled by many homeostatic mechanisms, so that despite variations in the fluid intake, despite the amount of fluid loss by perspiration on a hot and humid day, despite even massive hemorrhage, the total blood volume and the ratio between plasma and the formed elements are rapidly restored and maintained constant (see Table 11-1).

TABLE 11-1   Partial Composition of Blood Plasma (Chief Constituents)

Substance	Grams per 100 ml of Plasma
Water	91.000
Albumin	4.400
Globulin	2.300
Fibrinogen	0.300
Nonprotein nitrogen	0.036
Glucose (after fasting)	0.080
Sodium	0.335
Potassium	0.019
Calcium	0.010
Magnesium	0.003
Inorganic phosphorus	0.003
Organic phosphorus	0.020
Chloride	0.360
Bicarbonate	0.180

Blood plasma is a straw-colored fluid composed of about 91 per cent water and 9 per cent solids. The solids include a vast variety of substances. A discussion of all of them is clearly within the realm of biochemistry and beyond the scope of this textbook. Only a few of the more important constituents will be briefly mentioned.

Plasma Proteins Of all the blood constituents, perhaps the plasma proteins remain most constant. This great constancy has led many observers to deny that the plasma proteins represent a balance between the protein ingested and the protein utilized. That this is so, however, is indicated by the fact that in prolonged malnutrition plasma proteins decrease. But the usual dietary variations, mild hemorrhage, and wide changes in bodily activity all fail to produce a significant alteration in the plasma-protein concentration. Beyond question these blood constituents are exquisitely governed by very effective and dynamic homeostatic mechanisms.

The extraordinary efficiency and complexity of the physiology of man is illustrated by the fact that while the plasma proteins on the one hand are maintained constant by a series of mechanisms, the plasma proteins in turn function as a homeostatic mechanism to control other activities. For example, one of the most important roles of the plasma proteins is to regulate the body water balance.

If the human body were completely desiccated, it would lose about 65 per cent of its weight. In other words, over half of the body weight is made up of fluids. The total blood volume constitutes only about 9 per cent of the body weight; the remainder is in the tissues. Thus we say that the body possesses two fluid compartments: (1) **intravascular** and (2) **extravascular.** There is, at all times, a balance between these two compartments, so that the ratio remains constant. The plasma proteins help to maintain this ratio.

The capillary walls are semipermeable, which means that water and other substances of small molecular size can pass through the walls in either direction. But the plasma proteins are large molecules which normally cannot diffuse through the capillary wall. As a result there exists an osmotic relationship between the intra- and extra-vascular compartments. If large quantities of fluid are imbibed, the plasma proteins will be diluted and fluid will pass out of the capilllaries so that the ratio is rapidly righted. On the other hand, if there is a loss of plasma protein through a damaged kidney, the ratio will be upset, allowing an abnormal amount of fluid to enter the extravascular compartment. This condition is termed **edema.**

The plasma proteins, through their osmotic effect, not only regulate the fluid ratio between the two compartments but also aid in maintaining constant the total quantity of fluid within the body. For example, if one gulped a gallon or two of beer, both compartments would be flooded if a like quantity were not promptly excreted. When kidney physiology is studied, it will be learned that the osmotic state of the blood determines to a large extent the quantity of urine formed. The osmotic state is a function of the plasma proteins.

In short, the plasma proteins are large molecules which cannot diffuse through the capillary walls. They thus establish an osmotic gradient which serves (1) *to regulate the ratio between the fluid compartments* and (2) *to control the total body fluid.*

One of the plasma proteins is **fibrinogen.** This protein is fabricated in the liver and circulates in solution in the plasma. During hemorrhage it is converted into a gel called **fibrin.** This gel forms the stroma, or framework, of the blood clot and aids in stemming the hemorrhage.

Blood Sugar   Glucose is dissolved in the plasma and delivered to all the cells in the body to supply them with energy. It is one of the most important energy foods. Although the blood-sugar levels do not remain nearly so constant as do those of the proteins, nonetheless there are excellent homeostatic devices which control carbohydrate metabolism and keep the blood-sugar levels within a relatively narrow range despite wide variations in ingestion and bodily activity. The fasting individual has a blood-glucose level of about 80 mg per cent (80 mg glucose per 100 ml of blood). Abnormal variations from this norm are associated with widespread disorders which will be discussed later.

Electrolytes   The plasma contains varying quantities of many of the electrolytes such as sodium, potassium, magnesium, chlorides, phosphates, and bicarbonates. Like the other plasma constituents, these substances are found to exist in very constant concentrations. It will be seen that even slight variations of potassium, for example, may prove fatal, whereas an increase in the sodium concentration is accompanied by drastic water-balance shifts.

Other Substances   It is impossible to discuss even a small percentage of all the plasma constituents. Such substances as urea, uric acid, and creatine are important excretory substances. The plasma also contains a host of essential enzymes and hormones. The components necessary for the coagulation of blood are dissolved in the plasma. Finally, the respiratory gases (oxygen and carbon dioxide) must pass through the plasma en route to and from the red cells. In short, the plasma is a fluid containing a wide variety of substances all of which play important roles in the total physiology of man.

HEMOSTASIS

Scarcely a day passes in which a person does not injure himself, at least to the extent of allowing a drop or two of blood to escape from the vascular system. Men who shave daily certainly have the opportunity to examine the redness of their blood with annoying frequency. But such small injuries hardly evoke our serious attention. The bleeding is slight and ceases spontaneously. **Hemostasis** means the stoppage of bleeding. Hemostasis involves coagulation of blood, clot retraction, and vasoconstriction.

COAGULATION

Research into the mechanism of coagulation has been so fruitful that the most widely held concepts have undergone considerable modification in recent years. Even today there is not complete agreement as to the role of each factor, but all agree that there are two essential reactions: (1) **prothrombin** is converted to **thrombin,** and (2) **fibrinogen** is converted to **fibrin.**

Fibrin is a gel that becomes deposited in a network. The network then traps the formed elements of the blood to build a **clot.** As will be discussed below, the fibrin also retracts to pull the edges of the wound together.

Exactly how prothrombin is converted to thrombin is the subject of considerable research and debate. There is general agreement that once thrombin is formed it catalyzes the conversion of fibrinogen to fibrin. At the present writing there are at least six major theories purporting to explain the various conversions essential to clotting. They vary in detail. One of these concepts is outlined in Fig. 11-6. It will be noted that the platelets and also the plasma contain precursors of **thromboplastin.** The role of the **antihemophilic factor (AHF)** is not certain. It has been postulated that the rupture of platelets at the site of blood vessel injury is enhanced by AHF. In the absence of this factor, blood does not readily clot, probably because of inadequate thromboplastin formation.

Figure 11-6 indicates that prothrombin is formed in the liver, enters the circulation, and then is converted to thrombin under the influence of thromboplastin, **calcium, Ac-globulin,** and **Factor VII.** Thrombin, as it is formed, is also thought to catalyze the prothrombin reaction, but its major function is to bring about the conversion of fibrinogen to fibrin.

It will be noted that there are substances which inhibit each of the essential reactions, or destroy the end-products. Were it not for these substances, such as **heparin** and **antithrombin,** intravascular clotting would quickly prove fatal.

The formation of plasma thromboplastin requires from 3 to 5 minutes. The prothrombin-thrombin reaction takes 13 to 15 seconds. The formation of fibrin from fibrinogen occurs in less than 1 second.

Not only are there many theories of blood coagulation, but several different terms are often used to refer to the same factor. Table 11-2 lists some of these synonyms.

Stage I: Formation of Plasma Thromboplastin

Stage II: Formation of Thrombin

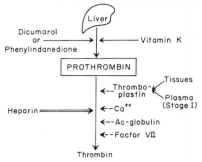

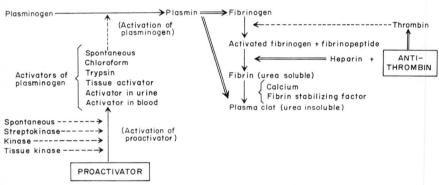

Stage III: Change of Fibrinogen to Fibrin

FIG. 11-6. Coagulation of blood. This is but one of several concepts which purport to outline the sequence of events essential to coagulation. The single arrow means "to give rise to"; the double arrow, "inhibits or destroys"; the broken arrow, "acts on"; and the box indicates that the enclosed substance is present in the blood. (Reproduced with the permission of F. C. Monkhouse.)

CLOT RETRACTION

The threads of fibrin form a network which traps blood cells and plasma. The clot then undergoes contraction. In the process of contraction, **serum** (defibrinated plasma) is squeezed out. Contraction is probably the result of shortening of the fibrin threads. Fibrin also clings to the edges of the opening in the blood vessel. Therefore, as the threads shorten, the clot becomes smaller and pulls the edges of the wound closer together. The force of contraction is about 9 mm Hg.

Clot retraction requires the presence of a large number of platelets.

Why retraction fails to occur if these platelets are not present is not known.

VASOCONSTRICTION

When arterioles and capillaries are injured they undergo constriction. This narrowing of the lumen of the vessel (vasoconstriction) is often complete enough to stem the flow of blood even in the face of high pressures. Vasoconstriction, under these circumstances, is thought to result from the liberation of **serotonin** from ruptured platelets at the site of injury.

TABLE 11-2   Synonyms for Clotting Factors

Factor I	Fibrinogen
Factor II	Prothrombin
Factor III	Thromboplastin, thrombokinase
Factor IV	Calcium
Factor V	Labile factor, proaccelerin, plasma Ac-globulin
Factor VI	Serum Ac-globulin, accelerin
Factor VII	Stable factor, proconvertin, SPCA (serum prothrombin conversion accelerator), cothromboplastin, autoprothrombin I
Factor VIII	Antihemophilic factor (AHF), antihemophilic globulin, thromboplastinogen, platelet cofactor I, plasma thromboplastic factor A
Factor IX	Plasma thromboplastin component (PTC), Christmas factor, platelet cofactor II, plasma thromboplastic factor B, autoprothrombin II
Factor X	Stuart-Prower factor
Factor XI	Plasma thromboplastin antecedent (PTA)
Factor XII	Hageman factor

PREVENTION OF COAGULATION

For many techniques it is necessary to prevent coagulation. If the mechanism of coagulation is understood, the various procedures used to prevent clotting will logically follow.

Mechanical Procedures   As has been stressed, clotting will not occur unless thromboplastin is formed. If blood is drawn into a syringe very carefully so that there is minimal damage to the skin, the only source of thromboplastin is from the platelets. If the syringe is coated with paraffin and the blood drawn most cautiously, the platelets will not be damaged and the thromboplastin will not be available to initiate the clotting mechanism. The paraffin smooths the walls of the glass syringe, thus preventing platelet damage.

Another mechanical procedure is to stir the blood sample with a glass rod. As the fibrin is formed, it will adhere to the glass rod and thus can be removed from the blood. Without fibrin there can be no clot. The blood is now said to be **defibrinated.**

Chemical Procedures   All the chemical procedures used to prevent co-agulation depend upon the inactivation or removal of one of the essential constituents of the clotting mechanism.

Heparin is one of the most widely used anticoagulants. It is extremely potent; only a few drops are required to prevent a large volume of blood from clotting. This substance is called heparin because it was first ex-tracted from the liver. It has now been found to exist in other tissues as well. Heparin acts in two ways: (1) it inhibits the conversion of pro-thrombin to thrombin, and (2) it inactivates thrombin. Its inactivating role is believed to be the more important. In any case, with no active thrombin available, fibrinogen cannot be converted to fibrin and coagula-tion is thus prevented.

In recent years, heparin not only has been used to prevent clotting for experimental purposes but is now being injected following surgical pro-cedures where it is desirable to diminish the possibility of intravascular clotting. Another substance which behaves like heparin is **hirudin,** which is extracted from the buccal glands of the leech. And there are now syn-thetic anticoagulants, such as **Dicumarol,** which are widely used in clini-cal medicine.

A common laboratory procedure to prevent coagulation is to precipi-tate the calcium. Without calcium, prothrombin is not converted to thrombin. Calcium can be precipitated by adding oxalates or citrates to the blood.

ABNORMALITIES OF HEMOSTASIS

Should blood fail to coagulate, the slightest injury might prove fatal. If coagulation were to occur intravascularly, serious impairment or even death would result.

Hemophilia   No blood disorder could be more inappropriately named. Hemophilia means, literally, "I like blood." In view of the fact that a person suffering with this disorder may readily bleed to death, the very sight of blood is a horrifying experience. The disorder is characterized by a failure of the clotting mechanism, so that even a small injury, such as a cut on a finger, may result in prolonged bleeding.

It is generally believed by hematologists that hemophilia is due to a lack or deficiency of the **antihemophilic factor (AHF).** Thus, the injec-tion of large quantities of normal blood into hemophiliacs proves very effective in controlling hemorrhage, at least temporarily. Hemophilia is an inheritable disorder and is seen most frequently in the male members of the family.

Thrombocytopenic Purpura   A condition characterized by subcutaneous hemorrhage is termed thrombocytopenic purpura. As the term indicates, there are very few thrombocytes (platelets) in the blood. As a result, clotting does not readily occur, any clots that do form fail to retract, and, in the absence of adequate serotonin concentration, vasoconstriction at the site of injury does not occur. Thus, minor trauma leads to uncontrolled bleeding into the subcutaneous space.

Thrombus and Embolus   A thrombus is a clot. The term is used clinically to designate an intravascular blood clot which is adherent to the vessel wall at its site of formation. An **embolus,** on the other hand, means "a piece." It is actually a piece of a thrombus which has broken free and has been carried by the circulating blood elsewhere, to become lodged in another vessel. Either a thrombus or an embolus may interfere with circulation, and if the involved vessel is large or supplies a vital organ, death may result.

BLOOD VOLUME

It is often advantageous to know the total quantity of blood in the body. As has been emphasized, considerable value is placed by the clinician upon the blood-cell count. But there are obviously many cases in which such a measure will be meaningless because it simply indicates the *concentration* of cells in the blood. In order to know the total cell number or the absolute amount of any other blood constituent, one must ascertain the concentration of that component and also the volume of blood. In other words, concentration times blood volume will give the total quantity of any substance in the blood.

METHOD OF DETERMINING BLOOD VOLUME

There are several methods of ascertaining the blood volume in man. One of these procedures, the so-called **dye method,** is relatively simple and is undertaken as an experiment in many student laboratories. A known quantity of an inert dye is injected into a vein. After a short period of time, an interval necessary to allow the dye to mix thoroughly with the blood, a sample of blood is drawn and then compared colorimetrically with known dilutions of blood and dye. The greater the blood volume, the less intense the dye will be because it will be more diluted.

A few actual figures will help to clarify this procedure. The dye most commonly employed in Evans' blue. It is particularly suitable because it has an intense color, it is innocuous, and it is only slowly eliminated from the circulation. Assume that 1 ml of the dye is injected into the arm vein. After adequate mixing, the drawn sample is compared with known dilutions and is found to compare to a dilution of 1:5,000. This must mean that the blood volume is 5,000 ml, or 5 liters. In actual practice,

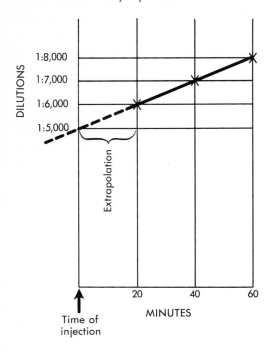

FIG. 11-7 Determination of blood volume. A dye is injected into the circulation and samples drawn every 20 minutes. The concentrations in the samples are compared with standard dilutions, the results plotted, and then extrapolated to time of injection.

several samples are drawn at 20-minute intervals. The concentration will be found to decrease progressively. A graph is then constructed and extrapolated back to the time of injection (Fig. 11-7). The concentration at the time of injection is then used for the blood-volume calculations. This is advisable because the dye is slowly but steadily eliminated from the circulation. By this method, as well as other more accurate but also more complicated procedures, the blood volume for a man of average size is found to be about 5 liters.

It is now more common to use radioisotopes to determine blood volume. The same dilution principle is employed. Radioactive iodine attached to globulin is selected because the iodine has a short half-life, it is easy to determine, and attached to globulin it does not readily leave the circulatory system. Red blood cells that have been labelled with radioactive chromium or radioactive iron are also used. By these means the total blood volume, the volume of plasma, and the volume of red cells may all be quickly and easily determined.

THE SPLEEN

The spleen is a large organ situated on the left side of the abdomen just below the diaphragm. The spleen is composed of a mass of sinuses containing various-sized openings. The arterial blood flows into the organ and is circulated about and through the sinuses to be gathered up finally by a series of veins.

The spleen is thus admirably designed and located to serve two important functions: (1) *to filter the blood and thus remove disintegrating red blood cells* and (2) *to act as a reservoir for blood.*

The blood held in reserve in the spleen has a very high cell count. Therefore, when this blood is added to the circulation, the circulating-blood-cell count increases. This is particularly advantageous following hemorrhage, for fluid is drawn into the vascular system from the extravascular compartment. As a result the hematocrit falls. But reflexly, the spleen is forced to contract, thus ejecting a high concentration of cells into the circulation. This mechanism, therefore, helps to restore the normal red-blood-cell count.

The exact nature of the reflex which controls splenic contraction has not been completely worked out. If the organ is denervated, it does not respond to hemorrhage and other conditions which demand increased blood. But just how hemorrhage evokes this response and through what pathways are still unknown.

TRANSFUSION OF BLOOD

There are many circumstances in which it is necessary to transfuse whole blood. Although it is often possible to use substitutes such as saline, glucose solutions, and plasma preparations, the fact remains that none takes the place of whole blood, and in many cases, whole blood is truly indispensable. Unfortunately, however, blood cannot be transfused into a person indiscriminately, because not all blood is the same. Some types of blood when mixed cause the formed elements to clump together. This is termed **agglutination,** which means "to paste." The cells stick together and form aggregates, and these masses may block vital vessels and lead to death.

BLOOD GROUPS

There are four basic types of human blood. Blood is classified according to the manner in which it reacts with other blood groups.

Group O   The serum of this group agglutinates the cells of all other blood groups. But the cells of this group are not agglutinated by any other sera.

Group A   This serum agglutinates the cells of the B and AB groups. The cells are agglutinated by the sera of O and B groups.

Group B This serum agglutinates the cells of A and AB. The cells are agglutinated by the sera of O and A groups.

Group AB The serum of this group does not agglutinate any cells. The cells, however, are agglutinated by the sera of all other groups.

THEORY OF BLOOD GROUPING

After studying the above classification, one will probably be convinced that blood grouping is an extremely complex and confusing process. This is not the case. If one basic principle is borne in mind, no confusion can arise. That principle states that *if the cells of the blood to be transfused will be agglutinated by the recipient's serum, the transfusion should not be made.* With that principle in mind, let us examine a few of the possibilities.

Assume that group A blood is to be transfused into a patient with group B blood. Is it safe? According to the classification, the cells of A blood are agglutinated by B serum. The answer is no; the transfusion should not be done.

Let us take another case. Assume that O blood is to be transfused into a patient with B blood. Is this safe? Here we find that the cells of group O blood are not agglutinated by *any* sera. Obviously, the transfusion is feasible. Theoretically, group O blood can be injected into anyone, because its cells are not agglutinated by any sera. For this reason, an individual with group O blood is termed the **universal donor.**

Finally, if group AB is examined, it will be seen that the serum of this blood does not agglutinate the cells of any blood. Theoretically, then, any type of blood can be transfused into a patient with AB blood. Such an individual is called a **universal recipient.**

One may well be wondering why group O blood can be transfused so safely if *its* serum agglutinates the cells of all other groups. The answer to this question is that when blood is transfused into a patient it is greatly diluted by the greater volume of the patient's blood, so that transfused serum becomes too dilute to agglutinate the host cells. And so we return to the basic principle, namely, that it is the cellular reaction of the transfused blood which is the deciding factor.

DETERMINATION OF BLOOD GROUP

The group into which a person's blood should be classified may be quickly and easily determined. It is, of course, a routine procedure in all hospitals. As a matter of fact, it is well for everyone to have his blood classified so as to avoid delay in cases of emergency.

A small amount of blood is diluted with saline, and then a drop of this mixture is added to two test sera, one belonging to group A and the

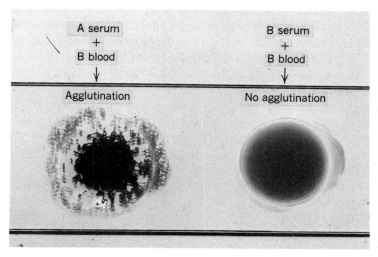

FIG. 11-8   Agglutination of blood. Procedure used to type blood.

other to group B. The examiner then observes whether or not agglutination has taken place. The clumping of the cells can be seen with the naked eye but is usually checked with a microscope (Fig. 11-8). Then the technician need only refer to Table 11-3 to determine the blood group. This table simply sets out in tabular form what has already been stated concerning each blood type. The minus sign indicates no agglutination, while the plus mark signifies agglutination.

Other types of blood have been described, but it is not within the scope of this book to include them all.

TABLE 11-3   Blood-group Determination

Group	Serum A	Serum B
O	—	—
A	—	+
B	+	—
AB	+	+

RH FACTOR

For years it has been known that in some cases, even though the bloods have been carefully and correctly classified, fatal results have followed transfusions. It is now known that some of these accidents are unquestionably due to the so-called **Rh factor.** The Rh factor is an **antigen,** which means "to produce **antibodies,**" and that is precisely what the Rh factor does. Thus if a person who does not possess the Rh factor receives transfused blood which does have it, his blood will form antibodies. But the recipient suffers no ill effects. The tragedy occurs when, at a future date, he is again transfused with Rh-positive blood. Now the antibodies which have previously formed cause the cells of the newly transfused blood to agglutinate.

People are classified as Rh positive or negative, depending upon whether or not this antigen is present. About 85 per cent of the white population are Rh positive. Other races seem to be 100 per cent Rh positive.

The Rh factor also has great importance in obstetrics. For example, it is possible for an Rh-negative woman to be pregnant with an Rh-positive fetus. As a result of the Rh factor in the blood of the embryo, the mother's blood soon develops antibodies. If the mother were then or later to receive a transfusion of Rh-positive blood, the transfused cells might be agglutinated. On the other hand, the Rh-negative mother with the Rh-positive antibodies may again become pregnant, and again carry an Rh-positive fetus. The Rh-positive antibodies may enter the fetus where they will destroy the blood of the developing embryo. Thus, the second child may be born dead, or at least seriously ill with an unusual type of jaundice (yellow skin). The sequence in these cases is that an Rh-negative woman married to an Rh-positive man delivers a healthy Rh-positive child. But the second pregnancy results in a stillborn, or a seriously ill, infant.

It is interesting to learn the origin of the term Rh. During the early phases of the experimental work which clarified this problem, it was discovered that the blood of the Rhesus monkey contained the antigen in question. For that reason the antigen has been assigned the designation Rh (Rhesus).

CROSS-MATCHING

Because blood contains many antigens in addition to those discussed above, it is best, in addition to determing the blood group of the donor and the recipient, to cross-match their bloods. In this procedure a sample of blood is drawn from each. Then cells from one are mixed with serum from the other and vice versa. To be absolutely certain when making a transfusion, no agglutination should occur in the cross-matching.

SUMMARY

Blood is a red and viscous fluid with a specific gravity of about 1.055. It is composed of **formed elements** and **plasma.** The percentage of red blood cells is called the **hematocrit.** It is normally 40 to 45 per cent. The total blood volume in the average man is about 5 liters.

The **red cells** are also known as **erythrocytes.** They are small, biconcave disks without nuclei. There are normally about 5,000,00 red cells per cubic millimeter of blood. They contain **hemoglobin,** a protein responsible for the carriage of oxygen by the blood. Oxygenated blood is red; reduced hemoglobin is blue. Red cells are formed by the red bone marrow, survive about 120 days in the circulation, and then disintegrate. The **spleen** serves as a blood reservoir with a high concentration of cells. Erythrocyte production by the bone marrow is controlled by the oxygen content of the blood.

There are only about 6,000 to 8,000 **white cells** or **leukocytes** per cubic millimeter of blood. The important types of white cells are (1) **lymphocytes,** (2) **monocytes,** (3) **neutrophils,** (4) **basophils,** and (5) **eosinophils.** Most of the white cells are also formed by the bone marrow; the lymphocytes and probably the monocytes arise from lymphatic tissue. The white cells function primarily to combat foreign agents. The cells migrate to the site of an infection, engulf the foreign particles, and destroy them. This engulfing process is termed **phagocytosis.** An excessive number of white cells is termed **leukocytosis.** It characterizes most acute infectious states. In **leukemia,** the white count may approach a half million, and this "blood cancer" behaves like other malignant diseases. An abnormally low white-blood-cell count is called **leukopenia.** It is customarily associated with many of the virus diseases.

The **platelets,** or **thrombocytes,** number about 300,000 per cubic millimeter of blood. They are essential to **hemostasis.**

Any condition in which the oxygen-carrying capacity of the blood is reduced is termed **anemia.** It may be caused by (1) a decrease in the number of red cells or (2) a reduction in the hemoglobin concentration.

The plasma is the fluid portion of the blood. It is a straw-colored fluid composed of about 91 per cent water and 9 per cent solids. The most important constituents are (1) the **proteins,** which control water balance and play a role in coagulation; (2) **blood glucose,** which is the basic source of cellular energy; and (3) the essential **electrolytes;** as well as many other constituents such as **enzymes, hormones, excretory substances,** and the **respiratory gases.**

Hemostasis depends upon the coagulation of blood, clot retraction, and vasoconstriction. Blood coagulation occurs when **prothrombin** is converted to **thrombin.** The thrombin then catalyzes the conversion of **fibrinogen** to **fibrin.** Fibrin forms the network of the clot and is responsible for the retraction of the clot. Vasoconstriction is brought about by **serotonin,** a substance carried by the platelets.

Blood falls into one of four groups, depending on its agglutinating properties. The four groups are termed **O, A, B,** and **AB.** If the cells of the donor blood will be agglutinated by the recipient's serum, the transfusion should not be made. *It is the cellular reaction of the donor's blood which is important.* The **Rh factor** is an **antigen** which, when given to an Rh-negative person, causes antibody formation. About 85 per cent of the white population are Rh positive.

QUESTIONS

1. What are the functions of the erythrocytes and leukocytes?
2. What is the normal blood volume and how may it be determined?
3. What is the function of the platelets?
4. Outline the mechanism of coagulation.
5. How may coagulation be prevented in drawn blood?
6. How may the type of a sample of blood be determined?

SUGGESTED READING

Gatson, L. M., "The Blood-clotting Factors," *New England J. Med.,* **270:**#5, 236–242, January 30, 1964; **270:**#6, 290–298, February 6, 1964.

Laki, K., and Gladner, J. A., "Chemistry and Physiology of the Fibrinogen-fibrin Transition," *Physiol. Rev.,* 44:#2, 127–160, April 1964.

Murray, J. F., "Systemic Circulation," *Ann. Rev. Physiol.,* 26: 389–420, 1964.

Ratcliff, J. D., "Circulation of the Blood," *Today's Health,* **35:**#1, 24–25, 50–51, January 1957.

Reich, C., "The Cellular Elements of the Blood," *Clin. Symposia,* 14:#3, 79–109, July-September 1962.

Zucker, M. B., "Blood Platelets," *Sci. American,* **204:**#2, 58–64, February 1961.

Cardiac Dynamics

THE HEART IS THE PUMP WHICH SUPPLIES THE ENERGY to propel the blood throughout the body. If the heart stops even briefly, irreversible changes occur and death quickly ensues. The importance of the heart cannot be overemphasized.

The problems with which the heart must cope are indeed complex. Not only is it required to pump blood continuously, but it is necessary for it to propel varying quantities of blood in accordance with body needs. There must obviously be highly delicate mechanisms to control this function. The study of the physiology of the heart resolves itself into two major considerations: (1) the means by which the heart pumps blood and (2) the mechanisms which control heart function. But before these problems can be approached, it is necessary to understand the basic principles of cardiac dynamics.

ANATOMY OF THE HEART

Figure 12-1 shows the heart in highly schematic fashion. In man, the heart weighs about 350 gm or about ¾ lb. The principal constituent of the heart wall is the **myocardium,** that is, **cardiac muscle,** which differs structurally and functionally from both skeletal and smooth muscle. The inner surface of the cardiac muscle is lined with a thin layer, termed the **endocardium.** On the outer surface of the myocardium is a slick serous membrane called the **epicardium.** The epicardium bends back to be continuous with the **pericardium** which surrounds the heart. Between the two membranes exists the **pericardial space** (Fig. 12-1). Normally, it contains a small quantity of fluid sufficient to lubricate the outer surface of the heart and thereby permit it to slide with minimum friction against the inner surface of the pericardium.

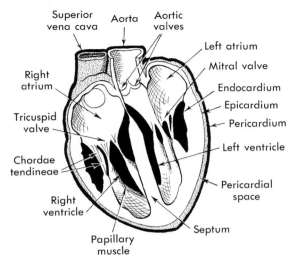

FIG. 12-1 Diagrammatic representation of the anatomy of the heart.

HEART CHAMBERS

The human heart contains **four cavities.** There are two **atria** and two **ventricles.** The atria are sometimes called **auricles,** the two terms being used interchangeably. Actually, auricle means "ear" and in the heart refers to the small outpouchings of the atria. Strictly speaking, the proper term for the entire structure is atrium, although auricle has gained widespread acceptance.

Shortly after birth, the opening between the right and left atria closes so that in the normal individual the atria do not communicate with one another. There is also a thick septum separating the two ventricles.

Blood enters the left atrium of the heart from the lungs. It then flows into the left ventricle which pumps it out into the aorta for distribution throughout the body. The blood returns from all parts of the body and is gathered into the superior and inferior venae cavae which open into the right atrium. The blood flows into the right ventricle to be pumped through the pulmonary arteries into the lungs. It returns via the pulmonary veins to enter the left atrium, thus completing the cycle (Fig. 12-2).

Examination of the heart discloses that the thickness of the wall varies in different chambers. The atrial walls are very thin, whereas those of the ventricles are thick and muscular, especially the left ventricular wall which is many times thicker than the right. The thickness of the wall is determined by the amount of cardiac muscle. The part of the heart muscle

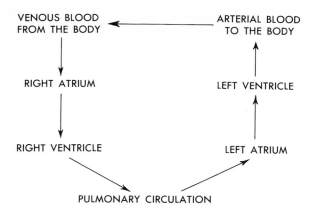

FIG. 12-2   The circulation pathway through the heart.

which does the most work becomes the largest. The atria, as will be pointed out subsequently, are required to do very little work. The left ventricle, on the other hand, must eject large quantities of blood rapidly against a very high pressure. This requires considerable energy.

HEART VALVES

There are four valves in the heart: (1) the **mitral valve** between the left atrium and left ventricle, (2) the **tricuspid valve** between the right atrium and right ventricle, (3) the **aortic valve** between the left ventricle and the aorta, and (4) the **pulmonic valve** between the right ventricle and pulmonary artery.

All of the valves, with the exception of the **mitral valve,** possess three leaflets or **cusps.** The mitral valve has only two cusps. The A-V valves are continuous with the endocardium, and their free ends are supported by delicate tendons called **chordae tendineae.** The chordae tendineae are seen to insert into the **papillary muscles.** If the direction of blood flow is kept in mind while examining the valves, it will be clear that they can open only in one direction and that this arrangement determines the flow of blood. The papillary muscles and the chordae tendineae prevent the A-V valves from opening in the opposite direction. This mechanism is of utmost importance to cardiac dynamics.

THE HEARTBEAT

In order to pump blood the heart must contract; then it must relax to allow more blood to enter it; then it must contract again. There are consequently two important cardiac phases: (1) the **contraction phase** and (2) the **relaxation phase.** The former is termed **systole,** which means "a contracting." The relaxation phase is called **diastole.** This term signifies "a dilatation" and, of course, during the relaxation phase blood enters the heart and causes it to be dilated.

OXYGEN REQUIREMENTS

Cardiac muscle, like all other body tissues, must receive a steady supply of oxygen for survival. The more active muscle is, the greater its oxygen requirement (Fig. 12-3). But there is one extremely important observation to be made from Fig. 12-3, and that is the *increased* oxygen demand after the cardiac output declines. In other words, the oxygen utilized by the heart increases with the initial length of the fiber and so does the work of the heart. But, according to Starling's law, after a critical point is reached the cardiac output falls off, while the initial length continues to increase. After this point is reached the heart still demands more and more oxygen, at the same time ejecting less blood. In this way a vicious cycle is set up which will be terminated by death if not properly treated. A fall in cardiac output delivers less blood to the tissues of the body in-

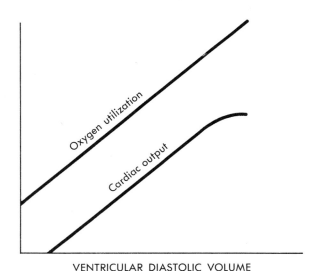

VENTRICULAR DIASTOLIC VOLUME

FIG. 12-3   Oxygen utilization in relation to Starling's law. Note that as the ventricular diastolic volume increases so does the cardiac output up to a critical point after which it decreases. This describes Starling's law of the heart. Oxygen utilization continues to increase even after cardiac output decreases.

cluding the cardiac muscle, and because of a shortage of oxygen the muscle is weakened and puts out even less blood.

OTHER REQUIREMENTS

Temperature All chemical reactions are influenced by temperature. Generally speaking, the higher the temperature, the more rapid will be the chemical reaction. Cellular metabolism consists of a series of complex chemical processes, the speed of which varies with temperature. Thus it is that the higher the temperature of the blood, the faster will be the heartbeat. But since the temperature of the blood is maintained by exquisitely sensitive homeostatic mechanisms within such a narrow range, this factor is not of great importance in the physiology of man.

Blood Constituents The blood contains a wide variety of substances, as was pointed out in the previous chapter. Several of these constituents modify heart action significantly. Thus, every physiological laboratory is equipped with a supply of Ringer's solution. This is a solution of electrolytes in a proportion which Ringer found necessary to maintain the perfused heart in normal activity. For example, if the isolated turtle or frog heart is perfused with isotonic sodium chloride (NaCl), it soon ceases to beat. It is necessary to include not only sodium and chloride but also potassium, calcium, and bicarbonate ions. Not only must these constituents be present, but they must appear in a very definite ratio. Table 12-1 gives the percentage composition of Ringer's solution.

TABLE 12-1   Percentage Composition of Ringer's Solution

NaCl	0.900
KCl	0.030
$CaCl_2$	0.025
$NaHCO_3$	0.020

Acidity Finally, it should be noted that a change in the acidity of the blood alters cardiac function. Usually, the reaction of the blood is maintained close to the neutral point (actually the pH is about 7.4), but under some conditions it does vary and evokes not only reflex responses but also direct cardiac changes.

ENERGY OF CONTRACTION

Cardiac muscle derives its energy for contraction from the transformation of adenosine triphosphate to the diphosphate form. Normally, diastole is long enough to permit complete recovery of the original essential compounds. This allows the heart to beat steadily for years. As a matter of fact, experiments using isolated hearts indicate that the heart muscle will beat for incredibly long periods of time so long as there is an adequate supply of oxygen and nutrients and so long as waste products are removed.

Abnormally, the heart rate may become so rapid, the rest periods so abbreviated that there is not adequate time for the resynthesis of the basic compounds. As a result, the heart fatigues and ceases to beat.

RHYTHM

Cardiac muscle, unlike skeletal muscle, has an inherent power of rhythmic contraction. It is true that the heart is liberally innervated by the autonomic nervous system which can modify the beat of the heart, but there is a fundamental rhythm to the normal heart muscle which is completely independent of any innervation. For example, if the heart is removed from an animal and perfused under optimal pressure with the proper constituents, it will continue to beat indefinitely. But that rhythm can be, and in man is, modified by the autonomic nervous system.

ORIGIN OF THE HEARTBEAT

If the living heart is watched, it is impossible to determine just where the contracting process begins. But through histological and physiological investigations, it is now known that the beat of the heart originates in the right atrium.

Sinoatrial Node Microscopically, a specialized spot of tissue may be discerned in the right atrial wall just at the point of entry of the superior and inferior venae cavae. This specialized tissue mass is composed of interwoven thin strips of modified cardiac muscle. It is termed the **sinoatrial node** (Fig. 12-4) and derives its name from *sinus,* which implies a dilated channel for venous blood, and *atrium,* which has already been described. The sinoatrial node is popularly referred to as the **S-A node.** There is excellent evidence to indicate that the heartbeat originates in the S-A node. For example, if heat is applied to the node, the heart rate increases, whereas if heat is applied to other parts of the atrium no such increase can be detected. Likewise, if the node is destroyed, there results a marked slowing of the heart. Destruction of a comparable area elsewhere in the atrium does not have this effect. This, and other evidence, indicates conclusively that the heartbeat originates in the sinoatrial node. It is for this reason that the node is referred to as the **pacemaker** of the heart.

The S-A node is supplied with fibers from both divisions of the autonomic nervous system. Impulses which arrive over these pathways modify the sinoatrial node and thus influence the heart rate.

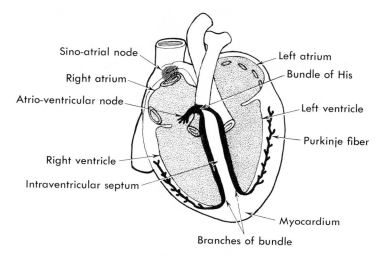

Sino-atrial node

Right atrium

Atrio-ventricular node

Left atrium

Bundle of His

Left ventricle

Purkinje fiber

Right ventricle

Intraventricular septum

Myocardium

Branches of bundle

FIG. 12-4   Conduction system of the heart. The beat is initiated by the sino-atrial node.

TRANSMISSION OF THE HEARTBEAT

After the heartbeat is initiated by the S-A node, the impulse spreads out over both atria in more or less concentric rings. There are thought to be no special pathways in the atria, and since the muscle acts as a syncytium all parts of it progressively contract as the impulse spreads. As a result of the manner in which the impulse spreads, the muscle immediately surrounding the sinoatrial node contracts first, and then more distant atrial areas subsequently join in. The pressure within the atria, therefore, slowly increases and then decreases.

Atrioventricular Node   The impulse spreads throughout the atria but is not transmitted across the atrioventricular septum which separates the atria from the ventricles. However, there is another specialized mass of tissue termed the **atrioventricular node.** This node is also made up of thin strips of interwoven specialized cardiac muscle and is similar, in this respect, to the sinoatrial node (Fig. 12-4). It is referred to as the **A-V node.**

The impulse from the atria activates the A-V node, and in this way the ventricles are activated. The atrioventricular node is the only pathway by which the impulse can be transmitted from the atria to the ventricles. If this node is destroyed, and it may be by disease, the atria and ventricles then beat completely independently of one another and at different rates. Such a condition is called **complete heart block.** On the other hand, if the disease process is not extensive, so that impulses do pass through the node but only after a considerable delay, or if not all the atrial impulses fire the A-V node, the disorder is spoken of as **partial heart block.** In such cases the atria may beat two or three times for every beat of the ventricles, but there is a definite ratio between the atrial and ventricular beats, indicating that some of the impulses are being transmitted.

Atrioventricular Bundle and Branches   The impulse does not fan out concentrically through the ventricles as it does in the atria. This is so because there is a ventricular conducting system. Figure 12-4 shows that there is a bundle of elongated tissue continuous with the atrioventricular node. It is called the **atrioventricular bundle of His** in honor of one of the men who first described it.

The bundle of His splits into two, each part of which is continuous with the long conducting pathway which passes to the individual ventricles (Fig. 12-4). These branches of the bundle, so-called **Purkinje fibers,** spread out in the ventricles. Thus the impulse is delivered to all parts of both ventricles almost simultaneously. As a result, the ventricles contract sharply and vigorously.

INDEPENDENT RHYTHMS

It has been pointed out that if the sinoatrial node, the pacemaker, is destroyed, the heart continues to beat but at a much slower rate. It has been found that the atrioventricular node also has an inherent rhythm, and when it is removed from the influence of the pacemaker it initiates its own impulse but at a much slower rate. This condition prevails following destruction of the pacemaker. Therefore, the slower heart rate can be assumed to be the inherent rate of the atrioventricular node.

Likewise, if the A-V node is destroyed as well as the pacemaker, then the atrioventricular bundle exerts its own inherent rhythm which is even slower than that of the A-V node. Finally, it can be shown that a small piece of cardiac muscle will beat even after it has been excised from the heart. Thus the musculature must have its own rhythm; but since it requires so much cardiac insult to demonstrate this inherent rhythm, the exact rate cannot be stated with certainty, although it seems clear that it is slower than the A-V bundle rate. Table 12-2 summarizes these relationships.

TABLE 12-2   Approximate Independent Rates per Minute for Various Parts of the Heart

S-A node	70–80
A-V node	60–70
A-V bundle	35–40
Musculature	About 30

Knowledge of the rhythm of the heart has yielded, in recent years, exciting practical applications. It is now possible to provide the patient with an artificial pacemaker which initiates ventricular contraction by the application of evenly spaced repetitive electrical impulses. The electrodes of the pacemaker may be applied to the skin of the chest (external pacemaker) or wires may be fixed to the myocardium directly (internal pacemaker).

ELECTROCARDIOGRAPHY

There is electrical activity associated with the contraction of cardiac muscle which may be recorded by suitable equipment. Such records have proved invaluable both in the physiology laboratory and clinically. A complete discussion of electrocardiography is clearly beyond the scope of this book. The primary principles are here summarized, first because such a study emphasizes basic physiological factors of cardiology, and second so that the student may, if he so desires, go beyond the limits of this course and familiarize himself with this important technique.

The instrument used to amplify and record the electrical activity of the heart is called the **electrocardiograph**. The record so produced is referred to as an **electrocardiogram** (**EKG** or **ECG**).

RECORDING TECHNIQUES

The first recordings of the electrical activity of the heart were made using a sensitive string galvanometer. In this instrument a string made of quartz-glass fiber and coated with silver is suspended between the two poles of an electromagnet. Variation of the current in the string causes it to move between the electromagnets. To obtain a recording of this movement a light is focused on the string so that it casts a shadow on photosensitive paper. The paper has a mechanism to move it at a steady, standard rate, thus after development, a permanent record of string movement results. More modern instruments utilize electronic amplification systems to amplify the cardiac action potentials sufficiently so that a pen is caused to move. Paper flows at a standard speed under the pen to obtain the record. The advantage of the newer method is that the record may be observed as it is being recorded and no development is necessary. In addition, polygraphs may be used in order to obtain the record from several **leads** simultaneously.

ELECTROCARDIOGRAPHIC LEADS

The electrodes may be placed directly on the heart, as is sometimes done in experimental animal work, or they may be attached to most any part of the body. The relative position of the two electrodes will, of course, influence the direction and amplitude of the record; therefore, a conventional system has been developed. The specific arrangement of the two electrodes is termed a lead.

Electrodes   The electrodes are generally made of metal and slightly concave so as to make good contact with the skin in the regions of the wrists and ankles. A jelly consisting of an electrolyte and an abrasive is first rubbed over the surface of the skin. The abrasive removes dead cells and other accumulations that would interfere with the conduction of the impulse. The electrolyte forms a surface between the skin and the metal electrode, and thus facilitates the conduction of the impulse. In place of the jelly, thin paper pads presaturated with an electrolyte solution are often preferred because they are inexpensive, less messy than the jelly, and convenient to use. The electrodes are securely held by means of wide rubber straps.

Standard Leads   The first electrocardiograms were made by Einthoven who attached electrodes to the two wrists and to the left ankle. These three electrodes could be used in three different combinations of two, which became known as the standard leads. They are: **Lead I,** right arm and left arm; **Lead II,** right arm and left leg; and **Lead III,** left arm and left leg.

If the arms are held extended to the sides, a triangle can be visualized connecting the two arms and the left leg. The heart then lies within the triangle. This triangle is known as **Einthoven's triangle** (Fig. 12-5). It has considerable significance in the analysis of the electrocardiogram.

Unipolar Limb Leads   The three standard electrodes are used, but two of them are connected, through suitable resistance, to a common terminal and then lead to the negative post of the electrocardiograph. The remaining electrode goes to the positive post. The following designations are used: **aVF** when the positive terminal is connected to the left leg, **aVR** when it is the right arm, and **aVL** when it is the left arm. These leads are also referred to as **augmented limb leads** because the magnitude of the deflections is increased by this wiring procedure. The augmented leads are now used as commonly as the standard leads because the record so obtained is determined almost exclusively by potentials from one particular limb. It is said that the record "views" the heart from the root of that limb.

Chest Leads   In this case, an indifferent electrode is formed by uniting all of the standard electrodes through resistance to a central terminal. The potential of the central terminal, therefore, remains at zero throughout the cardiac cycle. The positive terminal is connected to an electrode

LEAD I
RIGHT ARM – LEFT ARM

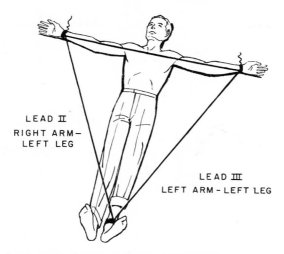

LEAD II
RIGHT ARM–
LEFT LEG

LEAD III
LEFT ARM – LEFT LEG

FIG. 12-5   Einthoven's triangle. The three standard leads form a triangle enclosing the heart.

which is placed on various areas of the chest. This electrode, then, is the
sole determinant of the observed deflections of the record. Six standard
positions on the chest are now commonly used. They are designated V_1,
V_2 up to V_6. The records have great diagnostic value.

Esophageal Lead   To obtain still another "view," so to speak, instead of
the chest electrode, an electrode is introduced into the esophagus and
then connected to the positive post.

ELECTROCARDIOGRAM

With the two electrodes attached to the body in any of the combinations
already described, while the patient is in the supine position, a record
such as shown in Fig. 12-6 is obtained. It will be noted that the record is
superimposed upon a graph. The lines upon the graph have been stand-
ardized so that electrocardiograms may be easily interpreted and compared. The vertical lines supply a time record; the horizontal lines
indicate the magnitude of response. The interval between two vertical
lines measures 0.04 second. It will be noted that every fifth vertical line
is heavier. The time interval between two heavy vertical lines is then
0.20 second. Before a record is taken, the instrument is adjusted so that
a current of 0.1 millivolt causes a vertical deflection of one horizontal

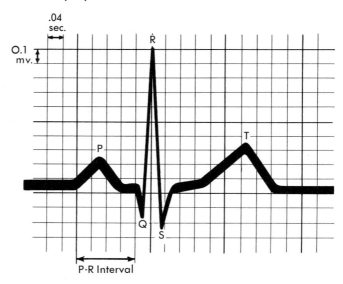

FIG. 12-6   The electrocardiogram. (See text for details.)

space. Every fifth horizontal line is also darker. In other words, a current of 0.5 millivolt will deflect the curve the distance between two heavy horizontal lines.

It will be recalled that the impulse responsible for contraction of the heart is initiated by the sinoatrial node. The impulse then fans out over the atria. Next the A-V node is excited, which transmits the impulse through the A-V bundle of His and its branches to activate the ventricles. As this impulse courses through the heart, the electrical manifestation of its position in relation to the three leads varies. It is for this reason that the record differs in each lead.

It should be understood that the record obtained in any one lead merely reflects the electrical activity which is associated with excitation of the cardiac muscle. Figure 12-6 depicts the more important waves which must be considered in order to interpret the electrocardiogram.

P Wave   The atria contract first. Therefore the electrical activity associated with this excitation causes the first deflection or wave on the electrocardiogram. Figure 12-6 shows that the curve is of moderate magnitude and smooth. This indicates that the impulse spreads relatively slowly throughout the two atria so that progressively more and more muscle depolarizes. By the time the last parts of the atria begin to contract, the muscle immediately surrounding the S-A node is already repolarizing. Thus the curve slowly builds up to a maximum and then tapers off. The direction of the P wave is usually upright in all three standard limb leads. However, this is not invariably true. It may also be found that the magnitude of the P wave differs in the three leads. It is the position of the heart which determines the magnitude and direction of each wave. Therefore, when an electrocardiogram is read, the amplitude and direction of each wave is calculated, and from such computations the axis of the heart is ascertained. This information is of vital clinical importance.

QRS Complex Excitation of the ventricles gives rise to complicated deflections. Accordingly, the wave is called a complex. In Fig. 12-6 it can be seen that the typical QRS complex usually contains three individual waves, the first of which is called the Q wave; the second, spikelike, upward deflection is the R wave; and the third is the downward S wave. The direction of these three components is not always the same in all three leads. Again, the direction and magnitude of these waves depend upon the position of the main axis of the heart in relation to Einthoven's triangle. The QRS complex represents the algebraic sum of the electrical activity emanating from each ventricle.

P-R Interval The P-R interval is the time measured from the beginning of the P wave to the beginning of the QRS complex (Fig. 12-6). This may seem confusing, and one may wonder why it is not called the P-Q interval. It happens that quite often there is no distinct Q wave, whereas there is usually a sharp R wave. Thus it has become the accepted practice to designate the interval P-R.

The P-R interval is the time which elapses between the beginning of atrial systole and the start of ventricular systole. In other words, it is the time required for the impulse to spread from the S-A node throughout the atria, plus the delay of the impulse in the A-V node and bundle, plus the conduction time through the branches to the ventricular musculature. This period of time usually occupies about 0.16 second. The significance of the P-R interval is, of course, to indicate the efficiency of the cardiac conducting system.

T Wave The P wave represents depolarization of the atria. The QRS complex expresses the resultant of depolarization of the ventricles and repolarization of the atria. The T wave is due simply to repolarization of the ventricles.

ELECTROCARDIOGRAM ANALYSIS

Again it must be emphasized that no attempt is being made to offer a comprehensive study of electrocardiography. This section on electrocardiogram analysis is designed to make it possible for the student to interpret a record sufficiently to augment his knowledge of cardiac physiology. Figure 12-7 shows a normal 12-lead electrocardiogram.

Artifacts The electrocardiograph will record electrical activity other than that originating in the heart. Therefore, it is essential that the subject be completely at rest while the record is being taken. If the individual is excited and moving about, the record will be distorted because skeletal-muscle contraction also gives rise to electrical activity. In addition, artifacts may be caused by poor contact between the electrodes and the skin. Defects in the instrument itself will alter the record. Therefore, the tracing should first be carefully examined for any discrepancies due to artifacts.

Heart Rate Perhaps the first measurement to make is the heart rate, as well as the regularity of the beat. One glance will show whether or not the rhythm is regular. Then, remembering that each vertical line demarcates 0.04 second, it is simple to calculate the heart rate. For example, if four P waves occupy approximately 75 vertical lines, that is, 15 heavy vertical lines, the heart rate must be about 80 beats per minute ($15 \times 0.2 = 3$ seconds for 4 beats thus $^{60}/_3 \times 4 = 80$ beats per minute). This is within the normal range.

Waves The record is now examined wave by wave. The normal record will show a distinct P wave, QRS complex, and T wave, as well as other less important deflections. The direction and magnitude of each wave are examined and compared with normal values. In some cases the record will disclose two or three P waves for every QRS complex. This

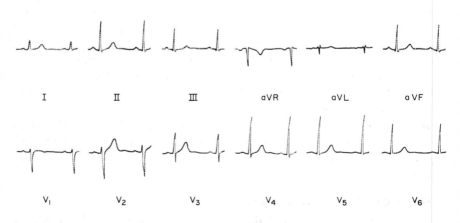

FIG. 12-7 A normal 12-lead electrocardiogram. Note that the direction and amplitude of the deflections vary in each lead.

indicates a partial heart block. On the other hand, there may be no relationship between the P waves and the QRS complex. This is indicative of a complete heart block, resulting in independent atrial and ventricular rhythms.

The configuration of each curve is also of importance. Ordinarily the P wave, for example, is round and smooth. In abnormal cases it may be flat, peaked, or even notched. If it is recalled that the P wave represents depolarization of the atria, then it becomes clear that these aberrant P waves must indicate abnormalities in the atrial musculature.

Not only are the waves carefully studied for configuration, duration, direction, and magnitude, but the intervals between the deflections are also measured. An abnormally prolonged P-R interval, for example, indicates a delay in the conduction of the impulse either in the atria or in the A-V system. These two possibilities can be differentiated by also calculating the duration of the P wave. If the duration of the P wave is normal and the P-R interval abnormally long, the delay must be present in the A-V conducting system.

Electrical Axis It has already been indicated that the direction and magnitude of each wave are determined by the position of the heart. Not only does the heart position influence the direction and amplitude of the waves, but so do other factors such as the relative size of the two sides of the heart and differences in conductivity in the two sides. The so-called **mean electrical axis** is determined by establishing the resultant of all these factors.

In order to calculate the mean electrical axis of the heart, the direction and magnitude of the QRS complex in any two leads are plotted upon an Einthoven triangle.

Deviations of the electrical axis from the normal range may indicate dilatation, hypertrophy, or a combination of the two of one side of the heart or the other, depending upon whether the axis deviates to the left or right. Such axis deviations may also be indicative of an impairment of transmission in the bundle branches. This disorder is referred to as **bundle-branch block.**

CARDIAC CYCLE

As has already been pointed out, the student should guard against the mistake of attempting to "explain" cardiac function on the basis of need. Clearly, a statement that the heart pumps more blood because the body needs more explains nothing. The physiologist attempts to ascertain (1) how the heart is apprised of the body needs and (2) how it alters its function to satisfy this increased demand. But before these two problems can be considered, it is necessary to examine the cardiac cycle in detail.

It has already been established that blood enters the right atrium, passes into the right ventricle, circulates through the lungs, then returns to the left atrium to enter the left ventricle and be pumped throughout the body (Fig. 12-2).

The pressure of the blood when it enters the right atrium is very close to zero. The activity in the right ventricle elevates that pressure to about 25 mm Hg, while at the same time the left ventricle increases the pressure of the blood ejected into the aorta to about 120 mm Hg. All these pressures are of course expressed in relation to atmospheric pressure.

When the heart muscle contracts, blood flows in only one direction because of the action of the valves. In other words, in the short period of one cardiac cycle, which at a normal heart rate of 70 per minute occupies less than a second, the valves must open and close rapidly, synchronously, and efficiently. Therefore, one must be able (1) to describe all the changes which occur during the cardiac cycle and (2) to explain *how* these alterations take place.

PHYSICAL PRINCIPLES OF PRESSURE RELATIONSHIPS

Since the major portion of our knowledge of cardiac dynamics has been deduced from the pressure curves to be discussed presently, it is first advisable to review basic physical principles of pressure relationships.

The pressure within a chamber represents the ratio between the size of the chamber and the volume of fluid forced into it. If the fluid does not fill the chamber, there is no pressure. In order to have positive pressure, the chamber must be overfilled, so to speak. Therefore, the greater the volume of fluid in ratio to the capacity of the chamber, the higher will be the pressure.

There is another factor to bear in mind at all times, and that is the material of which the compartment is made. If the chamber wall is in-elastic, then a small increase in volume will cause a great and sharp rise in the internal pressure. If the container is ideally elastic, as the volume increases, the size of the chamber will also increase. If these increments are proportional, the ratio between size and volume will remain constant and so will the internal pressure. Actually, of course, this degree of elasticity is seldom encountered. In the heart, for example, especially in the thin-walled and highly elastic atrium, a great increase in volume of blood produces only a slow and small elevation in pressure.

With these principles in mind, the student should now follow the ensuing discussion *wave by wave,* with the aid of Fig. 12-8. It is necessary to know what causes each wave in the curve in order to understand cardiac dynamics.

ATRIAL-PRESSURE CURVE

Starting with the atrial-pressure curve (Fig. 12-8), it is apparent that throughout the greater part of diastole the pressure within the atrium steadily increases. This is because of the fact that blood flows continuously into the atrium throughout diastole, and this increases the volume of blood in relation to the size of the chamber.

Next there is a sudden increase in pressure. This wave is caused by

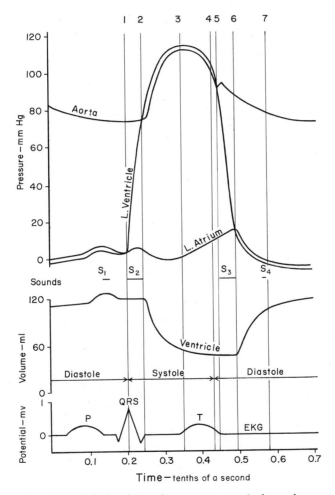

FIG. 12-8   Relationships of pressure, ventricular volume, heart sounds, and the electrocardiogram during the cardiac cycle.

atrial contraction. Contraction of the cardiac muscle decreases the size of the atrium, thereby increasing the internal pressure.

At line 1, systole begins. When the term systole is used without any qualification, it refers to the contraction of the ventricle. Contraction of the atria is termed **atrial systole.** At line 1, the ventricles begin to contract. This muscular activity, as it decreases the size of the ventricle, evokes a sharp rise in intraventricular pressure. It will be noted that before line 1 is reached the pressure in the ventricle is slightly lower than in the atrium. Fluid flows from higher-pressure areas to lower-pressure areas. Thus the blood flows from the atrium into the ventricle through the open A-V valve. But when the ventricle contracts, it is seen in Fig. 12-8 that the pressure within the ventricle greatly exceeds the intraatrial pressure. As a result there is a tendency for the blood to flow back into the atrium from the ventricle. But as soon as this reverse flow begins, the A-V valve is closed by the backward movement of the blood. The intraventricular pressure increase is so sudden and so sharp that the A-V valve actually bulges into the atrium. This bulging, reducing as it does the size of the atrial chamber, is responsible for the rise in atrial pressure.

Now there occurs a sharp fall in atrial pressure. This decrement is caused by two factors: (1) the stretching of the atrial wall by the contraction of the ventricles which pulls the A-V septum downward and thus enlarges the atrial chamber and lowers its pressure and (2) the rapid ejection of about 70 ml of blood from the chest cage. For all practical purposes, the thoracic cage is a closed chamber. Thus the intrathoracic pressure represents the ratio between the size of the chamber and the volume contained therein. If 70 ml of blood are ejected by the heart into the blood vessels, the thoracic cavity loses this volume and the intrathoracic pressure falls. Since the atria possess such thin walls, any change in intrathoracic pressure will influence intraatrial pressure.

The atrial-pressure curve next shows a slow increase in pressure. This increase is caused by blood which flows into the atrium from the great veins.

When ventricular pressure falls below that in the atrium, blood rushes into the ventricle, sweeping the A-V valve open in its onrush. The atrial pressure curve now falls, because a large volume of blood flows into the ventricle, which decreases the volume in the atrium and therefore lowers the pressure.

The cardiac cycle is now complete and ready to begin again.

VENTRICULAR-PRESSURE CURVE

Now ventricular pressure will be dissected and examined wave by wave. Since many of the events which take place in each chamber are influenced by activity elsewhere, there will of necessity be considerable repetition.

Starting once again at the extreme left of Fig. 12-8 the pressure in the ventricle is noted to be slightly lower than in the atrium. As a result, blood flows from the atrium through the open A-V valve into the ventricle. Therefore, as these two chambers steadily fill with blood, there is a progressive increase in pressure. The first deflection is caused by atrial systole, which forces blood more rapidly into the ventricle.

At line 1, systole begins. The ventricular wall contracts as a unit with great force; thus the intraventricular pressure increases sharply. As soon as the pressure within the ventricle exceeds the intraatrial pressure, that is, where the two lines cross, the blood reverses its direction and begins to flow back into the atrium. In so doing it forces the A-V valve closed. The ventricle now is a closed chamber. The wall is still contracting down upon the volume of blood within. This elevates the pressure rapidly. Since the volume of blood does not change, neither does the length of the cardiac fiber. In other words, between lines 1 and 2 the cardiac muscle of the ventricle is contracting **isometrically.** This part of the cardiac cycle is appropriately termed the **isometric-contraction phase.**

During diastole, the blood pressure in the aorta falls to about 80 mm Hg. The pressure in the ventricle at the beginning of systole is close to zero. In other words, during the isometric-contraction phase, the intraventricular pressure must be elevated about 80 mm Hg.

At line 2 on the ventricular-pressure curve, the intraventricular pressure exceeds the aortic pressure. As a result, the aortic valve is forced open and blood rushes out of the ventricle. The ventricle continues to contract vigorously and, despite the fact that blood is now being ejected, the pressure continues to mount to line 3. Because of the great pressure which has been built up between lines 2 and 3, blood leaves the ventricle very rapidly. This can be confirmed by noting the ventricular-volume curve at the bottom of Fig. 12-8. Accordingly the part of the cardiac cycle between lines 2 and 3 is termed the **rapid-ejection phase.**

The pressure in the ventricle beyond line 3 is seen to decline. But bear in mind that up until line 4 systole continues, that is, the ventricle continues to contract. The pressure falls off simply because blood is being ejected faster than the ventricle is contracting, thus altering the ratio between volume and capacity. A glance at the ventricular-volume curve indicates that blood continues to be ejected during this period, but more slowly than during the previous period. Consequently, this part of the cardiac cycle between lines 3 and 4 is called the **reduced-ejection phase.**

At line 4, systole ends. The ventricular wall begins to relax. The ventricle now contains very little blood. As a result, a precipitous fall in pressure begins. At line 5, the two curves cross, indicating that the ventricular pressure has fallen below the pressure in the aorta. The blood in the aorta now begins to reverse its flow into the ventricle but in so doing slams shut the aortic valve. The short period between the end of systole, line 4, and the closure of the aortic valve, line 5, is termed the **protodiastolic phase,** *proto* meaning "first." In other words, it is the first part of diastole.

Once again the ventricle is a closed chamber. The cardiac muscle continue to relax, but since no blood is entering the chamber, the length of the cardiac fiber remains unchanged. Hence, the part of the cardiac cycle between lines 5 and 6 is called the **isometric-relaxation phase.**

The fall in intraventricular pressure continues until it is lower than the pressure in the atrium. When it is, the two curves cross at line 6. Now the blood begins to flow into the ventricle from the atrium and, in so doing, opens the A-V valve. The volume of blood which, between lines 2 and 6, has collected in the atrium now rushes into the ventricle. Once again this fact may be confirmed if the ventricular-volume curve is noted. Appropriately, the part of the cardiac cycle between lines 6 and 7 is termed the **rapid-inflow phase.** Lastly, if the heart rate is slow there will be a short period during which there is relative quiescence

TABLE 12-3   Approximate Duration of the Phases of the Cardiac Cycle (in Seconds) at a Heart Rate of 72 per Minute

	Protodiastolic	0.04
	Isometric relaxation	0.08
Diastole 0.48	Rapid inflow	0.09
	Diastasis	0.18
	Atrial systole	0.09
	Isometric contraction	0.08
Systole 0.35	Rapid ejection	0.12
	Reduced ejection	0.15

throughout. This phase is called the **diastasis.** The cycle is complete and ready to begin again. Table 12-3 outlines the time relationships of the various cardiac phases.

AORTIC-PRESSURE CURVE

The aorta is more elastic than muscular. Therefore, changes in its capacity reflect its elasticity and not muscular contraction. The pressure in the aorta, at any time, just as in the chambers of the heart, simply reflects this relationship between the capacity of the vessel and the volume of blood contained.

Beginning once again at the extreme left of Fig. 12-8, aortic pressure is seen to be falling progressively. At this time the aortic valve is closed, and the volume of blood ejected into the aorta is flowing out into the vascular tree. It is true that the aorta, by its inherent elasticity, closes down upon the volume of blood, but not fast enough to maintain the pressure. Therefore, the volume decreases more rapidly than does the capacity, resulting in a fall in pressure. It is important to realize the role played by the elasticity of the great blood vessels. If the vessels were simply rigid tubes, like lead pipes, as soon as the heart ceased to eject blood, the pressure in the aorta would fall precipitously perhaps even to zero before the next ejection phase. In other words, *it is the elasticity of the aorta and large blood vessels which helps to maintain the blood pressure during diastole.*

At line 2 on the aortic-pressure curve, the aortic valve opens and a large volume of blood is ejected rapidly into the aorta. As a result, the pressure in the aorta increases. The wall of the aorta is stretched by the blood volume. If the vessels were completely rigid the capacity would remain constant while the volume rapidly increased and, thus, the aortic pressure would soar. The elasticity of the aorta and other large blood vessels, then, serves two functions: (1) to maintain the blood pressure during diastole and (2) to buffer the systolic pressure.

Between lines 3 and 4, the amount of blood being ejected by the ventricle is reduced; at the same time blood flows out of the aorta into the vascular tree. Since the outflow is greater than the flow into the aorta, the volume is reduced and so is the pressure.

Finally diastole begins. The pressure in the ventricle falls rapidly until the two curves cross. At this point, line 5, the blood begins to flow back into the ventricle but in so doing closes the aortic valve. The reverse flow is halted and forced in the normal direction, thus causing a sudden but only transient increase in the aortic pressure. This dip, or notch, in the aortic-pressure curve is known as the **incisura,** which means "a cutting into," that is, a notch.

After the flow of blood in the aorta has once again become smooth and unidirectional, the aortic pressure steadily decreases until the aortic valve opens once again.

The curves shown for aortic and ventricular pressures are based upon the classic work of Wiggers and Hamilton done in the early 1930's. The dynamics of ventricular ejection have recently been reinvestigated using more modern equipment. Curves obtained in this way are reproduced in Fig. 12-9.

It is immediately obvious that the configuration of the ventricular pressure curve differs from the original curves, but the most striking fea-

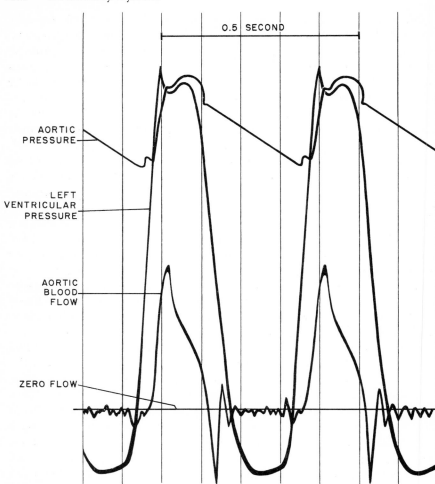

FIG. 12-9 Relationships of left ventricular pressure, aortic pressure, and aortic blood flow during the cardiac cycle. Note that in contradistinction to the curves in Fig. 12-8, ventricular pressure exceeds aortic pressure only at the beginning of the ejection phase. When it falls below aortic pressure, the velocity of aortic blood flow decreases. (Reproduced, with permission, from M. P. Spencer, and F. C. Greiss, *Circulation Res.*, **10**:274, 1962.)

ture of this new study is the demonstration that for only a short period during systole is the ventricular pressure higher than that of the aorta. It has long been assumed that there must be a higher pressure in the ventricle than in the aorta and that this pressure gradient is necessary in order to move the blood from the heart into the aorta.

An interesting feature of the new investigation is the simultaneous recording of blood flow in the aorta. This is made possible by the use of an electromagnetic flowmeter which is a transducer that surrounds the blood vessel and does not impede the flow. It will be noted that the rate of blood flow in the aorta increases during the time that ventricular pressure exceeds that of the aorta. But as soon as the pressure gradient is reversed, that is, when the ventricular pressure falls below that of the aorta, the rate of aortic blood flow rapidly decreases, stops (at zero flow), and then reverses.

It appears, as has long been assumed, that it is the positive pressure gradient that is responsible for the ejection of blood from the ventricle and for the increasing acceleration of that ejection during the rapid ejection phase. However, during the reduced ejection phase, there is a negative pressure gradient which opposes the flow of blood and brings it to a halt. An analogy to driving a car is helpful. To propel the car with increasing acceleration, energy, provided by the engine, is required. Now if the gears are disengaged, the car does not immediately stop, but, because of its mass, continues to move forward. To stop it rapidly requires opposing force. Apparently the same is true in the heart. The blood has mass. The positive pressure gradient accelerates it; the negative pressure gradient decelerates it. It finally stops and reverses.

CARDIAC-VALVE FUNCTION

The anatomy of the heart valves has been outlined. It was noted that the valves are attached to the heart wall at one end and free at the other. The heart valves are moved by two forces: (1) the pressure of the blood and (2) eddy currents.

BLOOD PRESSURE

It has been seen that significant pressure changes take place in the heart during the cardiac cycle. Sometimes the pressure is higher in the atria than in the ventricles, and at other times the reverse is true. Likewise, for a fraction of a second the pressure is higher in the ventricles than in the large vessels, and then this relationship is reversed. These pressure changes are fundamentally responsible for the opening and closing of the valves. The valves possess no inherent energy; they move simply as straws in the wind. Thus, when the atrial pressure exceeds the pressure in the ventricles, the blood flows into the ventricles and in so doing sweeps the A-V valves open. When the ventricle begins to contract, the intraventricular pressure exceeds the atrial pressure and blood begins to flow back into the atria.

EDDY CURRENTS

As the blood pours into the ventricle from the atrium, it does not simply pile up until the chamber is filled. Instead it sweeps around the walls to set up what are termed **eddy currents.** The blood flows behind the valves and thus begins to float them to the closed position. As more and more blood fills the ventricle, the greater become the eddy currents. At the same time, the blood flow into the ventricles is lessening. In other words, throughout diastole there is an increasing force acting to close the valves and a progressively weaker force holding them open. Therefore, just before systole begins, the A-V valves are almost closed. The sudden increase in intraventricular pressure when the ventricle contracts now reverses the flow of blood and completes the closure of the valves.

The eddy currents, then, do not close the valves, but they initiate the process and in so doing prevent an undue amount of blood from being regurgitated into the atrium when the ventricle contracts.

It is interesting to note that if there is a delay in the conduction of the impulse from the atrium to the ventricle, there will be a period just before systole when so little blood is flowing into the ventricle that no eddy currents are set up. As a result, the valve remains wide open. Now, when the ventricle contracts, a considerable quantity of blood regurgitates into the atrium before the valve can close. This is clearly a waste of energy.

HEART SOUNDS

In view of the fact that a large quantity of blood flows through the heart rapidly, not in a steady stream but rather in a stop-and-go pattern, it is not surprising to find that very definite sounds emanate from the heart during the cardiac cycle. The physician uses a **stethoscope** to listen to these sounds. The instrument is so named because *stethos* means "chest" and *skopeo* means "I examine." In other words, it is an instrument to examine the chest. The physician employs the stethoscope to examine the heart and lungs. The stethoscope consists of an exploring head, which is in some cases merely a metal cone and in other instances a small diaphragm. This is connected to two rubber tubes which lead to ear plugs. In this way the sounds from the chest are transmitted by the rubber tubes to the ears of the examiner. The stethoscope does not, in any way, magnify the sound. It is a simple conduction system. One can listen to heart sounds without an instrument. If the ear is placed close to the chest, the heart sounds will be clearly detectable. This was the accepted procedure before the invention of the stethoscope.

The sounds which arise from the normal heart are heard to be vigorous, clear-cut, and regular. The defective heart usually alters these sounds. It is appropriate, therefore, to speak of normal and abnormal heart sounds.

NORMAL SOUNDS

It is easy to detect two distinct normal heart sounds. In some cases a third sound may also be heard. It is actually present in almost all individuals and is considered to be a normal constituent. However, in many people it is too faint to be detected without special equipment.

First Sound   In Fig. 12-8 there is a tracing of the heart sounds. This record serves to place the sounds in their exact relationship to the cardiac cycle. It can be seen that the first heart sound occurs at the beginning of systole. A glance at the pressure curves indicates that at this instant there is a great deal of commotion in the heart which could readily account for the sound. Several events are believed to contribute to the production of the first heart sound.

In the first place, as soon as the ventricle begins to contract, the reverse flow of blood slams the A-V valve closed. This can be compared to the closing of a door. The harder one shuts a door, the louder will be the noise, and so it is in the heart. The more vigorously the ventricle contracts, the louder the first sound.

A fraction of a second after the A-V valves close, the aortic and pulmonic valves open. One has but to observe children at play to realize the fact that a door (or valve) can produce as much noise when opened as when closed. Actually, the great pressure in the ventricle snaps the valves open and sets them to vibrating. This vibration gives rise to sound waves which are heard as a part of the first heart sound.

As soon as the aortic and pulmonic valves open, a great quantity of blood, under high pressure, rushes forth. This has two effects: (1) it causes the walls of the aorta and pulmonary arteries to vibrate, and (2) it causes the ventricular walls to vibrate. This activity also contributes to the production of the first heart sound.

There is no doubt but that the valvular action, especially the closing of the A-V valve, is the major contributor to the production of the first heart sound, but the other factors should not be ignored. It can be said that the first heart sound is heard at the beginning of systole and is caused by (1) *the closing of the A-V valves,* (2) *the opening of the aortic and pulmonic valves,* (3) *the vibration of the ventricles, and* (4) *the vibration of the major vessels.*

Second Sound   Figure 12-8 indicates that the second heart sound begins at the onset of diastole. At this time there are again many events which contribute to this sound. The major contributor is the closing of the aortic and pulmonic valves. A fraction of a second later the A-V valves open; thus they also participate in the production of the second sound.

It has been explained previously that the incisura is caused by the rebound of blood from the closed aortic and pulmonic valves. This rebound evokes an abrupt increase in pressure and, as a result, causes the walls of the aorta and pulmonary arteries to vibrate. These vibrations produce sound. Finally, the sharp fall in pressure in the ventricle is said to make the ventricular wall quiver.

Again it can be said that, although the valve action is mainly responsible for the second heart sound, it is not the only factor. The second heart sound which begins at the onset of diastole is caused by (1) *the closing of the aortic and pulmonic valves,* (2) *the opening of the A-V valves,* and (3) *the vibration of the large vessels and ventricles.* The second heart sound ends after the A-V valves open.

The two major heart sounds serve to identify the particular phase of the cardiac cycle in which the heart is at any time. If one listens to a normal heart, one will hear lub-dub—lub-dub—lub-dub. Table 12-3 outlines the length of systole and diastole. It is seen that at the normal heart rate of about 72 beats per minute, diastole is considerably longer than systole. Thus, one hears lub-dub—pause, lub-dub—pause. The lub is the first heart sound and marks the beginning of systole. The dub is the second heart sound and indicates the onset of diastole. There is then a brief pause before systole begins again.

The two major normal heart sounds are of great importance to the physician. Their intensity and quality indicate the vigor of cardiac-muscle contraction in the normal man. In the defective heart they mark the phase of the cardiac cycle and thereby serve to place any abnormal sounds correctly. As will be seen, an abnormal sound heard in systole indicates a very different condition than a pathological sound heard during diastole.

Third Sound   As already indicated, the third heart sound is usually very faint and difficult to hear in the average person without special amplifying equipment. Figure 12-8 shows that this sound is present during the rapid-filling phase. It is thought to be due to the vibrations of the walls of the ventricles occasioned by the rapid inrush of blood from the atria.

ABNORMAL SOUNDS

Gallop Rhythm   If the heart is beating very rapidly and if the third sound is audible, three distinct sounds will be heard in rapid sequence. The effect will be similar to that of a galloping horse—thus the name. But since the third sound is not usually heard, this is not the customary cardiac activity which leads to gallop rhythm.

In most cases the presence of a gallop rhythm indicates serious heart damage. There are, to be sure, many cardiac afflictions which demonstrate this finding. For our purposes, it is enough to say that the gallop rhythm is a common abnormal cardiac sound associated with serious heart ailments.

Murmurs A murmur is a soft sound. In a sense it resembles the sound produced by forcible expiration with the mouth partially open. To understand cardiac murmurs, it is necessary to appreciate two basic factors which govern the production of sound resulting from fluid flowing through a tube. It is an easily demonstrable fact that fluid flowing at a moderate rate through a smooth tube produces no sound. If the velocity of that flow is increased, a point is reached at which sound is heard. Therefore, the first factor which determines the production of sound is the **velocity of the flow.** But the velocity at which sound will be produced depends upon the **internal surface of the tube.** If the surface is rough, the sound will be produced at a lower velocity. Therefore, it can be said that sound produced by the flow of fluid in a tube is determined by (1) the velocity of the flow and (2) the nature of the inner surface of the tube. The sound is actually produced by turbulence which causes the walls of the tube to vibrate. If the flow is smooth, there will be no turbulence and therefore no sound. But when high velocities are attained, there is turbulence and obviously this agitated state is enhanced by the presence of roughened walls.

In view of the fact that a high velocity of flow is capable of producing sound, it might be thought that if the circulatory rate were to increase considerably a murmur would be heard. In many cases this is precisely what happens. The velocity of a fluid through a tube is inversely proportional to the diameter of the tube. In other words, the narrower the tube, the faster the flow at that point. To see that this is correct one need only recall that a river seems hardly to move where it is wide but when it narrows the velocity becomes very rapid. The openings between the heart chambers are narrow. Therefore the blood flow is rapid at these points. During severe exercise, the flow of blood through such narrow apertures may become so fast as to exceed the critical velocity at which turbulence is produced. As a result, a murmur will be heard. Obviously this murmur does not reflect the presence of heart disease.

On the other hand, there are many cardiac abnormalities which give rise to murmurs even when the general circulatory rate is normal. Often one or more of the valves will be narrowed. Such narrowing is referred to as **stenosis,** which simply means "a narrowing." As a result, the velocity of blood flow through the narrow opening is very swift even at normal circulatory rates. Therefore, every time blood flows through this orifice a murmur is produced. If the cardiac cycle is kept in mind, it will be possible to relate any murmur to the valve in question. For example, if the A-V valves are narrowed, then the murmur will be detected during diastole, notably during the rapid-inflow phase. If the aortic or pulmonic valves are stenosed, the murmur will be heard during systole, most conspicuously during the rapid-ejection phase. A seasoned clinician can readily differentiate between the two A-V valves or between the pulmonic and aortic valves by moving the head of the stethoscope about until the murmur is heard at maximum intensity. This location will indicate the defective valve.

Usually, when a valve is narrowed or stenosed, it is also roughened by the same process. Therefore the murmur produced by stenosis is due to (1) *the constricted opening which increases the velocity of blow flow* and (2) *the roughened wall which reduces the critical velocity at which turbulence is produced.*

In some cases, the valves close incompletely or insufficiently to prevent the backflow of blood. This type of disorder is termed **insufficiency** or **regurgitation.** Thus we speak of **aortic, mitral, tricuspid,** or **pulmonic insufficiency** or **regurgitation.** As will be seen in subsequent chapters, both stenosis and insufficiency throw an extra load upon the heart. They are also both associated with murmurs. In the case of stenosis, the murmur is caused by the increased velocity of the blood and the roughening of the walls which result in turbulence. But the murmur in an insufficient valve requires another explanation. In this case the blood is allowed to flow back into a heart chamber. In so doing it collides with blood which is entering that chamber in the normal direction. The collision causes turbulence and vibration and therefore sound.

Again the examiner must listen most carefully in order to place the murmur in relation to the cardiac cycle. For example, if he hears lub-hiss-dub—lub-hiss-dub, he knows that the murmur is occurring during systole. Having established this fact he must, by moving the stethoscope about, ascertain whether the A-V valves are producing the sound or whether the disturbance is in the aortic or pulmonic valves. If it is the latter, there is probably an aortic or pulmonic stenosis; if the A-V valves are responsible, they are probably insufficient, thus allowing blood to regurgitate into the atria during systole.

SUMMARY

The greater **the initial length of the fiber,** the more forceful will be the contraction. The initial length is determined by the amount of blood which enters the ventricle during **diastole.** The greater the force of contraction during **systole,** the more blood will be ejected. Accordingly, the output of the heart increases up to a critical point, with increasing diastolic filling. This is **Starling's law of the heart.**

The heartbeat originates in the **sinoatrial node.** The impulse spreads concentrically throughout the atria to be picked up by the **atrioventricular node.** This node then transmits the impulse throught the **atrioventricular bundle and branches,** thus activating the ventricles almost simultaneously. The sinoatrial node is called the **pacemaker.** If the atrial impulse does not get through to the ventricles, the ventricles beat independently of the atria. This condition is termed **complete heart block.** **Partial heart block** is a state characterized by an undue delay or incomplete transmission of the impulse to the ventricles.

The **electrocardiograph** is an instrument which records cardiac electrical activity. The three standard leads which make up Einthoven's triangle are **lead I,** left arm and right arm; **lead II,** right arm and left leg; **lead III,** left arm and left leg. The unipolar leads are designated **aVR, aVL,** and **aVF.** The chest leads are numbered V_1 through V_6. The record produced by the electrocardiograph is termed the **electrocardiogram (EKG).** The **P wave** is caused by depolarization of the atria. The **QRS complex** is due to depolarization of the ventricles plus the deflection caused by atrial repolarization. The **T wave** represents ventricular repolarization. The **P-R interval** is the time measured from the beginning of the P wave to the beginning of the QRS complex.

During diastole, blood enters the atrium and flows through the open A-V valve into the ventricle. Therefore, the pressure in both chambers slowly increases. When the atrium contracts, there is an increase in pressure in both chambers. At this point systole begins. The ventricle contracts vigorously and causes a sharp increase in pressure. The blood begins to flow back into the atrium but in so doing completely closes the A-V valve which has already been partially shut by the action of **eddy currents.** The ventricle now becomes a closed chamber. The wall is contracting isometrically. This constitutes the **isometric-contraction phase.** When the ventricular pressure exceeds the aortic pressure, the aortic valves open. Blood now rushes from the ventricle during the **rapid-ejection phase.** But because of the continued, vigorous ventricular contraction, the pressure in both the ventricle and the aorta continues to increase until the **reduced-ejection phase** occurs, during which the pressure in both chambers falls. Systole ends at that point. The very first part of diastole is termed the **protodiastolic phase.** During this period the pressure in the ventricle falls below that of the aorta and the blood reverses its direction, starts to flow back, and in so doing closes the aortic valve. The blood rebounds in the aorta and causes the **incisura.** The ventricle is a closed chamber. The wall relaxes isometrically. This is the **isometric-relaxation phase.** Finally, the pressure in the ventricle falls below that of the atrium, and blood rushes in during the **rapid-inflow phase.** The cycle is now ready to begin again.

During the cardiac cycle, two and sometimes three distinct **heart sounds** are heard. They are usually detected by the use of a **stethoscope.** The first heart sound occurs at the beginning of systole. The second heart sound commences at the end of systole. The third sound, to be heard, usually requires the aid of amplifying equipment. It is present during the rapid-filling phase. If a valve is narrowed, the disorder is termed **stenosis.** The narrowing increases the velocity of blood flow through the opening, so as to produce turbulence, vibration, and sound called a **murmur.** Murmurs may also be caused by a valve which fails to close completely, a condition referred to as **insufficiency** or **regurgitation.**

QUESTIONS

1. What is Starling's law of the heart?
2. Trace the course of the impulse from the pacemaker through the heart.
3. Draw a typical electrocardiogram and explain each deflection.
4. Draw the superimposed pressure curves for the atrium, ventricle, and aorta. Label fully. Also include curves to represent ventricular blood volume, EKG, and heart sounds.
5. What causes the heart sounds?
6. How do murmurs differ from normal heart sounds?

SUGGESTED READING

Harary, I., "Heart Cells in Vitro," *Sci. American,* 206:#5, 141–152, May 1962.

Lentz, J., "Messages from your Heart: the Electrocardiogram," *Today's Health,* 41:#6, 26–27, 50, June 1963.

Milnor, W. R., "Heart," *Ann. Rev. Physiol.,* 24: 169–198, 1962.

Podolsky, R. J., "The Mechanism of Muscular Contraction," *Am. J. Med.,* 30:#5, 708–719, May 1961.

Scher, A. M., "The Electrocardiogram," *Sci. American,* 205:#5, 132–141, November 1961.

Shah, P. M., Shodki, S. J., and Luisada, A. A., "A Revision of the 'Classic' Areas of Auscultation of the Heart. A Physiologic Approach," *Am. J. Med.,* 36:#2, 293–300, February 1964.

Cardiac Control

13

AT THIS TIME IT SHOULD BE EVIDENT HOW THE HEART CONTRACTS and the sequence of events which transpires during each beat. In the discussion of the origin and transmission of the heartbeat, it was noted that the pacemaker has an intrinsic rhythm of about 70 beats per minute. However, this inherent cadence can be altered by many and diverse forces. Not only is it possible to change the *rate* at which the heart works, but the *force* with which it contracts may also be varied. In any analysis of the efficiency of the heart as a pumping organ, one must consider both of these factors.

In general terms, it can be said that the function of the heart is to propel an adequate quantity of blood to satisfy body needs. It has been noted that during exercise the oxygen requirements of contracting skeletal muscle increase sharply. This demand can be met only by a greater supply of oxygenated blood. The respiratory system oxygenates the blood; the circulatory mechanism delivers it to the tissues. With this information as a starting point, the physiologist must explain how the heart function is altered to meet these varying requirements. Our problem here is to analyze the factors which control the rate and force of contraction of the heart. We shall see that there are mechanisms which act directly upon the heart and other factors which influence heart action through reflex pathways.

CARDIAC OUTPUT

Throughout this discussion the term **cardiac output** will be employed. By definition, *cardiac output is the quantity of blood ejected by one side of the heart in one minute.* Under normal conditions the volume of blood put out by both sides of the heart is the same. Therefore, to calculate the quantity of blood pumped by the heart as a whole, it is neces-

265

sary to multiply the cardiac output by 2. However, it should be realized that under some circumstances the two ventricles may pump different amounts of blood.

CALCULATIONS OF CARDIAC OUTPUT

In order to compute cardiac output, it is necessary to know the **heart rate** and the **stroke volume.** The heart rate is simply the number of times the heart beats per minute. The stroke volume is the quantity of blood ejected by each beat (stroke) of the heart. The average heart pumps about 70 ml of blood, a little over four tablespoons, with each beat, and the usual heart rate is approximately 72 per minute. Therefore, the cardiac output, in this case, would be 5,040 ml (70 × 72). In other words, this heart pumps about 5 liters of blood per minute.

DETERMINATION OF CARDIAC OUTPUT

As has just been mentioned, if the stroke volume and heart rate are known, the cardiac output can be easily calculated. The heart rate is simple to determine but the stroke volume is not. Accordingly, other methods must be sought.

Fick Principle   Cardiac output may be calculated from the amount of oxygen consumed per minute and the amount of oxygen taken up by the blood as it passes through the lungs. These relationships are expressed by the Fick principle as follows:

$$\text{Cardiac output} \atop \text{(ml/min)} = \frac{\substack{\text{oxygen consumed per minute} \\ \text{(ml/min)}}}{\substack{\text{arterial O}_2 \text{ content} \\ \text{(ml O}_2/\text{ml blood)}} - \substack{\text{venous O}_2 \text{ content} \\ \text{(ml O}_2/\text{ml blood)}}}$$

To determine the volume of oxygen consumed per minute, the subject breathes from a known volume of oxygen for a period of time. Six to 10 minutes usually suffices. Then by ascertaining the oxygen remaining, the amount consumed can be calculated. A sample of arterial blood is drawn for the determination of arterial content. But because the oxygen content is not the same in the blood of all the veins, the so-called mixed venous blood must be used. This is the venous blood just before it enters the right heart. Such a sample is obtained by **cardiac catheterization.** A small-bore tube is introduced into an arm vein and then moved through the vein until the tip of the tube enters the right atrium. A sample of blood is then withdrawn and the oxygen content determined. Using the Fick equation the cardiac output may now be determined.

Dye Method   Cardiac catheterization introduces certain difficulties and objections, therefore the dye method is often used instead of the procedure just outlined. In this method, a known quantity of dye, usually Evan's blue, known also as T-1824, is injected into an arm vein. A catheter in an artery leads the blood through a transducer sensitive to dye concentration. The elecrical impulses resulting from the transducer activate a recorder so that a record is obtained of the concentration of dye in the arterial blood following the injection. Such a record (Fig. 13-1) shows a rising line which then falls but not to the base line because of recirculation of the dye. If the transducer has been properly calibrated, it is possible to determine, from the record, the average concentration of dye that passed in the arterial blood in one circulation. The time may also be calculated, then:

$$\frac{\text{Cardiac output}}{\text{(ml/min)}} = \frac{\text{dye injected}\ \text{(mg)}}{\text{average concentration} \times \text{time}\ \text{(mg/ml)}\quad\text{(min)}}$$

Radioisotope Method   A radioisotope may be substituted for the dye. By means of a scintillation detector similar results will be obtained. The isotope of preference is generally I^{131} combined with albumin to hold it in the circulation. By means of an external scintillation detector placed over the aorta a record may be obtained which obviates the necessity of putting a catheter in an artery. The calculation is a bit more involved, but the results are comparable to the dye method and the Fick procedure.

Ballistocardiography   It is also possible to determine the cardiac output by use of the **ballistocardiograph.** This is an instrument which records the small movements of the body caused by the ejection of blood from the heart and by other aspects of the cardiac cycle. Such a record contains a series of waves. It has been shown that the magnitude of the waves bears a relationship to the cardiac output. In order to calculate cardiac output it is necessary to estimate the cross-section of the aorta. This is

FIG. 13-1   Determination of cardiac output, dye method. Typical curve obtained after injection of dye in a vein. By determining the average concentration under the curve and _t_, time, the cardiac output can be calculated.

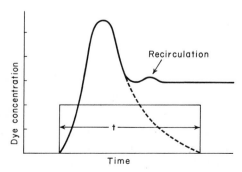

done by x-ray. The calculations are very complex but in general the results agree with other methods.

VARIATIONS IN CARDIAC OUTPUT

At rest the cardiac output, in man, is about 5 liters per minute. Under other conditions it may change. In some cases of cardiac abnormalities, it is decreased. Under other conditions, such as exercise, it may increase to as much as 30 or 35 liters per minute.

Relationship of Heart Rate and Cardiac Output   If the curve representing ventricular blood volume is kept in mind (Fig. 12-7), the relationship between heart rate and cardiac output is easier to understand. As the heart rate increases, the length of diastole decreases (Table 13-1). The greatest volume of blood enters the ventricle during the rapid inflow phase. Thereafter the flow decreases. Thus, as the heart rate increases from a very low rate to about 90 beats per minute, there is very little change in the final diastolic volume (Fig. 13-2). Because cardiac output is equal to heart rate times stroke volume, in the range 50 to 90 beats per minute, the cardiac output is seen to increase as the heart rate increases, since the stroke volume does not decrease proportionately. In the range 90 to 140 there is not much change in cardiac output (Fig. 13-3) simply because as the rate increases, the filling time decreases and so the stroke volume falls proportionately with the increase in rate, so long as the venous pressure remains constant. Finally, however, at very fast rates the filling time is so short that the stroke volume falls faster than the rate increases, thus the cardiac output progressively decreases. From this discussion it should be clear that a change in heart rate does not always indicate a comparable change in cardiac output.

TABLE 13-1   Length of Systole and Diastole at Various Heart Rates

Heart Rate, beats/min	Systole, seconds	Diastole, seconds
50	0.41	0.79
60	0.39	0.61
70	0.36	0.49
80	0.34	0.41
110	0.30	0.25
170	0.23	0.12

Exercise   A change in muscular activity evokes a comparable alteration in cardiac output. If exercise is not too severe, the respiratory and circulatory changes usually prove adequate to supply completely the in-

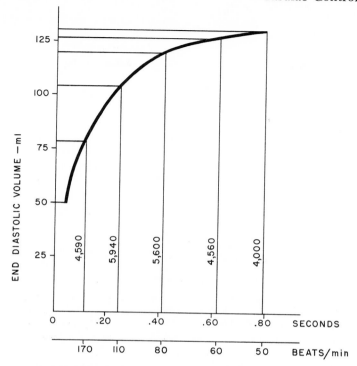

FIG. 13-2 Relationship of end diastolic volume to heart rate. A theoretical filling curve is used and a constant ventricular residue of 50 ml assumed. The figures on the vertical lines are calculated cardiac outputs in ml/min. Time values represent length of diastole. This relationship is valid only if venous pressure stays constant.

creased body demands. In such a case no oxygen debt accrues, there is a minimum of fatigue, and the exercise may be continued for a prolonged period. However, there is an upper limit to the capacity of the heart; if the severity of the exercise is such as to exceed this capacity, then an oxygen debt does accrue and the activity can be maintained for only a short period of time. The complex mechanisms which keep the heart in step with bodily activity will be considered later. Suffice it here to say that violent exercise may bring about an increase in cardiac output up to about six times the resting cardiac output. The difference between the resting cardiac output and the maximum cardiac output is termed the **cardiac reserve.**

Body Surface Area The cardiac output varies with the body surface area. That is, the larger the individual the greater the cardiac output.

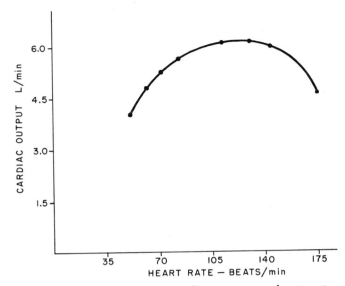

FIG. 13-3 Relationship of cardiac output to heart rate. Using values shown in Fig. 13-4, one can see that over a broad range increasing heart rate does not significantly alter cardiac output so long as venous pressure does not change.

Thus, to compare cardiac output values, the **cardiac index** is often used. The cardiac index is obtained by dividing the cardiac output, expressed in liters, by the surface area, expressed in square meters. The surface area of the average adult is about 1.7 square meters. Accordingly, the average cardiac index is about 3.3 (5.6/1.7) liters/min/m².

Other Normal Activities The cardiac output is found to vary following a large meal, during emotional bouts, in pregnancy, and during sleep. It is common knowledge that many persons die of a heart attack immediately following a heavy meal or while emotionally aroused. The processes of digestion utilize oxygen; accordingly, the load placed upon the heart is increased. If the heart is already defective, if it already has very little reserve power, then the extra load may be enough to "push it over the hill," so to speak, thereby initiating a vicious cycle which terminates in death. The same may be said for the excitement attendant on an emotional crisis.

At complete rest or during sleep, the cardiac output, as one would expect, diminishes. The demands of the body are at their lowest ebb, and therefore the stroke volume and heart rate decrease until just enough blood is pumped to meet these needs.

Pathological Conditions It should be understood that if the heart is defective the cardiac output may be severely altered. It will be seen, however, that even a grossly pathological heart can eject a normal quantity of blood for a time, but there is a progressive deterioration until a critical point is reached at which cardiac ouput can no longer keep pace with body needs. At this time death is imminent.

If there is **aortic insufficiency,** for example, part of the blood ejected during systole regurgitates into the ventricle during diastole. This is obviously an inefficient process, for a large quantity of blood must be pumped only to flow back into the heart. If 25 per cent of the ejected blood backwashes, in order to supply the normal body needs the heart must pump approximately 25 per cent more blood than does the normal heart. The young, vigorous heart can easily handle this load *but at a price,* and the price is progressively hypertrophy, increasingly greater loads, and ultimate and untimely death.

If the aortic valve is **stenosed,** in order to pump the normal quantity of blood through that narrow aperture in the usual period of time, the ventricle must contract more vigorously. This, too, constitutes an added load and leads to the same fatal results.

There are pathological conditions outside the heart which may eventuate in abnormal cardiac ouput. For example, it has already been noted that a condition known as **anemia** is characterized by a decreased oxygen-carrying capacity of the blood. Therefore, in order to meet tissue oxygen needs, each unit of blood must be circulated more rapidly. In short, the cardiac output must be increased. This is precisely what happens.

In a condition termed **hyperthyroidism,** all the metabolic processes of the body operate at an increased tempo. As a result, the total utilization of oxygen is augmented proportionately. Since the arterial blood is normally close to 100 per cent saturated with oxygen, the only way these increased oxygen needs can be met is to increase the cardiac output. Again, a sequence of events brings about this result.

The mechanisms which control the heart will now be considered.

STARLING'S LAW OF THE HEART

It has already been pointed out that the greater the initial length of the cardiac fiber, the more forceful will be the contraction. The initial length of the cardiac fiber is determined by the quantity of blood which flows into the ventricle during diastole. The force of the contraction then determines the amount of blood ejected by the ventricles during systole. In other words, the stroke volume is directly related to the diastolic volume up to a critical point (Fig. 12-3). This relationship is termed **Starling's law of the heart.** Since an interplay between volume and force of contraction exists, we need consider only the factors which determine the diastolic filling of the ventricle in order to appreciate how the heart is controlled.

HEART RATE

If all other factors remain constant, a change in heart rate will alter diastolic filling. As the heart rate increases, the diastolic interval progressively decreases. Accordingly, less blood distends the ventricle and it contracts with less force. Conversely, with a slow heart rate, diastole is long, a large volume of blood enters, stretches the ventricle, and therefore ventricular contraction is vigorous. By this inherent mechanism, the force of contraction is attuned to the entering volume of blood which, in turn, depends upon the heart rate.

VENOUS PRESSURE

There are two factors which determine ventricular filling: (1) the **length of diastole,** which is a function of the heart rate, and (2) **venous pressure.** If the heart rate is kept constant but the venous pressure elevated, more blood will be forced into the ventricle then at normal pressures. Clearly, if the venous pressure is high, then even during a very brief diastole a large quantity of blood will rush into the ventricle resulting, according to Starling's law of the heart, in a greater stroke volume. If both stroke volume and heart rate increase, then cardiac output will be markedly raised.

When the dynamics of circulation are considered, the factors which control venous pressure will be discussed. But for the moment it should be understood that the venous pressure is a very important factor which controls the heart directly and acts by virtue of Starling's law.

This relatively simple mechanism is nonetheless highly effective and self-regulatory. As the venous pressure increases, more blood enters the ventricle during diastole. Therefore, the ventricle contracts more vigorously during the next systole and ejects a greater quantity of blood. Since the heart is now putting out a supranormal quantity of blood, the veins will be drained more rapidly and this, in turn, reduces the venous pressure. As the venous pressure falls so does the cardiac output, until the normal venous pressure is once again established.

ARTERIAL PRESSURE

The arterial pressure, just like the venous pressure, plays an important role in determining diastolic filling. Let us assume that during diastole circulatory changes have taken place which result in a sudden elevation of arterial blood pressure. Let us say that the aortic pressure just before the aortic valve opens has been about 80 mm Hg. Now the aortic diastolic pressure suddenly increases to 100 mm Hg. The ventricle will contract with the same force as it did previously, because the initial length of the fiber is unchanged. It is easy to understand that, because of the higher arterial pressure, not so much blood will be pumped out of the ventricle during systole. In other words, the same force of contraction will eject less blood against a head of pressure equal to 100 mm Hg than it formerly did against only 80 mm Hg. Consequently, at the end of the systole, there will be a considerable residue of blood in the ventricle.

Again, to use actual figures, assume that normally the ventricle contains 120 ml of blood, of which 70 ml are ejected during systole. Then, during diastole, another 70 ml of blood enter the ventricle. But in the illustration above, because of the elevation of arterial pressure, there remains a residue of possibly 70 ml instead of the usual 50 ml. During the very *next* diastole, about 70 ml of blood will flow into the ventricle. This 70 ml plus the residue of 70 ml give a total ventricular filling of 140 ml of blood. This quantity of blood will stretch the cardiac fibers more than the usual 120 ml did and, according to Starling's law, the ventricle will contract more forcefully. The greater force of contraction will eject, even against the added head of pressure, the customary 70 ml of blood. Therefore, the cardiac output which fell for just one beat because of the elevated arterial pressure is now restored to normal. And so long as the arterial pressure remains high, the 70-ml residue will persist. As soon as the arterial pressure falls, the ventricle will eject 90 ml of blood and leave the usual 50 ml as a residue.

These are purely arbitrary figures; as a matter of fact, it takes more than one beat for the necessary readjustments to occur. But the point should be clear that the heart is controlled directly by the arterial pressure. It is true that the heart must work harder in order to eject the normal volume of blood against a higher head of pressure, but in so far as the body is concerned, the astonishing fact is that the cardiac output tends to remain normal despite the elevated blood pressure.

It should be evident, even at this point, why chronic high blood pressure usually leads to cardiac failure. The cardiac output, even in marked hypertension, is within the normal range, but in order to accomplish this feat the heart muscle works much harder than it does in an individual with normal pressure.

CARDIAC-VALVE DEFECTS

The fundamental fact that the force of cardiac-muscle contraction is a function of its initial length explains how the heart reacts directly to altered conditions. It has already been seen how an elevated venous pressure increases the cardiac output, and it has been noted that even in the face of an elevated arterial pressure cardiac dynamics are quickly altered and maintain the cardiac output within the normal range. The same basic principle explains how a heart with very serious valvular defects can, for a considerable period of time, maintain a normal cardiac output.

For example, let us consider a case of **aortic insufficiency.** Because the aortic valve does not close adequately, blood regurgitates from the aorta into the ventricle during diastole. There is, therefore, an insufficient quantity of blood delivered to the tissues. However, the blood which re-enters the ventricle is added to the normal complement of blood during the next diastole. Thus the ventricle is stretched more than it normally is and contracts with greater vigor. Consequently, a larger volume of blood is ejected—great enough, in fact, so that even though part of it regurgitates there is still the normal quantity available for tissue needs. This compensation for valvular defects is carried out at a price. The ventricle is stretched more than it normally would be; thus it performs more work and in so doing utilizes more oxygen. This excess work results in **hypertrophy,** that is, a growth or increase in size of the cardiac muscle. The bigger muscle requires more oxygen. There is thus estab-lished a vicious cycle so that, as the years go by, the ventricular volume during diastole becomes larger and larger until the critical point on the curve is reached after which an increase in diastolic volume results in a diminished ventricular contraction. At that point cardiac failure is imminent.

Only aortic insufficiency has been discussed, but it can be appreciated that an **aortic stenosis** would evoke a similar sequence of events.

INFLUENCE OF CHEMICALS ON THE MYOCARDIUM

It has already been pointed out that the chemical composition of the blood exerts a very definite influence upon the activity of cardiac muscle. In view of the fact that dynamic homeostatic mechanisms maintain the blood composition so constant, we need consider only a few of the con-stituents which are apt to vary more than the others.

OXYGEN

Since all the tissues of the body utilize oxygen, it is quite possible to alter significantly the oxygen content of the blood. However, in most cases, rapid adjustments quickly restore the oxygen level to normal. In severe exercise, it is possible to utilize so much oxygen that the blood-oxygen saturation diminishes. Fortunately, the cardiac muscle continues to function normally for a prolonged period of time even in the face of a low oxygen content. It is only when the blood-oxygen level becomes extremely low that the cardiac muscle is affected directly. Thus, for all practical purposes, we can conclude that variations in the oxygen concentration of the blood have very little direct control over the function of the heart.

CARBON DIOXIDE

Carbon dioxide, as well as oxygen, is a respiratory gas and is thus influenced by alterations in bodily activities. Again, in severe exercise, CO_2 may be produced so rapidly as to accumulate in the circulating blood stream.

It has been shown that excessive CO_2 depresses the sinoatrial node and thereby slows the heart rate. If the CO_2 concentration is high enough, the atrioventricular node may likewise be depressed and heart block may develop. Carbon dioxide has another direct effect upon the heart; it relaxes the cardiac muscle. In moderate concentrations, therefore, CO_2 may function to improve cardiac efficiency. A slow heart is more efficient than a fast one, all other factors being equal, because each time the heart beats, valves must be opened and closed and pressures must be elevated. These are activities which utilize energy and thus reduce the energy available for pumping blood—the primary function of the heart. Carbon dioxide slows the heart, allows more time for ventricular filling, and at the same time relaxes the muscle, thereby permitting the cardiac muscle to attain a greater initial length at any venous pressure. This results in a more vigorous and efficient contraction.

In short, the heart under the influence of moderately elevated concentrations of CO_2 beats more slowly and more vigorously, that is, more efficiently. However, if the concentration of CO_2 exceeds a critical level, heart block may result.

During severe exercise, lactic acid as well as CO_2 is produced. This substance seems to affect the heart like CO_2. Both products are acid and in high enough concentrations may actually increase the acidity of the blood. As will be discussed later, the acidity of the blood is so carefully controlled that it rarely varies. As a matter of fact, even small deflections may prove fatal. A slight increase in acidity will affect the heart as CO_2 does, but any significant change may result in complete cardiac arrest.

EPINEPHRINE

Epinephrine is a potent substance secreted by the medullary cells of the adrenal glands. It is therefore a normal constituent of the blood. Epinephrine is also available commercially and has wide clinical application. In many cases of cardiac arrest, it is injected directly into the cardiac muscle with dramatic results. This substance has been instrumental in saving many lives. Epinephrine causes the myocardium to beat faster and more vigorously. When the adrenal glands are studied, it will be learned that in an emergency (that is, when man is threatened and must react rapidly and vigorously) epinephrine is speedily poured into the blood stream. This hormone has widespread effects, one of which is to strengthen the force and increase the rate of cardiac contraction. As a result, the cardiac output is augmented and more blood is made available to the reacting tissues of the body.

The influence of epinephrine on the force of ventricular contraction has been shown very clearly by Sarnoff and his co-workers. Figure 13-4 shows that the stroke work (force of contraction) at any venous pressure increases with stimulation of the stellate ganglion, or with increasing doses of norepinephrine. The Starling relationship is demonstrated by increasing venous pressure. Thus, this experiment shows that there is a family of curves expressing the relationship between end diastolic pressure and stroke work which vary with the level of norepinephrine.

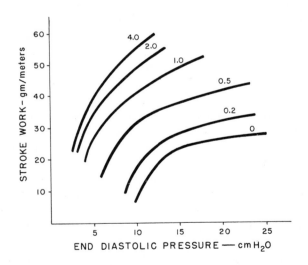

FIG. 13-4   Relationship of stroke work to end diastolic pressure. The numbers on the curves represent frequency of stimulation of the left stellate ganglion. A similar family of curves was obtained using varying doses of norepinephrine instead of stellate stimulation. (Reproduced, with permission, from S. J. Sarnoff, et al, *Circulation Res.*, 8:1108–1122, 1960.)

REFLEX CONTROL OF THE HEART

Every reflex arc has, as its basic components, a receptor, an afferent pathway, a synapse, an efferent pathway, the effector (muscle or gland), and usually facilitatory and inhibitory superstructures which modify the reflex action. Before analyzing reflexes which govern the heart, it is necessary to outline the cardiac innervation.

INNERVATION OF THE HEART

The autonomic nervous system innervates smooth muscle, cardiac muscle, and glands. Accordingly, all the fibers which supply the heart muscle belong to this part of the nervous system. The nerves may be divided into two groups: (1) the **vagus nerve,** which belongs to the parasympathetic division, and (2) the **accelerator nerves,** which are members of the sympathetic system.

Vagus The vagus nerve is also known as the **tenth cranial nerve.** It is a mixed nerve, that is, it contains both motor and sensory components. We are here concerned with the motor fibers which arise from cells in the medulla oblongata and pass down with the other components in the vagus nerves to innervate the heart (Fig. 13-5). Some of the fibers innervate the sinoatrial node, while others supply the atrioventricular node. However, it is generally held that none of the vagal fibers passes to the ventricular musculature. Thus, all the control which the vagus exerts must be directed through the specialized nodal tissue.

Stimulation of the vagi causes marked slowing of the heart (Fig. 13-6). At the same time the force of atrial contraction is decreased. But because the atria now pump less blood into the ventricles, the force of ventricular contraction also decreases and so does the stroke volume. Thus, although the vagal fibers do not innervate the ventricle, the ventricle is nonetheless influenced.

If the excitation is intense and prolonged, partial or complete heart block may be produced. In other cases, however, intensive stimulation simply produces cardiac arrest so that the entire heart ceases to beat. It is interesting to note that when arrest is produced, after a few seconds, contraction once again takes place even though the stimulation is maintained. This phenomenon is known as **vagal escape.** In other words, the heart escapes from the influence of the vagus.

In normal man, there is a steady conduction of impulses in the vagal fibers which innervate the heart. There is thus a "braking" action upon the heart. This constant vagal surveillance is termed **vagal tone.** If both vagi are cut, the heart rate immediately increases. This experiment simply demonstrates that normally there is vagal tone. Destruction of the vagal

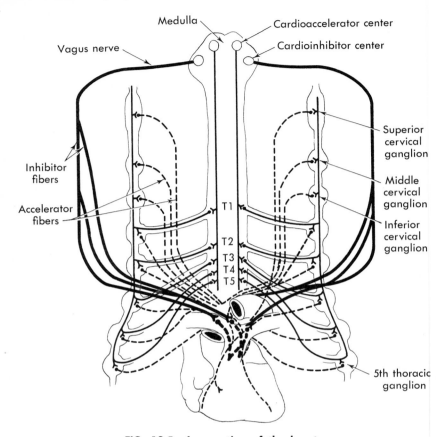

FIG. 13-5 Innervation of the heart.

fibers removes the persistent inhibition on the heart, thus permitting the heart to speed up.

One should visualize the heart under the influence of a steady stream of inhibitory impulses. If these impulses are decreased, the heart rate will increase; if the impulses are increased, the rate will decrease. In other words, the vagal activity alone is capable of altering heart rate in either direction.

Membrane potential studies recorded from the area of the pacemaker go a long way toward explaining how vagal stimulation inhibits the heart (Fig. 13-7). It can be seen that vagal stimulation results in hyperpolarization. At the end of the period of vagal stimulation, the resting membrane potential is about 9 mv greater than prior to stimulation. It is

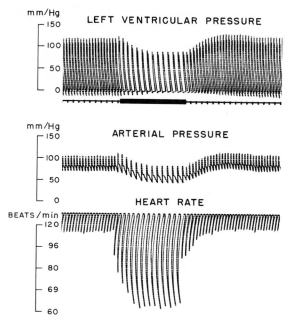

**FIG. 13-6   Influence of vagal stimulation on car-
diac function. Note the sharp decrease in rate and
ventricular pressure. As a result the arterial pressure decreases.**

also to be noted that during stimulation the characteristic prepotential
does not develop, nor is there an action potential. Contraction, then, is
completely inhibited.

Accelerator Nerves   The sympathetic-nervous-system fibers arise from
cell bodies which reside in the lateral-horn substance of the first five

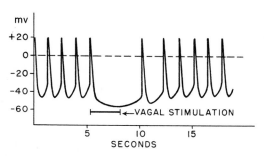

**FIG. 13-7   Influence of vagal
stimulation on the pacemaker
potentials of the sinus venosus
of the frog heart. Hyperpolarization results; the potential
does not rise to threshold level
and firing does not occur.**
(Reproduced, with permission, from O. F. Hutter, and W. Trautwein, *J. Gen. Physiol.,*
39:715, 1956.)

thoracic segments of the spinal cord (Fig. 13-5). Some preganglionic fibers pass to the sympathetic chain and end in ganglia at the same level. Others are projected to the superior, middle, and inferior cervical ganglia. Postganglionic fibers arise in the three cervical ganglia and also in the five thoracic ganglia and stream to the heart. These fibers innervate both the S-A and A-V nodes as well as the myocardium of the atria and ventricles.

Stimulation of these fibers, as the name suggests, accelerates the heart. The function of the accelerator nerves is just the opposite of the role of the vagal fibers. There is apparently a steady stream of impulses flowing through the accelerator nerves. Thus we may speak of **accelerator tone** as well as vagal tone.

Not only does stimulation of the sympathetic fibers accelerate the heart, but the force of contraction also is increased (Fig. 13-8). Both of these

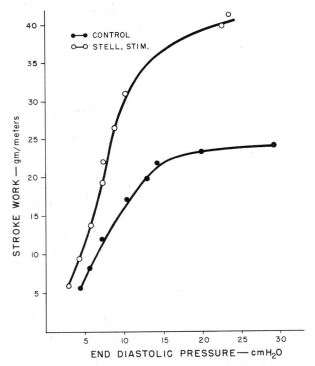

FIG. 13-8 Influence of sympathetic stimulation on force of ventricular contraction. At all end diastolic volumes the force of contraction is greater when the stellate ganglion is stimulated. (Reproduced, with permission, from S. J. Sarnoff, et al, *Circulation Res.*, 8:1108–1122, 1960.)

responses contribute to the increased cardiac output characteristic of exercise.

If the pacemaker potentials are recorded and the accelerator fibers stimulated, the major influence is to steepen the slope of the prepotential (Fig. 13-9). Accordingly, threshold voltage is more quickly attained and the action potential is generated sooner than it would have been in the absence of stimulation. It is also to be noted that the overshoot progressively increases.

It has been postulated that the vagus inhibits cardiac muscle by increasing its permeability to potassium, thereby increasing the resting potential. Sympathetic stimulation is thought to increase the permeability to sodium, thus permitting a more rapid build up to threshold voltage.

Coordination of Innervation The heart is under dual control: the vagus slows the heart, and the accelerator fibers speed it. Both exert their effects constantly. It is analogous to a tug of war. If one influence weakens, the other will predominate and cardiac function will be altered accordingly. Thus we may conclude that heart rate may be varied in four ways or in any combination of these ways: (1) increased activity of the vagus, (2) decreased vagal activity, (3) increased activity of the accelerator nerves, or (4) decreased activity of the accelerator nerves.

As one might suspect, these influences do not function independently of one another. In driving a car one can hold his foot lightly upon the brake and still increase the speed of the car by stepping on the gas pedal, but as everyone realizes it is far more efficient to remove the braking

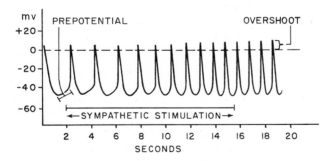

FIG. 13-9 Influence of sympathetic stimulation of the pacemaker potentials of the sinus venosus of the frog heart. The slope of the prepotential increases, thereby reaching threshold level sooner, thus increasing heart rate. The overshoot also progressively increases. (Reproduced, with permission, from Hutter and Trautwein, *J. Gen. Physiol.*, **39**:715, 1956.)

action while accelerating. The same is true of the heart. Conversely, it is possible to slow a car by braking while still holding down the gas pedal, but again the desired result is produced more efficiently by removing the accelerating influence while braking.

The braking and accelerating effects on the heart are integrated in the medulla oblongata. Here are located the so-called **cardioinhibitor** and **cardioaccelerator centers** (Fig. 13-5). These centers may be stimulated or inhibited. The efferent component of the reflex arc originates at this point. Afferent impulses impinge upon these centers reciprocally, bringing about activation of one and simultaneously inhibition of the other and thus effectively controlling heart rate.

RECEPTORS AND REFLEX RESPONSE

It has been pointed out that there is, throughout the body, specialized nervous tissue sensitive to specific changes in the environment, both external and internal. Such tissue is termed a receptor. Thus we find strategically placed receptors sensitive to changes in (1) arterial blood pressure, (2) venous blood pressure, and (3) the chemical composition of the blood. Herein lies the means for informing the heart of conditions needing attention.

Pressoreceptors   These receptors, as the term indicates, are sensitive to changes in blood pressure. As will be seen when the dynamics of circulation are considered, the cardiac output is one of the major determinants of arterial blood pressure. It has been emphasized that the pressure in any system reflects the ratio between the capacity of the system and the volume contained therein. With this in mind, it is easy to understand that, if the heart pumps more than the normal amount of blood into the arteries, the arterial pressure must increase. Likewise it has been indicated that the pressure in the large veins is, in part, a function of cardiac activities. Therefore, the value of having the heart apprised of both arterial and venous pressure should be obvious.

Figure 13-10 shows that where the common carotid artery bifurcates into the internal and external carotid arteries there is a noticeable swelling. This enlargement is termed the **carotid sinus.** The walls of this sinus are lined with pressoreceptors. From this area arise afferent neurons which join the **glossopharyngeal nerve** or **cranial nerve IX** to pass to the medulla. The fibers end in synaptic union within the cardioaccelerator and cardioinhibitor centers.

There are similar pressoreceptors lining the arch of the aorta (Fig. 13-10) in an area called the **aortic sinus.** Afferent fibers from these receptors join the vagus nerve to terminate in the medulla oblongata. Thus the reflex arc for the reaction of the heart to arterial pressure changes is

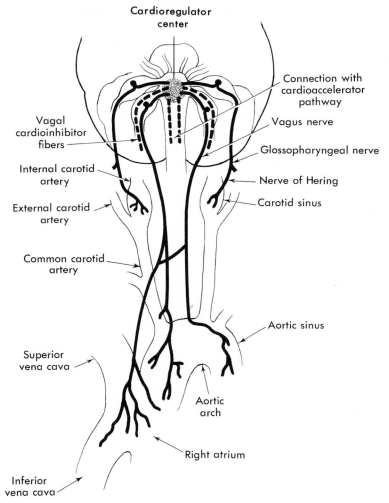

FIG. 13-10 Nervous regulation of the heart. Pressoreceptors in the aortic sinus, the carotid sinus, and perhaps in the great veins, monitor the blood pressure.

complete. A fluctuation in arterial pressure activates the pressoreceptors; the impulse is conveyed by the afferent fibers in cranial nerves IX and X to the medulla where contact is made with both cardiac centers. Efferent fibers of the sympathetic and parasympathetic nervous systems then convey impulses to the heart, and suitable adjustments follow.

To test this mechanism, let us assume that there is a sudden rise in arterial blood pressure. As a result, the pressoreceptors are activated and impulses flow into the cardiac centers. Thus the heart is slowed. Slowing of the heart along with other circulatory changes tends to diminish cardiac output which aids in reducing arterial blood pressure. On the other hand, should the arterial blood pressure fall, through the same reflex mechanism the heart rate will be increased, cardiac output augmented, and the pressure brought back to normal. There is, then, an inverse relationship between arterial blood pressure and heart rate. When pressure increases, heart rate decreases, and vice versa. For example, it is common knowledge that the heart rate markedly increases following massive hemorrhage. One can now explain why this occurs. The inverse relationship between blood pressure and heart rate is known as **Marey's law of the heart.**

There are also pressoreceptors in the large veins where they enter the right atrium. These receptors are sensitive to changes in venous pressure. When the venous pressure increases, the receptors are fired and impulses pass to the medulla via afferent neurons in the vagus. Here they impinge upon the cardiac-control centers and effect an increase in heart rate. This mechanism is termed the **Bainbridge reflex.** The effectiveness of this reflex should be made clear. It has already been pointed out that an increase in venous pressure forces more blood into the ventricle during diastole and, as a result, the stroke volume is augmented. The increased venous pressure through the reflex arc just outlined also speeds the heart. Since cardiac output is equal to the product of stroke volume and heart rate, it is obvious that an increased venous pressure markedly elevates cardiac output.

Chemoreceptors   As this term implies, there are receptors in the vascular system which are sensitive to a change in the composition of the blood. Specifically, they react to alterations in the oxygen and carbon dioxide content, and to the acidity of the blood.

The chemoreceptors are located in association with the carotid and aortic sinuses in small masses of tissues called the **carotid** and **aortic bodies.**

If the oxygen content of the blood falls, a condition termed **hypoxemia,** the heart rate is increased as is the force of contraction. It was long thought that the chemoreceptors of the carotid and aortic bodies were responsible for this result. The fact is, however, that if the hypoxemia is limited to these peripheral chemoreceptors, cardiac function is either unchanged, or diminishes. Accordingly, other receptors must be responsible. It has been suggested, but not proven, that hypoxemia stimulates cardiac function by a direct action on the medullary centers.

The carotid and aortic chemoreceptors are probably primarily concerned with respiration and have little, if anything, to do with the regulation of cardiac function.

SUMMARY

The function of the heart is to pump an adequate quantity of blood to meet tissue requirements. The amount of blood ejected by one side of the heart in one minute is termed the **cardiac output.** The quantity of blood expelled by one ventricle per beat is called the **stroke volume.** Cardiac output is equal to stroke volume times the heart rate. In the average-sized man, it amounts to about 5 liters per minute.

Cardiac output may be increased about six times over resting norms. The greatest values are recorded during violent exercise, at which time as much as 30 liters a minute may be pumped by each ventricle. The cardiac output is also elevated during emotional crises, after a large meal, and in the latter months of pregnancy. During sleep, the cardiac output diminishes somewhat. Pathological conditions such as hyperthyroidism and anemia are associated with an elevated cardiac output.

An increase in venous pressure will force more blood into the ventricle and thereby elevate stroke volume. The **pressoreceptors** in the great veins are stimulated and initiate a reflex increase in heart rate. The increased heart rate with large stroke volume results in a markedly elevated cardiac output. The mechanism by which venous pressure controls heart rate is called the **Bainbridge reflex.** The arterial pressure also determines the diastolic volume by varying the residue left in the ventricle at the end of systole.

Carbon dioxide in high blood concentrations slows the heart and relaxes the cardiac muscle. This serves to augment stroke volume and increase the efficiency of the heart. Epinephrine speeds the heart and increases the vigor of myocardial contraction.

The heart is innervated by both branches of the autonomic nervous system. The **vagus nerve** belongs to the parasympathetic division. It functions to slow the heart. The **accelerator nerves** are sympathetic fibers. Their opposing influences are coordinated in the **cardioinhibitor** and **cardioaccelerator centers** in the medulla. Afferent fibers impinge upon these centers and complete the arcs required for reflex control.

Heart rate is regulated through reflex pathways by (1) arterial pressure, (2) venous pressure, and (3) the chemical composition of the blood. The pressoreceptors sensitive to arterial-blood-pressure changes are located in the **carotid** and **aortic sinuses.** An elevation of arterial blood pressure effectuates a decrease in heart rate. The inverse relationship between blood pressure and heart rate is termed **Marey's law of the heart.**

QUESTIONS

1. What is the definition of cardiac output?
2. What is the relationship between cardiac output and heart rate?
3. Under what conditions does cardiac output vary?
4. Discuss the nervous control of the heart.
5. Discuss the mechanical control of the heart.
6. Discuss the chemical control of the heart.

SUGGESTED READING

Astrand, P. O., Cuddy, T. E., Saltin, B., and Stenberg, J., "Cardiac Output During Submaximal and Maximal Work," *J. Appl. Physiol.,* **19**:#2, 268–274, March 1964.

Matranga, F. C., "Look to Your Heart," *Today's Health,* **36**:#4, 42, 62–63, April 1958.

Ratcliff, J. D., "How Your Doctor Tests Your Heart," *Today's Health,* **35**:#12, 42–43, 52–53, December 1957.

Rushmer, R. F., and Smith, O. A., Jr., "Cardiac Control," *Physiol. Rev.,* **39**:#1, 41–68, January 1959.

Sarnoff, S. J., and Mitchell, J. H., "The Regulation of the Performance of the Heart," *Am. J. Med.,* **30**:#5, 747–771, May 1961.

"The Carotid Sinus," *Spectrum,* **6**:#5, 120–121, March 1, 1958.

Blood Pressure

14

EVERYONE, AT ONE TIME OR ANOTHER, HAS HAD HIS BLOOD PRESSURE TAKEN. It is the object of this chapter to discuss the significance of the blood pressure. But first, it is necessary to survey the circulatory tree and its ramifications, then to consider the methods for determining blood pressure, and finally its regulation will be analyzed. After these basic considerations are assimilated, the student will be in an excellent position to understand the blood pressure at rest, during exercise, and in diseased states.

ANATOMY OF THE BLOOD VESSELS

Blood vessels are everywhere present in the body. Even the most insignificant scratch may release a drop or two of blood. Since blood is normally found only within the vessels, it must follow that the scratch has severed a tiny vessel. But not all vessels are so small. The aorta, for example, which is connected with the left ventricle of the heart, is a very large vessel. In man it measures about 1 to 2 in. in diameter. One could easily insert two or three fingers. In short, there are blood vessels of all dimensions. These vessels differ not only in size but also in structure and function.

CIRCULATORY TREES

The aorta is the largest blood vessel in the body. Thus it may be likened to the trunk of a sturdy tree. From this trunk many good-sized limbs branch. These are termed **arteries.** The large arteries split into progressively smaller arteries. Finally, after the size and structure of the wall has changed significantly, the smaller vessels are termed **arterioles.** The arterioles finally arborize into a tremendous number of tiny thin-walled struc-

287

tures called **capillaries.** Thus a typical tree is visualized, with the aorta as the main trunk and the capillaries as the terminal twigs. This constellation may be called the **arterial tree.**

There is also a **venous tree.** Once again the twigs are the capillaries. Thus we can refer to the arterial and venous ends of the capillaries. The venous ends merge into increasingly larger vessels which are referred to as **venules.** The venules, in turn, unite to produce small **veins,** which lead to larger and larger vessels until they form two large veins (the **superior** and **inferior venae cavae**) which are continuous with the right atrium of the heart.

BLOOD-VESSEL WALL

If samples of the aorta, an artery, an arteriole, a capillary, a venule, and a vein are examined, it will be found that they all display distinctive histological characteristics. The aorta is the largest of all. The wall is very thick, and there is a broad elastic layer which is of paramount physiological significance.

The arteries are smaller than the aorta, and their walls are thinner. It is important to recognize that in the arteries the elastic layer has been partially supplanted by smooth muscle.

The arterioles have practically no elastic component, but they do possess a very thick muscular ring, innervated by the autonomic nervous system. When this smooth muscle contracts, the diameter of the vessel is decreased. Accordingly, the amount of blood which flows through the arteriole may be controlled and, as will soon be seen, the arterial blood pressure is varied.

The capillary wall is one cell thick. The wall is so thin that the fluid portion of the blood, the plasma, with all its constituents except the proteins, may pass through this barrier in either direction. This is not true of any other part of the circulatory tree. Thus it becomes evident that the aorta, arteries, arterioles, venules, and veins are conducting systems, which convey the blood to and from the capillary network. The traffic of substances between the blood and the tissues takes place only in the capillaries, because only they possess a thin, semipermeable wall.

The venules resemble the arterioles. True, the wall is much thinner, but it contains a functional muscular layer which can alter the lumen of the venule. The veins are larger, but their walls are thin. Actually the pressure in the venous side of the circulation is so low that these thin-walled vessels are adequate to support it. Some veins possess valves, whereas the arteries and arterioles do not. These are one-way doors, so to speak, so that blood can flow only toward the heart and not in the reverse direction.

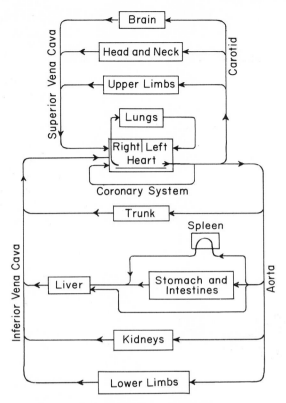

FIG. 14-1 Diagrammatic representation of the circulatory routes.

CIRCULATORY ROUTES

In order to understand the dynamics of circulation it is important to realize that the blood does not circulate through a simple, one-channel system connecting one side of the heart with the other. As seen in Fig. 14-1, there are many parallel routes that the blood may take from the major arterial and venous systems. Because of these parallel routes, pressures in one part of the circulation may be drastically altered without necessarily altering the pressure elsewhere.

HOW BLOOD PRESSURE IS MEASURED

When the physician measures blood pressure, as already stated, he is concerned with the arterial blood pressure. However, in some cases it is necessary to determine also the venous pressure. The technique is different in each case.

ARTERIAL-BLOOD-PRESSURE DETERMINATION

Figure 14-2 illustrates the usual equipment employed for determining the arterial blood pressure. The instrument is called a **sphygmomanometer.** It can be seen to consist of a cuff which is wrapped about the arm and then inflated. The term sphygmomanometer is derived from the Greek terms *meter,* "to measure," *manos,* meaning "thin," and *sphygmo,* denoting "pulse." When the cuff is inflated, as we shall see, the blood supply to the forearm, wrist, and hand is occluded. Hence the pulse cannot be felt at the wrist. Then the cuff is slowly deflated until the pulse can be felt or the blood gushing through the vessels can be heard with a stethoscope. The old-time physicians used to take the pulse and describe the first appearance of the pulse as being "thin." Hence is seen the origin

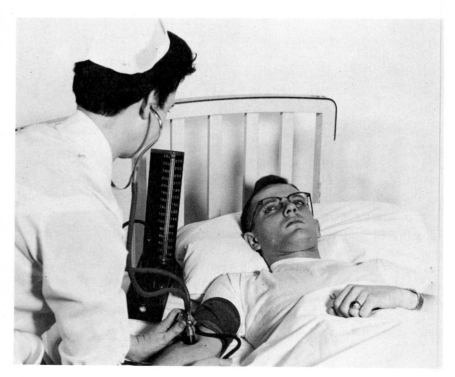

FIG. 14-2   Determination of arterial blood pressure with sphygmomanometer and stethoscope.

of the term sphygmomanometer. The apparatus also includes a mercury or aneroid manometer which is connected to the cuff.

The technique, essentially, is to inflate the cuff by means of a bulb as shown. The cuff is inflated until the pressure exceeds the arterial systolic blood pressure. Then air is slowly released and the systolic and diastolic pressures are noted. It will be recalled that the pressure within the aorta, and therefore within all the arteries, varies. It reaches a peak during systole and then steadily decreases during diastole. The pressure at the peak is termed **systolic pressure;** the lowest pressure attained during diastole is referred to as the **diastolic pressure.** Consequently, when blood determinations are made, both systolic and diastolic pressures are noted. These are reported as systolic/diastolic. For example, in a normal young person this might be 120/80.

When the cuff is inflated, a point is finally reached at which the pressure within the cuff exceeds the systolic pressure. If one were to place a stethoscope on the arm just below the cuff, no sound would be heard, because the cuff prevents the blood from flowing through the subjacent arteries. The pressure in the cuff is then slowly reduced until a sound can be detected. The noise is produced by the blood flowing through the partially constricted artery just beneath the cuff. The examiner glances at the manometer and notes the pressure at this point. This represents the systolic pressure, expressed in millimeters of mercury.

The cuff is further deflated while the examiner continues to listen. As more and more blood flows through the underlying vessel, the quality of the sound will change. Finally, the experienced physician can detect a sudden muffling of the sound. This is due to the fact that the lumen of the vessel is no longer constricted and normal blood flow is reestablished. The physician notes the manometer reading at this point and records it as the diastolic pressure. If the cuff is further deflated, a point is soon reached at which all sound disappears. At this time blood is flowing steadily through the artery; there is no turbulence and hence no sound. Some authorities insist that the complete cessation of the sound indicates diastolic pressure. The difference in pressure between muffling and complete disappearance is only about 5 mm Hg.

It has been stated that there is a change in the quality of the sound as the cuff pressure is gradually reduced. Four distinct sounds were described by a Russian scientist named Korotkov. Accordingly, these sounds are referred to as the **sounds of Korotkov.**

In experimental animals it is possible to ascertain the arterial blood .pressure in the same manner, but most often it is found to be more accurate and satisfactory to measure it directly by placing a cannula or hypodermic needle, which is attached to a mercury manometer, into the artery. This procedure makes possible a very accurate measure of the arterial blood pressure.

VENOUS-PRESSURE DETERMINATION

The venous pressure, just like the arterial pressure, may be measured either directly or indirectly. The direct procedure is to insert a hypodermic needle into a vein and then connect it to a water manometer. It will be noted that a mercury manometer is used to ascertain arterial blood pressure whereas a water manometer is employed for venous-pressure measurement. The difference is due to the fact that arterial pressures are so much higher than venous levels. The venous pressure is rarely equal to more than 10 or 20 mm of mercury. Water, which is about 13.5 times lighter than mercury, is used for accuracy.

The indirect method for determining venous pressure is not nearly so accurate as the indirect arterial-blood-pressure technique but nonetheless does afford a worthwhile approximation.

One way of obtaining a rough estimate of the venous pressure is to have the patient lie flat on his back. The examiner then slowly elevates the subject's hand until the veins on the back of the hand collapse. The height of the hand above the subject's heart is measured. Since blood has a specific gravity close to that of water, the distance gives a rough measure of the venous pressure expressed in centimeters of water (Fig. 14-3). In other words, if the veins on the back of the hand collapse when the hand is 25 cm above the heart, the venous pressure is said to be approximately 25 cm H_2O.

A more accurate indirect method is to employ a small glass chamber which is placed over a vein, usually on the back of the hand. The glass chamber is sealed to the skin with collodion so that it will be airtight. The chamber is attached to a water manometer. Air is now slowly pumped into the glass chamber until the vein is seen to collapse. The reading at this point is noted and represents the venous pressure. When the venous pressure is determined by the glass-chamber procedure, the vein utilized must be at the level of the heart. Otherwise, the forces of gravity will significantly alter the findings. It can be seen that this procedure is similar to the usual method for determining arterial blood pressure. They both utilize equipment which can exert pressure over the vessel. When the vessel is finally compressed completely by this air pressure, the assumption is made that the required force represents the venous blood pressure. This assumption is, for all practical purposes, valid because the blood-vessel walls are thin and pliable and thus offer little or no resistance themselves. They remain round and patent primarily because of the pressure

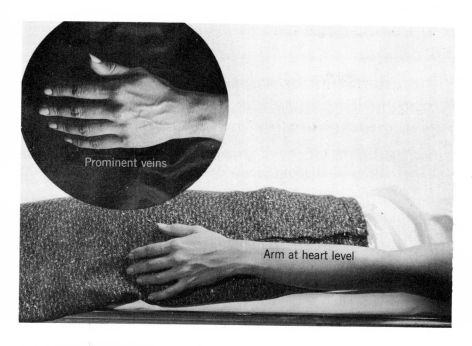

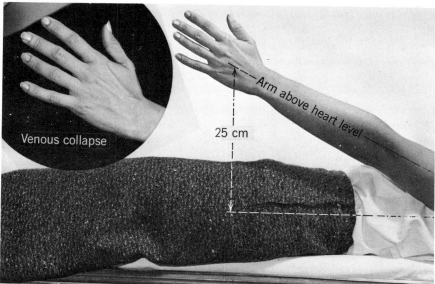

FIG. 14-3 Estimation of venous pressure. The arm is elevated until the hand veins collapse. The distance above the level of the heart gives a rough measure of venous pressure expressed in cm H$_2$O.

of the blood within. Therefore a force equal to the blood pressure must be exerted from without in order to collapse them.

REGULATION OF ARTERIAL BLOOD PRESSURE

In considering the pressure changes within the heart, it was emphasized that the pressure within any closed system is the result of the capacity of the system, on the one hand, and the volume of fluid within the system, on the other. If this ratio of capacity to volume is borne in mind, the following discussion of blood pressure within the circulatory trees will be easily grasped.

PHYSICAL PRINCIPLES

When we speak of a person's blood pressure, we usually refer to his arterial blood pressure as measured in the brachial artery while in the sitting position. The pressure varies greatly between the arteries and the veins, and even among the various arteries there is a wide difference in pressure. Thus to obtain meaningful and comparable values, the clinician uses the brachial artery. This vessel has been selected because it is conveniently located and readily accessible.

For the moment, let us assume that we are dealing with only one vessel which is attached to the left ventricle of the heart. Also, let us imagine that this vessel possesses rigid walls and that there is a stopcock at the end which can control the amount of fluid which leaves the vessel. The pressure within this tube can be measured anywhere between the heart at one end and the stopcock at the other. In this simple model it should be easy to understand that the pressure will be determined by a combination of three factors: (1) *the amount of blood pumped into the vessel,* (2) *the viscosity of the blood,* and (3) *the amount of blood allowed to leave the vessel.* Since blood viscosity normally remains constant, we need not consider this factor any further.

Cardiac Output and Peripheral Resistance   The amount of blood which enters the vessel is the cardiac output, that is, the quantity of blood ejected by one ventricle during one minute. The rate at which the fluid leaves the system is determined by the stopcock. It has just been mentioned that the arterioles possess a heavy, functional muscle ring. These vessels can vary the size of their lumina; they thus act as stopcocks.

If the stopcock were to be closed completely, then, as the heart continued to pump blood into the system the pressure would progressively increase until the vessel burst. On the other hand, if the stopcock were wide open, the blood would flow out as fast as it was pumped in and there would be very little pressure. From these two extremes it should be evident that the pressure within this simple system is determined by the amount of blood within the vessel at any one time. We have assumed that the walls were rigid, and therefore the capacity must remain constant. Clearly, then, the more fluid forced into the container, the higher the pressure.

The volume of fluid within the vessel determines the pressure. This amount is governed by the cardiac output and by the resistance offered to the flow of blood by the stopcock at the opposite end. As already stated, in the arterial tree this resistance is supplied by the arterioles. The arterioles, being away from, or peripheral to, the heart and arteries where the pressure is ascertained give rise to a force which is referred to as **peripheral resistance.** This peripheral resistance is varied by the contraction or relaxation of the smooth muscle in the arteriolar walls.

In summary, the two important regulating forces of arterial blood pressure are (1) cardiac output and (2) peripheral resistance. If, as in our model, the walls of the vessels were rigid, we would not have to consider any other factors. But it will be recalled that the walls of the aorta and large arteries are highly elastic.

Elasticity   Returning once again to the basic principle that the pressure in any system reflects the ratio between the capacity and volume, it can be seen immediately that the elasticity of the vessel wall must be taken into consideration because, by virtue of this elasticity, the size of the system varies. If the aorta were so distensible that any increase in blood volume was accompanied by a comparable increase in the size of the vessel, the ratio between capacity and volume would be unchanged and so would the pressure. In other words, the greater the elasticity of the aorta and large arteries, the less the pressure will increase during the rapid-ejection phase of the heart. Thus, it can be concluded that *the elasticity of these vessels buffers the systolic pressure.*

In the model endowed with rigid walls, the pressure would decrease very rapidly during diastole because the heart would be pumping no blood into the system, yet blood would be pouring out of the other end. Since capacity cannot change in the rigid model, any decrease in blood volume rapidly lowers the pressure. But if, as in man, the aorta and large arteries are elastic, during diastole, while the blood is coursing into the arterioles and capillaries, the capacity of the aorta and large arteries is also decreasing. True, the decrease in capacity is not so great as the volume shrinkage, but still the fall in pressure during diastole is not nearly so great as it would be were the vessel walls rigid.

Without entering into complicated calculations, what has been said should suffice to indicate that the elasticity of the aorta and large arteries serves to buffer the systolic arterial pressure and to support the diastolic arterial pressure. In the normal young adult, these vessels are highly elastic. As one grows older, the elasticity diminishes; in some cases, these vessels become truly rigid. As a result, the systolic and diastolic arterial pressures which differ by only about 40 mm Hg in the young healthy person may vary by more than 100 mm Hg in the individual with sclerosis (hardening) of the large vessels.

CONTROL OF PERIPHERAL RESISTANCE

The three vital determinants of arterial pressure are (1) cardiac output, (2) peripheral resistance, and (3) the elasticity of the large vessels. In Chap. 13 the cardiac output was considered in detail and should be reviewed at this time. The elasticity of the vessels varies with age and with other relatively irreversible factors. The peripheral resistance, on the other hand, can and does fluctuate significantly in response to (1) **nervous** and (2) **chemical stimuli.**

Nervous Mechanisms   The peripheral resistance, that is, the opposition offered to the flow of blood beyond, or peripheral to, the point at which arterial blood pressure is determined, is a function of the muscular arterioles. This is smooth muscle which is innervated by nerves belonging to the so-called autonomic nervous system. This layer of circular muscle either contracts or relaxes in response to impulses which arrive via these nerve fibers. For the most part, such impulses cannot be controlled voluntarily. By that is meant that one can at will move his arm or wink his eye but cannot cause his blood vessels to **constrict** (close down) or **dilate** (open up). It is true that emotion-laden thoughts do bring about such alterations. For example, the recall of a particularly embarrassing situation may elicit blushing. The word **blush** is derived from a term which means "to redden," which is, of course, just what occurs. One reddens because the arterioles in the involved area dilate and thus permit more red blood to enter the superficial skin vessels, giving to the skin a red, flushed appearance. This illustration demonstrates that there is higher-brain-center supervision over the arterioles. For the most part, however, this nervous mechanism is a reflex; that is, the alterations brought about are involuntary and in response to a stimulus such as an undue rise or fall in the arterial blood pressure itself.

It has been pointed out that at the bifurcation of the common carotid artery there is an outpouching termed the **carotid sinus.** This area is lined with receptors called **pressoreceptors** sensitive to a change in arterial blood pressure. There are also pressoreceptors in the arch of the aorta and probably elsewhere in the body. The pressoreceptors initiate impulses which are conducted to the brain stem. In the brain stem there are clusters of nerve cells which collectively make up the **vasoconstrictor** and **vasodilator** centers (Fig. 14-4). The cells in these centers give rise to fibers which either directly or indirectly innervate the smooth muscle in the walls of the arterioles. Consequently, any alteration in arterial blood pressure will cause the pressoreceptors to fire. The impulses so initiated will be conducted to the vasoconstrictor and vasodilator centers and from there to the arterioles.

Here, then, is the basic mechanism for self-regulation of blood pressure. When the pressure rises, generalized vasodilatation occurs. This increase in the caliber of the arterioles decreases the peripheral resistance and thus allows more blood to drain off more rapidly. It may be likened to a puncture in a tire. If the hole is small, it may be possible to pump air into the tire as rapidly as it escapes. Thus the pressure will remain con-

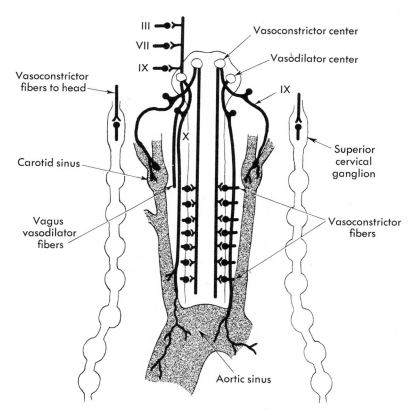

FIG. 14-4   Reflex control of the arterioles. Alteration in blood pressure activates pressoreceptors in the aortic and carotid sinuses. As a result the arterioles are either reflexly constricted or dilated.

stant. But if the hole is large, the air will be dissipated faster than it enters and the pressure necessarily falls.

It will be recalled that when the arterial blood pressure increases, through a reflex mechanism in accordance with Marey's law, the heart is slowed. This tends to reduce cardiac output. Now we learn that at the same time there is a generalized reduction in peripheral resistance. If cardiac output and peripheral resistance *both* decrease, obviously there will be a significant fall in arterial blood pressure. In other words, by virtue of the carotid- and aortic-sinus mechanisms, the blood pressure regulates itself.

The importance of this arrangement cannot be overemphasized. Figure 14-5 shows the results of a simple experiment in which an animal is slowly bled while the arterial blood pressure is continuously recorded. It can be seen that there is very little change in blood pressure until 20 to 30 per cent of the total blood volume is lost, and only after a reduc-

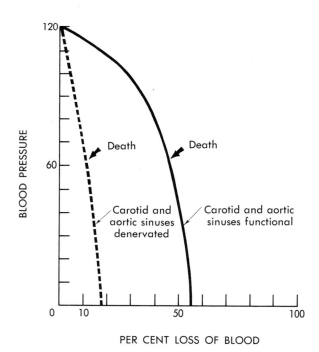

FIG. 14-5   Protective function of the pressoreceptors. With the sinus mechanisms functional, a significantly greater blood loss can be tolerated.

tion of about 40 per cent does the animal succumb. Figure 14-5 also reveals that if the carotid and aortic sinuses are denervated there is a sharp fall in pressure from the very beginning, and after a loss of approximately 10 per cent of the blood volume death ensues. It should be evident why there is this notable difference. As soon as hemorrhage begins in the normal animal, the very slight and almost imperceptible fall in arterial blood pressure activates the carotid and aortic mechanisms which reflexly increase cardiac output and markedly augment peripheral resistance. These changes compensate for the loss of blood, so that there is very little alteration in arterial pressure. However, a point is finally reached at which even these effective mechanisms are overwhelmed. Thereafter the pressure falls progressively until levels incompatible with life are reached.

These vascular reflexes have a functional significance in far less dramatic situations. For example, when one jumps out of bed in the morning, there is a change from the horizontal to the vertical position. The force of gravity tends to pull the blood to the legs and away from the brain. But just as soon as this happens the pressure in the carotid and aortic sinuses decreases. As a result, cardiac output is stepped up and generalized vasoconstriction increases the peripheral resistance. These changes elevate the blood pressure and assure an adequate blood flow to the vital centers in the brain.

There are also believed to be pressoreceptors, other than in the carotid and aortic sinuses, elsewhere in the body, for example, in the heart and lungs. However, these possible mechanisms await further clarification.

Chemical Control The peripheral resistance offered by the arterioles is controlled not only by arterial and venous blood pressures but also by the chemical composition of the blood. It will be recalled that there are chemoreceptors in the carotid and aortic bodies. The blood flows constantly through these structures, and thus any deviation from the normal may be rapidly detected by the chemoreceptors. If there is (1) a decrease in **oxygen concentration** or (2) an increase in **acidity,** generalized vasoconstriction results. The student may wonder how vasoconstriction can benefit man in such a condition. To clarify the problem it is necessary to know that carbon dioxide, which acts directly upon the vasoconstrictor center in the medulla, also causes sharp local responses upon the arterioles. This is an efficient mechanism, because as a muscle contracts it produces CO_2 which in that area causes arteriolar dilation and thus permits more blood to supply the actively contracting muscle. In other words, a high CO_2 concentration in the blood acts directly upon the smooth muscle of the arterioles and causes them to relax. And yet CO_2 impinges upon the vasoconstrictor center and produces a generalized vasoconstriction. The problem then is to explain how these seemingly conflicting results are reconciled.

If one will visualize the city water-supply system for a minute, the problem will be clarified. The city maintains a constant water pressure in its mains. In your house you can vary the amount of water which leaves the faucet by simply changing the opening, that is, by making it bigger or smaller. When the faucet is wide open the flow is at a maximum, and there is no way to increase it. But, and this is the important point, if while the faucet is wide open the city were to increase the pressure in the mains, the water would gush more plentifully from the faucet.

This analogy may be transposed to man. The arterioles are the faucets; the aorta and large arteries are the mains. Thus, when a muscle contracts it produces CO_2 and this dilates the local arterioles (opens the faucet). For most degrees of exercise, this local effect suffices. But if the effort becomes severe, the CO_2 content may build up in the general circulation. It will act upon the vasoconstrictor center in the brain stem to cause a generalized vasoconstriction of arterioles which do not supply active muscles, such as the arterioles which serve the gastrointestinal tract. Consequently, there will be an elevation in blood pressure (in the mains, so to speak), and this forces more blood through the dilated arterioles which supply the contracting muscles. It should be evident that man is endowed with a very ingenious and effective mechanism for ensuring an adequate supply of blood to the muscles commensurate with their activity.

Epinephrine is another substance which exerts powerful effects upon the arterioles. It acts directly upon the smooth muscle and causes it to contract. Here, then, is still another means available to man for elevating the pressure in the mains, that is, the large vessels. During violent exercise, epinephrine is poured into the blood stream. This results in an elevation of pressure, thereby forcing more blood through the dilated arterioles which serve the muscles.

A substance closely related to epinephrine, that is, **norepinephrine,** is liberated by most of the postganglionic sympathetic fibers. This is the substance, then, that is responsible for vasoconstriction which results in response to sympathetic activation.

Other vasoconstrictor substances normally found in the circulation are **angiotensin** and **serotonin.** Angiotensin is formed in the blood from the reaction of renin and angiotensinogen. Renin is a product of the kidneys, and angiotensinogen is a globulin produced by the liver. Serotonin, as already mentioned, is released by the platelets. The resulting vasoconstriction is important in the control of bleeding.

REGULATION OF VENOUS PRESSURE

Although the circulatory system is a closed one, it is nonetheless possible to have very different conditions prevail in various parts of the system. For example, in patients with chronic high blood pressure, the arterial level may be well above 200 or 300 mm Hg; yet the venous pressure may be within the normal range. On the other hand, in congestive heart failure, the venous pressure may rise markedly with no change on the arterial side. As a matter of fact, in the latter instance the arterial blood pressure may actually decrease. It is obvious from these examples that there must be separate and distinct factors involved in each of the circulatory trees.

PHYSICAL PRINCIPLES

It was learned that the arterial pressure depends upon how much blood is pumped into the arteries (that it, the cardiac output) and how much leaves the system, as determined by the peripheral resistance. In so far as the veins are concerned, the physical principles are the same. The venous pressure is measured somewhere between the arterial tree and the heart. The pressure between these two points must represent the balance between how much blood enters the veins from the arterial side and how much blood is removed from the veins by the heart. It is true that no more blood can flow through the venous system than flows through the arterial system. Thus, in the final analysis, the venous flow simply reflects the output of the left ventricle of the heart. But, as already indicated, the pressure in the two sides may vary widely.

The blood flows from the veins into the right side of the heart. If there is a stenosis of the tricuspid valve, that is, if the valve between the right atrium and ventricle is narrowed, there will be an increased resistance to the flow of blood out of the veins. Hence, the venous pressure will increase and remain elevated. The high pressure now forces the normal quantity of blood through the constricted aperture. The same result is obtained if the right ventricular muscle weakens and pumps less blood. The residue builds up the venous pressure so that now the ventricle is stretched more during diastole. This restores its output to normal, but the venous pressure remains elevated.

CONTROLLING MECHANISMS

There are four important factors which alter venous blood and therefore modify venous pressure. They are (1) the *massaging action of the neighboring muscles,* (2) *venomotor activity,* (3) *intrathoracic pressure,* and (4) *gravity.*

Massaging Action of the Muscles It has already been mentioned that the veins contain one-way valves. Figure 14-6 shows that the veins in many parts of the body course along in close association with the muscles. When these muscles contract, the veins are squeezed, or milked. Because of the presence of valves, the blood can pass from the squeezed area in only one direction, that is, toward the heart. Obviously, then, the more vigorously and rapidly the muscles contract, the greater will be this milking action forcing the blood toward the heart, and the greater will be the pressure of the blood in the larger veins. This is one of the extremely important mechanisms by which circulatory adjustments are made during exercise.

Venomotor Activity Not very much is known concerning venomotor activity. It has been established that the veins can change in size. In

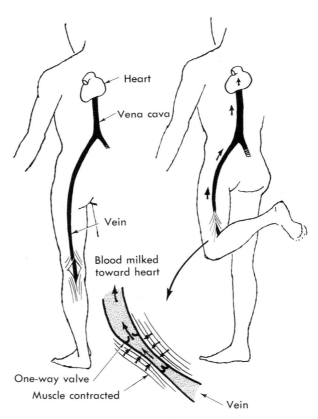

FIG. 14-6 Influence of muscle contraction on venous blood flow.

other words, it is known that venoconstriction is possible. But the mechanisms by which these changes are brought about remain indefinite. Nonetheless, it is a fact that the veins possess a huge capacity and, as a result of venomotor activity, this capacity may be greatly altered. The pressure in the veins, as in any other closed system, represents the ratio between blood volume and capacity. Thus, if the capacity decreases as a result of venomotor change, then the venous pressure will be elevated.

In this connection there is still another possibility that has recently been given considerable support by authorities in this field. The **liver** has many functions. Heretofore much emphasis has been placed on the role this large organ plays in the metabolic processes. Now, however, there is general agreement that the liver is also important in circulatory dynamics. Close histological study discloses that the liver contains large sinusoids capable of holding relatively great quantities of blood. It has been estimated that well over a liter of blood can be contained within the liver. In view of the fact that the total blood volume is of the order of 5 liters, it can be seen that this is a considerable amount. It is thought that appropriate reflex mechanisms bring about alterations in the caliber of the blood vessels leading into and out of the liver. In this way, the quantity of blood contained within the organ can be varied. It should be clear, then, that if, in addition to generalized venoconstriction, circulatory changes were evoked which sharply decreased the volume of blood within the liver as much as a liter or more would be forced into the venous system, which would strikingly increase venous pressure.

Intrathoracic Pressure During respiration there are marked oscillations in the pressure within the chest cavity. This cavity, or chamber, is termed the **thorax;** the pressure within the thorax is known as **intrathoracic pressure.**

The thorax is a closed chamber; therefore the intrathoracic pressure at any time must reflect the ratio between the capacity of that chamber and the volume within. The capacity of the thorax is altered by the chest muscles and also by contraction and relaxation of the diaphragm (Fig. 14-7). When a person inspires, he enlarges the thorax by pulling the ribs out and up, and the diaphragm down. This results in a decrease in the intrathoracic pressure. During expiration, the diaphragm is brought up, and the ribs go down and in. The thoracic capacity is reduced, and the intrathoracic pressure must increase. It will be learned when respiration is studied in detail that the lungs are elastic and stretched. Thus, even at the end of a normal expiration, the lungs tend to decrease in size by virtue of their own elasticity. In other words, they tend to pull away from the chest wall. This enlarges the intrathoracic cavity and thus decreases the intrathoracic pressure. The net result of all these factors is to

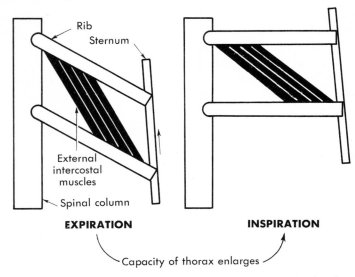

EXPIRATION **INSPIRATION**

Capacity of thorax enlarges

FIG. 14-7   Effect of inspiration on thoracic capacity. During inspiration the ribs are elevated, thereby enlarging the thorax. This lowers intrathoracic pressure.

produce a negative pressure within the thorax during both normal inspiration and normal expiration. When we speak of a negative pressure, we mean a pressure less than atmospheric pressure, which is equal to 760 mm Hg at sea level. This negative pressure during quiet inspiration is about −6.0 mm Hg. During quiet expiration it is approximately −2.5 mm Hg. However, during increased activity, as in exercise, respiration is markedly augmented. The chest wall and the diaphragm make great excursions, so great, in fact, that the intrathoracic pressure during a large, forceful inspiration may reach −40 mm Hg, whereas during a forced expiration it may be increased to +40 mm Hg. If one were to seal a tube into the chest wall and connect it to a mercury manometer, the column of mercury would be seen to go up and down during the respiratory cycle. The more violent the respiratory effort, the greater would be the mercury excursions, finally showing a difference of about 80 mm Hg (−40 to +40).

These changes in intrathoracic pressure markedly affect venous flow because the veins are thin walled, and as they traverse the intrathoracic space, they are influenced by any pressure changes in that space. A fluid will flow from a high-pressure area to an area of low pressure. The rate of flow will vary proportionately with the pressure differential. Clearly, the lower the intrathoracic pressure, the greater will be the pressure differential between the blood in the thoracic veins and in the veins outside the thorax.

It is true that during a strenuous expiration the intrathoracic pressure soars far above the venous pressure and at this time the great veins will be completely closed. There will be no venous flow. But the one-way valves prohibit the backward flow of blood. Therefore, if the venous flow is greatly enhanced during deep inspiration and momentarily halted during forced expiration, the net result is still an over-all increase in venous flow.

It should be evident that an increase in respiration aids venous return to the heart and thus represents an extremely vital cog in the total machinery by which greater tissue needs are supplied by the circulatory system.

Gravity Man, having assumed an upright position, severely taxes his circulatory system. The heart is placed relatively high. Blood must travel up some 4 ft from the lower extremities to the heart. The vessels which transport this blood, the veins, have very thin walls incapable in themselves of supporting this high column of blood. Fortunately, these veins are surrounded by the various muscles of the lower extremities and trunk which lend the much-needed support.

Gravity tends to prevent the blood from returning to the heart. If the leg and trunk muscles are paralyzed, the veins alone cannot oppose this force. As a result, the blood pools in the veins instead of returning to the heart. If this condition is not corrected, the output of the heart fails, inadequate oxygen is delivered to the brain, and the individual loses consciousness. Fortunately, with loss of consciousness the individual falls, becomes horizontal instead of vertical, the force of gravity no longer pulls the venous blood away from the heart, and the individual quickly recovers. He recovers unless some well-meaning citizen attempts to render first aid and returns him to a sitting or standing position!

In the upright position the force of gravity is successfully opposed by muscle tone. In order to remain upright, various muscles of the legs and trunk must remain contracted and rigid. These are the muscles which also support the veins. When one walks or runs, the muscles contract more vigorously and thus actually milk the blood toward the heart in the manner already outlined. Ordinarily, these mechanisms suffice to overcome gravity. But it is well known that soldiers standing at attention for long periods of time, especially in warm weather, often faint. This is due to the lack of a massaging action. The blood slowly pools in the veins, the venous return to the heart lessens, and finally the cardiac output decreases to a point incompatible with consciousness.

Pilots of modern aircraft also must cope with a circulatory problem. Pulling out of a dive, the force of gravity is multiplied several times. The force drawing the blood down and therefore away from the heart may be 5 to 10 g's (gravity) or even more. Under such conditions the pilot will black out, that is, lose consciousness because of the failure of adequate blood to reach the heart. In order to operate modern aircraft in combat maneuvers, it is necessary for the pilot to be enveloped in a pressurized suit. The pressure of the suit supports the veins against these great forces and permits the blood to flow back into the heart. The faster the dive, the more sudden the pull out, the greater must be the pressure in the suit. For this purpose, ingenious valves have been devised which automatically vary the suit pressure according to the g's developed.

Whether or not active venoconstriction operates to oppose the force of gravity is not yet clear. Some authorities contend that, when the gravitational force decreases venous return and therefore cardiac output, the carotid and aortic reflexes bring about venoconstriction which would tend to prevent pooling. Whether or not this mechanism does actually function in this manner, the fact remains that by far the most effective opposition to gravitational pull is afforded by the skeletal muscles which surround the veins.

VARIATIONS IN BLOOD PRESSURE

AT REST

Even when man is completely at rest, there are important variations in the blood pressure in different parts of the circulatory system. Figure 14-8 shows representative mean pressures in the arterial and venous trees. The velocity of the blood is also depicted. From this illustration several important facts may be gleaned. First, it should be noted that there is a progressive fall in pressure. The pressure, according to this illustration, is highest in the aorta and lowest just before the blood enters the right atrium from the great veins. The sharpest fall in pressure occurs in the arterioles. It will be recalled that this is the site of the so-called peripheral resistance. Energy is utilized in overcoming resistance. This energy is the blood pressure. Consequently, the greater the resistance, the lower will be the pressure *beyond the point of resistance.*

The blood velocity, on the other hand, remains relatively constant until the capillaries are reached. At this point the velocity decreases sharply. A curve representing the cross-sectional area has been superimposed. As the cross-sectional area increases, the velocity decreases. Thus the velocity and area curves go in opposite directions. In other words,

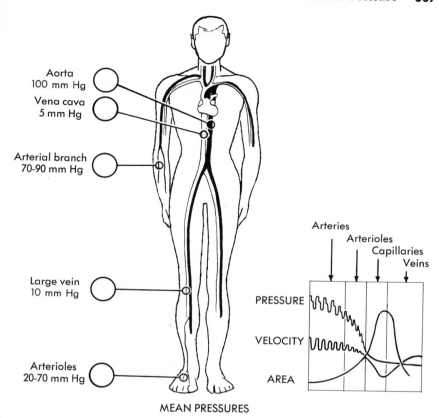

MEAN PRESSURES

FIG. 14-8   Pressure and velocity in various parts of the circulatory system. Note that the pressure decreases progressively throughout the circulation, but the velocity of blood flow is lowest in the capillaries.

because of the tremendous *total* cross-sectional area of the capillaries, the blood flow is very slow. This is, of course, advantageous and allows the blood components adequate time to diffuse in and out of the capillaries and tissues.

Although the pressure may vary in different parts of the circulatory system, at rest the pressure in any one area remains reasonably constant. The arterial pressure in the brachial artery (in the arm) in normal young adults is about 120 mm Hg systolic and 80 mm Hg diastolic. If the pressure is measured in the femoral artery (in the thigh) while the subject is erect, it will be found to be considerably higher because of the influence of gravity. The venous pressure as measured close to the heart is almost zero.

DURING EXERCISE

During exercise there is an increased heart rate, an elevation of the arterial and venous pressures, and increased cardiac output. The rise in arterial pressure is due entirely to greater cardiac output. The over-all peripheral resistance decreases. It is true that there is vasoconstriction in some areas, but in the active muscles there is vasodilatation which more than offsets constriction elsewhere. This is clearly shown by the fact that cardiac output may increase 5 or 6 times while arterial blood pressure increases, at the most, only two times. The decrease in peripheral resistance which permits the arterial system to accommodate this large cardiac output with only a twofold increase in pressure is mostly due to vasodilatation in the muscles evoked by the high production of CO_2.

The major problem is to explain the remarkable increase in cardiac output during exercise. Cardiac output is determined by the heart rate and the stroke volume. The increased heart rate is probably the result of impulses from higher centers, centers that drive the skeletal muscles and, as an important corollary, the cardiac muscle as well. In addition, the contracting muscles send impulses to the medullary centers to increase accelerator activity. This accelerator (sympathetic) activity also increases the force of contraction, thus improving stroke volume. But, at the same time, there must be increased venous pressure to fill the ventricle adequately in the face of decreasd filling time occasioned by a fast heart rate. The increased venous return during exercise is caused by: (1) greater cardiac output, (2) decreased arteriolar resistance, (3) pumping action of the contracting muscles, and (4) pumping action of increased respiratory activity.

In addition, there may be venoconstriction which would decrease the relatively large capacity of the venous system, thereby elevating venous pressure. Finally, most of the parallel circulatory systems shown in Fig. 14-1 undergo vasoconstriction during exercise. This greatly diminishes the blood supply to the viscera making that large volume of blood available to the major circulation through the muscles.

As already emphasized, in order to maintain or increase stroke volume while the heart is beating rapidly, there must be faster diastolic filling of the ventricle. This can only result if the pressure differential between the atrium and ventricle increases. The greater venous return increases the atrial pressure; a more vigorous atrial contraction increases it further. A decreased ventricular residue lowers the ventricular pressure at the end of systole. In addition, there is evidence that during vigorous cardiac activity the pressure in the ventricle at the beginning of the rapid inflow phase may become negative. All of these alterations increase the atrial-ventricular pressure gradient which drives blood into the ventricle. At very fast heart rates, atrial contraction and the period of negative ventricular pressure would occur simultaneously, thus creating the maximal atrial-ventricular pressure differential.

It is interesting to note that during exercise the mean blood pressure remains elevated; however, soon after exercise ceases, it falls below the resting level. Most of this fall is due to a very low diastolic pressure. The heart rate also slows. These changes, that is, low diastolic pressure and slow heart rate, are probably due to sinus pressoreceptor activity. During exercise the reflexes are suppressed, perhaps dominated by higher center drive from the cerebral cortex and hypothalamus. But as soon as exercise ceases, the sinus pressoreceptors are freed to slow the heart and dilate arterioles which have been constricted during exercise. Accordingly, the cardiac output and the peripheral resistance decrease, thus lowering the mean arterial blood pressure.

HYPERTENSION

The term hypertension has reference to high blood pressure in the arterial system. Until the heart begins to fail, as a result of long-standing hypertension, the venous pressure is usually within normal range. Chronic systolic pressure in excess of about 160 mm Hg is considered abnormal. Despite the chronic high arterial blood pressure the pressoreceptors continue to function. If external pressure is applied to the carotid sinus of a hypertensive patient, his blood pressure will fall, just as it does in a normal subject. Action potential studies disclose that immediately following the onset of hypertension there is vigorous firing in the buffer nerves, but this progressively diminishes. In other words, at first the pressoreceptors respond as they always do when the pressure is elevated. But progressively they cease to do so, thus ultimately becoming acclimated to the high pressure. It is as though the regulator had been reset.

The cause of hypertension, in most cases, is increased peripheral resistance. This may result from a variety of causes. In some instances the mechanism of the increased peripheral resistance has not been determined. These cases are referred to as **essential hypertension.** Hypertension may result from: (1) **kidney disease,** (2) a tumor of the adrenal medulla known as a **pheochromocytoma,** (3) and **arteriosclerosis,** that is, a thickening of the walls of the arterioles with a concomitant narrowing of the lumen which increases resistance.

HEMORRHAGE

The loss of blood is a very common experience. In most cases, very little need be done about it except to let nature take its course. But the manner in which nature operates is of interest to the physiologist. If the laceration is a minor one, a clot will rapidly form, and there will not be sufficient loss of blood volume to evoke any significant cardiovascular changes.

But if the laceration is very large or if the individual has hemophilia, the clotting mechanism may be overwhelmed and a considerable quantity of blood lost before the hemorrhage can be controlled. The normal blood volume is about 5 liters. The loss of more than 2 liters of blood may prove fatal.

Figure 14-9 shows the sequence of compensatory reactions which may maintain the victim until the bleeding is halted and, in extreme cases, transfusion of whole blood is instituted. Let us assume that the accident has severed many arteries and veins. There will, of course, be a simultaneous diminution of both arterial and venous pressure.

Arterial Reactions   The decrease in arterial blood pressure activates the pressoreceptors in the carotid and aortic sinuses. The heart rate is in-

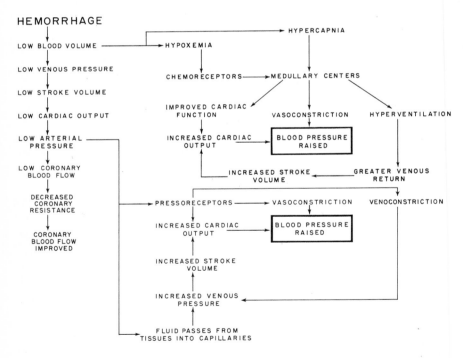

FIG. 14-9 The physiological consequences of hemorrhage. These mechanisms maintain blood pressure within a viable range unless over about 40 per cent of the total blood volume is lost.

creased, and there is generalized vasoconstriction. In the face of lowered venous pressure, the greater heart rate probably does not increase the cardiac output significantly, but the greater vasoconstriction may effectively maintain the arterial blood pressure within the normal range.

As the blood volume decreases, the tissues will extract more and more oxygen from the blood. At the same time, the carbon dioxide concentration of the blood will increase because of the small blood volume. In other words, there is less blood to carry the molecules of carbon dioxide, and so each unit of blood must transport more of that substance. These changes activate the chemoreceptors and bring about even greater vasoconstriction.

Venous Reactions The low venous pressure is combated to some extent by the increased respiration which is reflexly brought about. The respiratory efforts lower the intrathoracic pressure, and blood is attracted toward the heart. There is also venoconstriction, which diminishes the capacity of the venous vascular tree, and this serves to maintain the venous pressure. In addition, the viscera contribute a significant volume of blood. But if these mechanisms are overwhelmed, cardiac output decreases to such an extent that vasoconstriction cannot compensate for it. There is then a fall in arterial blood pressure until a level incompatible with life is reached.

Capillary Reactions Hemorrhage evokes important events at the capillary level. It is here that the fluid leaves and reenters the vascular system. Due to the low blood pressure, fluid is drawn from the tissues into the capillaries. This helps compensate for the fluid loss. Finally, there is reflex contraction of the spleen which forces blood into the vascular system, blood which possesses a high concentration of cells. The splenic mechanism then functions to restore the cellular component of the blood whereas the capillaries operate to replenish the fluid element.

LOSS OF CONSCIOUSNESS

If hemorrhage continues unabated, the compensatory mechanisms just outlined will be overwhelmed, the blood pressure will fall, and the individual will lapse into unconsciousness. Loss of consciousness also occurs if the cardiac output decreases sharply, or if there is a massive decrease in peripheral resistance. In both cases the blood pressure falls below the level compatible with consciousness.

SUMMARY

There are two circulatory trees, the **venous** and the **arterial**. The **aorta** gives off many **large arteries** which arborize into **smaller arteries,** then into **arterioles,** and finally into **capillaries.** The capillaries then re-form into **venules,** which join to form **small veins,** then **larger veins.** Finally, the **inferior** and **superior venae cavae** meet to enter the right atrium of the heart.

These vessels differ in size and structure. The aorta and large arteries are notably elastic. The smaller arteries and arterioles are conspicuously muscular. The capillaries are only one cell thick and are admirably suited for diffusion. The veins are generally thin walled and contain some smooth muscle.

Pressure in any part of the system may be determined if a needle is introduced into the vessel and attached to a **manometer.** In man, arterial pressure is determined with the use of the **sphygmomanometer.** Venous pressure may be estimated by elevating the hand until the veins collapse, or by sealing a chamber over a vein and pumping air into it until the veins are seen to collapse. When arterial pressure is determined, it is expressed in millimeters of mercury as systolic over diastolic pressure. The values are based upon points of reference derived from the **sounds of Korotkov.**

The arterial pressure is controlled by the **cardiac output** and the **peripheral resistance.** The peripheral resistance is regulated by **vasomotor activity.** The elasticity of the aorta and large vessels buffers systolic and supports diastolic pressure. The elasticity usually diminishes with age and in numerous diseased states.

If the arterial blood pressure falls, the pressoreceptors in the carotid and aortic sinuses reflexly increase the peripheral resistance. This restores the pressure to within normal limits.

Venous pressure is regulated by (1) **the massaging action of the muscles,** (2) **venomotor activity,** (3) **intrathoracic pressure,** and (4) **gravity.**

There is a progressive decrease in blood pressure from the aorta to the large veins. The greatest decrement takes place in the arterioles because of the resistance at this point. The blood velocity falls rapidly in the capillaries because of their great cross-sectional area.

During exercise the cardiac output increases up to about 6 times the resting level, but the peripheral resistance decreases because of great vasodilatation in the muscles. The cardiac output is increased by sympathetic drive from higher centers and from the active muscles. Stroke volume is maintained or is increased by elevated venous pressure caused by greater cardiac output, decreased arteriolar resistance, pumping action of contracting muscles and respiratory movements, and shunting of blood from the viscera.

Hypertension results from increased peripheral resistance which may be the result of **kidney disease, pheochromocytoma,** or **arteriosclerosis.**

Numerous circulatory mechanisms effectively compensate for loss of blood unless over approximately 40 per cent of the total volume is lost. A sharp fall in arterial pressure causes loss of consciousness. This may occur as a result of hemorrhage or massive vasodilatation.

QUESTIONS

1. Outline the method of determining arterial blood pressure.
2. What are the major factors that control arterial blood pressure?
3. What role does the elasticity of the aorta play in circulatory dynamics? Explain.
4. What are the major factors that control venous pressure?
5. Why is the blood velocity lowest in the capillaries?
6. Outline the blood pressure alterations that occur in response to exercise.

SUGGESTED READING

Dean, V., "Measuring Venous Pressure," *Am. J. Nursing,* **63:**#10, 70–72, October 1963.

Green, H. D., and Kepchar, J. H., "Control of Peripheral Resistance in Major Systemic Vascular Beds," *Physiol. Rev.,* **39:**#3, 617–686, July 1959.

"Hypotension," *Therapeutic Notes,* **65:**#7–8, 168–173, July-August 1958.

Maxwell, M. H., and Prozan, G. B., "Renovascular Hypertension," *Prog. Cardiovasc. Res.,* **5:**#1, 81–117, July 1962.

Pascarelli, E. F., and Bertrand, C. A., "Comparison of Blood Pressures in the Arms and Legs," *New England J. Med.,* **270:**#14, 693–698, April 2, 1964.

Zweifach, B. W., "The Microcirculation of the Blood," *Sci. American,* **200:**#1, 54–60, January 1959.

15

Capillaries and Lymphatic System

THE CIRCULATION FUNCTIONS TO TRANSPORT OXYGEN, carbon dioxide, meta-bolic end-products, nutrients, hormones, and enzymes. But the arteries and the veins are impermeable; thus there can be no transfer of any of these substances between blood and tissue cells. The capillaries, however, are not impermeable, and it is at this level that the all important ex-changes occur. In addition, there is an entirely separate system, the lym-phatic system, that serves to remove various substances from the tissue spaces and to return them to the circulation.

CAPILLARIES

It has been calculated that there are about 3,600,000,000 capillaries in the circulatory system of man. To be sure, each capillary has a very small cross-sectional area, but the cross-sectional area of all of the billions of capillaries added together is large, about 4,500 square centimeters com-pared to 4.5 cm² for the aorta. Since the velocity is inversely proportional to the cross-sectional area, it can be easily calculated that the velocity of blood in the capillaries is about $\frac{1}{1000}$ what it is in the aorta. The slow flow in the capillaries permits the important interchange of substances to take place.

ANATOMY

The capillary walls are extremely thin. They are composed of but a single layer of endothelial cells. Two sets of pores have been described: (1) a set of small pores that allow passage of substances with a molecular weight not greater than 250,000, and (2) large pores permitting much larger molecules to pass. Electron microscope studies show the presence of intracellular vesicles packed tightly in layers in the capillary endothelium.

314

It is thought that the large pores are really these vesicles. The transfer of large molecules may consist of the material being taken up in a vesicle which then becomes pinched off. The term **cytopemphis** has been given to this process, rather than pinocytosis, in order to convey the idea that substances are being transmitted through the cytoplasm rather than utilized by the cell, as is the case in pinocytosis.

The permeability of the capillary wall is not the same throughout the body. The capillaries of the brain are least permeable; those of the liver most permeable.

The true capillaries do not have smooth muscle and therefore cannot undergo constriction. However, there is a **precapillary sphincter** placed between the arteriole and the true capillary. This sphincter can constrict and thereby alter the flow and pressure in the capillary. In most capillary beds there are also **A-V shunts** which connect the arteriole and venule by a short, direct route. The A-V shunt has smooth muscle and thus its lumen size can be altered. If the A-V shunt is open the blood will take the route of least resistance and consequently bypass the capillaries.

CAPILLARY FUNCTION

It is extremely difficult to determine capillary pressure, but by means of very fine pipettes which can be introduced directly into a capillary, and by other means it has been determined that the normal capillary pressure in most areas of the body is about 30 mm Hg about midway between the arteriole and venule. Closer to the arteriole it is higher, reaching about 40 mm Hg. At the venule end it is generally about 20 mm Hg. These figures, however, can and do vary markedly.

Variations in capillary flow and pressure result from (1) the arterial pressure, (2) the status of the precapillary sphincters and the A-V shunts, and (3) the venous pressure.

Temperature and Color of the Skin It is common experience that sometimes the skin is bright red and hot while at other times it is deathly pale and cold. The color and temperature of the skin are in good measure functions of capillary activity. Oxygenated blood is red, whereas blood devoid of its oxygen is relatively blue. Blood surrenders its oxygen as it passes through the capillary networks. The more rapidly blood flows through the capillaries, the less oxygen it will give up. In other words, the rate of capillary blood flow determines the color of the skin. When the flow is rapid, the skin is red. If the capillary flow is sluggish, so that much of the oxygen is transferred to the tissues, then the skin will appear blue.

Color possesses two qualities: (1) **hue** and (2) **intensity.** Skin hue is a function of the **rate** of blood flow. The intensity of the skin color depends upon the **thickness** of the layer of blood flowing in the subjacent capillary bed. The thicker this layer, the more intense the color. The thickness of the layer is determined by capillary activity. If all the precapillary sphincters constrict, there will be relatively little or no blood just beneath the skin surface. If they dilate, the layer of blood will be considerably more dense.

These observations can be summarized by saying that an intensely red skin is due to a rapid blood flow through dilated vessels whereas a very pale skin with a blue tinge is the result of constricted vessels through which the blood flows very slowly.

The **temperature** of the skin is determined primarily by the rate of blood flow, although the thickness of the layer of blood beneath the skin is also a factor. If the blood flow is fast and if the capillaries are dilated, the skin not only appears intensely red but also feels hot. Such a condition is highly characteristic of an inflamed area, such as a boil.

Triple Reaction   If one draws the point of a pencil or a probe across an area of skin, a red line develops. If this procedure is repeated several times, a red flare spreads on both sides of the line. Shortly thereafter the red line is seen to become swollen and elevated. From stroking the skin, three distinct events have occurred: (1) a **red line,** (2) a **flare,** and (3) a **wheal** (meaning "ridge"). These three results are collectively referred to as the **triple response.**

The mechanisms by which these three changes take place have been carefully investigated by Sir Thomas Lewis. The first response, the red line, is due to capillary dilatation beneath the area which has been stroked. This primary dilatation is caused by mechanical stimulation. Even if all the nerves in the area are destroyed, the red line still results. This experiment indicates that this is a purely mechanical phenomenon.

The second reaction of the triad, the red flare, is more complex. It results from dilatation of the arterioles which supply the capillaries in the area stimulated. This dilatation has been found to be in response to the so-called **axon reflex.** Figure 15-1 shows that there are sensory fibers from the skin and from the arterioles which join into a common sensory pathway. It is believed that the impulses evoked by stroking the skin pass to the point of union and then down the branch to the arteriole. Arteriolar dilatation results. The evidence for this theory is compelling. If the common sensory pathway above the point of union is severed, the response is still present. But if, after cutting the nerve, time is allowed for degeneration of the terminal branches of the nerves, then the reaction can no longer be elicited.

The third response, the wheal, is the result of increased capillary permeability. This response, like the red line, is due simply to mechanical stimulation. Because of increased permeability, fluid from the capillaries

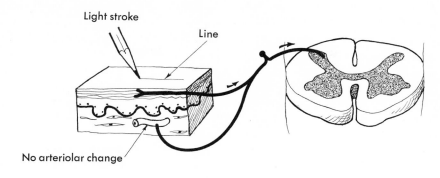

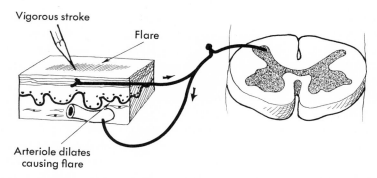

FIG. 15-1   Axon reflex. When the skin is stroked vigorously, impulses ascend the sensory nerve and also are conducted antidromically, that is, back to the arteriole which dilates, thus permitting more blood to enter the area, thereby producing the flare.

oozes into the tissue spaces beneath the line and causes it to swell and appear elevated.

Most investigators believe that the triple response is caused by the liberation of **histamine** which follows mechanical stimulation. This conclusion has many implications and finds practical application in the treatment of hives as well as other allergic disorders. Hives is a skin manifestation characterized by masses of swellings or wheals. If histamine is an important agent responsible for such swellings, then it is logical to expect that antihistaminic drugs should prove efficacious in counteracting the disturbance. As a matter of record, the antihistaminic drugs have proved their value in these cases.

FORMATION OF TISSUE FLUID

The transfer, or exchange, of substances between the capillaries and the tissue spaces is considered to be a purely passive process. That is, only physical forces determine the exchange of plasma and tissue fluid and the movement of solute. In so far as is known, there is no active transfer.

Plasma, with the exception of the very large protein molecules, is capable of moving through the wall of the capillary to enter the tissue spaces. Similarly, the fluid that normally occupies the tissue spaces can pass into the capillary circulation. These transfers depend upon the resultant of the hydrostatic (blood) pressure on the one hand; the osmotic pressure on the other.

Hydrostatic Pressure   Movement of fluid through any semipermeable membrane depends upon the gradient of hydrostatic pressure between the two sides. In the case of the capillaries it is very difficult to determine accurately either the pressure within or without. It is generally assumed, however, that the pressure in the capillary at the arteriolar end is about 40 mm Hg. This hydrostatic force tends to drive the blood plasma through the capillary wall into the tissue spaces.

Fine needles have been introduced into the tissue spaces in an attempt to measure the tissue pressure, that is, the pressure of the fluid in the tissue spaces surrounding the capillaries. Values of a mm of Hg or two are generally recorded. Recently, Guyton has published figures using a new technique in which small capsules are implanted and after the inflammatory reaction has subsided the pressure within the capsule is measured. With this technique it would appear that the interstitial fluid is about − 6.5 mm Hg. Reference will be made to these findings below, but for the moment assume that there is a driving force of about 40 mm Hg forcing fluid out of the capillaries.

Osmotic Pressure   The plasma proteins cannot readily pass through the capillary membrane; accordingly they are responsible for the osmotic attraction, or pressure, which causes fluid to move from the tissue spaces into the capillary blood.

The osmotic pressure of the plasma in the capillaries is about 26 mm Hg. Because there is usually so little protein in the tissue fluid, the osmotic pressure is very low, perhaps as low as 1 mm Hg. The resultant of these two forces would be 25 (26 − 1). This force drives fluid into the capillary.

It can be seen, then, that since the hydrostatic pressure is higher than the effective osmotic pressure, fluid should leave the capillary under a driving force of 15 mm Hg (40 − 25). But as the blood continues on through the capillary, the pressure falls to perhaps 20 mm Hg or lower.

In other words, it would now be below the osmotic pressure and therefore fluid would flow back into the capillary. Thus a circulation out of and then into the capillary is visualized (Fig. 15-2). This concept was first proposed by Starling and is referred to as **Starling's hypothesis.**

The work of Guyton, however, suggests that under normal circumstances such a circulation probably does not occur. His finding of an interstitial fluid pressure of − 6.5 mm Hg indicates that the osmotic pressure is much greater than the mean blood pressure in the capillaries. There is therefore suction, so to speak, that keeps the tissue spaces dry. According to this concept, the tissue fluid that is present probably comes from intracellular metabolism rather than from the circulating plasma.

Of course, capillary hydrostatic pressure is not the same in all capillaries. Beyond question, if the hydrostatic pressure exceeds the osmotic pressure, fluid will pour out of the capillaries. The same result follows if capillary permeability is increased, thereby permitting protein to filter out.

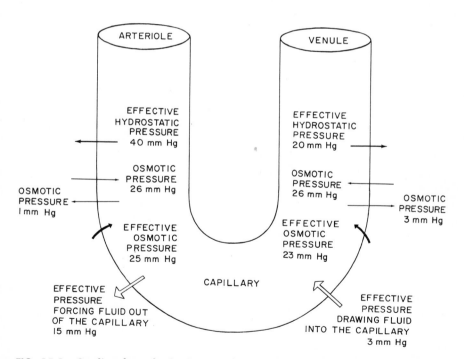

FIG. 15-2   Starling hypothesis. Due to the resultant of hydrostatic and osmotic forces, fluid leaves the end of the capillary near the arteriole and returns close to the venule.

LYMPHATIC SYSTEM

Not all of the fluid that exists in the interstitial spaces, either as a result of exudation from the capillaries or as a result of intracellular metabolism, is removed by transfer back into the capillaries. In addition, there is some protein loss from the blood. Finally, there are various substances formed in the cells, including protein, which must be introduced into the circulation. The lymphatic system serves this function, and it also provides another mechanism for draining the interstitial spaces.

ANATOMY

The lymphatics are a network of fine vessels which begin as a series of closed tubes about the size of capillaries. These thin-walled delicate lymphatic capillaries are composed of but a single layer of flat endothelial cells. They are characterized by being blind, that is, closed at one end. Upon close examination it is found that connective-tissue fibrils stretch from the capillary walls to merge with the surrounding tissues. These fibrils are extremely important because they support the capillaries in such a way as to keep them open. If it were not for this arrangement, the tissue pressure would collapse the capillaries and thereby frustrate their function of draining the tissue spaces.

The capillaries are continuous with the lymphatic vessels which, in turn, unite with others to form even larger channels. Ultimately there result two main trunks: (1) the **right lymphatic duct** and (2) the **thoracic duct.** These main lymphatic vessels serve unequal areas. In Fig. 15-3 it can be seen that the thoracic duct receives lymph from both lower extremities, the lower part of the abdomen, the left thorax, the left half of the head, and the left upper extremity. The right lymphatic duct drains only the right upper extremity, the right thorax, and the right half of the head. The right lymphatic duct is smaller than the thoracic duct. It empties into the right innominate vein. The thoracic duct drains into the left innominate vein.

In structure, the lymphatic vessels resemble veins. They are also equipped with one-way valves which are essential for the movement of lymph through them.

The superficial veins of the forearm are readily visible, but the superficial lymph vessels are not. However, infection (of a finger, for example) may spread to the entire extremity, and a red streak, termed **lymphangitis,** may develop.

All along the lymph channels there are swellings, termed **lymph nodes.** They are composed of a meshwork of fibers enclosed in a fibrous capsule. Nests of lymph nodes are found in various parts of the body such

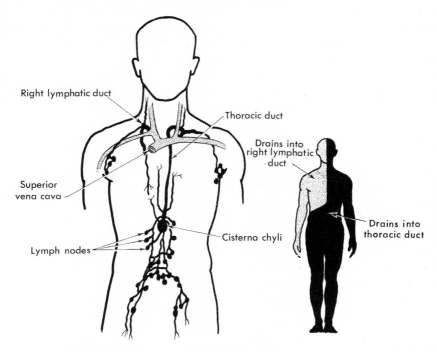

FIG. 15-3 **Diagrammatic representation of the anatomy of the lymphatic system.**

as the axilla, the antecubital space, and the groin. In some cases the lymph nodes become inflamed. This condition is called **lymphadenitis.**

LYMPH FORMATION

By definition, only when fluid enters the lymphatic system does it become lymph. Accordingly, three fluids are involved: (1) blood plasma, (2) interstitial (tissue) fluid, and (3) lymph. The forces responsible for the formation of tissue fluid have been discussed. For some time it was thought that lymph was formed by an active process by which the fluid was secreted into the lymph capillary. Now it is known to be a purely passive process. As the tissue fluid forms the pressure increases. It is this pressure that drives the fluid into the lymph capillary. Because of the presence of fine fibrils, the lymph capillary is prevented from collapsing. The lymph capillary is highly permeable; thus there is no osmotic pressure, only the external hydrostatic pressure to drive the fluid into the vessel.

LYMPH FLOW

Once lymph enters the capillaries, it moves as a result of two factors: (1) as more lymph forms, it pushes the lymph already present ahead, and (2) the contraction of muscles and the bulging of arteries when they pulsate, squeeze the lymph vessels. Since these vessels have a closed end, and by virtue of the one-way valves, the lymph is milked toward the outflow into the venous system. Changes in intrathoracic pressure also affect lymph flow as they do venous flow.

The actual lymph pressure is not known, but it can be surmised that it rarely exceeds 5 mm Hg when the subject is lying down. The pressure in the large, central lymphatic trunks is less than 0.5 mm Hg. But during activity in the upright position, and in cases of inflammation, pressures as high as 50 mm Hg are possible.

EDEMA

There is a steady formation of tissue fluid; consequently, drainage of the tissue spaces must proceed at the same rate as tissue fluid formation. It has been seen that the fluid leaves the capillaries at the arteriolar end and some returns to the blood stream at the venular end of the blood capillary whereas the remainder is drained by the lymph vessels. If it forms faster than it is removed, the fluid will accumulate in the tissue spaces and cause a swelling. This excessive accumulation of fluid in the tissue spaces is termed **edema.**

It will be recalled that the rate of fluid formation depends upon the resultant of (1) the **blood pressure,** (2) the **tissue pressure,** and (3) the **osmotic pressure.** If the hydrostatic force far outweighs the osmotic force, the rate of fluid formation in the tissue spaces will be very rapid. The quantity of fluid present in the tissue spaces depends simply upon the rate of formation versus the rate of drainage.

Lymphatic Obstruction   Everyone appreciates the fact that if water is left running in a sink which has a clogged drainpipe the sink will eventually overflow. This is precisely the situation in conditions where the lymph vessels become obstructed. The formation of lymph continues, but there is inadequate drainage from the tissue spaces. Thus the fluid can do only one thing—accumulate. In other words, edema results.

Figure 15-4 shows an individual with obvious edema. This person is afflicted with an organism called *filaria,* which has an affinity for the lymph vessels where it multiplies at an incredible rate and in so doing literally plugs the lymphatic channels. The condition is called **elephantiasis** because, as the picture clearly indicates, the swollen extremities resemble the legs of an elephant.

FIG. 15-4   **Elephantiasis. The tremendous swelling is due to fluid accumulation caused by blockage of the lymphatic vessels.** (Reproduced, with permission, from R. P. Strong, "Stitt's Diagnosis, Prevention, and Treatment of Tropical Diseases," McGraw-Hill, Blakiston Division, 1944.)

Nutritional Edema   Figure 15-5 demonstrates the results of an inadequate intake of protein. This condition is very common during wartime when prisoners are fed a protein-poor diet for long periods of time. It will be recalled that large protein molecules do not pass through the capillary wall. They are thus responsible for the osmotic force which opposes the

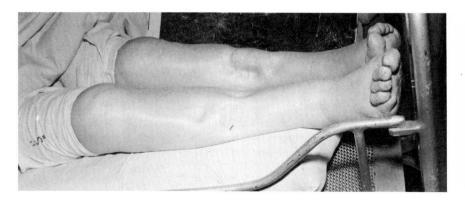

FIG. 15-5   **Nutritional edema. Leg edema caused by inadequate protein intake.** (Reproduced, with permission of Wide World Photos, Inc.)

outpouring of fluid from the vascular tree. When the protein concentration of the blood decreases, the rate of formation increases and thus may overwhelm the drainage system. Edema results.

Cardiac Edema   Individuals with heart disease notice that their feet and ankles swell. In the more terminal stages of heart failure there is even more generalized edema, and fluid may accumulate in the abdominal cavity, causing marked abdominal swelling. This condition is termed **ascites.** Cardiac edema is caused by the abnormally high venous pressure. When the heart fails, blood accumulates behind it and steadily increases the venous pressure. This increase in venous pressure causes a higher capillary pressure. An elevated capillary pressure favors filtration through the capillary wall. The rate of fluid formation of tissue fluid exceeds the rate of drainage. Edema results.

Traumatic Edema   Various types of injuries which traumatize the tissues result in increased capillary permeability. For example, a sharp blow to most parts of the body causes swelling. The swelling is due to the accumulation of fluid in that area. Trauma, by increasing capillary permeability permits protein to escape thereby reducing osmotic pressure. Since the hydrostatic pressure remains virtually unchanged, the balance is upset and fluid pours into the tissue spaces.

SUMMARY

Capillaries are extremely small vessels with thin walls through which fluid exchange with the tissue spaces occurs. Capillaries do not have smooth muscle. Flow is controlled by the **precapillary sphincters** and the **A-V shunts.** Because of the tremendous total cross-sectional area, blood flow in the capillaries is very slow. The pressure is about 30 mm Hg.

The temperature and color of the skin are controlled by capillary blood flow. Stroking the skin gives rise to the **triple reaction** which consists of (1) **red line,** (2) **flare,** and (3) **wheal.**

The movement of fluid into and out of the capillaries depends upon the resultant of hydrostatic and osmotic pressures. According to the **Starling hypothesis** fluid leaves the capillary at the arteriolar end and returns to the capillary close to the venule.

Lymph capillaries are very fine vessels which have one end blind, or closed. They are freely permeable so that fluid and protein can easily enter to form **lymph.** The lymph, by virtue of its continuing formation and the massaging action of muscles and pulsating arteries, moves along the **lymphatic vessels,** through **lymph nodes** to return, ultimately, to the venous circulation. The lymph pressure is generally very low, on the order of a few mm Hg, but during exercise and in inflammation the pressure may rise to 50 mm Hg.

If tissue fluid forms faster than it can be removed there is accumulation in the tissue spaces, a condition termed **edema.** Edema occurs following lymphatic obstruction, elevated venous pressure, trauma, and protein deficiency.

QUESTIONS

1. Explain why blood flow is slower in the capillaries than anywhere else in the circulation.
2. In the pulmonary capillaries the hydrostatic pressure is not higher than about 7 mm Hg. In which direction will fluid move between tissue spaces and capillary blood? Why?
3. Explain the mechanism for each component of the triple reaction.
4. Why does lymph flow accelerate in exercise?
5. What is the status of the capillary circulation when the skin is hot and intensely red?
6. Why does protein deficiency cause edema?

SUGGESTED READING

Elias, H., "Histology and Dynamics of Capillaries and Arteries," *Dental Dig.,* **56:** 440–443, 489–493, 536–539, 1950.

Kahlson, G., "New Approaches to the Physiology of Histamine," *Persp. Biol. Med.,* 5:#2, 179–197, Winter 1962.

Kramar, J., "Endocrine Regulation of the Capillary Resistance," *Science,* **119:** 790–792, 1954.

Mayerson, H. S., "The Lymphatic System," *Sci. American,* **208:**#6, 80–90, June 1963.

16

Circulation through Special Organs

THERE ARE REGIONS OF THE BODY in which the circulation differs from that observed generally or else has special properties which warrant closer attention. It will be seen that the coronary circulation not only is of vital importance to the well-being of the whole organism but is controlled by factors specific to its needs. Likewise, it will be learned that the delicate brain tissue is assured a steady supply of blood by elaborate self-regulating mechanisms. In this chapter the circulation through the heart, brain, lungs, liver, and spleen will be analyzed.

CORONARY CIRCULATION

In discussing cardiac dynamics, it has been repeatedly emphasized that the function of the heart is to deliver blood in adequate quantities to all the cells of the body. Blood is essential to the continued survival of the cells. The heart itself is composed of cells which also must be nourished and which produce waste products necessitating removal. The blood that flows through the heart chambers is not utilized for these vital processes. The heart, like all other organs, has its own highly specialized circulatory apparatus, in this case the **coronary system.** The term coronary means literally "a crown," and this implies encirclement. It should be recalled that the coronary vessels do, in fact, encircle the heart.

The importance of the coronary system cannot be overemphasized. If the blood supply to one kidney is interrupted, that kidney will die, but the body can survive with the other one alone. If the circulation to a limb is halted, the extremity may require amputation, but the individual continues to live. However, if the blood supply to the heart is blocked, the cardiac cells die, contraction ceases, and therefore the entire circulation of vital blood comes to a standstill. A steady and adequate cardiac

326

circulation must be maintained. It has been seen that, during exercise, cardiac output may be increased tenfold or more. To prevent heart damage, the coronary flow must be increased at least as much. A complete understanding of the physiology of exercise therefore requires a knowledge of the mechanisms by which coronary circulation keeps step with the work of the heart.

ANATOMY OF CORONARY VESSELS

Coronary Arteries   Figure 16-1 shows the coronary vessels. It will be noted that **two coronary arteries** spring from the aorta just beyond the aortic valve. In other words, as soon as the blood leaves the left ventricle, part of it enters the coronary arteries for distribution to the cardiac muscle.

Unfortunately, the coronary arteries are functionally **end arteries.** This means that the two vessels are more or less independent of each

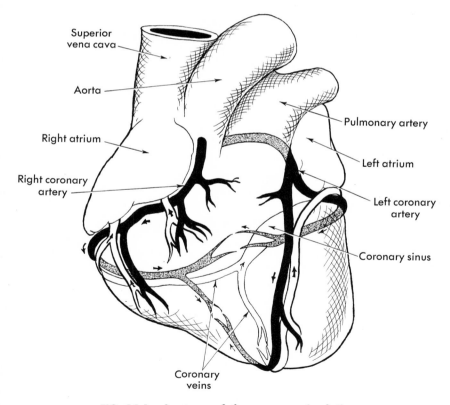

FIG. 16-1   Anatomy of the coronary circulation.

other. In contrast, in most organs of the body, the various blood vessels meet with one another so that, if one is blocked, the blood from another vessel may still nourish the tissues. But in the heart, if one of the coronary arteries is suddenly occluded, no blood is delivered to the heart muscle ordinarily supplied by that artery. That part of the heart dies and is known as an **infarct**. Of course, if only a small vessel is plugged, only a limited part of the heart muscle will become non-functional, and life may still be sustained. However, if a large area of the heart is destroyed, the heart becomes no longer capable of doing its work, and death ensues.

Coronary Veins The two coronary arteries arborize into numerous arterioles and then into capillary beds where the actual exchange of vital substances takes place. These capillaries then reunite into larger and larger vessels, the so-called **coronary veins** which deliver the blood to the right atrium. In addition to this drainage system, there are **Thebesian veins** which short-circuit the blood directly from the capillaries and smaller veins into the ventricles. And finally, there are the almost completely ignored **anterior cardiac veins** which ascend on the front wall of the right ventricle to end directly in the right atrium. In other words, there are at least three routes by which venous blood from the heart muscle can be returned to the general circulation. The major volume of coronary blood drains through the coronary sinus, but a goodly percentage is returned via the anterior cardiac veins. The Thebesian veins seem to play only a very minor role.

REGULATION OF CORONARY BLOOD FLOW

In order to nourish the heart wall, the quantity of blood flowing through the coronary system must keep step with the work of the heart. It will be recalled that as the initial length of the cardiac fiber increases so does the work of the heart and the demand for oxygen. At this time it is necessary to outline the factors which regulate coronary flow in accordance with varying demand.

The amount of blood flowing through a vessel at any time is the resultant of two factors: (1) the force driving that blood, that is, the blood pressure, and (2) the size of the vessel. Football players will readily appreciate these two factors. The weakest player can go through the opposing line if the hole is large enough, but when the gap is small, then a great deal of force, or pressure, is required. The same applies in the circulatory system. If the diameter of the inside of the vessel is large, there is little resistance to the flow of blood. But if the lumen becomes smaller, then considerable force is required to drive the blood through.

Logically, then, we must examine the factors which regulate the coronary-vessel caliber and the coronary blood pressure. It will be seen that the size of the vessels may be varied by (1) the activity of the nervous system, (2) the chemical composition of the blood, and (3) mechanical forces.

Nervous Control   The coronary arteries and especially the small branches called arterioles are innervated by nerves which control the size of the lumen of those vessels. One set of nerves causes the vessels to **constrict,** that is, to close down or decrease in caliber. Other nerves allow the vessels to relax or **dilate.** If the blood pressure is held constant, then the larger the coronary vessels, the greater will be the blood supply to the heart wall. In other words, the coronary blood flow can be controlled by the activity of the nervous system. By virtue of such nervous control, the necessary alterations in coronary blood flow during exercise may be executed. It should be emphasized that this is just one method; there are others. Man has several lines of defense, so that should one fail all is not lost. The situation may be likened again to a football team. If the forward wall is penetrated, there is the secondary to make the tackle. Should they fail, there is usually the safety man in position representing a third line of defense. Returning once again to the coronary blood flow, it will be seen that the nervous system, the chemical composition of the blood, and mechanical forces function in concert in normal man. Thus, if all the nerves which innervate the heart were to be cut, the coronary blood flow would still keep pace with demand because of the remaining safety factors.

Chemical Control   The blood contains many substances which affect the caliber of the blood vessels. The more important constituents which act in this manner are oxygen, carbon dioxide, epinephrine, and lactic acid. In addition, there are substances, administered either by mouth or by injection, which markedly alter the caliber of the coronary vessels.

For our purposes, it is enough to say that a shortage of oxygen causes the coronary vessels to dilate as does an excess of carbon dioxide, lactic acid, and epinephrine. During exercise, the tissues consume oxygen and thus lower the oxygen content of the blood. Simultaneously the cells produce CO_2, the actively contracting muscles liberate CO_2, and the adrenal glands are stimulated to pour epinephrine into the blood stream. It should be evident that all these substances produce the same result— dilatation of the coronary vessels. Thus, more blood is permitted to flow to the heart muscle and thereby satisfies the increased demand.

For reasons not clearly defined, the coronary vessels sometimes go into a **spasm,** an involuntary muscular contraction. In other words, the muscle in the wall of the coronary vessel contracts and thus reduces the lumen of that vessel. Such a condition may prove fatal because of the resulting reduced blood supply to the cardiac muscle. For this, drugs such as **amyl nitrite** and **nitroglycerin** are used by the physician to relieve the spasm.

These drugs cause a dramatic dilatation of the coronary vessels, and if administered promptly may save the patient's life.

Mechanical Control   The coronary vessels are embedded within the wall of the heart. Consequently, during muscular contraction the cardiac muscle squeezes the vessels and thus reduces their caliber. However, soon after the ventricle begins to contract, the aortic valve opens and the pressure within the aorta sharply rises (Fig. 16-2). Since the coronary arteries arise from the aorta, an elevation in pressure also takes place in the coronary vessels, thereby driving the blood through the squeezed vessels. In short, the coronary flow during the cardiac cycle depends upon the balance of two opposing factors: (1) the squeezing effect (**intramural pressure**) of the contracting cardiac muscle and (2) the aortic blood pres-

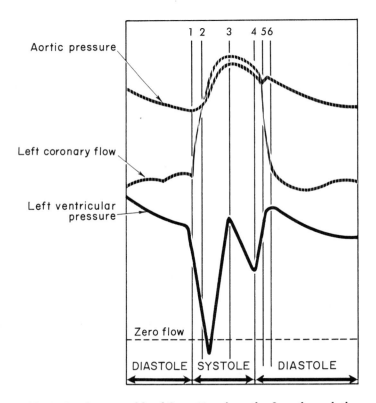

FIG. 16-2   Coronary blood flow. Note how the flow through the left coronary vessel varies during the cardiac cycle. Flow in the right coronary vessel does not vary nearly as much because the driving force (aortic pressure) is the same, but the resistance (intramural pressure) is far less.

sure. In the normal heart, even during exercise, these two factors tend to balance one another so that an adequate coronary blood supply may be assured.

Figure 16-2 should be studied in detail at this time. It will be noted that at the extreme left of this figure the coronary blood flow is steadily falling. It will also be seen that the aortic pressure is diminishing at the same rate. These two lines are parallel. This is to be expected, because the ventricle is at rest, intramural pressure is negligible, and therefore the coronary flow is solely the function of aortic pressure. As the aortic pressure decreases throughout diastole, so does the coronary flow.

At line 1 the coronary flow falls precipitously. It will be noted that the fall begins just before line 1. At this time the atria are contracting. At line 1 the ventricles begin to contract. The pressure within the heart rises sharply, and therefore the intramural pressure increases proportionately. This intramural pressure opposes the flow of blood in the coronary vessels and, as can be seen, the flow decreases markedly. It diminishes to the point at which there may be no forward flow at all, and as shown, at the peak of intramural pressure the flow may actually be reversed, the blood being squeezed back into the aorta. But at line 2 the aortic valve opens. Now the pressure in the aorta rises, opposes the great intramural pressure, and succeeds in overcoming it so that once again blood flows through the coronary vessels. The curve, therefore, is seen to rise until line 3 is reached.

At line 3 aortic pressure begins to fall off, but the ventricle is still contracting. This is the reduced-ejection phase. In short, the intramural pressure remains high while the aortic pressure falls off; therefore, the coronary flow diminishes. At line 4, systole ends, the ventricle relaxes, and intramural pressure decreases. The more the intramural pressure falls, the greater becomes the coronary blood flow. At line 6, the ventricle is completely relaxed, intramural pressure is once again at a minimum, and consequently the coronary blood flow is solely determined by the aortic pressure. The cycle is ready to begin again.

In pathological conditions the situation is quite different. Just one example will be offered to illustrate this point. Let us assume that there is stenosis or narrowing of the aortic valve. The opening between the left ventricle and the aorta is markedly constricted. In order to drive the normal quantity of blood through this small aperture, the ventricular muscle must contract and therefore squeeze the coronary vessels abnormally. This, as just explained, will cut down the coronary blood flow. Now assume further that the aortic valves do not close completely. Blood, instead of being forced through the coronary vessels, will regurgitate into the ventricle. It should be evident that such a valvular disorder will markedly decrease the coronary blood flow because the aortic pressure falls sharply during diastole. Lastly, in order to cope with this condition, the heart is doing more work and demanding more oxygen. It should be clear that the heart, under these conditions, is not being adequately nourished.

CORONARY BLOOD FLOW AT REST

The coronary flow in man must be estimated by indirect methods. The flow in an average sized man is thought to be about 250 ml per minute. If data from animal experiments can be extrapolated to man, then approximately 85 per cent of the total flow passes through the left coronary artery and only 15 per cent through the right coronary artery.

CORONARY BLOOD FLOW IN EXERCISE

During exercise, the pressure of the blood entering the right side of the heart, that is, the venous pressure, is elevated by mechanisms previously discussed. Accordingly, the Bainbridge reflex is set off which causes the heart to beat more rapidly. The high venous pressure also forces a large quantity of blood into the heart during diastole. This stretches the cardiac fibers, and the force of contraction during the next systole is augmented. Hence, the large volume of blood is ejected; in other words, the stroke volume is increased. The combination of increased heart rate and elevated stroke volume raises the cardiac output to as much as six times the resting cardiac output, which averages about 5 liters. In other words, during exercise one side of the heart is capable of ejecting about 7 gallons of blood per minute. This is truly a remarkable feat. One has but to compare the time required to pump 7 gallons of gasoline into a car to be convinced of the true import of this phenomenon.

In order to attain and maintain this output, the heart must slave and literally eat up its own oxygen supply. To nourish these hardworking cells, the coronary blood flow must be increased many times. How is this accomplished?

Even before exercise begins, the very thought of the effort evokes widespread alterations. Through nervous control the blood vessels which supply the cardiac muscle are dilated and thus allow blood to flow through them more readily and in larger quantities. At the same time, arterial blood pressure increases. When exercise actually begins, venous pressure is elevated. Cardiac output increases, and the arterial blood pressure rises further. This rise in pressure forces large quantities of blood through the dilated coronary vessels.

The circulation of blood in the coronary system is, to a great extent, self-regulating. Thus, in exercise for example, the greater cardiac work utilizes more oxygen from the coronary blood flow. The vessels dilate whenever the oxygen content of the coronary blood decreases. Accordingly, there is less resistance to flow and the flow increases thereby bringing in oxygen at a faster rate. Whether it is the shortage of oxygen per se, or an end-product of increased metabolism that is directly responsible for the dilatation, is not known.

CORONARY OCCLUSION

About a half million people in the United States die as a result of heart disease each year. A large fraction of these deaths result from **coronary occlusion.** The term occlusion means "to close." Closure of the coronary vessels, as has already been pointed out, can and often does prove fatal. The vessels may be closed by spasm or by a clot; the result is essentially the same.

Whether or not death will result from coronary occlusion depends simply upon the size of the vessel and how much cardiac reserve is present. If the heart is "on its last legs," then even if a small area is deprived of blood the loss may prove too great. On the other hand, even a healthy heart can be suddenly halted should a large vessel be occluded and deprive a major portion of the heart of its nourishment. But even if the heart is not completely embarrassed by the occlusion, it will be irreparably damaged. The area normally supplied by the occluded vessel does not regenerate. It must forever be carried as so much dead weight by the remaining healthy tissue of the heart. Thus this dead area, the infarct, not only contributes nothing to the work of the heart but actually proves to be a burden. The healthy cardiac muscle must do its own work plus that of the infarct and also carry the dead weight. This excess load takes its toll, so that although sudden death has not resulted, the victim's life is often shortened.

Figure 16-3 shows the sequence of events which follows as a proximate result of coronary occlusion. It can be seen that the end result is death. The coronary occlusion results in an infarct which, as already explained, weakens the contraction of the heart muscle. Less blood is pumped. This results in low arterial blood pressure and reduced coronary blood flow. As a sequel of the weakened contraction, there will also be a residue left in the ventricle. The next load of blood added to this residue will dilate the ventricle and, according to Starling's law, cause the heart to beat more forcibly. If the heart possesses adequate reserve, this may serve to compensate for the infarct. The lowered arterial pressure through the carotid-sinus reflex, according to Marey's law, increases the heart rate. Increased heart rate plus increased stroke·volume may very well bring the cardiac output back to normal. But clearly this is accomplished by greater work of the heart, which eventually takes its toll. The dilatation, it will be recalled, demands more oxygen; the resulting hypertrophy of

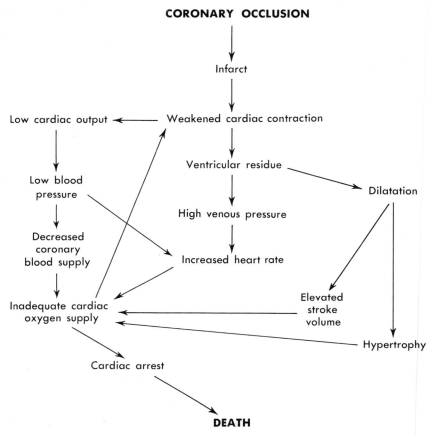

FIG. 16-3 Coronary occlusion. Sequence of events likely to occur following occlusion of a large coronary vessel.

the cardiac muscle utilizes more oxygen; the faster heart rate consumes more oxygen. In short, the coronary blood supply must be increased above normal, but as a result of the low cardiac output the coronary blood supply is below normal. A vicious cycle has been established; cardiac arrest will terminate the cycle perhaps within a few seconds, or possibly only after years. The outcome depends upon the size of the infarct in relation to the reserve of the heart.

CEREBRAL CIRCULATION

It has been pointed out that, if the circulation which nourishes the heart is stopped or proves inadequate, the heart will cease to beat and death will quickly ensue. There are other vital organs which also require a continuous supply of blood The brain contains numerous centers which cannot function for more than a short period of time in the absence of oxygen. It has been estimated that if the blood supply to the brain is stopped for longer than about 6 to 10 minutes irreversible changes take place. Clearly, the blood supply to the brain must be assured; it will be seen that there are excellent mechanisms designed to guarantee cerebral circulation.

Figure 16-4 shows the main vessels which carry the blood to and from the head. These are the carotid arteries and the jugular veins. Since man normally assumes the upright position, there is no great problem of venous return as is experienced from areas below the level of the heart. The force of gravity actually assists the venous circulation and enhances cerebral drainage. But, at the same time, it is necessary to pump blood to the brain against gravitational force. Therefore, any decrease in cardiac output or in arterial blood pressure will markedly affect cerebral circulation.

There is still another factor which must be considered. That is the fact that the brain is encased by inelastic tissues. The brain itself is covered by the tough and inelastic dura, and both the brain and its coverings are surrounded by the skull. If the blood pressure within the cerebral vessels rises significantly, serious consequences will ensue.

In short, the blood supply to the brain must be steady and the pressure must be maintained within a relatively narrow range. What are the mechanisms which assure these results?

REGULATION OF CEREBRAL CIRCULATION

We have already examined many factors which regulate the general circulation. Any change in the general circulation will be reflected in the cerebral blood flow. But in addition there are specific mechanisms initiated within the brain itself. Thus we may speak of the cerebral circulation as being regulated by (1) **extrinsic** and (2) **intrinsic mechanisms.**

Extrinsic Control   Figure 16-4 shows that the common carotid arteries bifurcate into the internal and external branches in the neck. It will be recalled that the extremely important carotid sinus and bodies are located at this junction. In other words, the pressoreceptors and chemoreceptors are strategically located so as to be able to guard the cerebral circulation. These receptors test the pressure and analyze the chemical composition of the blood just before it enters the brain. Any deviation from the normal is in this way detected, and rapid and appropriate alterations are made which result in a return to normal values.

For example, when man assumes the upright position, gravity draws the blood away from the brain and tends to pool it in the lower extremities. This trend, if unchecked, will deprive the brain of sufficient oxygen

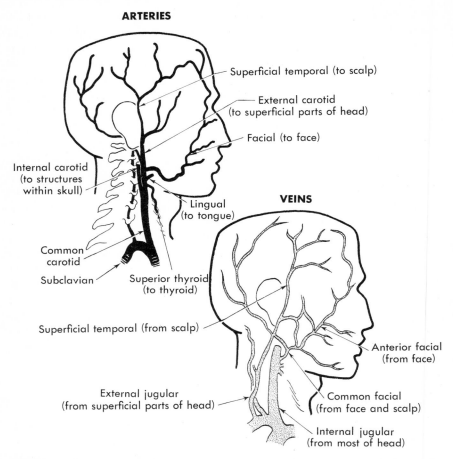

ARTERIES

Superficial temporal (to scalp)

External carotid
(to superficial parts of head)

Facial (to face)

Internal carotid
(to structures
within skull)

Lingual
(to tongue)

VEINS

Common
carotid

Subclavian

Superior thyroid
(to thyroid)

Superficial temporal (from scalp)

Anterior facial
(from face)

External jugular
(from superficial parts of head)

Common facial
(from face and scalp)

Internal jugular
(from most of head)

FIG. 16-4 Diagrammatic representation of the arteries and veins supplying the head and neck.

and the individual will quickly lose consciousness. However, before this situation occurs, the pressoreceptors in the carotid and aortic sinuses fire warning signals into the medulla. Through appropriate nervous pathways, these impulses are conducted to the heart and to all the arterioles throughout the body. Heart rate is increased, which tends to augment cardiac output, and the peripheral resistance becomes greater. The combination of higher cardiac output and greater peripheral resistance elevates the blood pressure and so overcomes the force of gravity, thus maintaining the cerebral blood supply within normal limits.

Likewise, if for any reason the oxygen concentration in the blood should diminish, and this may follow various pulmonary disorders, the chemoreceptors in the carotid and aortic bodies increase cardiac output and peripheral resistance. As a result, more blood flows through the brain. And so, even though each unit of blood is deficient in oxygen, more units reach the brain and compensate for oxygen deficiency.

Intrinsic Control   Between the brain and the skull, there is a small space which separates the two structures. This is referred to as the **intracranial space,** and the pressure therein is termed the **intracranial pressure.** Under abnormal conditions, the intracranial pressure may increase significantly. For example, in a disease commonly referred to as "water on the brain" **(hydrocephalus),** the intracranial pressure may be unusually great. If the blood pressure were to remain within normal limits, no blood could flow through the cerebral vessels because they would be occluded by the greater external force. But by a combination of intrinsic and extrinsic factors, this fatal result is prevented. As the intracranial pressure increases, the blood flow through the brain will be impaired and carbon dioxide will accumulate. This substance, as has already been pointed out, has two effects. First, it will cause the cerebral arterioles to dilate, though if the intracranial pressure is great they may be prevented from dilating. However, the CO_2 also impinges upon the vasoconstrictor center and produces a generalized increase in peripheral resistance throughout the body. This elevates the blood pressure and serves to force the blood through the cerebral vessels despite the increased intracranial pressure. In other words, by this mechanism any increase in intracranial pressure evokes a comparable rise in cerebral blood pressure. Consequently, the blood pressure tends to remain higher than intracranial pressure, and a continuous cerebral blood flow is assured.

Carbon dioxide, acting on the brain, has still another effect. It will be learned later that this substance is a powerful respiratory stimulant. As respiration increases, the venous return to the heart is augmented, as outlined in the previous chapter. This increased venous return elevates cardiac output. Thus, as a result of the accumulation of CO_2 within the brain, the peripheral resistance and the cardiac output are raised. The resulting higher blood pressure restores the cerebral blood flow to within normal limits.

In healthy young adults, in the supine position, the cerebral blood flow normally is about 55 ml per 100 gm of brain per minute. Thus for a brain of average weight, 750 ml per minute of blood flows through the cerebral circulation.

CEREBROSPINAL FLUID

Anatomical Considerations   The brain is covered by three thin layers collectively called the **meninges,** a term derived from *meninx,* meaning "a membrane." Actually, there are three membranes. There is a very delicate covering closely adherent to the brain substance called the **pia mater.** The outer, tough, inelastic layer is the **dura mater,** and between these two is a weblike membrane appropriately termed the **arachnoid.** The space between the pia and the arachnoid is referred to as the **subarachnoid space.** This cavity is continuous with a similar one which surrounds the spinal cord. The subarachnoid space is filled with a fluid known as the **cerebrospinal fluid (CSF).**

Function   The cerebrospinal fluid serves at least two important functions. First, it acts as an elastic protective covering which surrounds the delicate nervous tissues. This thin layer of fluid which envelops the brain and spinal cord serves as a cushion and buffers it against trauma. Second, the cerebrospinal fluid can change in volume. This is extremely important because, as previously pointed out, the skull is inelastic and therefore any pressure changes within the cranium may subject the brain to possible damage. However, the volume of cerebrospinal fluid may alter over a considerable range and thus serve to compensate for other intracranial volume changes. Here, then, is a mechanism which functions to maintain intracranial pressure within the normal safe range.

Production and Fate   There are four large brain cavities termed **ventricles.** Projecting into each of the lateral ventricles is a mass of tissue richly supplied with capillaries. These masses are termed **choroid plexuses.** The best available experimental evidence indicates that the cerebrospinal fluid is formed by these plexuses. However, there are good reasons to believe that the CSF is not simply a filtrate of the blood plasma. No doubt some of it forms as tissue fluid does elsewhere in the body, that is, as a resultant between the blood pressure on the one hand and the osmotic attraction of the proteins on the other. But the larger part of the cerebrospinal fluid appears to be formed by an active secretory process of the cells of the choroid plexus.

There are two major reasons for concluding that CSF is, at least partially, formed by an active process: (1) CSF and plasma differ markedly in composition and (2) if the circulation of CSF is blocked, truly high pressures develop. A study of the CSF reveals that some substances do not penetrate the cerebral capillary walls at all while others do so only very slowly. Thus a barrier between the blood and brain tissue has been envisioned. It is commonly referred to as the **blood-brain barrier.** The mechanism by which these capillaries differ, in this respect, from others throughout the body is not known.

The blood-brain barrier functions to protect the extremely sensitive neural tissue. It prevents a wide variety of substances, potentially injurious to neural tissue from passing. On the other hand, it maintains, probably by active secretion, the all important ionic concentration of the fluid bathing the neural tissue. As is to be expected, water and the respiratory gases move through the barrier readily.

The cerebrospinal fluid circulates through the ventricles and the subarachnoid space ultimately to be returned to the venous blood. The arachnoid is equipped in places with granulations, termed **arachnoidal granulations,** also called **arachnoid villi.** They are prolongations of the arachnoid layer through the dura into the superior sagittal sinus and into the parasinusoidal spaces (Fig. 16-5). The arachnoid villi are the major site of fluid transfer from the arachnoid space into the venous system. Because the sinuses cannot collapse, in the upright position of man the pressure within the sinuses must be negative. It is, therefore, less than the hydrostatic pressure of the CSF and thus fluid moves from the arachnoid space into the sinuses. It is probably a purely passive process.

The total amount of cerebrospinal fluid in man is difficult to calculate, but it is estimated to be about 125 ml, that is, just about a cupful.

Abnormalities The most serious result of abnormalities in the circulation of the cerebrospinal fluid is a condition termed **hydrocephalus.** As the term indicates, this is a condition of excessive fluid within the cranium. It may result from: (1) overproduction of cerebrospinal fluid, (2) an obstruction to the circulation of the fluid, or (3) inadequate absorption. In any case, the fluid accumulates in the ventricles and creates considerable pressure which progressively destroys the brain tissue. In children, and this condition occurs most frequently in young ones, the pressure may become so great as actually to enlarge the skull.

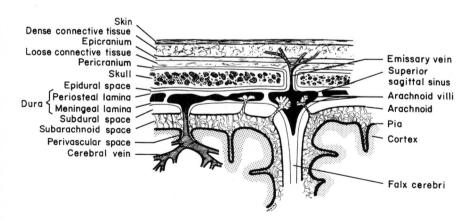

FIG. 16-5 Relationship of the meninges, the arachnoid villi, and the dural sinuses. Cerebrospinal fluid circulates in the subarachnoid space and then returns to the venous blood via the arachnoid villi. (From E. L. House, and B. Pansky, "A Functional Approach to Neuroanatomy," McGraw-Hill, 1960. Used by permission.)

HEADACHES

The problem of headache necessarily leads one through an endless maze of physiology, medicine, and psychiatry. A complete review of the subject is clearly not indicated in this text, but there are some types of headaches which are related to alterations in the cerebral circulation and can therefore be profitably mentioned at this time.

Arterial Dilatation   The dilatation or enlargement of the arteries both within and without the skull may cause headache. It has been shown that if the vessels which supply the scalp dilate, the pain-sensitive and inelastic tissue which makes up the scalp is stretched, thus producing the characteristic pain of a headache. Likewise, if the large vessels which supply the brain itself dilate, the pain-sensitive tissue is stretched, and again this may result in headache.

The causes of arterial dilatation are too numerous to discuss. It is this type of headache which can be most successfully alleviated by drugs such as aspirin.

Intracranial Pressure   Headaches are very commonly experienced in cases of elevated intracranial pressure. However, there is reasonably good evidence to indicate that the pain is not due to the raised pressure per se. Pain customarily seems to result from stretching tissue, and the elevated pressure beneath the skull would tend to compress rather than stretch such tissues. The explanation seems to be that the mechanism which causes the raised pressure also produces the pain. For example, if a tumor were to develop within the brain substance and grow, it would stretch the tissues and cause pain. It would, at the same time, raise the intracranial pressure. But in this instance it would be a mistake to say that the pain is caused by the elevated intracranial pressure.

High Blood Pressure   People who suffer from hypertension have frequent and sometimes continuous headaches. The mechanism of such pain is probably twofold. In the first place, the elevated pressure stretches the vessels and the pain-sensitive tissues which surround them. In the second place, high blood pressure is associated with increased intracranial pressure. This latter pressure may stretch the arachnoid and give rise to pain.

PULMONARY CIRCULATION

ANATOMY OF PULMONARY VESSELS

The blood is pumped by the right ventricle into the pulmonary artery (Fig. 16-6). This artery immediately bifurcates into two main branches, one of which passes to the left lung and the other to the right lung.

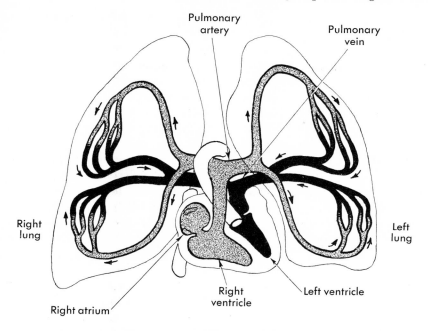

FIG. 16-6   Diagrammatic representation of the pulmonary circulation.

These branches, in turn, arborize into smaller arteries and arterioles and finally the typical network of capillaries. The pulmonary capillaries then re-form into venules and veins, and finally the large pulmonic vein enters the left atrium of the heart. It can be seen that the pulmonic circulation is a separate, lesser system consisting of two small trees, the pulmonic arterial and venous trees.

PULMONARY BLOOD PRESSURE

In the normal, healthy man, it is obvious that the same amount of blood must flow through the pulmonic system per minute as flows through the greater or systemic circulation. It was seen that the left side of the heart pumps over 5 liters of blood per minute. Thus the right ventricle must eject a comparable amount. In view of the fact that cardiac output is one of the major determinants of blood pressure, it may be imagined that the pulmonic arterial blood pressure would be about the same as the systemic arterial blood pressure. But this is not the case. The pulmonary blood pressure is very low. In the pulmonic artery, the systolic pressure is about 25 mm Hg, and the diastolic pressure is usually close to 10 mm Hg.

The first conclusion to be drawn from these facts is that the peripheral resistance in the pulmonic circulation is considerably less than it is in the systemic circulation. This must be so because the arterial blood pressure is determined by (1) cardiac output and (2) peripheral resistance. Since cardiac output in both systems is identical, it must follow that the peripheral resistance in the lungs is far less than elsewhere in the body.

There is yet another observation to be made from these same data. Although the cardiac output in both sides is the same, the pulse pressure (the difference between the systolic and diastolic pressures) is quite different. This we find to be about 40 mm Hg (120 − 80) in the general circulation, but only about 15 mm Hg (25 − 10) in the pulmonic system. As already discussed in detail, the pulse pressure reflects three factors: (1) cardiac output, (2) peripheral resistance, and (3) the elasticity of the vessels. We have seen that the cardiac output of both sides of the heart is identical. We have concluded that the peripheral resistance in the lungs is low. The conclusion that the elasticity is markedly greater in the pulmonic system than it is elsewhere becomes inescapable. The elasticity, it will be recalled, buffers the systolic and supports the diastolic pressure. The greater the elasticity, the less will be the rise in pressure during the ejection of blood, and the fall during diastole will also be diminished. These results are dramatically exemplified by the pulmonary system.

In view of the fact that the mean pulmonary artery pressure is less than 20 mm Hg and the pressure of the blood returning to the left atrium is close to 0 mm Hg, it becomes obvious that the hydrostatic pressure in the pulmonary capillaries must be lower than it is in other capillary beds of the body. A value of 7 mm Hg for the pulmonary capillary pressure is probably an accurate estimate. The osmotic pressure of the blood flowing through the pulmonary system, however, is the same as elsewhere, that is, about 26 mm Hg. It can, therefore, be easily calculated that the blood osmotic pressure dominates and results in movement of fluid into the pulmonary capillary throughout its length. This serves as a highly important protective mechanism. Because of these pressure gradients, fluids that inadvertently enter the lungs diffuse into the pulmonary capillaries.

There are conditions, however, in which the pulmonary pressure becomes elevated (see below). When this pressure exceeds the osmotic pressure of the blood, conditions are reversed and fluid now leaves the capillaries to accumulate in the thorax. This condition is termed **hydrothorax.**

Intrathoracic Pressure   The alterations in intrathoracic pressure as a result of respiration markedly influence pulmonary blood flow and pressure. It will be remembered that during forceful inspiration the intrathoracic pressure is lowered and that this encourages blood to flow from the venae cavae into the right side of the heart. As a result, more blood is pumped by the right side of the heart. But, at the same time, the lungs are expanded, and consequently the pulmonary vessels are stretched, thereby greatly increasing their capacity. So, although more blood is pumped into the pulmonary system, the greatly increased capacity causes a sharp depression in pulmonic blood pressure, and very little blood enters the left side of the heart during inspiration. In other words, during inspiration the blood pools in the pulmonary vessels. But during expiration the lungs decrease in size, and this reservoir is therefore squeezed into the left side of the heart, thereby elevating the output of the left ventricle. If one then determines arterial blood pressure, he will find that it varies and that these oscillations may be related to breathing. Figure 16-7 shows that during inspiration the pressure progressively falls, then during expiration it rises. These findings are consistent with the mechanisms just described.

Pulmonary-vasomotor Activity   The arteries and arterioles of the pulmonary system contain a layer of smooth muscle and are innervated by the autonomic nervous system. In addition to these anatomical observations, there is also physiological evidence that the pulmonic vessels are capable of vasomotor changes. Actually, however, these alterations seem to be of little importance to the pulmonary circulation. The great elasticity of the vessels and the changes which occur as a result of respiration seem to outweigh any possible vasomotor alterations.

Resistance of the Left Side of the Heart   The normal left side of the heart easily accommodates as much blood as is presented to it. However,

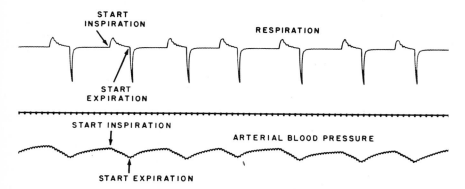

FIG. 16-7   Influence of respiration on arterial blood pressure. Upper record shows respiration recorded using a pneumotrachograph. Lower tracing is the arterial blood pressure. The frequency response of the amplifier was reduced and the sensitivity increased; thus the systolic and diastolic variations are markedly dampened and the respiratory variations exaggerated to show clearly the rise with inspiration and the fall during expiration.

if the left ventricle is failing, it contracts feebly, leaving a large residue in the ventricle at the end of each systole. Hence, there is a resistance to the flow of blood from the pulmonary veins into the left side of the heart. Blood slowly but steadily pools in the lungs. For example, let us assume that normally 70 ml of blood enter the left side of the heart but now, as a result of a residue, only 69 ml can enter. This leaves 1 ml in the pulmonary system, but after 10 beats it is 10 ml, and after 100 beats it is 100 ml. This pooling of blood increases the pulmonary pressure. Consequently, the normal quantity of blood is forced into the left side of the heart, but the pool remains in the pulmonary system. In other words, the pulmonic pressure has been elevated. And so it is found that, as the left side of the heart grows weaker and weaker, the pulmonary pool and pressure progressively increase.

The same result will be obtained by any abnormality in the left side of the heart which exerts resistance to the flow of blood from the pulmonary system into the heart. Such a condition, for example, could be mitral stenosis, that is, a narrowing of the mitral valve which lies between the left atrium and the left ventricle.

HEPATIC AND SPLENIC CIRCULATION

The circulation of blood through the liver, spleen, and kidneys has specific peculiarities which make it advisable to discuss these organs individually. Here only the hepatic and splenic circulation will be considered. In the section concerned with excretion, the dynamics of blood flow through the kidneys will be studied.

THE LIVER

The hepatic circulation is unusual in that it receives both arterial and venous blood. The arterial blood enters via the **hepatic artery.** The **portal vein** brings venous blood from the splanchnic areas (Fig. 16-8). In the human subject it has been estimated that the combined blood flow through the liver is approximately 1,400 ml per minute, which is close to 25 per cent of the cardiac output. More detailed studies indicate that about 20 per cent of the blood enters the liver through the hepatic artery and 80 per cent via the portal vein. Apparently there is a sensitive compensatory mechanism which decreases the volume in one system when that in the other increases. More important, it has been demonstrated that for short periods the combined inflow may markedly exceed, or fall below, the volume drained by the hepatic veins. These observations indicate that there are vasomotor changes within the liver which, in effect, control the volume of blood therein contained at any particular time.

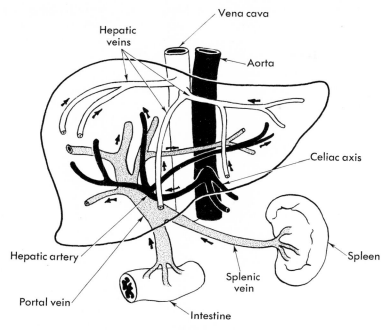

FIG. 16-8 Diagrammatic representation of the hepatic and splenic circulation.

In addition, the hepatic artery is capable of vasomotor alterations. Thus, there are apparently reflex mechanisms available which can strikingly and rapidly alter the liver blood volume. Since this large organ holds over a liter of blood, variations in its volume exert important effects on the general circulation. For years it has been known that as the heart progressively fails the liver enlarges because of the accumulation of blood. This reaction has always been considered to be due to the elevated venous pressure. The impression now, however, is that the hepatic pooling may be due to reflex adjustments which serve to remove a large volume of blood from the general circulation and, in this way, reduce the burden on the failing heart. The reflex mechanisms responsible for liver circulatory adjustments have still to be defined, but the impression is growing that they may play a more important role in general circulatory dynamics than heretofore has been ascribed to them.

The interesting aspect of the hepatic circulation is that the hydrostatic pressure in the liver capillaries must be very low. The resistance in the hepatic arterioles must be very high. This follows from the fact that blood enters the hepatic artery at a mean pressure of about 90 mm Hg.

But by the time the junction of the hepatic and portal blood is reached the pressure is lower than that of the portal system; otherwise there could be no portal flow. In the portal vein the pressure is usually less than 10 mm Hg; in the hepatic veins it is close to zero. The pressure in the liver capillaries, then, can hardly be more than 5 mm Hg. As in the lungs, this low hydrostatic pressure should permit the blood osmotic pressure to attract fluid into the circulation along the entire length of the capillary. However, the liver capillaries are so permeable that protein readily moves through their walls. This reduces the osmotic pressure so low that fluid does not move into the circulation.

THE SPLEEN

It has just been emphasized that the liver represents an important blood-storage depot. The spleen serves a similar function. Just how large the splenic reserve is in man is not accurately known. However, it has been calculated that the spleen can contribute about 250 ml of blood to the general circulation during severe exercise. Under these conditions the total blood volume is found to increase between 25 and 30 per cent. In other words, well over a liter of blood is added to the circulation. This volume of blood is drawn from the various blood stores in the liver, spleen, great veins, skin, and perhaps the lungs.

Alterations in splenic volume are brought about in a manner considerably different from that noted elsewhere. The capsule surrounding the organ contains smooth muscle innervated by the sympathetic nervous system. Activation of these fibers results in contraction of the capsule so that the spleen is squeezed and the contained blood forced into the draining veins. Pressures up to 100 mm Hg have been recorded in the splenic veins under such conditions. Splenic contraction occurs in response to hemorrhage, the administration of some anesthetic agents, and following emotional bouts, as well as in response to other forms of stress. Apparently, an effective stimulus for splenic contraction is either a fall in blood pressure or hypoxemia. If the carotid sinus and bodies are denervated, there is no response. Conversely, it has been demonstrated that a rise in pressure causes enlargement of the spleen which is a passive process probably brought about by the reflex dilatation of the splenic arterioles and constriction of the veins.

The blood which leaves the spleen is very rich in formed elements. Thus, following severe hemorrhage, the fluid component of the blood is replenished because of the pressure alterations between the capillaries and the tissue spaces. The formed-element portion is returned toward normal by splenic concentration. The question arises as to how the spleen concentrates the blood in this manner. It is thought that the squeezing action of the capsule serves this purpose. Rhythmic splenic contractions occur normally, at least in lower animals and presumably in man as well. If there is concurrent splenic venous contraction, the output from the spleen would remain constant, but the internal splenic pressure would be markedly elevated. It is thought that this high pressure serves to filter the fluid out of the blood, leaving a cell-free residue. The filtered fluid is ultimately returned to the circulation via lymphatic drainage.

SUMMARY

The **heart** muscle is supplied by **two coronary arteries** which spring from the aorta close to the aortic valve. These are **end arteries.** The **coronary veins** return the blood to the heart chambers by the **coronary sinus,** the **anterior cardiac veins,** and the **Thebesian veins.** The amount of blood which flows through the coronary vessels per unit time depends on (1) the size of the vessels and (2) arterial pressure. The caliber of the coronary vessels is controlled by (1) the nervous system, (2) chemical constituents of the blood, and (3) mechanical factors. Occlusion of a coronary blood vessel by spasm or a blood clot deprives the area supplied by that vessel of oxygen and produces an **infarct.** Consequently, a greater load is placed upon the remaining healthy cardiac muscle. Normal coronary blood flow is 250 ml per minute.

The blood supply to the **brain** is regulated by (1) **intrinsic** and (2) **extrinsic** mechanisms. The carotid and aortic sinuses stand guard over the entrance to the cranial vault. Any pressure change evokes reflex cardiac and vasomotor activity which functions to return the pressure to within the normal range. The carotid and aortic bodies are sensitive to the chemical composition of the blood and thus assure that the oxygen content of the blood which flows to the brain is adequate. If the **intracranial pressure** increases, cerebral blood flow is diminished and carbon dioxide accumulates. Thus, generalized vasoconstriction and local vasodilatation occur. Normal cerebral blood flow is about 750 ml per minute.

The brain is covered by **meninges,** which consist of a **pia mater,** the **arachnoid,** and the **dura mater.** Between the pia and arachnoid is the **cerebrospinal fluid.** This fluid functions to cushion the brain and also serves to maintain constant cranial volume. The cerebrospinal fluid is formed by the **choroid plexus.** The fluid flows slowly through the brain and around the brain and spinal cord and is absorbed into the venous blood, thus forming a cerebral extravascular circulation. Excessive production, obstruction to the circulation, or inadequate absorption of the fluid leads to **hydrocephalus. Headaches** are usually caused by stretching of cerebral pain-sensitive tissues.

The **pulmonary blood pressure** averages about 25 mm Hg systolic and 10 mm Hg diastolic. The low mean pressure indicates that the pulmonary peripheral resistance is less than in the greater circulatory tree. The low pulse pressure signifies that the elasticity of the pulmonary system is very great. Pulmonary flow varies markedly with respiration. As a result, arterial blood pressure falls during inspiration and rises during expiration.

The **hepatic circulation** is unique in that it receives both arterial and venous blood. The arterial blood enters via the hepatic artery, the venous through the **portal vein.** These vessels may constrict or dilate and thus alter the volume of blood held within the liver sinusoids. Accordingly, this large organ plays a major role in circulatory dynamics, since it can withdraw or add relatively large quantities of blood to the general circulation. The **spleen** possesses a somewhat similar function. It too can add blood to the circulating blood volume. But more important, the blood from the spleen is very rich in cells. Therefore, following hemorrhage, contraction of the spleen helps to restore not only the volume, but also the formed elements.

QUESTIONS

1. Describe the factors that control coronary circulation.
2. Why does coronary flow vary during the cardiac cycle?
3. Discuss the mechanisms that regulate cerebral circulation.
4. Trace the course of the cerebrospinal fluid.
5. Why are the pressures in the pulmonary artery different from those in the aorta?
6. How do the liver and spleen influence circulatory dynamics?

SUGGESTED READING

Brauer, R. W., "Liver Circulation and Function," *Physiol. Rev.,* 43:#1, 115–213, January 1963.

Lassen, N. A., "Cerebral Blood Flow and Oxygen Consumption in Man," *Physiol. Rev.,* 39:#2, 183–238, April 1959.

Ratcliff, J. D., "Circulation of the Blood," *Today's Health,* 35:#1, 24–25, January 1957.

Sevelius, G., "Coronary Artery Blood Flow," *Prog. Cardiovasc. Dis.,* 5:#1, 19–31, July 1962.

Willman, V. L., "Anatomy and Physiology of the Heart in Congenital Heart Disease," *Am. J. Nursing,* 60:#2, 190–195, February 1960.

PART

Respiratory System

Mechanisms of Breathing

17

THE TERMS RESPIRATION AND BREATHING are *not* synonymous. Strictly speaking, breathing is only a part of respiration. The familiar movements of the chest and the diaphragm, and the resultant flow of air into and out of the lungs, are properly included in the category of breathing. Respiration, however, is more inclusive. The study of respiration considers (1) the movement of air into the lungs, (2) the passage of oxygen from the lungs into the pulmonary blood, (3) the transportation of oxygen by the blood to all the cells of the body, (4) the utilization of oxygen and the production of carbon dioxide by the cells, (5) the carriage of carbon dioxide by the blood to the lungs, (6) the passage of this gas from the blood into the lungs, (7) the movement of air out of the lungs.

Respiration is conveniently divided into two phases: (1) **external** and (2) **internal** respiration (Fig. 17-1). The latter is concerned only with the utilization of oxygen and the production of carbon dioxide and other metabolites by the cells and, therefore, is also referred to as **cellular respiration.** External respiration, on the other hand, includes all the other steps just listed. In this section, very little will be said about internal respiration, since it is a highly complex and very specialized subject. Our attention will be focused upon breathing and the chemical means by which the respiratory gases are transported by the blood and then released to the tissue cells.

It has been emphasized many times that respiration and circulation are, in essence, one system dedicated to a single purpose. That purpose is to deliver an adequate supply of oxygen to the tissues and to remove the products of metabolism. A moment's reflection will convince the reader that respiration and circulation are completely interdependent; one cannot function successfully without the other. Only for the purpose of clarity are they considered separately.

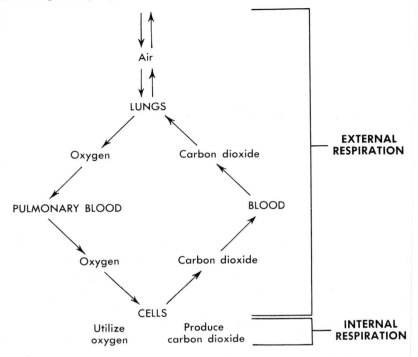

FIG. 17-1 External and internal respiration. Internal respiration involves all the intracellular processes.

BREATHING APPARATUS

The breathing organs include much more than just the lungs. The lungs are large, elastic sacs, but they possess no capacity of independent movement. Thus it is that, for expansion and contraction, other structures are needed. Therefore, it is necessary to consider (1) **the lungs and accessory equipment** and (2) **the thoracic cage.**

LUNGS

Figure 17-2 demonstrates the lungs of man in their anatomical relationship to the heart and the thoracic cage. It can be seen that there are two lungs, one on each side. They are extremely elastic and, when examined in the living state, feel somewhat like a sponge. They occupy by far the major part of the thorax. The heart is considerably smaller and lies between the lungs.

Pleura A fine, moist, glistening membrane covers the outer surfaces of the lungs. This membrane not only envelops the lungs but also serves as the inner lining of the thoracic cage (Fig. 17-2). As the thoracic cage and lungs move during the inspiratory movements, the two layers of this membrane slide against one another. The area between these two pleural layers is called the **intrapleural space.**

Accessory Structures   In order for air to enter the lungs, it must first traverse the nose and sometimes the mouth. In either case, the air ulti-

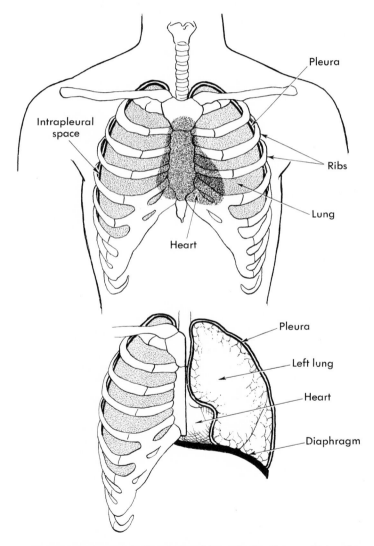

FIG. 17-2   Anatomical relationships of the lungs. Note the intrapleural space.

mately passes through the **pharynx.** The nose is the preferred route, because the nasal passages are particularly designed for this purpose. The nasal openings are lined with tiny hairlike structures called **cilia.** These hairy projections trap particles of dust and other foreign bodies and, by means of a wavelike action, actually move foreign products down into the throat to be ushered into the stomach and destroyed. In addition, the vascular system in the nasal passages is close to the surface and effectively arranged to warm the inspired air. Figure 17-3 shows that the air passes through the **larynx,** which is the voice box; the long cartilaginous tube called the **trachea;** the two major **bronchi,** one going to each lung; increasingly smaller and smaller bronchi and **bronchioles;** until the terminal, dead-end, saclike structures, the **alveoli,** are reached. The actual exchange of the respiratory gases takes place between the alveoli and the blood which flows through very fine neighboring capillaries. All the other structures just mentioned serve merely as air passageways; no gaseous transfer takes place in them.

Blood Supply   It will be recalled that the blood, to be oxygenated, is pumped by the right side of the heart into the pulmonary arteries. These vessels then arborize into progressively smaller branches until finally the capillaries are reached. Although each capillary is minute, there are so many of them that their combined surface area is truly tremendous. This

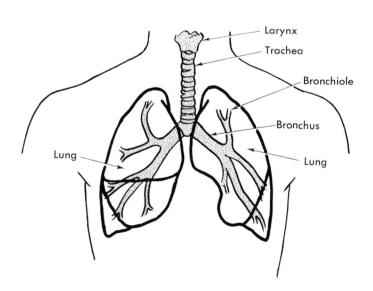

FIG. 17-3   The respiratory passageways. The bronchioles terminate in the tiny saclike alveoli.

great surface area, of course, makes possible a very rapid exchange of the respiratory gases. It has been estimated that the total surface area of the pulmonary capillaries is about 100 sq m, that is, approximately the floor space of a large room! The blood, after it has been oxygenated, is collected into the pulmonary veins and delivered to the left side of the heart.

But just as the heart receives little or no nourishment from the great quantity of blood which flows through its chambers, the lungs are also only poorly supplied by the blood coursing through the pulmonary vessels. The nutrition of the lung tissue is derived from oxygenated arterial blood delivered to the lungs by the **bronchial arteries.**

THORACIC CAGE

The thorax, or thoracic cage, as it is often called because of the characteristic architecture of the ribs, is essentially a closed chamber.

Ribs The ribs which form the walls of the thoracic cage are progressively smaller toward the neck. The ribs are joined to each other by two sets of muscles: (1) the **internal intercostal muscles** and (2) the **external intercostal muscles.**

There are 12 pairs of ribs. The upper 10 pairs sweep around front and join, either directly or indirectly through cartilaginous connections, the breastbone or **sternum.** The lower two pairs are free in front and are, accordingly, called **floating ribs.**

Diaphragm The diaphragm is a gently curving musculotendinous sheet which bounds the bottom of the thoracic cage (Fig. 17-2). It is attached peripherally to the lateral walls of the thorax, thus, in effect, converting the thoracic cage into a closed chamber.

The diaphragm, in its normal, relaxed position, curves upward. When the diaphragmatic muscles contract, the diaphragm is straightened. In other words, the central portion which curves up now is flat or even directed down. This has the effect of enlarging the thoracic cage. At the same time the abdominal viscera are squeezed by the descending diaphragm, and if the abdominal wall is not tensed it will bulge with each respiration.

Thoracic Movements Everyone is familiar with the thoracic movements associated with the breathing act. It is possible to control the respiratory movements and thus study the activity. First hold the chest wall rigid. Now take a slow breath. You will notice as you do this that there is a definite bulging of the abdomen. This is caused by the descent of the diaphragm, which compresses the abdominal viscera. On the other hand, it is possible to inspire without moving the abdomen, but in this case the chest must expand. If this activity is studied carefully, it will be seen that the chest moves out and up. There is actually a hingelike action of the ribs at their attachment to the spinal column behind (Fig. 17-4). In order to bring about this outward and upward movement of the ribs, several muscles must contract in a coordinated manner. These muscles are so arranged between the ribs that when they shorten the ribs are pulled up. It may be thought that contraction of these muscles would draw the two ribs, to which they are fixed, together. This does not occur, because the ribs are fixed at their attachment to the vertebral column and the external intercostal muscles are fixed to the upper rib closer to the vertebra than the lower attachment. Therefore, on a simple leverage principle, shortening of the muscle elevates the lower rib. In short, each lower rib is raised, and since the first rib is fixed the entire thoracic cage moves upward and outward. There are also short muscles which join each vertebra with the rib below it. Thus, when they shorten, the ribs are elevated. These two groups of muscles work together.

Quiet expiration is a passive process. During this act, the muscles just described simply relax, and the chest wall collapses, so to speak. But in some cases, expiration is quite forceful. One can readily drive the air out of the lungs with great force. To do this several muscles must contract.

It has been mentioned that contraction of the diaphragm pulls the dome down and thus enlarges the thoracic cage during inspiration. For forceful expiration, the abdominal muscles contract vigorously squeeze the abdominal contents, and thus force the diaphragm upward.

In brief, there are a series of muscles which can enlarge the thoracic

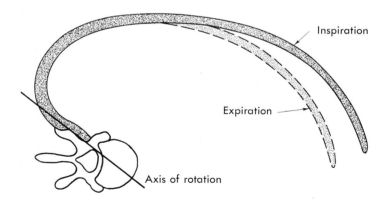

FIG. 17-4   Hinge action of the ribs. In this drawing, one is looking down on the spinal cord and ribs. During expiration the ribs are drawn up and by their rotary action also swing out. As a result, the thorax is enlarged.

cage and another group of muscles which can decrease its size. We shall now see what relation these changes have to breathing.

MOVEMENT OF AIR

In order to furnish the tissues with oxygen, the air first must be brought into the lungs. Then it passes into the pulmonary blood stream. At the same time, carbon dioxide leaves the blood and enters the lungs. To rid the lungs of this substance, the air in the lungs must be exhaled. The movement of air in and out of the lungs is one of the basic requisites of respiration.

INSPIRATION

We have noted that during inspiration many muscles contract which lower the diaphragm and move the chest wall forward and upward. The effect of both of these activities is to enlarge the size of the thoracic cavity.

Intrapleural Pressure   If Fig. 17-5 is analyzed, it will be seen that if the lungs could not expand, the enlargement of the thoracic cage would cause a sharp decrease in the pressure within the space between the lungs and the chest wall, the so-called intrapleural space. But the lungs are elastic and so, as soon as the intrapleural pressure falls as a result of thoracic enlargement, the lungs expand. There is another reason why the lungs follow the thorax, and that is **surface tension.** If two pieces of wet plate glass are placed together, it is very difficult to separate them. The force holding them is a manifestation of surface tension. The two moist pleural layers are together at the beginning of inspiration. When the thorax enlarges, these layers tend to pull away from one another, but the negative intrapleural pressure on the one hand and the surface tension on the other resist this divorce. Therefore, as the thorax expands so do the lungs.

When we speak of the intrapleural pressure as being negative, we mean that the pressure within the pleural space is less than atmospheric pressure. Atmospheric pressure at sea level is 760 mm Hg. During normal, quiet inspiration the pressure in the intrapleural space is about 754 mm Hg. To express it in its more common form, the intrapleural pressure during this type of breathing is about -6 mm Hg ($760 - 754$).

If inspiration is forced, deep, and rapid, as it is during heavy exercise, the intrapleural pressure throughout the inspiratory act may be as much as 40 mm Hg below atmospheric pressure (-40). This great negative pressure, it will be recalled, exerts a profound influence on venous return.

Intrapulmonary Pressure   Because of the negative intrapleural pressure and the surface tension, the lungs expand when the thorax enlarges. The

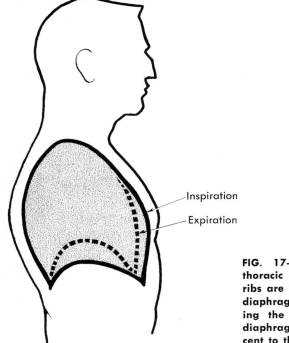

Inspiration

Expiration

FIG. 17-5 Respiratory changes in thoracic size. During inspiration the ribs are brought up and out and the diaphragm descends, thereby enlarging the thorax. Movements of the diaphragm contribute about 80 per cent to this enlargement.

increase in size of the lungs makes the pressure within, that is, the **intrapulmonary pressure,** fall below atmospheric presure. Since the lungs are connected with the outside through the respiratory passages, air now moves from the higher atmospheric pressure to the lower intrapulmonary pressure. In other words, the only reason air moves into the lungs during inspiration is because the pressure within the lungs is lower than the pressure of the outside air. The lungs and chest do not expand because of the entry of air; it is just the other way around. The air moves in because the chest and lungs expand.

Surface Tension   It has already been mentioned that there is an attraction between the two pleural layers. This attraction, or surface tension, keeps the layers from being separated. Thus, as the thorax expands, so do the lungs. But the inner surfaces of the lungs are moist too and thus should adhere, thereby opposing lung expansion, or, if the lungs are expanded, this inner surface tension should cause the lungs to collapse. It is now known that this does not occur because of the presence, within the lungs, of a substance, termed **surfactant,** which effectively decreases surface tension. Surfactant, which is thought to be a lecithin product, permits the inner surfaces of the lungs to separate during inspiration. During expiration, if surfactant were not present, the surface tension would become greater as the lung size decreased and finally the alveolar sacs would collapse altogether (**atelectasis**).

EXPIRATION

Passive Expiration   In normal, quiet breathing, no muscular activity is required for expiration. For this reason this phase is called passive. During inspiration the chest is raised and the diaphragm is lowered. If the muscles responsible for these movements cease to contract, and thus relax, the chest will fall and the intra-abdominal pressure will push the diaphragm back up to its resting position. As a result of these changes, the size of the thorax is diminished.

A decrease in the size of the thoracic cage increases the intrapleural pressure, and therefore the lungs, because of their inherent elasticity, return to their resting position. This raises the intrapulmonary pressure. When the intrapulmonary pressure becomes greater than the surrounding atmospheric pressure, the air will move out of the lungs. Again we see that the prime factor which governs the movement of air is a differential in pressures.

At this point, a clear distinction between intrapleural and intrapulmonary pressure must be made. The former refers to the pressure in the small space *between* the thoracic wall and the lungs, the latter to the pressure *within* the lungs. During normal, passive expiration, the intrapulmonary pressure rises above atmospheric pressure; it is for this reason that air is expired. But throughout expiration the intrapleural pressure remains subatmospheric. And at the end of expiration, before the next breath is drawn, the intrapleural pressure is about −3 or −4 mm Hg.

One will immediately wonder how the intrapulmonary pressure can increase above the intrapleural pressure. The elasticity of the lungs accounts for this difference. The lungs are actually too small for the thorax because they fail to grow as much during the developmental period as does the thorax. Therefore, even at the end of a normal expiration, the lungs remain partially stretched. This stretch tends to pull the lungs away from the thoracic wall. But as the lungs are drawn away, the intrapleural pressure decreases and creates a differential between intrapleural and intrapulmonary pressures. This differential at the end of expiration is about 3 or 4 mm Hg and is just equal to the force exerted by the elasticity of the lungs.

With these facts clearly in mind the findings expressed in Table 17-1 can be understood.

TABLE 17-1 Intrapleural and Intrapulmonary Pressures

	Intrapleural Pressure, mm Hg	Intrapulmonary Pressure, mm Hg
Quiet inspiration	—6	—3
Forced inspiration	down to —40	down to —37
Passive expiration	—3	+3
Forced expiration	up to +40	up to +40

Forced Expiration During exercise, expiration changes from a simple, passive movement to a very definite, strong, and forceful act. The various muscles already described come into play and pull the chest down and move the diaphragm up. As indicated in Table 17-1, the intrapleural pressure increases sharply. Thus, the intrapulmonary pressure rises and air is rapidly expelled.

Forced expiration is utilized not only in response to exercise but also to expel foreign objects from the respiratory passages, as in coughing. In this case the epiglottis (the cap, so to speak, over the major air passages) remains closed while the expiratory muscles are vigorously contracted (Fig. 17-6). Since air is temporarily prevented from leaving the lungs, both the intrapleural and intrapulmonary pressures are built up to their maximal levels. Then, suddenly, the glottis is opened and a blast of air rushes through the trachea, effectively ejecting any foreign object or mucous deposit which may be lodged therein.

Pneumothorax It has been noted that even at the end of expiration, in the resting position of the thorax, the lungs remain stretched so that the intrapleural pressure is below atmospheric pressure. Obviously, if an opening were to be made in the thoracic wall, air would rush into the pleural space. The term **pneumothorax** means "air in the thorax" or, more specifically, in the intrapleural space. Once air enters this space, there is no longer any counterforce exerted against the elasticity of the lungs, and they collapse.

Air may enter the thorax through the chest wall or through an opening in the lungs. It does not matter how air gets into the intrapleural space; the result is collapse of the lungs. A pneumothorax may occur accidentally, or it may be deliberately produced in the treatment of various pulmonary diseases, notably tuberculosis. So long as the pleural space is open to the atmosphere, the respiratory movements cannot cause the lung to expand. Therefore, this procedure allows the lung to rest and heal.

When the opening into the pleural space is closed surgically or heals, the air in the intrapleural space is slowly absorbed, and simultaneously the lung expands to its normal size and position. Now, once again, it can participate in breathing.

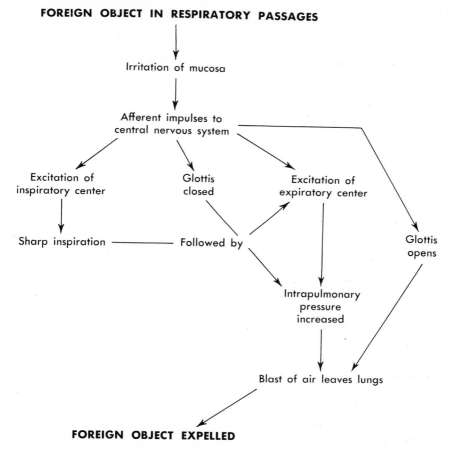

FOREIGN OBJECT IN RESPIRATORY PASSAGES

Irritation of mucosa

Afferent impulses to central nervous system

Excitation of inspiratory center

Glottis closed

Excitation of expiratory center

Sharp inspiration —————— Followed by

Glottis opens

Intrapulmonary pressure increased

Blast of air leaves lungs

FOREIGN OBJECT EXPELLED

FIG. 17-6   Cough reflex. The sequence of events essential for the expulsion of irritating substances in the respiratory passages.

QUANTITY OF AIR BREATHED

The quantity of air which passes through the lungs in one minute is termed the **ventilation.** The ventilation clearly is a product of the rate of breathing and the amount of air drawn in during each inspiratory effort. The usual breath contains about 500 ml of air. The average breathing rate is about 16 per minute. In other words, the ventilation under normal conditions is of the magnitude of about 8 liters per minute (16 × 500).

The quantity of air normally inspired with each breath is termed the **tidal volume.** It is easy to demonstrate that a considerably greater quantity of air than this can be inspired. Also, after the normal expiration ends, it is possible voluntarily to expel more air from the lungs. Therefore when we speak of the quantity of air breathed it is necessary to define the conditions. Table 17-2 shows the different values. It can be seen that

TABLE 17-2   LUNG VOLUMES

Residual volume	1,500 ml
Expiratory reserve volume (supplemental)	1,000 ml
Tidal volume	500 ml
Inspiratory reserve volume (complemental)	3,000 ml
Vital capacity	4,500 ml

even after a maximal expiratory effort some air still remains in the lungs. This air makes up the **residual volume.** It amounts to about 1,500 ml. Before the infant takes his first breath the lungs contain no air, but after that very first breath they forever hold a residue which is never expelled. This fact is the basis of a very important criminological procedure. It is thus possible to determine whether an infant was born dead or died after being born alive, simply by removing the lungs and placing them in water. If the lungs float they must contain air, which means that the child took at least one breath or, in other words, was born alive. If the infant was born dead, the lungs contain no air and will not float.

After a normal inspiration of about 500 ml, it is possible to draw into the lungs approximately an additional 3,000 ml of air. This extra air is termed the **inspiratory-reserve volume.** Likewise, after an average expiration, it is possible to expel an additional 1,000 ml from the lungs, the so-called **expiratory-reserve volume.**

Taking all these values together, it can be seen that, if one inspires all the air possible and then expels as much as possible, the quantity so expired will be about 4,500 ml (Table 17-2). The quantity of air expelled by a maximal expiration after the greatest inspiration is termed the **vital capacity.**

ROLE OF THE DIAPHRAGM

The importance of diaphragmatic movements in the movement of air is made clear when it is realized that the surface area of the diaphragm is about 270 cm². Accordingly, the diaphragm needs to descend only 1 cm in order to enlarge the thoracic capacity by 270 cm³. Normally, in quiet respiration, the diaphragm moves about 1.5 cm. In forced breathing it has a range of up to 7 cm. Since only about 500 ml of air move in quiet breathing, it can be calculated that diaphragmatic movements account for about 80 per cent of this volume.

COMPLIANCE

The lungs are elastic sacs. They can be stretched, they will resist stretch, and they recoil when released. The difference between the intrapleural and intrapulmonic pressures is termed the **transmural pressure.** Transmural pressure is really the pressure which exists across the wall of the lung. When the intrapleural pressure is lower than the intrapulmonic pressure, the lungs expand. The relationship between the change in transmural pressure and the change in lung volume is termed **compliance.** For example, in the normal, young adult, lung compliance is about 300 ml per mm Hg. This means that for each mm Hg of transmural pressure the lung size changes 300 ml.

In many disorders the elasticity of the lungs is altered, making it more difficult for them to expand. In such instances, the compliance decreases so that a transmural pressure of 1 mm Hg will change the lung volume less than the normal 300 ml.

DEAD SPACE

No exchange of oxygen or carbon dioxide takes place in the respiratory passageways from the nostrils to, but not including, the alveoli. The volume of air contained by these passageways is called the **anatomical dead space.** On the average, the anatomical dead space amounts to about 150 ml. Thus, if 500 ml of air are inspired, only about 350 ml reach the alveoli, where the exchange of gases occurs. During expiration the first 150 ml expired will be found, therefore, to contain the same percentage of the respiratory gases as does room air.

The anatomical dead space can vary only moderately (through bronchiolar contraction or dilatation). The **physiological dead space,** also called virtual or effective dead space, is defined as the space within the lungs and passageways which, just prior to expiration, contains air of the same composition as room air. The anatomical and physiological dead spaces are equal in the normal person. But should some of the alveoli become nonfunctional, then the physiological space would be larger.

The physiological dead space may be calculated if the concentration of one of the respiratory gases in the expired air and alveolar air, and the volume of the expired air are known. For example, if the amount of CO_2 in the alveolar air is 6 per cent, in the expired air 4 per cent, and the volume of expired air is 500 ml, then:

$$\frac{500}{6} = \frac{X}{4} = 334$$

Thus, 334 ml represents the quantity of alveolar air in the expired air. The physiological dead space is equal to $500 - 334$, or 166 ml.

It should be understood that the anatomical dead space can be increased by the use of tubes. For example, if one breathes through a tube with a capacity of several hundred ml, quite clearly the total dead space will be greater than the tidal volume, and unless great respiratory efforts are made, there will be no renewal of air in the alveoli.

Normal ventilation at rest is about 8,000 ml per minute. If the dead space is 150 ml, then alveolar ventilation will be 5,600 ml per minute (350 × 16). Ventilation is increased by faster or deeper breathing, or both. But at any ventilation, alveolar ventilation will be greater if the depth of breathing is increased rather than the rate. For example, if tidal volume is 500 ml and the rate 50 per minute, ventilation will be 25,000 ml per minute (500 × 50) and the alveolar ventilation will be 17,500 (350 × 50). But if the tidal volume is increased to 1562.5 and the rate is 16 per minute, then the ventilation is still 25,000 ml per minute (1562.5 × 16), however the alveolar ventilation becomes 22,600 (1412.5 × 16). Clearly, the best way to increase alveolar ventilation is by increasing the depth rather than the rate. On the other hand, deep breathing requires a larger energy output to overcome the elastic recoil of the lungs. In conclusion, greatest efficiency is obtained by increasing both rate and depth.

SUMMARY

The exchange of the gases oxygen and carbon dioxide between man and his environment is termed **respiration. External respiration** embraces a consideration of (1) the movement of air into the lungs, (2) the passage of oxygen from the lungs into the pulmonary blood, (3) the carriage of oxygen by the blood to all the cells of the body, (4) the transportation of carbon dioxide by the blood to the lungs, (5) the passage of carbon dioxide from the blood into the lungs, (6) the movement of air out of the lungs. **Internal respiration** is a study of the utilization of oxygen and the production of carbon dioxide by the cells. The movement of air into and out of the lungs is called **breathing.**

The **lungs** are large elastic sacs which almost fill the thoracic chamber. They are covered by the **pleura** which is reflected back over the inner surface of the thorax. Between the two pleural layers is the **intrapleural space.** Air traverses the **nose** and **mouth,** passes through the **pharynx, larynx, trachea, bronchi, bronchioles,** and finally reaches the **alveolar sacs** from which oxygen passes into the pulmonary blood system. Blood, to be oxygenated, is pumped to the lungs by the right side of the heart through the **pulmonary arteries.** After oxygenation, the blood returns to the left side of the heart via the **pulmonary veins.** The lungs receive nutrition by way of the **bronchial arteries.**

To move air into the lungs, it is necessary to increase the size of the thoracic cage. This lowers the **intrapleural pressure,** and the lungs expand, thereby decreasing the **intrapulmonary pressure.** The air then moves from the relatively higher atmospheric pressure to the lower-pressure area within the lungs. **Surfactant** lowers the surface tension within the lungs.

The **tidal volume** is about 500 ml. The **inspiratory-reserve volume** is approximately 3,000 ml. With maximal expiratory effort an additional 1,000 ml of air, the **expiratory-reserve volume,** may be forced out. There is always some air which remains in the lungs. It amounts to about 1,500 ml and is called the **residual volume.** The **vital capacity** is about 4,500 ml and is the quantity of air which can be expelled by a maximal expiration after a maximal inspiration.

The normal respiratory rate varies from 14 to 18, with an average of 16 per minute. The term **ventilation** is defined as the quantity of air which passes through the lungs in one minute. It is equal to the respiratory rate times the tidal volume (16 × 500), or about 8 liters, in the average man.

Compliance expresses the relationship between the change in **transmural pressure** and the change in lung volume. It is normally about 300 ml per mm Hg.

The **anatomical dead space** is the volume of air contained in the respiratory passageways in which no gas exchange occurs. The **physiological dead space** is the space in the respiratory system which contains unaltered air. Both the anatomical and physiological dead spaces average about 150 ml.

QUESTIONS

1. What is the difference between internal and external respiration?
2. Trace the route air must take in passing from the nose into the alveolar sacs of the lungs.
3. What is the difference between intrapleural and intrapulmonary pressure?
4. Why does air move into the lungs during inspiration?
5. What is meant by the term "vital capacity"?
6. How can compliance be determined in man?

SUGGESTED READING

Bendixen, H. H., Smith, G. M., and Mead, J., "Pattern of Ventilation in Young Adults," *J. Appl. Physiol.,* **19:**#2, 195–198, March 1964.

Clements, J. A., "Surface Tension in the Lungs," *Sci. American,* **207:**#6, 120–130, December 1962.

Fenn, W. O., "The Mechanism of Breathing," *Sci. American,* **202:**#1, 138–148, January 1960.

Kane, I. J., "The Lungs in Health and Disease," *Today's Health,* 34:#2, 42–45, February 1956.

Kory, R. C., Callahan, R., Boren, H. G., and Syner, J. C., "The Veterans Administration-Army Cooperative Study of Pulmonary Function. 1. Clinical Spirometry in Normal Men," *Am. J. Med.,* 30:#2, 243–258, February 1961.

Mead, J. "Mechanical Properties of Lungs," *Physiol. Rev.,* 41:#2, 281–330, April 1961.

Control of Breathing

18

WE HAVE SEEN THAT WITH NORMAL BREATHING about 8 liters of air are exchanged in the lungs each minute. At sea-level atmospheric pressure, this volume is enough to supply the body with oxygen and to eliminate the carbon dioxide. If an individual engages in very light exercise, such as reaching across the table for another helping, the actively contracting muscles produce more than their usual quantity of CO_2; this causes local dilatation in those particular muscles. Consequently, the blood flow in that region is increased. In addition, the active tissues may extract a larger volume of oxygen from the blood. These two mechanisms, (1) **greater local blood flow** and (2) **increased oxygen extraction,** usually prove adequate to supply the tissue needs. But if greater exercise is indulged in, such as running up a flight of stairs, such purely local adjustments do not suffice. It proves necessary to bring about not only all the changes in the cardiovascular system already discussed but also comparable adjustments in breathing. In other words, ventilation must be increased. It is the object of this chapter to analyze the mechanism by which breathing is controlled in man.

INVOLUNTARY CONTROL

It is general knowledge that breathing can be voluntarily controlled at least within broad limits. However, one does not ordinarily think about breathing, nor is it necessary to remind oneself to breathe. During sleep and even unconsciousness, breathing continues. During exercise, respiratory rate and depth increase quite automatically. In this chapter the involuntary mechanisms will be considered, and then we shall examine to what extent man can control his breathing voluntarily. Finally, abnormalities of breathing will be briefly discussed.

367

ANATOMICAL CONSIDERATIONS

Respiratory Nerves   The muscles utilized in inspiration and expiration are skeletal muscles. The axons which innervate the chest muscles arise from cell bodies which lie within the anterior-horn substance of the spinal cord and thus are **spinal nerves.** The **phrenic nerves** innervate the diaphragm. These unusual axons arise from cells in the anterior-horn substance up in the neck and descend throughout the chest to innervate the diaphragm. Precisely how this unique arrangement comes about is not within the scope of this text. Suffice it to say that during embryonic development the diaphragm is actually in the neck region and is innervated by spinal nerves which originate in that area. With further development, the diaphragm descends to its final position and brings its nerves with it.

Respiratory Center   In quiet breathing, only a few muscles of the thoracic cage are active. During more vigorous excursions, the expiratory muscles become more energetic. Finally, a degree of breathing may be reached in which even the facial and neck muscles participate. It is apparent that all these muscles must be coordinated in order to execute breathing in the most efficient manner. The center of coordination is called the **respiratory center.** This center consists of cells which give rise to axons which course to the nuclei of the cranial nerves in that region. In addition, other axons descend into the spinal cord and terminate on the cells of the phrenic and other spinal nerves. In other words, the respiratory center is similar to a central switchboard in a large building; it may send out impulses to a few or to many muscles.

The location of the respiratory center has been established in several different ways. In the first place, the brain of an animal may be sectioned (cut across), starting high and progressively cutting lower and lower. This technique demonstrates that it is possible to cut across the brain stem above the medulla and still have the animal survive and continue to breathe. If the section is made just below the medulla, at the point where the brain stem and the spinal cord join, then respiration is paralyzed and the animal dies. Secondly, it is possible, with the aid of very fine electrodes, to stimulate small areas of the brain. When such an exploration is carried out, a region is found which when stimulated causes typical respiratory movements. From such procedures it has been concluded that the respiratory center is located in the upper two-thirds of the medulla and extends up into the pons.

The concept of the respiratory center being a discrete, circumscribed cluster of specialized cells has been seriously questioned. There is little doubt that the medulla is essential to respiration, and it is the reticular formation that is intimately involved. But whether the part of the reticular formation concerned with respiration is specific for this function is not clear. Stimulation experiments indicate that one part of the medullary reticular formation is responsible for inspiration and another part for expiration. Thus it is the practice to speak of an inspiratory and an expiratory center. Recent evidence, however, indicates that the cells responsible for inspiration and expiration are intermingled. Anatomically, then, it is probably an error to visualize separate centers, but from a functional viewpoint this is permissible.

Rhythmicity Breathing, quite obviously, is rhythmic. But whether this rhythmicity is due to an inherent property of the respiratory center, or to factors which influence the respiratory center, is the question. For some time it was held that the center, if completely uninfluenced by extrinsic forces, produces **apneusis,** which is a sustained inspiration. This conclusion has been challenged by a demonstration that even when the center is completely isolated from all other possible influences, rhythmic breathing still continues. According, it has been postulated that the respiratory center possesses an inherent rhythmicity, a rhythmicity that can be markedly altered by extraneous factors. There is, however, no evidence for the presence of pacemaker neurons which possess an intrinsic rhythm. The characteristic rhythm is thought to be due to self re-excitation between the inspiratory and expiratory neurons.

Pneumotaxic Center In the brain stem, above the medulla, is another nest of cells which has been termed the **pneumotaxic center.** These cells give rise to very short processes which course down to the respiratory center. Likewise, there are short fibers from the respiratory center which are directed up to the pneumotaxic center. In brief, the two centers are interconnected, forming a closed circuit which, as we shall learn, is of considerable importance in hyperventilation.

REFLEX CONTROL

The respiratory center receives impulses from many areas of the body, including the cerebral cortex. Those from the cerebral cortex result in voluntary control of breathing. All others enter into reflex patterns.

Hering-Breuer Reflex The cells that make up the inspiratory center fire impulses to the inspiratory muscles, the thorax expands, and therefore so do the lungs. In the lungs there are receptors sensitive to stretch. Accordingly, as the lungs expand, these receptors fire more and more rapidly. The impulses so initiated are propagated by afferent neurons in the vagal nerves to the inspiratory center which, as a result, is inhibited (Fig. 18-1). Impulses may also go directly to the expiratory center to fire it. At any rate, inspiration ends and expiration occurs. This reflex was described first by Hering and Breuer in 1868.

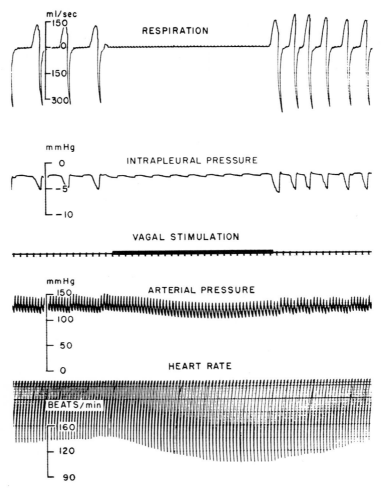

FIG. 18-1 Influence of vagal stimulation. To obtain this polygraph recording, the central end of the cut vagus was stimulated. Complete cessation of breathing resulted. Note small respiratory efforts in the intrapleural pressure record. However, these are too small to move air. Also note that during cessation of breathing, the cyclic variations in the arterial pressure are absent.

If the vagi are cut, rhythmic breathing continues, but it becomes slower and deeper (Fig. 18-2). When the reflex is functional, stimulation of the inspiratory center causes increased rate and depth of breathing. The greater inspiratory activity causes a rapid and strong inspiratory effort. And because of the stimulation, the inspiratory center is more diffi-

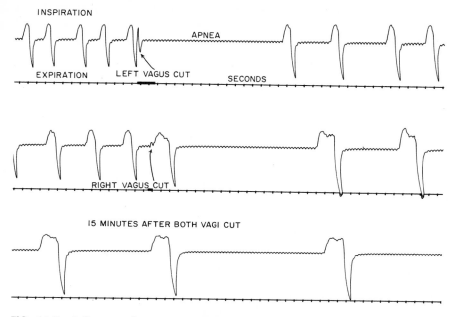

FIG. 18-2   Influence of vagotomy. Respiration becomes slower and deeper following section of both vagi.

cult to inhibit. Thus, the lungs must be stretched more before there is a sufficient barrage of impulses to stop inspiratory activity. The end result is faster and deeper breathing.

Pneumotaxic Reflex   It is thought that, when the inspiratory center fires, it not only sends impulses to the appropriate muscles but also directs impulses up short neurons to the pneumotaxic center. This center, in turn, is activated and sends inhibitory impulses down to the inspiratory center as well as stimulatory impulses to the expiratory center. As a result, inspiration is halted and forceful expiration follows.

The evidence indicates that in normal, quiet breathing the pneumotaxic center does not operate. Apparently it functions only in conditions which demand maximal ventilation. It may thus be regarded as an auxiliary mechanism, a second line of defense, to augment the Hering-Breuer reflex or to substitute for it if need be.

Carotid- and Aortic-body Reflexes   It will be recalled that in the carotid and aortic bodies there are receptors sensitive to changes in the chemical composition of the blood. As a result of the impulses initiated by these receptors, widespread cardiovascular changes are brought about. In addition, alterations in breathing occur.

The chemoreceptors are most sensitive to the O_2 content of the blood. If **hypoxemia,** that is, an abnormally low oxygen content of the blood, is present, these chemoreceptors are fired. The impulses are conducted to the respiratory center where they stimulate the inspiratory cells. Just as in the case of increased CO_2 stimulation, these cells cause a more rapid inspiration and, in combination with the Hering-Breuer reflex, bring about deeper breathing also. Thus, through the aortic- and carotid-body reflexes, ventilation is increased whenever hypoxemia exists. Carbon dioxide and an increase in acidity also stimulate the chemoreceptors.

Blood-pressure Reflexes   Just what role the pressoreceptors in the carotid and aortic sinuses play in the control of breathing remains conjectural. These receptors are extremely important in the regulation of circulation, but the evidence seems to indicate that under normal circumstances they have no influence upon breathing. It is true that, if the blood pressure is suddenly and sharply increased, by virtue of these pressoreceptors breathing will be inhibited or may cease entirely. But it is difficult to see what physiological purpose this mechanism serves.

Muscle Reflexes   Whenever a muscle contracts, the proprioceptors initiate impulses which are necessary for awareness of the position of a limb as well as for muscular coordination. These impulses also fire into the respiratory center and bring about an increase in ventilation. That this phenomenon is not due to a change in the chemical composition of the blood as a result of muscular contraction can be easily shown. In the first place, the movement of a small group of muscles in one limb will not cause demonstrable alteration in the blood chemistry. Secondly, the limb may be removed from the body, left connected only by the nerve, and even in this drastic preparation contraction of the limb muscle increases ventilation. Thus, even before there are changes in the venous blood pressure and prior to any alteration in the blood chemistry, ventilation is reflexly increased.

DIRECT CHEMICAL CONTROL

The inhalation of air containing 5 or 10 per cent CO_2 causes a striking increase in ventilation (Fig. 18-3). Hypoxemia also increases ventilation as does a change in the acidity of the blood. A change in the CO_2, O_2, or pH of the blood alters breathing not only because of their influence on the chemoreceptors in the carotid and aortic bodies but also because of a direct effect on the reticular formation.

Carbon Dioxide   There is normally only about 0.04 per cent carbon dioxide in the inspired air. No measurable alteration in ventilation occurs until the inspired air contains at least 1 per cent CO_2. When it contains 4 per cent, ventilation is doubled. At higher concentrations the ventila-

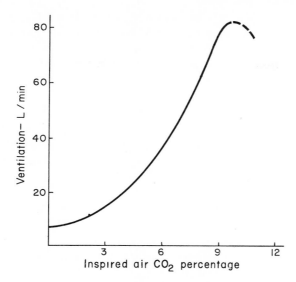

**FIG. 18-3 Influence of carbon dioxide on ventila-
tion. CO_2 in the inspired air in excess of about 10
per cent becomes intolerable or causes unconsciousness.**

tion increases very sharply until a maximum of about 80 or 90 liters per
minute is reached. Most individuals can tolerate about 10 per cent CO_2
in the inspired air, but higher concentrations produce great discomfort
and then depression and unconsciousness. Ultimately respiratory paralysis
will result and therefore the curve (Fig. 18-3) at this point falls sharply.

It is somewhat more meaningful to express ventilation in terms of the
partial pressure, P, of CO_2 in the blood. An increase of as little as 2.5
mm Hg doubles ventilation. The normal P_{CO_2} is 40 mm Hg. If this is
increased to 60 mm Hg, ventilation increases over tenfold.

When the P_{CO_2} is altered, the pH of the blood may be changed. For
some time it was debated as to whether the effective respiratory stimulus
is the alteration in CO_2 or the resultant change in pH. It is now generally
agreed that both alter respiratory center activity.

But just how CO_2 evokes increased ventilation is a major unanswered
question. CO_2 does not usually have a direct stimulatory function. In
addition, it has been found that the influence of CO_2 is markedly decreased during sleep. These observations suggest that there may be inhibition of the respiratory center and that CO_2 acts by depressing the neurons
responsible for the maintenance of this inhibition. In other words, it is
similar to the action of releasing a brake.

Acidity   If the acidity of the blood is increased so is ventilation. However, the quantitative aspects must be kept in mind. The maximum increase evoked by severe acidosis, that is, a blood pH of 7.0, is only 4 to 5 times normal. CO_2 can produce a tenfold increase. In addition, except in truly pathological states, the pH of the blood does not vary as extensively as depicted. Normally the blood pH is about 7.4 and it rarely falls below 7.3.

Oxygen   Hypoxemia actually depresses the respiratory center. Yet when the per cent oxygen in the inspired air is decreased, ventilation increases. This increase, however, is due completely to the activation of the carotid and aortic body chemoreceptors. When these receptors are denervated, hypoxemia results in decreased ventilation.

Cerebrospinal Fluid   If CO_2 is added to the cerebrospinal fluid, a striking increase in ventilation occurs. CO_2 readily passes the blood-brain barrier; thus any change in blood CO_2 is rapidly reflected in the CSF. It has been shown, however, that it is not the CO_2, per se, in the CSF that is responsible for ventilatory stimulation but rather the resultant change in CSF pH. Since the blood is effectively buffered, the normal shifts of CO_2 concentration do not change the pH greatly. But the CSF has no buffer systems; consequently there is a great change in pH when CO_2 is added. Thus it has been suggested that the ventilatory influence of CO_2 may depend upon the change in pH of the CSF. If this proves correct, it is no longer necessary to assume that CO_2 in the case of the respiratory center has a stimulatory effect but depresses all other tissues studied.

INTERACTIONS

Hypoxemia does not significantly influence ventilation until the P_{O_2} falls below about 60 mm Hg. But if this experiment is carried out while the P_{CO_2} is held constant, the inverse relationship between ventilation and arterial oxygen tension can be shown at P_{O_2} levels above 100 mm Hg. This means that when the P_{CO_2} is not controlled any increase in ventilation evoked by hypoxemia lowers the P_{CO_2} which then inhibits respiration.

The reverse experiment is also revealing, that is, one in which the sensitivity to changes in P_{CO_2} is studied at different P_{O_2} levels. As the P_{O_2} decreases, the sensitivity to P_{CO_2} increases. Of particular interest is the fact that all the lines come to a common origin at the base line, that is, zero ventilation (Fig. 18-4). This is the threshold value for P_{CO_2}. The threshold value is very close to the normal P_{CO_2}. If the P_{CO_2} is lowered below threshold value by hyperventilation, breathing ceases in the sleeping subject, or while under anesthesia. In most conscious subjects, however, breathing continues, which indicates that breathing is not only

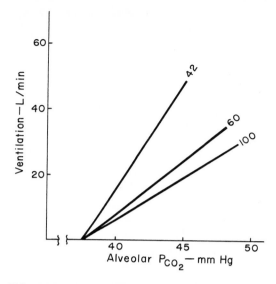

FIG. 18-4   Interaction of P_{CO_2} and P_{O_2} in the control of breathing. The numbers at the ends of the lines indicate the P_{O_2}. Note that the lower the P_{O_2}, the greater the increase in ventilation for any change in P_{CO_2}. (Reproduced, with permission, from B. B. Lloyd, M. G. M. Jukes, and D. J. C. Cunningham, *J. Exp. Physiol.,* **43**:214, 1958.)

under carbon dioxide control, but also depends upon cerebral activity.

The combined effect of hypoxemia and hypercapnia on chemoreceptor activity is greater than the sum of the two acting separately. It has been suggested that CO_2 affects the blood flow to the chemoreceptors. The carotid and aortic bodies have a copious blood flow. There are, however, shunts which can divert the blood away from the receptors. Thus, it is thought that when the P_{CO_2} rises there is dilatation of the shunt so less blood flows to the receptors, thereby resulting in stagnant hypoxemia. This would explain the CO_2 effect alone. When there is also low P_{O_2} plus limited blood flow to the receptors, the influence would be greatly exaggerated.

VOLUNTARY BREATHING

In the beginning of this chapter the statement was made that breathing can be controlled voluntarily, within limits. By that we mean that it is possible to hold one's breath, but not indefinitely. Likewise, one may volitionally hyperventilate, but this procedure also brings about changes which make it impossible to continue for a prolonged period.

BREATH HOLDING

It will prove very instructive if the reader will hold his breath as long as he can. First, it will become evident that there is a time limit. Second, if he will analyze the mechanisms which finally succeed in overcoming his voluntary effort, he will afford himself an excellent review of the devices which control breathing.

Voluntary Mechanism   There are numerous conditions which result in complete cessation of breathing, so-called **apnea**. But here we are concerned more with the arrest of breathing which is accomplished voluntarily. All volitional activity is initiated in the cerebral cortex. Accordingly, there must be neurons which course from the cerebral cortex to the respiratory center. Through these nerve routes it is possible to send impulses which will either inhibit or stimulate either the inspiratory or the expiratory cells in the respiratory center. In other words, it is possible to arrest breathing anywhere in the respiratory cycle. It is also quite simple to change one phase, such as expiration, without altering the other phase.

Limits of Breath Holding   As growing children we took great delight in seeing how long we could hold our breath. In most cases the greatest effort failed to arrest breathing for much more than a minute or two. Yet under ideal circumstances it is possible to hold one's breath for considerably longer than that. In fact, there are some individuals who have succeeded in holding it longer than 15 minutes!

While breathing is stopped, the production of CO_2 continues. The concentration of this gas in the alveolar air and in the blood will come to an equilibrium rapidly. Thereafter, CO_2 simply accumulates in the blood. Even though breathing has been arrested, the circulation of blood, of course, continues. It has been stressed that this gas is a very potent respiratory stimulant. Therefore, while the breath is being held, the stimulation to the inspiratory center becomes increasingly greater. Finally, a point is reached at which the drive to the center is greater than the voluntary control. At that point breathing begins anew, despite one's efforts to prevent it.

If the physiological mechanisms just outlined are kept in mind, it is easy to devise a means of increasing the length of breath holding. One very effective method is to hyperventilate for a period of time prior to the test. This diminishes the concentration of CO_2 in the blood. It then takes longer for the CO_2 to build up to a point where voluntary inhibition is overcome.

While breathing is stopped, the oxygen content diminishes and thus the chemoreceptors are activated. Although this drive is not so strong as the CO_2 influence, nonetheless it contributes. Consequently, if an individual hyperventilates before the test by breathing a gas mixture containing a high concentration of O_2, he will be able to hold his breath longer. True, the blood is normally about 97 per cent saturated with oxygen, but pushing that concentration up to 99 or even 100 per cent does help.

HYPERVENTILATION

Voluntary hyperventilation by the mechanism already described causes a progressive lowering of the CO_2 content of the blood. This is so because the outside air contains only a trace of CO_2. Consequently, the more rapidly it is passed through the lungs, the greater will be the CO_2 pressure gradient between the pulmonary blood and the alveolar air, and so the faster will be the loss of CO_2 from the body. This is often referred to as "washing out" the CO_2. Since the loss is greater than the production, the CO_2 content of the blood falls.

If one hyperventilates for a period of time by breathing very deeply and somewhat more rapidly than normal, he becomes dizzy, perhaps even giddy, and then fatigue overpowers him so that the effort cannot be continued. There are many reasons for this sequence of events. First, the washing out of CO_2 permits a generalized vasodilatation. It will be recalled that CO_2 acts upon the vasoconstrictor center; in its absence vasodilatation results. The blood pressure falls, and the blood supply to the brain decreases. Second, the diminished CO_2 content of the blood by shifting the O_2 dissociation curve (see Chap. 19) reduces the quantity of O_2 delivered to the tissues. This fact may well account for the fatigue. Third, the decreased CO_2 content, if great enough, will cause the blood to become more alkaline. The quantity of ionized calcium in the blood therefore decreases and this may result in **tetany,** a condition characterized by muscular spasm and pain. As a matter of fact, cramps while swimming have been attributed to this mechanism. It is said that the hyperventilation induced by exercise and the cold water causes a loss of CO_2, tetany, and muscle pain.

VOLUNTARY CONTROL OF BREATHING
FOR NONRESPIRATORY PURPOSES

Speaking   In order to force the proper amount of air past the vocal cords at the optimal pressure, it is necessary to control breathing voluntarily. In speech, there is little problem in this respect, since an individual can take a breath whenever he desires without interrupting significantly the con-

tinuity of speech. But in singing, of course, the control of breathing is a
very important factor. The phrasing of the song and the length of time
that each note must be held determine when one can breathe. In the
more difficult operatic arias, this often presents a limiting factor.

Coughing   When a foreign body becomes lodged in the air passages,
reflex and voluntary mechanisms swing into action. These include the
closure of the glottis and the forcible contraction of the thoracic cage
which increases intrapulmonary pressure. Then the glottis is suddenly
forced open, and a blast of air passes up the respiratory ducts. This
functions to blow out the foreign body. When one has a cold, there is
usually mucous formation in the respiratory passages. The resulting
cough reflexes prevent the mucus from reaching the lungs (Fig. 17-6).

Straining   To initiate urination or defecation often requires a great increase in intra-abdominal pressure. This is brought about by straining.
The glottis is closed and the thoracic muscles as well as the diaphragm
and abdominal muscles are contracted. Consequently, there is a decrease
in the size of the abdominal cavity, and the pressure is increased.

ABNORMAL BREATHING

The increase in ventilation caused by greater activity is not properly
considered to be a form of abnormal breathing. But there are many
disorders which result in alterations in respiration which are relevant
to this discussion.

CHEYNE-STOKES BREATHING

Cheyne-Stokes breathing is characterized by a periodic increase and decrease in the depth of breathing. The rate of breathing may also wax and
wane, but the outstanding change is in the periodic variation in the
amplitude (Fig. 18-5).

This type of breathing is sometimes seen when there is increased
intracranial pressure or when the individual is under the influence of
a narcotic agent. Apparently the sensitivity of the respiratory center is
dulled. Thus, a much higher than normal concentration of CO_2 is required to bring about inspiration. Consequently, for a time, there is
apnea, that is, no breathing at all. The CO_2 builds up; the O_2 diminishes.
Finally, through the chemoreceptor drive and the direct action of CO_2,
breathing begins. This double drive causes breathing to become increasingly deeper, but at last the CO_2 is diminished and the O_2 has
increased so that the drive ceases. Breathing now becomes progressively
more shallow; because of the lack of sensitivity of the center it waits too
long to become active again, and a period of apnea takes place. Put

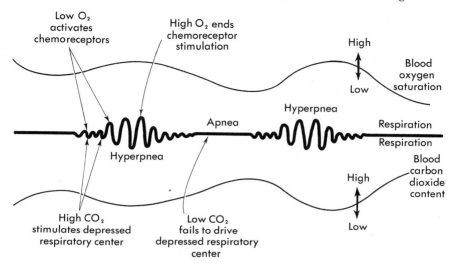

FIG. 18-5 Cheyne-Stokes breathing.

more simply, it is an illustration of "overshooting the mark" due to diminished sensitivity of the respiratory center.

DYSPNEA

Dyspnea is the term applied to labored breathing. The individual feels and looks as though he cannot catch his breath. There is actually only a small increase in the depth of breathing and a slight augmentation in the rate so that ventilation is increased, but the cardinal finding is the apprehension. It has been shown that dyspnea results when the tidal-volume/vital-capacity ratio increases. Normally the tidal volume is about 500 ml, and the vital capacity, in young adults, averages 4,500 ml. The normal ratio then is about 1:9. But in many abnormal conditions, the vital capacity is diminished, and at the same time the tidal volume is increased. For example, in severe congestive heart failure, there is often an accumulation of fluid in the thorax which diminishes vital capacity. The increased venous blood pressure, through a reflex mechanism, will increase the tidal volume. Therefore the ratio may become, let us say, 1:3. It has been shown that the greater this fraction, the more severe the dyspnea.

Of course dyspnea may occur in the complete absence of any organic changes. It may be due to psychological factors. The individual may be unduly apprehensive and fully convinced that he cannot catch his breath even though breathing is quite normal.

KUSSMAUL BREATHING

Kussmaul breathing is very deep, only slightly rapid, and generally accompanied by a sigh. It is highly characteristic of acidosis usually caused by diabetes mellitus or uremia. A shift of the reaction of the blood to a more acid state excites the chemoreceptors. As a result, breathing becomes deeper. But though the tidal volume increases, there is usually no change in the vital capacity, and therefore this type of breathing is quite different from dyspnea.

CHOKES

Workers who labor in pressure chambers in deep waters suffer from the "bends" if they are returned to sea-level pressure too rapidly. More recently it has been found that aviators who ascend to over 35,000 ft with great speed suffer with the same condition. The symptoms and signs, in both cases, are caused by the liberation of nitrogen from the blood. Bubbles form which cause the various findings. One such disorder is called the **chokes**. The breathing becomes shallow, rapid, and then labored. There are usually fits of coughing, great apprehension, and sometimes even loss of consciousness. Although it is known that the nitrogen bubbles are responsible for the disorder, the exact mechanism cannot yet be described.

SUMMARY

The complex sequence of events essential to breathing is coordinated by the **respiratory center** located in the **reticular formation** of the upper two-thirds of the medulla and lower part of the pons. The rhythmicity of breathing is thought to be an inherent characteristic of the respiratory center. This basic rhythm is modulated by sensory input and also direct chemical influence.

Expansion of the lungs during inspiration initiates the **Hering-Breuer reflex.** Other reflexes involve the carotid and aortic chemoreceptors and pressoreceptors, and also the **pneumotaxic** center. Activation of muscles and joints stimulate proprioceptors which fire impulses to excite the respiratory center.

Carbon dioxide increase, and oxygen and pH decrease, all activate the respiratory center. An increase in blood P_{CO_2} can raise ventilation tenfold or more. The exact mechanism is not known. It may be due to alteration of pH of the cerebrospinal fluid. Hypoxemia stimulates respiration solely through peripheral chemoreceptors.

Breathing may be suspended **(apnea)** or markedly increased **(hyper-**

ventilation) voluntarily. During apnea the P_{CO_2} increases until the breath can no longer be held. Hyperventilation, by lowering P_{CO_2} and slightly raising P_{O_2}, increases breath holding time.

Breathing is voluntarily controlled in speaking, coughing, and straining. **Cheyne-Stokes breathing** is an abnormal condition caused by a lowered sensitivity of the respiratory center. **Dyspnea** is labored breathing which usually results when the ratio between the tidal volume and the vital capacity increases. **Kussmaul breathing** is a very deep type of breathing which is usually found in acidosis. The **chokes,** caused by rapid atmospheric pressure changes, evokes coughing, dyspnea, and sometimes loss of consciousness.

QUESTIONS

1. How does the Hering-Breuer reflex control respiration?
2. What is the function of the pneumotaxic center?
3. What role do the carotid and aortic bodies play in respiratory control?
4. What factors limit the length of time the breath can be held?
5. How does carbon dioxide influence respiration?
6. How does CO_2 change the effect of O_2 on breathing?

SUGGESTED READING

Bennett, D., Jayson, M., and Rubenstein, D., "The Perception of Dyspnea," *Dis. Chest,* **43**:#4, 411–417, April 1963.

Brown, H. W., and Plum, F., "The Neurologic Basis of Cheyne-Stokes Respiration," *Am. J. Med.,* **30**:#6, 849–860, June 1961.

Creighton, H., and Coulter, W. W., Jr., "The Whys of a Pulmonary Function Test," *Am. J. Nursing,* **60**:#12, 1771–1774, December 1960.

Kane, I. J., "The Lungs in Health and Disease," *Today's Health,* **34**:#2, 42–45, February 1956.

Smith, C. A., "The First Breath," *Sci. American,* **209**:#4, 27–35, October 1963.

Tenney, S. M., "Respiration," *Ann. Rev. Physiol.,* **23**: 123–152, 1961.

19 Transport of Respiratory Gases

IN OUTLINING THE SCOPE OF THE TERM RESPIRATION, it was mentioned that the transportation of oxygen from the lungs to the tissues and the carriage of carbon dioxide from the tissues to the lungs are important aspects of this subject. But in order for the blood to perform these functions, it must first be saturated with oxygen. The oxygen must pass from the lungs into the blood. Similarly, after the blood has carried the carbon dioxide to the lungs, it leaves the blood and passes through the epithelial membranes to enter the alveolar spaces. Therefore, before the transportation of the respiratory gases can be considered, we must first explain the mechanisms by which these gases pass in and out of the blood.

PHYSICS OF RESPIRATION

In the study of cardiac dynamics it was expained that the blood pressure is expressed in millimeters of mercury. The pressure of gases is designated in the same units. In the atmosphere, the pressure of the air simply reflects the weight of a column of air above the earth. Air has mass, thus is attracted by gravity. It presses down upon the earth's surface, and at sea level it will support a column of mercury 760 mm high. Therefore we say that the normal atmospheric pressure at sea level is 760 mm Hg. But what is the pressure of the oxygen in the air? And what influence does temperature have over the volume and pressure of the gas? In order to answer these questions, the pertinent gas laws will be briefly considered.

GAS LAWS

Dalton's Law of Partial Pressure Let us assume that a volume of oxygen is put into a bag and the pressure measured and found to be 100 mm Hg. Now if an equal volume of nitrogen is introduced into the same bag, it too will exert a pressure equal to 100 mm Hg. It is true that both gases

382

together exert a pressure of 200 mm Hg. But each gas has the same pressure whether it occupies the chamber exclusively or in company with other gases. Phrased more succinctly, Dalton's law states that *in a mixture of gases, each gas exerts the same pressure as though it alone occupied the total volume.*

Avogadro's Principle This principle states that *all gases which have the same volume at the same temperature and the same pressure will contain the same number of molecules.* A liter of oxygen at a pressure of 760 mm Hg and a temperature of 20°C will contain exactly the same number of molecules as, let us say, a liter of carbon dioxide or of any other gas under these same conditions.

Boyle's Law If a million molecules of a gas are contained in a small space, they will exert a greater pressure than if they are allowed to occupy a much larger chamber. Boyle's law states that *the pressure of a gas is inversely proportional to its volume so long as the temperature is kept constant.*

Charles' Law The pressure that a gas exerts in a closed chamber is a function of molecular movement. Molecules move rapidly and at random. The faster they move, the greater the pressure exerted by the gas. The rate of molecular movement is a function of temperature. At absolute zero (−273°C), all molecular activity ceases. Therefore at that temperature a volume of gas would exert no pressure. The higher the temperature, the greater the pressure. Charles' law states that *the pressure of any gas is directly proportioned to its absolute temperature so long as the volume remains constant.* This can be verified by a simple illustration. One has only to check the pressure in a tire the first thing in the morning and then again after the car has been driven for a bit to prove that the pressure varies with the temperature of the air in the tube.

Boyle's law and Charles' law may be combined to express the relationship between pressure, temperature, and volume as follows:

$$\text{Pressure} = \frac{\text{temperature}}{\text{volume}}$$

MOVEMENT OF GAS

Oxygen moves from the alveolar space into the pulmonary blood stream. Simultaneously, carbon dioxide passes from the blood into the alveolar air. For a considerable period of time, it was held that the epithelial membrane separating the alveolar air and the pulmonary blood possessed a secretory ability which served to move the gases. This concept has been disavowed. The factors which determine the movement of the respiratory gases are (1) partial pressure of the gases, (2) permeability of the membranes, (3) chemical reactions in the blood, (4) rate of pulmonary circulation, and (5) size of the alveolar surface area.

Partial Pressure of the Gases A gas moves from a high-pressure area to an area of lower pressure. The differential between the pressure of oxygen in the lungs and in the blood suffices to drive the gas through the membranes and into the blood. The same is true of carbon dioxide. Using Dalton's law it is possible to calculate the magnitude of these pressures.

Figure 19-1 shows the simple instrument used to collect a sample of alveolar air. One simply breathes through the tube until the tidal vol-

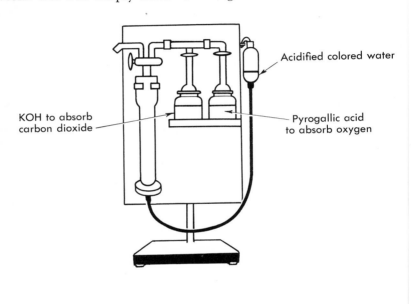

Acidified colored water

KOH to absorb
carbon dioxide

Pyrogallic acid
to absorb oxygen

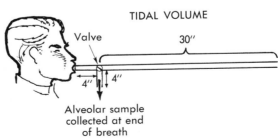

TIDAL VOLUME

Valve   30″

4″   4″

Alveolar sample
collected at end
of breath

FIG. 19-1 Analysis of alveolar air. The subject expires through the tube. Just before the end of expiration, the valve is turned and the last part of the sample is collected in a bag connected to the short side-arm. The sample is then analyzed, using the equipment shown above.

ume has almost completely expired. Then the valve is turned, and the very last part of the expired volume is trapped. This is the alveolar-air sample. It can be studied with the aid of the gas analyzer shown in Fig. 19-1. In this instrument the volume of the sample air is measured. Then the air is passed over a chemical which removes the CO_2. The volume of the sample is measured again. The difference between the first and second volume is, of course, the volume of CO_2. Next the gas is run through a chemical which absorbs the O_2. For the third time the volume is measured. The difference between the second and third measurements equals the volume of O_2 contained in the sample mixture.

By means of this procedure the percentage composition of the alveolar air may be measured with considerable accuracy. Let us assume that the analysis reveals the following percentage composition:

Oxygen	15
Carbon dioxide	5
Nitrogen	80
	100

If the atmosphere pressure is 760 mm Hg, the total pressure within the lungs must be the same. But in the alveoli there is another gas which we have not yet considered. It is **water vapor.** The temperature of the body remains relatively constant, and therefore the vapor emitted from the moist surfaces of the body, such as the lungs, remains constant and exerts a pressure of about 47 mm Hg. In other words, the alveolar air is made up of four gases: (1) **nitrogen,** (2) **oxygen,** (3) **carbon dioxide,** and (4) **water vapor.** If the total pressure is 760 mm Hg and the water-vapor partial pressure is 47 mm Hg, then

$$\begin{array}{r} 760 \text{ mm Hg} \\ - \ 47 \text{ mm Hg} \\ \hline 713 \text{ mm Hg} \end{array}$$ equals the total pressure of nitrogen, oxygen, and carbon dioxide

Knowing the percentage of each of these gases, it is a simple matter to calculate the partial pressure of each. For example, for oxygen:

$$713 \times 0.15 = 107 \text{ mm Hg}$$

For carbon dioxide:

$$713 \times 0.05 = 35.7 \text{ mm Hg}$$

The partial pressure of these gases in the blood can also be determined. When this is done, it is found that the pressure of oxygen in the pulmonary blood is always lower than the partial pressure of oxygen in the alveolar air. Therefore, oxygen moves from the alveolar space into the pulmonary blood stream. Conversely, the pressure of carbon dioxide in the pulmonary blood is always higher than the carbon dioxide partial pressure in the alveolar air. Consequently, carbon dioxide leaves the blood.

The partial pressure of the respiratory gases in the alveolar air depends, of course, upon the concentration of these gases in the inspired air. Atmospheric air contains the following percentage composition:

Nitrogen	79.0
Oxygen	20.9
Carbon dioxide	Trace

If a gas mixture with less than 20 per cent oxygen were to be breathed, then the alveolar-oxygen partial pressure would decrease accordingly. As a result, the pressure of oxygen in the blood would diminish. In short, there is a gradient; the partial pressure of oxygen is highest in the atmospheric air, lower in the alveolar air, and lowest in the blood. It is by reason of this gradient that oxygen moves into the blood. The gradient for carbon dioxide is just the reverse, being highest in the blood and lowest in the atmosphere (Table 19-1). Carbon dioxide, therefore, moves out of the blood.

Permeability of the Membranes   Two very thin membranes separate the alveolar air from the pulmonary blood. They are (1) the lung epithelium and (2) the capillary wall. These thin membranes are in such intimate contact that they often appear to be but one membrane. But still they represent a barrier through which the respiratory gases must pass. The driving force is the differential in partial pressures. The membranes offer resistance to the movement of the gases. The greater the permeability, the less the resistance. Membrane resistance is usually expressed by what is termed the **diffusion coefficient.** The diffusion coefficient, also called the diffusion capacity, is defined as the amount of gas which passes across the membranes per minute per millimeter difference in tension of the gas on the two sides of the membranes. The diffusion capacity for oxygen is normally about 20 ml/min/mm Hg. Carbon dioxide is much greater, being approximately 400 ml/min/mm Hg. The diffusion coefficient expresses the rate of diffusion not only through the lung epithelium and the capillary wall but also through the thin layer of moisture lining the alveoli, the interstitial fluid between the alveolar membrane and the capillary membrane, the plasma, and the red cell membrane. The fact that CO_2 is far more soluble in water than is O_2 contributes significantly to its greater diffusion coefficient.

The diffusion coefficients for both the respiratory gases are great enough to permit equilibration to occur, at rest, very soon after the blood enters the pulmonary capillaries. For example, it has been estimated that the pulmonary capillaries hold about 60 ml of blood. If the cardiac output is 6000 ml per minute, the blood must be renewed in the pulmonary capillaries 100 times per minute. To put it another way, each particle of blood takes about 0.6 second to pass through the pulmonary capillaries. At rest, the O_2 uptake is 250 ml per minute. In 0.6 second, 2.5 ml of O_2 must diffuse into the blood. The diffusion capacity for O_2 is 20 ml/min/ mm Hg. At rest, at the beginning of the pulmonary capillary, the O_2 partial pressure difference between alveolar air and the blood is 60 mm Hg ($100 - 40$). According to the diffusion coefficient, 0.2 ml O_2 will diffuse each 0.6 sec per mm Hg. With a driving force of 60 mm Hg, 12 ml would diffuse. This is far greater than the 2.5 ml that actually does diffuse, but as oxygen enters the blood, the P_{O_2} in the blood increases, and therefore the driving force decreases. As a result, at the beginning of the capillary the uptake is great and then progressively lessens. Within the first third of the capillary almost the entire oxygen load diffuses into the blood. This provides a large reserve factor. Carbon dioxide equilibrates even faster.

In many abnormal conditions, such as pneumonia and silicosis, the permeability of the membranes is sorely interfered with and the movement of the gases is impaired. It is for this reason that in advanced pulmonary cases, the patient is placed under an oxygen tent. He now breathes a mixtures of air containing mostly oxygen. Instead of the alveolar air containing 15 per cent oxygen, it may hold 20 or 30 per cent or more. Assuming that it contains 30 per cent, the partial pressure of oxygen is about 214 mm Hg (713×0.30). This high pressure aids in driving oxygen through the abnormal membranes.

Chemical Reactions in the Blood The chemical combinations which take place in the blood and make it possible for the blood to carry large quantities of the respiratory gases will be discussed in detail later. It is enough to say here that the efficiency of these reactions determines the movement of the gases. If these chemical combinations permitted each milliliter of blood to carry only 1 ml of oxygen, then after that milliliter had entered, regardless of the gradient, no more would move across the membranes. But, by way of contrast, if these reactions were so efficient as to permit a much larger quantity of oxygen to be carried, of course more would move into the blood. Therefore we can conclude that the efficiency of these chemical processes determines the rate at which the respiratory gases move.

Rate of Pulmonary Circulation   The more rapidly the blood moves through the lungs, the more oxygen it will take up per unit time. If the circulation were to stop completely, the pressure of the respiratory gases on both sides of the membranes would soon become equal and gas interchange would cease. Conversely, the faster the blood flows, the greater the gradient and therefore the more rapid the movement of the respiratory gases.

Alveolar Surface Area   Under varying conditions the size of the alveolar surface area changes. For example, during shallow breathing not all of the alveoli may open. Deeper breathing opens these sacs, thereby increasing the total surface area. If all other factors are kept constant, it is obvious that the larger this surface area, the greater will be the rate at which the gases move.

TRANSPORT OF OXYGEN

The factors which determine the movement of oxygen from the alveolar air into the blood have been discussed. It was mentioned that the chemical reactions within the blood are of prime importance. The quantity of oxygen carried in physical solution in the blood is extremely small. It has been calculated that if oxygen were carried in physical solution alone man would require over 200 liters of blood in order to survive. The normal blood volume, it will be recalled, is about 5 liters. By far the greater percentage of the oxygen is carried in chemical combination.

HEMOGLOBIN

As has already been pointed out, the characteristic color of the blood is a function of an iron protein pigment called **hemoglobin.** Oxygen enters into a loose combination with hemoglobin by virtue of the iron contained within the hemoglobin molecule. Hemoglobin combines with oxygen as follows:

$$\text{Hemoglobin} + \text{oxygen} = \text{oxyhemoglobin}$$
$$\text{Hb} \quad + \quad O_2 \quad = \quad HbO_2$$

Oxygen Capacity   The maximum quantity of oxygen which the blood can carry is termed the **oxygen capacity** and is determined by the amount of hemoglobin present. One gram of hemoglobin can combine with 1.34 ml of oxygen. The blood of man contains approximately 15 gm of hemoglobin per 100 ml of blood. Therefore, the oxygen capacity of 100 ml of blood is about 20 ml (15×1.34). This is commonly expressed as volumes per cent. Thus we say that the oxygen capacity of the blood is 20 volumes per cent.

Oxygen Dissociation Curve   The fact that oxygen unites with hemoglobin in a reversible manner has been emphasized. The quantity of oxygen which combines in this way is determined by the partial pressure of oxygen. If the pressure is increased, more oxygen and hemoglobin unite; when the partial pressure of oxygen falls, the hemoglobin surrenders a portion of the oxygen.

The dissociation curves of human blood are shown in Fig. 19-2. Such curves are derived by the use of a series of **tonometers.** A tonometer is simply a tube in which a small quantity of blood is introduced along with a mixture of gas. Let us assume that in a series of tonometers we have only blood and pure oxygen but that in each tonometer the oxygen pressure varies. Let us further assume that it is 10 mm Hg in the first, 30 in the next, 50 in the third, and so forth. The tonometers are then slowly rotated so as to spread the blood in a thin layer along the inner surface and thus encourage equilibration between the oxygen in the tonometer and in the blood. The tonometers are rotated in a water bath heated to 37°C in order to simulate body temperature. After a period of time sufficient to allow equilibration, the blood is analyzed and the **oxygen content** determined. If the blood is found to contain 5 volumes per cent, for

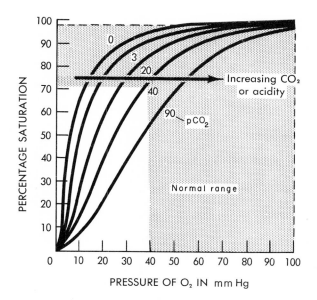

FIG. 19-2   Oxygen dissociation curves. Note that by increasing the CO_2 or the acidity the values are shifted to the right; thus for any P_{O_2} hemoglobin holds less oxygen.

example, it is said to be 25 per cent saturated, since 20 volumes per cent equals 100 per cent saturation. In this way, the first curve in Fig. 19-2 is constructed. The procedure is repeated with varying quantities of carbon dioxide, and the results are plotted as indicated.

An understanding of the oxygen dissociation curves is essential. It will be recalled that when a person breathes air at sea-level atmospheric pressure, the partial pressure of oxygen in the alveolar air is about 100 mm Hg. The oxygen partial pressure in the blood will then be below but close to this figure. If the oxygen dissociation curves are examined, it will be seen that at 100 mm Hg the blood is almost completely saturated regardless of the carbon dioxide pressure. Actually, the normal carbon dioxide pressure in the arterial blood is about 40 mm Hg. If we follow the appropriate curve for this value, it will be evident that the blood must leave the lungs about 97 per cent saturated. To put it another way, each 100 ml of blood as it leaves the lungs contains 19.4 ml of oxygen (0.97 × 20).

From a study of these curves it can be seen that increasing the oxygen partial pressure in the lungs beyond 100 mm Hg is of no particular advantage. The blood-oxygen saturation may be pushed to 100 per cent, but since it is normally 97 per cent saturated, the gain is not great. Conversely, it is obvious that the partial pressure of oxygen can be reduced considerably below normal without depriving the blood of much of its oxygen load. It will be noted that even when the partial pressure is cut in half, reduced to 50 mm Hg, the oxygen saturation of the blood is still over 80 per cent, a saturation which readily serves most functions. In short, it can be concluded that the oxygen partial pressure in the lungs can vary over a wide range and still the blood will be adequately saturated.

Let us now turn our attention to the lower oxygen pressures, that is, the pressures which prevail in the tissues. When the blood reaches the capillaries, some of its oxygen passes through the capillary membrane and enters the tissue spaces. It does so because the partial pressure of oxygen in the tissue spaces is less than it is in the blood. According to the pressure gradient, oxygen moves from the blood into the tissues. The actual pressure of oxygen in the tissues varies widely, depending upon the activity of the particular tissue. But let us assume for the moment that it is about 35 mm Hg. Consulting the dissociation curve marked "40," we find that the blood will now be only 70 per cent saturated. It will contain about 14 volumes per cent of oxygen. In other words, each 100 ml of blood has surrendered to the tissues about 5.4 ml of oxygen. If the tissue being supplied is muscle which now begins to contract vigorously, it will utilize oxygen at an accelerated rate, the partial pressure will drop, and more oxygen will leave the blood. Thus the venous blood returning from actively contracting muscle may contain only 8 volumes per cent of oxygen or even less. The increased extraction of oxygen by the tissues is the first line of defense. It is, of course, limited by the quantity of oxygen present. Consulting the dissociation curves once again, it can be seen that in order to reduce the oxygen saturation below 10 per cent would require extremely low tissue pressures. It is doubtful that this limit is reached even in the most exhausting forms of exercise.

Influence of Carbon Dioxide   As indicated by the dissociation curves, the quantity of carbon dioxide contained in the blood definitely influences the oxygen saturation at any given partial pressure. For example, if the partial pressure of oxygen in the blood is 40 mm Hg, it can be seen that at a carbon dioxide partial pressure of 40 the blood will be about 75 per cent saturated. But if the CO_2 is only 20 mm Hg, then the saturation is about 85 per cent. As will be discussed presently, the carbon dioxide content of the blood varies, being highest in the blood as it leaves the capillaries and lowest in the blood as it departs from the lungs. This change favors the uptake of oxygen in the lungs where the carbon dioxide content is low. In the tissues the rising carbon dioxide concentration encourages the divorce of oxygen from the hemoglobin. As has just been explained, if the carbon dioxide partial pressure in the blood increases from 20 to 40 mm Hg, the blood will give up about an additional 10 per cent of its oxygen load.

HYPOXIA

The word **hypoxia** is a general term which means inadequate oxygenation. It may refer to inadequate oxygenation of the air, the blood, or the cells. **Hypoxemia,** on the other hand, specifically signifies a decreased oxygen saturation of the blood. A complete absence of oxygen would be termed **anoxia,** but this extreme condition is rarely encountered. Therefore, the preferred term hypoxia is used. It has been said that, in the final analysis, everyone dies from hypoxia. This simply means that after the heart ceases to beat, for whatever reason, the tissues are no longer supplied with oxygen, their essential metabolic processes grind to a stop, and death ensues. A consideration of hypoxia, then, is of considerable importance. In the following discussion, hypoxia refers to inadequate oxygenation of the cells.

Hypoxemic Hypoxia   This seemingly pleonastic term implies that the hypoxia is due to an inadequate uptake by the blood of oxygen. The inadequate oxygenation of the cells may come from many causes, but one reason is a decreased arterial oxygen saturation. This state may result from pneumonia in which the accumulation of fluids in the lungs impairs the transfer of oxygen from the alveolar air into the blood. It may also be associated with paralysis of the respiratory muscles, as in infantile paralysis, in which inadequate ventilation causes a sharp reduction in the partial pressure of oxygen in the alveolar air. It may be a result of drowning, breathing insufficient quantities of oxygen, or exposure to high altitudes where the partial pressure of oxygen is greatly reduced. The net result is to reduce the saturation of the arterial blood, thereby depriving the tissues of an adequate suppy of oxygen. The tissues extract a large percentage of the available oxygen, but if the supply is very low, the large extraction ratio is frustrated.

Anemic Hypoxia   Hemoglobin is essential to the transportation of oxygen. If the concentration of hemoglobin is reduced below its normal value of about 15 gm per 100 ml of blood to about 7.5 gm, that is, a 50 per cent reduction, the oxygen content of the blood will also be 50 per cent of normal. True, all the hemoglobin is completely saturated, but there is not enough hemoglobin to carry an adequate supply of oxygen molecules. This condition is termed **anemia**. The individual compensates in two ways: (1) by increasing the tissue extraction of available oxygen and (2) by increasing the rate of blood circulation by mechanisms previously discussed. Whether or not these changes compensate for the reduction of the oxygen content depends, of course, upon the degree of anemia.

Stagnant Hypoxia   Many disorders of the cardiovascular system, such as cardiac failure, shock, arterial spasm, and emboli, may result in a marked slowing of the flow of blood through the capillaries. In this case the tissue extracts practically all the oxygen contained in the blood. But after this quantity of oxygen has been removed, there is no more available, and the slow movement of the blood fails to bring in a new supply fast enough to care for tissue needs.

Histotoxic Hypoxia   If the blood contains its normal content of oxygen and if the blood flow is normal, the tissues may still suffer from inadequate oxygenation because of interference with the utilization of the available oxygen. Many poisons block the essential metabolic processes, so that the available oxygen is not used and the cells suffer from hypoxia —in this instance, histotoxic hypoxia.

Effects of Hypoxia   Apparently, hypoxia afflicts the nervous system first. Thus, the early indications of this condition result from malfunction of nervous tissue. It does not matter what has produced the hypoxia. It may be caused by an ascent to altitudes beyond 18,000 ft, an excessive intake of alcohol, the inhalation of carbon monoxide from a faulty gas heater or from the exhaust of a car, or inhalation of a gas anesthetic. In any case, the individual first has a feeling of well-being, of euphoria; this may prove fatal, because feeling well he makes no effort to protect himself. It is well known, for example, that pilots are extremely reluctant to use their oxygen equipment, insisting that they have no need for it. But it is easy to demonstrate that their abilities are severely handicapped under hypoxic conditions; they are simply unaware of their impediments.

Ultimately there is loss of coordination; the individual staggers and is unable to execute discrete movements. Finally vision and memory fade, and then unconsciousness develops. If the hypoxia is not promptly relieved, death will soon follow.

All types of hypoxia, with the possible exception of the histotoxic variety, evoke widespread physiological changes as a result of the activation of the chemoreceptors in the carotid and aortic bodies. Ventilation is increased, thus serving to augment the partial pressure of oxygen in the alveolar air, and the circulatory rate is elevated, thereby delivering the available oxygen to the tissues more rapidly. If the degree of hypoxia is not severe, that is, if the arterial oxygen partial pressure does not decrease below about 50 or 60 mm Hg, these compensatory mechanisms may suffice to protect the individual.

There are other, slower changes which occur in cases of chronic hypoxia, as for example in persons who live at high altitudes. In such individuals the red-blood-cell count and the amount of hemoglobin increase. In addition, there are changes in the endocrine glands and especially the adrenal cortex which in some manner assist the individual in his acclimatization to these adverse conditions. Thus we see that in communities located 14,000 to 15,000 ft above sea level the residents have high erythrocyte counts, characteristically barrel-shaped chests, and other physiological adaptations which make it possible for them to carry out an amazing load of work at this altitude. In contrast, people who visit in such places usually become breathless and quickly fatigued.

HYPEROXIA

It has been known for well over half a century that the inhalation of pure oxygen produces profound toxic effects. Convulsions, edema of the lungs, and even death may result. But despite considerable investigation of this problem it is still not possible to state why breathing high concentrations of oxygen should have these deleterious consequences. In some manner, the very high partial pressure of oxygen interferes with the metabolic processes, but just how remains to be elucidated.

There are conditions, however, in which it is highly desirable to increase the oxygen content of the blood. If the hemoglobin is already completely saturated, breathing air with above normal partial pressure of oxygen cannot increase the quantity carried by hemoglobin. But the quantity carried in physical solution can be increased. As already mentioned, at normal oxygen pressures this volume is very low, but if the subject is placed in a so-called **hyperbaric chamber** in which the total air pressure is increased, and if he then breathes oxygen at these pressures, the partial pressure of oxygen can be increased to very high levels. The amount of oxygen carried in physical solution is directly proportional to the partial pressure of oxygen. By means of breathing oxygen in a hyperbaric chamber, the pressure can be increased high enough to force as much as 5 ml of O_2 into physical solution in 100 ml of blood. In other words, even if the blood had no hemoglobin it would still contain enough oxygen to satisfy normal demands. This procedure is now being extensively investigated for use during various operations which interfere with circulation. Hyperbaric chambers are also reported to have a dramatic use in cases of impending gangrene, that is, death of tissue due to oxygen deprivation.

TRANSPORT OF CARBON DIOXIDE

We have learned that oxygen is carried primarily in chemical union with hemoglobin. Approximately 20 per cent of the transported carbon dioxide is carried in this way. About 10 per cent, is transported in physical solution, while the rest is found in chemical combination as the bicarbonate ion.

HEMOGLOBIN MECHANISM

Carbon dioxide combines with an NH_2 group in the hemoglobin molecule to form a so-called carbamino acid, sometimes referred to as **carbhemoglobin** or **carbaminohemoglobin**. The reaction is as follows:

$$\text{Hemoglobin} + \text{carbon dioxide} = \text{carbhemoglobin}$$

$$\text{HbNH}_2 \quad + \quad \text{CO}_2 \quad = \quad \text{HbNHCOOH}$$

Hemoglobin not only functions to carry carbon dioxide in this way, but it also serves another purpose. Hemoglobin is normally combined with a base and thus can make this base available for union with the bicarbonate ion.

It is true that the base can be provided by other compounds, but it is most readily available from the hemoglobin because this substance markedly changes its acid strength with different degrees of oxygenation. For example, when the hemoglobin loses its oxygen to the tissues, it becomes a weaker acid and therefore can surrender more base to combine with the bicarbonate. In short, hemoglobin directly transports CO_2 and at the same time assists in the carriage of this substance in the bicarbonate form.

Carbon Dioxide Content   In considering the transport of oxygen, we refer usually to the **oxygen saturation.** Since oxygen is carried almost exclusively by hemoglobin, the degree of saturation of the hemoglobin is an accurate measure of the quantity of oxygen carried. However, it is also feasible to refer to the **oxygen content,** which simply describes the actual volumes of oxygen per 100 ml of blood carried. Since only a small percentage of CO_2 is carried in combination with hemoglobin, the degree of saturation would not necesarily present a very accurate picture of the quantity of CO_2 carried. Therefore, we refer only to the **carbon dioxide content** which is expressed in volumes per cent.

Carbon Dioxide Dissociation Curve   Again, by the use of tonometers, it is possible to bring blood into equilibrium with various gas mixtures. When the results are plotted, the curves shown in Fig. 19-3 are obtained. It can be seen that the quantity of CO_2 carried by the blood is a function of the partial pressure of that gas. The higher the pressure, the greater the concentration in the blood.

It will next be observed that the quantity of CO_2 in the blood at any partial pressure depends on the degree of oxygenation. The less oxygen

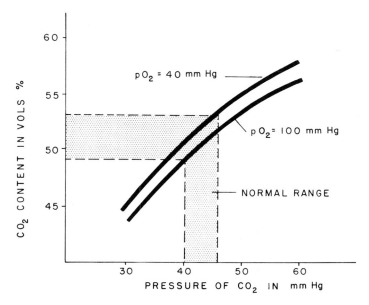

FIG. 19-3   Transport of CO_2. The quantity of CO_2 carried by the blood is a function of P_{CO_2} and P_{O_2}.

carried by the blood, the more CO_2 it can transport. The change is not so great as observed in the oxygen dissociation curve, but it is nonetheless quite significant.

Since the alveolar air, under normal conditions, contains about 5.5 per cent CO_2, the partial pressure of CO_2 must be close to 40 mm Hg. In the venous blood the partial pressure of CO_2 is usually about 46 mm Hg. If the dissociation curve is now used, it will be found that in the venous blood, where the CO_2 pressure is 46 mm Hg and the oxygen content about 15 volumes per cent, the CO_2 content will be about 56 volumes per cent. But when the blood passes through the lungs it gains O_2 and loses CO_2 so that the arterial blood, as shown on the curve, will now contain only about 52 volumes per cent. In other words, each 100 ml of blood, as it passes through the lungs, gives up about 4 ml of CO_2 and accepts about 5 ml of O_2.

Actually, the ratio between the CO_2 liberated and the O_2 taken up depends upon the type of foodstuffs metabolized, as will be discussed later. Suffice it here to say that this ratio ($CO_2:O_2$) is termed the **respiratory quotient.** It ranges from 0.7 to 1.0, with an average, on a mixed diet, of 0.82.

CARBONIC ANHYDRASE

The greatest volume of CO_2 is carried as the bicarbonate ion. Before the CO_2 can enter the red blood cell, it must pass through the plasma. There is water in the plasma with which the CO_2 can combine. However, only a relatively small quantity of bicarbonate is formed in the plasma. But in the red cell, this same reaction between CO_2 and H_2O proceeds far more rapidly. The reason for the difference in the speed of these reactions is the presence of a catalyst, **carbonic anhydrase,** in the red blood cells.

Because of the presence of carbonic anhydrase, more bicarbonate ions are formed in the erythrocyte than in the plasma. Since bicarbonate is freely diffusable through the red-cell membrane, the excess bicarbonate passes from the erythrocyte into the plasma until equilibrium is established. But though the bicarbonate ions are now in equilibrium, there are more anions in the plasma. To bring about ionic balance, other anions —the chloride ions—move into the red cell. In other words, as the bicarbonate moves out, the chloride moves in, thus maintaining ionic balance. This movement of Cl^- is called the **chloride shift.**

EXCHANGE OF RESPIRATORY GASES

All the important mechanisms responsible for the transportation of the respiratory gases have been discussed. In review, two conditions will be

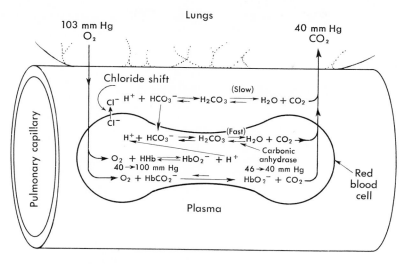

FIG. 19-4 Exchange of respiratory gases in the lungs.

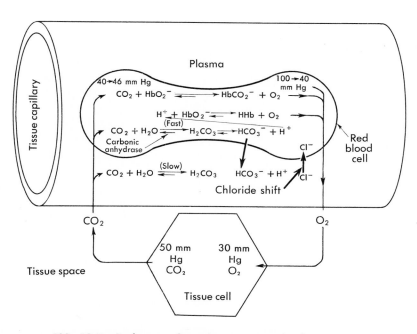

FIG. 19-5 Exchange of respiratory gases in the tissues.

illustrated: (1) as they prevail in the lungs (Fig. 19-4) and (2) as they exist in the tissues (Fig. 19-5).

IN THE LUNGS

Table 19-1 shows the partial pressure of O_2 and CO_2 in various areas. Such a compilation makes apparent the gradients. In the presence of such gradients, oxygen moves into the blood in the lungs and, simultaneously, CO_2 leaves.

TABLE 19-1   The O_2 and CO_2 Partial-pressure Gradients

Area	Partial Pressure, mm Hg	
	Oxygen	Carbon Dioxide
Inspired air	158	0.3
Expired air	116	32.0
Alveolar air	103	38.0
Arterial blood	100	40.0
Venous blood	40	46.0
Tissues	35	50.0

The O_2 enters the plasma where a small quantity is carried in physical solution. The remainder diffuses into the erythrocyte, as shown in Fig. 19-4. Here it unites with the hemoglobin. Thus, CO_2 is displaced, that is, the carbhemoglobin is broken down to liberate CO_2 which then diffuses out of the red cell, traverses the plasma and the membranes, and enters the alveolar air. The oxygenation of hemoglobin makes it a stronger acid. In other words, there is greater ionization, making available hydrogen ions which combine with the bicarbonate ions to form H_2CO_3. Under the influence of carbonic anhydrase, this carbonic acid breaks down into CO_2 and H_2O. The carbon dioxide then diffuses out into the alveolar air. Because of the lower CO_2 pressure in the alveolar air, some of the CO_2 carried in the plasma as bicarbonate also diffuses out, but since this reaction is faster in the erythrocytes, less bicarbonate is left in the cells. Bicarbonate diffuses in and chloride leaves to maintain ionic balance.

As a result of these reactions, the blood leaves the lungs containing close to 20 volumes per cent of oxygen and about 52 volumes per cent of carbon dioxide.

IN THE TISSUES

Figure 19-5 shows another red cell in a tissue capillary. Here the reactions are just reversed. In the tissues, the partial pressure of carbon dioxide is higher than it is in the blood and therefore this gas moves into the circulating blood stream. In the plasma it combines slowly with H_2O to form carbonic acid which then ionizes into HCO_3^- and H^+. About 10 per cent of the CO_2 combines in physical solution with the plasma, but most of it continues on into the red cell. Here, in the presence of carbonic anhydrase, it unites rapidly with water. Consequently, there are more bicarbonate ions formed in the cell than in the plasma. The excess diffuses out, and to keep ionic equilibrium, chloride ions move into the cell.

Because of the utilization of oxygen by the tissues, the partial pressure here is low. Therefore, oxygen diffuses out of the blood. Likewise, as indicated above, the reduced hemoglobin is less acid and therefore can surrender some of its base to form with the bicarbonate ion. In short, in face of all these changes, ionic acidity of the blood is not significantly altered.

When the blood leaves the capillaries, it contains about 56 volumes per cent carbon dioxide and about 15 volumes per cent oxygen. These figures vary, of course, depending upon the activity of the tissue supplied.

SUMMARY

According to **Dalton's law of partial pressures,** each constituent of a mixture of gases exerts the same pressure as it would if it occupied the same space alone. **Avogadro's principle** states that all gases which possess the same volume at the same temperature and pressure will contain the same number of molecules. **Boyle's** and **Charles' laws** show that the pressure of a gas varies directly with the absolute temperature and inversely with the volume.

The respiratory gases move between the blood and the alveolar space in accordance with (1) the partial pressure of the gases, (2) the permeability of the membranes, (3) the chemical reactions in the blood, (4) the rate of the pulmonary circulation, (5) the size of the alveolar surface area.

Oxygen is transported by the blood in chemical combination with hemoglobin. Each gram of hemoglobin can carry approximately 1.34 ml of O_2. Since each 100 ml of blood normally contain about 15 gm of hemoglobin, the **oxygen capacity** is close to 20 volumes per cent. The degree of hemoglobin saturation is determined by the partial pressure of O_2. The partial pressure of carbon dioxide influences the ability of hemoglobin to carry oxygen. The higher the CO_2 partial pressure, the less saturated will be the hemoglobin with O_2.

Hypoxia means inadequate oxygenation. **Hypoxemia** refers specifically to a reduced oxygen content of the blood. Thus, there are **anemic hypoxia, stagnant hypoxia, hypoxemic hypoxia,** and **histotoxic hypoxia.** Changes in the circulatory and respiratory systems can compensate for mild hypoxia, but in severe cases there are alterations in the nervous system which give rise to a feeling of well-being, then to loss of coordination, visual disturbances, loss of consciousness, and death. The inhalation of oxygen under high pressure increases the amount carried in physical solution.

About 10 per cent of the carbon dioxide is carried in physical solution, 20 per cent is combined with hemoglobin as **carbhemoglobin,** and the remainder is integrated with bicarbonate ion. The CO_2 content depends on (1) the partial pressure of CO_2 and (2) the degree of saturation of hemoglobin with O_2. The reaction of CO_2 with H_2O proceeds more rapidly in the cells than in the plasma because of the presence there of **carbonic anhydrase.** The excess bicarbonate so produced diffuses out and chloride moves in, to maintain ionic equilibrium. This is known as the **chloride shift.**

The blood leaves the lungs containing about 20 volumes per cent of oxygen and 52 volumes per cent of CO_2. It returns to the lungs bearing about 15 volumes per cent of O_2 and 56 volumes per cent of CO_2. On a mixed diet, about 5 volumes per cent of oxygen is taken up by the tissues, with the production of only about 4 volumes per cent of carbon dioxide. The $CO_2:O_2$ ratio is called the **respiratory quotient.** It averages about 0.82 on a mixed diet.

QUESTIONS

1. What factors determine the rate at which respiratory gases move between the blood and the alveolar spaces?
2. What is the difference between the terms oxygen capacity and oxygen content?
3. How is the diffusion coefficient determined?
4. What is the significance of the oxygen dissociation curves?
5. What role does carbonic anhydrase play in the transport of carbon dioxide?
6. Why does one breathe more deeply and rapidly at high altitude?

SUGGESTED READING

Ayres, S. M., Criscitiello, A., and Grabovsky, E., "Components of Alveolar-arterial O_2 Difference in Normal Man," *J. Appl. Physiol.,* **19:**#1, 43–47, January 1964.

Fenn, W. O., "The Mechanism of Breathing," *Sci. American,* **202:**#1, 138–148, January 1960.

Gordon, I. B., and Katz, L. N., "Hypoxia and the Pulmonary Musculature," *Persp. Biol. Med.,* **5:**#3, 275–292, Spring 1962.

Scholander, P. F., "The Master Switch of Life," *Sci. American,* **209:**#6, 92–106, December 1963.

Walker, J. E. C., Wells, R. E., Jr., and Merrill, E. W., "Heat and Water Exchange in the Respiratory Tract," *Am J. Med.,* **30:**#2, 259–267, February 1961.

White, J., "Closed-chest Cardiac Massage," *Am. J. Nursing,"* **61:**#7, 57–59, July 1961.

Special Respiratory Problems

20

MAN SUBJECTS HIMSELF TO MANY CONDITIONS which place unusual demands upon the respiratory mechanism. These include exercise and ventures to high above sea level as well as far below sea level. These special problems are considered primarily because they afford a good opportunity for review of basic respiratory and circulatory physiology. In addition, tests of pulmonary function and procedures of artificial respiration are included.

TESTS OF PULMONARY FUNCTION

There are now available a remarkable battery of tests of pulmonary function. Some of these procedures, however, are extremely complex or require such elaborate equipment and techniques that they are seldom used outside the well-equipped research laboratory. Only a few of the more common tests will be discussed here.

VITAL CAPACITY

The vital capacity can be readily measured by the use of a **spirometer** or similar volume recorders. The subject simply inspires maximally and then expires completely into the spirometer. In most instances there is no record of the patient's vital capacity through the years or prior to the present illness. Therefore it is necessary to compare the obtained value with that predicted from the use of an equation which takes into consideration height and age. Usually, a decrease in vital capacity indicates a reduction in functioning lung tissue as occurs with pneumonia, carcinoma, fibrosis, and pulmonary congestion. On the other hand, the decrease may be due simply to an inability to expand the chest. Normal adult males have a vital capacity of 4 to 6 liters.

MAXIMAL BREATHING CAPACITY

The maximal breathing capacity is the greatest volume of gas that can be breathed per minute. To obtain this value, the subject is instructed to breathe as deeply and as rapidly as possible for 15 seconds into a recording system. It is of utmost importance that as little resistance as possible exist in the apparatus. Even then each laboratory should establish its own series of normal values in order to calibrate the equipment. If the subject cooperates so as to give a maximal effort and if the machine is well calibrated, the test is a highly significant one. By the use of formulas which take into consideration surface area, age, and sex, it is possible to predict what the maximal breathing capacity should be in any subject. A comparison of this figure with the obtained value is then made. Although a reduction in maximal breathing capacity is not indicative of any single disorder, it does show a reduction in muscular force or an increase in airway resistance. If the patient's maximal breathing capacity is reduced out of proportion to a decrease in vital capacity, an obstruction of the airways or a disorder known as emphysema is indicated. Normal young adult males have a maximal breathing capacity of 125 to 175 liters per minute.

TIMED VITAL CAPACITY

Usually the same information can be obtained from the timed-vital-capacity test as from the maximal-breathing-capacity evaluation. And, since this test is far simpler and less exhausting to the patient, it is to be preferred. The subject simply makes a forced expiration into a 6-liter spirometer. The apparatus must be equipped with a device that records the total expired volume and also that emitted in 1, 2, or 3 seconds. The normal individual is able to expire 83 per cent of his vital capacity in 1 second, 94 per cent in 2 seconds, and 97 per cent in 3 seconds. In cases of obstructive pulmonary disease, these values will be reduced.

ARTERIAL BLOOD MEASUREMENT

The final proof as to whether or not the respiratory system is performing its task lies in the status of the respiratory gases in the arterial blood. On the other hand, normal arterial values may be maintained in the face of pulmonary dysfunction, but in so doing there remains a sharply reduced respiratory reserve. For this reason, pulmonary function tests as well as arterial blood measurements must be performed and evaluated in the light of one another. The determinations of significance in the arterial blood are the partial pressure of oxygen, the oxygen content and saturation, the total and plasma carbon dioxide content, and the plasma acidity.

EXERCISE

It should be clearly understood that to explain the sequence of physiological events responsible for the alterations in ventilation that occur due to exercise is one of the major problems in the entire field. Physiologists have succeeded in describing various isolated mechanisms that are probably involved, but the complete story has yet to be told. Some of these mechanisms are portrayed in Fig. 20-1, but it should be realized that there is little unanimity concerning either their validity or their importance. All that can be done here, then, is to offer a brief summary of current thinking.

Magnitude of Respiratory Alterations The increased tissue needs performing light exercise can be met with little or no change in ventilation. At rest the venous blood contains only about 5 volumes per cent less O_2 than the arterial blood. Since the arterial blood normally contains about 20 volumes per cent, there remains another 15 volumes per cent in the venous blood. During exercise this reserve is drawn upon. In vigorous exercise the muscles may use 15 or 20 volumes per cent. Increased oxygen extraction from the blood results due to: (1) .lower tissue P_{O_2}, (2) in-

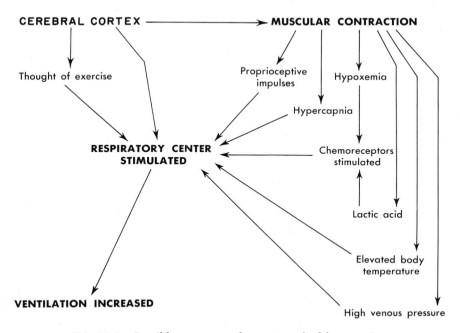

FIG. 20-1   Possible sequence of events evoked by exercise.

creased tissue P_{CO_2}, and (3) increased temperature which, like increased P_{CO_2}, shifts the O_2 dissociation curve to the right.

Not only is more O_2 extracted from each ml of blood, but more ml of blood per unit time enter the capillaries of contracting muscles due to: (1) local vasodilatation evoked by locally produced CO_2, (2) increased cardiac output, and (3) elevated arterial blood pressure.

At the resting level of ventilation, that is 8000 ml per minute, about 5600 ml of air containing 1120 ml of O_2 are presented to the alveoli per minute. At rest, only about 250 ml of O_2 enter the blood per minute. From these figures it would seem that at least a fourfold increase in O_2 extraction by the muscles could be supplied with no increase in ventilation. Ventilation, however, does increase.

In very vigorous exercise the oxygen utilization increases from 250 ml per minute up to 4 to 5 liters per minute. The CO_2 expired rises from the resting level of about 200 ml per minute to approximately 6 liters per minute. This means that the RQ, which is usually about 0.8 rises over unity to 1.5 or even 2.0. The blood lactate level arises from 10 mg per cent to approximately 150 mg per cent. Ventilation increases from 8 liters per minute to over 100 liters per minute.

Chemical Control   During exercise, more O_2 is used, more CO_2 is produced, and the pH of the venous blood decreases. It is understandable, therefore, that great research efforts have been made to explain the characteristic increase in ventilation during exercise in terms of the chemical changes. These efforts have consistently failed. There is no good evidence, at the moment, for chemoreceptors anywhere but in the arterial system. In addition, the respiratory center is served by arterial blood. There is general agreement that even during very strenuous exercise the chemical composition of the arterial blood rarely changes. Thus, it is difficult to understand how CO_2, O_2, or pH changes can regulate ventilation in exercise.

It has been suggested that the aortic and carotid chemoreceptors become more sensitive during exercise than at rest, and thus small alterations in CO_2 or O_2 could evoke large changes in ventilation. It is a fact that the inhalation of 100 per cent O_2 during exercise diminishes ventilation. Perhaps there are circulatory changes during exercise that markedly reduce the blood supply to the chemoreceptors so that there is stagnant hypoxemia at the receptor site and thus even small changes in the arterial P_{O_2} could have an augmented influence. As yet there is little evidence to support these suggestions.

Neural Control   There must be a barrage of impulses from higher centers in order to activate the skeletal muscles during exercise. Hyperventilation can be produced voluntarily, indicating the presence of pathways from the cerebral cortex to the respiratory centers. It is highly conceivable, then, that the cortical drive to the skeletal muscles responsible for exercise also drives the skeletal muscles necessary for breathing. In addition, there is good evidence that the muscle and tendon proprioceptors give rise to impulses which are propagated to the respiratory center, thus resulting in increased ventilation.

It must be remembered that stimulation of the respiratory center alone does not explain increased ventilation. Unless there is some self-inhibitory mechanism within the so-called respiratory center itself, increased stimulation could only lead to a deep, sustained inspiration (apneusis). This is probably prevented, and increased ventilation brought about, by the various feed-back mechanisms already described. These include: (1) an interplay between the inspiratory and expiratory neurons, (2) the Hering-Breuer reflex, and (3) the pneumotaxic reflex.

HIGH ALTITUDE

It has been emphasized that it is the partial pressure of oxygen that constitutes the driving force that causes oxygen to enter the blood. The lower this pressure, the less oxygen that enters. As one ascends from sea-level the atmospheric pressure decreases. At sea-level the pressure is 760 mm Hg. At 18,000 ft it is about one-half this value and at 50,000 ft it is only 87 mm Hg. In order to be able to calculate the P_{O_2} of the alveolar air at various altitudes it is necessary to know the percentage composition of the alveolar air of these altitudes. From these figures the P_{O_2} of the arterial blood can be estimated using the oxygen dissociation curves.

As the atmospheric pressure becomes less, hypoxemia will develop which will evoke hyperventilation. Hyperventilation will increase the percentage of oxygen in the alveolar air and decrease the percentage of carbon dioxide. Thus, unless actual determinations are made, precise calculations cannot be carried out based on the atmospheric pressure alone. However, sample values will be given to illustrate the problem of respiration at high altitude.

It will be recalled that the water vapor in the alveolar air exerts a pressure of 47 mm Hg. This is a function of temperature and thus does not significantly change. The partial pressure of CO_2 is, under normal conditions, about 40 mm Hg. Together they exert a pressure of 87 mm Hg. It can be seen, immediately, that if the total atmospheric pressure at 50,000 ft is only 87 mm Hg, there could be no oxygen in the alveoli, even if the subject were to breathe pure oxygen To be sure, hyperventilation would lower the P_{CO_2}, but even so the P_{O_2} would still be far below levels compatible with life. In order to survive at these altitudes and beyond, it is necessary to use either a special mask that will deliver oxygen under pressure, or else to have the entire compartment pressurized. The latter is the most common solution.

It has been determined that at 10,000 ft, when breathing air, the arterial blood P_{O_2} is about 70 mm Hg and the arterial blood saturation about 90 per cent. It may be thought that this would provide more than adequate oxygen for normal function. However, even this slight reduction produces very definite physiological alterations in circulation and respiration and also in one's physical efficiency. At lower altitudes, the alterations become so slight as to be difficult to measure, but it is generally agreed that at about 5,000 ft, alterations do occur. If one ascends much over 20,000 ft without an oxygen mask or pressurized equipment, he soon loses consciousness.

People who reside at high altitude do become acclimatized to some extent. The major alteration is increased red blood cell production and increased hemoglobin. As a result each unit of blood is capable of carrying a greater load of oxygen. Once acclimatized, work may be effectively performed at altitudes over 20,000 ft, and some individuals can maintain consciousness, at least for several minutes, as high as 30,000 ft.

DEEP SEA

As one descends beneath sea-level, the pressure rapidly increases because of the weight of the water. For every 33.3 ft descent, the pressure increases by 1 atmosphere. Thus at 100 feet below sea-level the pressure is 4 atmospheres (at sea-level it is 1). At 300 ft it is 10 atmospheres.

Submarines are constructed so that the pressure within the submarine is the same as at sea-level, but this means that the walls must be very strong to withstand the pressures beneath the seas. This severely limits the depth to which they can go. To go deeper it is necessary to increase the pressure within the container so as to counterbalance the outside pressure. Under these conditions there are marked physiological changes.

As already mentioned, breathing oxygen at high pressures causes tissue damage. In some manner, as yet not clarified, intracellular processes are deranged. To prevent this result, the percentage composition of oxygen in the air supplied at high pressures is decreased as the pressure increases. Accordingly, the partial pressure of oxygen delivered to the blood can be maintained within normal ranges.

A more serious problem is nitrogen narcosis. The amount of nitrogen dissolved in the body fluids is a function of the pressure. At pressures over about 5 or 6 atmospheres so much nitrogen is dissolved in the body fluids that it exerts an anesthetic effect on the brain. Clearly, the percentage of nitrogen, as well as the percentage of oxygen, in the compressed air delivered to the deep-sea diver must be reduced. To do this, another gas must be substituted. Helium is generally used for this purpose, since it appears to have no deleterious effects, even at very high pressures.

The final problem is to remove the CO_2 produced by the diver. As the pressure increases, the CO_2 is compressed and thus the volume of gas exchange must be increased proportionately.

ARTIFICIAL RESPIRATION

In many instances, it is necessary to administer artifical respiration. Since the procedure may be lifesaving, it is essential that it be carried out promptly and efficiently. For years it has been known that the more prompt the resuscitation, the better the chance of survival. But only recently has experimental work revealed just how urgent this matter truly is. Of equal importance is the efficiency of the method.

Prior to the Second World War, reports began to appear in the scientific literature which cast grave doubts upon the belief that the so-called prone-pressure or **Schafer method** of artificial respiration was the most effective. As a result of the work of many investigators, some of them working in the armed forces, definite evidence accumulated which made it mandatory to discard the old Schafer method in favor of more efficient procedures.

Research has been carried out upon (1) experimental animals; (2) human volunteers, who have subjected themselves to breath-holding tests; (3) fresh cadavers; (4) sick and injured persons who have stopped breathing; (5) individuals who have been given drugs which paralyze breathing.

MOUTH-TO-MOUTH METHOD

By far, this is the most efficient procedure, and it is now recommended above all others. To carry it out, one simply places his mouth over the open mouth of the subject and then forces his breath into the lungs of the subject. In this manner a large volume of air can be forced into the subject. The natural recoil of the chest generally suffices to expire the air. The procedure is then repeated. This should be carried out at a rate approximating the normal respiratory rate of 16 per minute.

The advantage, of course, lies in its simplicity and in the large volume of air that can be moved by this procedure. In addition, the CO_2 in the air forced into the subject serves to stimulate his own respiratory center. The disadvantage is the reluctance to engage in mouth-to-mouth contact under certain conditions. Further, if there is obstruction in the air passageways, expiration may not automatically occur to an effective degree.

ARM-LIFT/BACK-PRESSURE METHOD

Because there may be circumstances in which mouth-to-mouth resuscitation is not desirable, the arm-lift/back-pressure procedure is presented in detail. It is more involved than mouth-to-mouth but when carried out correctly it is highly effective. When this method was tested on cadavers and on individuals who had been given drugs to paralyze breathing, it was found possible to maintain a tidal volume of over 1,000 ml.

Position of Subject   Figure 20-2 indicates that the subject is placed face down in the prone position. The elbows are bent and the hands placed one upon the other. The face is turned to one side with the cheek upon the hands.

Position of Operator   The operator kneels on either the right or the left knee at the head of the subject, facing him. One knee is placed at the side of the subject's head close to the forearm. The opposite foot is placed near the elbow. The hands, as indicated in the figure, are positiond upon the flat of the victim's back in such a way that the heels lie just below a line running between the armpits. With the tips of the thumbs just touching, the fingers are spread downward and outward.

Compression Phase   The operator rocks forward until the arms are approximately vertical. He then allows the upper part of his body to

FIG. 20-2   **Arm-lift/back-pressure method of artificial respiration: compression phase.**

exert slow, steady, even, downward pressure. This forces air out of the lungs. The elbows should be kept straight and the pressure exerted almost directly downward on the back.

Position for Expansion Phase The operator now releases the pressure and commences to rock slowly backward. His hands are placed upon the subject's arms above the elbows, as shown in Fig. 20-3.

Expansion Phase The operator draws the subject's arms upward and toward himself. Enough lift should be applied so that resistance and tension are felt at the subject's shoulders. Then the subject's arms are returned to the ground. This completes the full cycle. The arm lift expands the chest by pulling on the chest muscles, arching the back, and relieving the weight on the chest. As a result, air rushes into the lungs.

This cycle is repeated about 12 times per minute at a steady, uniform rate. The compression and expansion phases should occupy about equal time.

NECESSITY FOR PROMPT ACTION

No matter how efficient the method is, the chances of survival depend strikingly upon the speed of action. The values in Table 20-1 emphasize this fact. A series of animals were asphyxiated and then 1 to 5 minutes

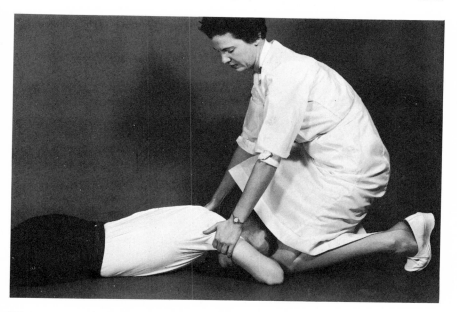

FIG. 20-3 Arm-lift/back-pressure method of artificial respiration: expansion phase.

allowed to elapse before artificial respiration was instituted. The table shows that, if only 1 minute intervened from the cessation of breathing to the initiation of resuscitation, 98 per cent survived. However, if 5

TABLE 20-1

Elapsed Time, Min	Per Cent Survival
1	98.00
2	72.00
3	47.00
4	22.00
5	0.05

minutes elapsed, practically none of the animals lived. The conclusion from these figures is inescapable that, in order to resuscitate a victim, first aid must be begun without delay.

USE OF CARBON DIOXIDE

Artificial respiration is resorted to in any instance in which the individual has ceased to breathe but circulation is still operative. The procedure is carried out in order to keep the blood adequately oxygenated and thereby prevent irreversible damage to the brain as well as other tissues. No matter how efficient the method, it is only a substitute, and usually a poor one, for normal breathing. Therefore, it is desirable to reestablish normal breathing as soon as possible. The most potent stimulus to breathing is a high blood concentration of CO_2. If artificial respiration is carried out effectively, the blood-oxygen saturation will be kept high, but at the same time abnormal quantities of CO_2 may be washed out of the body, thus unduly lowering the concentration in the blood. Therefore, while the respiratory center is dulled for one reason or another, the most potent stimulant is being removed. The reestablishment of normal breathing may thus take a prolonged period. It is for this reason that in many cases when proper equipment and qualified personnel are available the victim is made to breathe a gas mixture containing 3 to 5 per cent CO_2. In this way the CO_2 content of the blood is kept high and can act to stimulate the respiratory center to automatic activity at the earliest possible moment. Of course, there are instances where the use of CO_2 is contraindicated. This gas, in very high concentrations, acts as a narcotic and actually depresses the respiratory center. Thus, if an individual has ceased breathing as a result of asphyxia, the CO_2 content will be unduly high; in such cases CO_2 can be administered only after artificial respiration has been carried out long enough to assure a return of the blood chemistry to within normal values.

ARTIFICIAL RESPIRATOR

The methods outlined above are useful only in an emergency and then can be carried out only for limited periods of time. For somewhat longer periods the so-called **resuscitator** is used. This consists of a mask that is placed over the mouth and nose. The mask is connected to a pump that blows air under adequate pressure into the mouth and nostril. The pump then reverses itself and creates a negative pressure that causes expiration. But for very long periods of artificial respiration, such as is required for patients with paralysis of the respiratory muscles, the artificial respirator, or **iron-lung** as it is popularly called, is used.

The artificial respirator is a large metal tank in which the patient is placed with only his head outside the chamber. The patient's neck is surrounded by a rubber seal so as to keep the tank airtight. The pressure within the tank is decreased and increased alternately. When the tank pressure is negative, air is drawn into the subject's lungs; when it is positive, the air is forced out. The pressure can be regulated so as to adjust the tidal volume at the desirable level.

SUMMARY

The efficacy of the pulmonary system may be evaluated by the use of tests that determine the **vital capacity, maximal breathing capacity, timed vital capacity,** and the **oxygen** and **carbon dioxide content** of the arterial blood.

Marked respiratory and circulatory adjustments occur during exercise. Because little or no change in arterial CO_2, O_2, or pH occurs even during very heavy exercise, it is difficult to explain the increase in ventilation on this basis. Possibly the blood supply to the chemoreceptors diminishes during exercise, thus making them more sensitive to small blood changes. Also the neural drive essential for exercise to occur probably stimulates the respiratory center. In addition, there are impulses from contracting muscles. Increased venous pressure and temperature changes also stimulate respiration.

At **high altitude** the total atmospheric pressure is too low to drive adequate oxygen into the blood. First changes occur at about 5,000 ft. Consciousness is lost at over 20,000 ft. For ascent to higher altitudes, oxygen masks, or pressurized equipment, is required. Increased red blood cell production and increased hemoglobin provide a measure of protection.

In **deep-sea** diving the very high pressures increase the oxygen and nitrogen dissolved in the body fluids. High oxygen content deranges intracellular processes. Excessive nitrogen is narcotic. For normal function at high pressure the oxygen and nitrogen content of the air must be lowered and the air volume increased adequately to remove the compressed CO_2.

Artificial respiration is required when breathing is inadequate to maintain the proper alveolar gas composition. **Mouth-to-mouth** breathing is the simplest procedure and the most effective. The **arm-lift/back-pressure** method is also effective. Whatever procedure is used, it should be initiated within a few minutes after cessation of breathing. A mechanical **resuscitator,** if available, is best. For prolonged periods of artificial respiration, the **artificial respirator** is used.

QUESTIONS

1. Which test of pulmonary function would disclose partial obstruction in the trachea?
2. Explain the sequence of circulatory and respiratory changes evoked by exercise.
3. Determine the oxygen content of the arterial blood from the following values:
   Hemoglobin, 15 gm/100 ml
   Atmospheric pressure, 300 mm Hg
   Per cent O_2 in alveolar air, 16
   Per cent CO_2 in alveolar air, 4
4. In view of the fact that the oxygen saturation of the blood cannot be increased over 100 per cent and it is normally about 97 per cent, why does breathing compressed air have a deleterious effect?
5. Compare the advantages and disadvantages of the mouth-to-mouth and the arm-lift/back-pressure methods of artificial respiration.
6. Why is urgency required in initiating artificial respiration?

SUGGESTED READING

Comroe, J. H., Forster, R. E., Dubois, A. B., Briscoe, W. A., Carlsen, E., "The Lung," 2nd ed., Year Book Medical Publishers, Chicago, 1962.

Dubois, A. B., "Respiration," *Ann. Rev. Physiol.,* 26: 421–452, 1964.

Fenn, W. O., "The Mechanism of Breathing," *Sci. American,* 202:#1, 138–148, January 1960.

Horton, G. E., "Office Testing of Pulmonary Function," *Am. Practitioner,* 13:#7, 431–441, July 1962.

Kearney, P. W., "When the Heart Stops," *Today's Health,* 38:#11, 14, 80–81, November 1960.

Southworth, H., "Cardiorespiratory Resuscitation," *Am. J. Med.,* 26:#3, 327–330, March 1959.

PART 5

Alimentary and Excretory Systems

The Mouth

21

WE NOW TURN OUR ATTENTION TO THE VERY IMPORTANT STUDY of the digestion and utilization of foodstuffs and the elimination of waste products. **Food** may be defined as nutritive material absorbed or taken into the body to provide for growth, work, or repair and for the maintenance of the various metabolic processes. It can be seen that according to this definition foods not only embrace **carbohydrates, proteins,** and **fats** but also include **vitamins** and **minerals** which are essential to health.

In emergency situations, nutritive materials may be introduced into the body through a nasal or rectal tube or even by injection beneath the skin or into a vein. However, under normal circumstances, food begins its journey through the body in the mouth.

FOOD INTAKE

The intake of food has been shown to be under the control of the **hypothalamus.** If a lesion is placed in the **ventrolateral nuclei** of the hypothalamus, the animal does not eat and actually starves to death even though an abundance of food is available. In contradistinction, a lesion involving the **ventromedial** nuclei causes the animal to eat practically continuously so that the weight gain is incredible. These nuclei in the hypothalamus are looked upon as being facilitatory (lateral), and inhibitory (medial) centers. The inhibitory center, also called the **satiety center,** is thought to function by inhibiting the lateral nuclei. The lateral nuclei, referred to as the **feeding center,** in some way give rise to appetite. They may also be responsible for the so-called hunger contractions of the stomach, but this is only part of the drive for food. Even if the hunger contractions are prevented, the animal with a ventromedial lesion still has a voracious and insatiable appetite. Whatever the specific mecha-

415

nisms, it seems clear that the lateral nuclei of the hypothalamus facilitate them.

The sensitive cells in the lateral and medial nuclei of the hypothalamus are said to be **glucoreceptors** in that they seem to be responsive to the glucose concentration of the blood. Thus, when the glucose concentration of the blood falls, as it does between meals, the glucoreceptors in the lateral nuclei are activated and by virtue of the firing of these cells, appetite is generated. When food is taken in and the glucose concentration of the blood is increased, the medial nuclei are activated, they inhibit the lateral nuclei, and the drive for food ceases.

Conceivably, this **glucostatic** mechanism in the hypothalamus can be altered, thus accounting for the abnormal food intake characteristic of some individuals.

THE TEETH

Man, as well as some other animals, first develops a temporary set of teeth, the so-called **primary, deciduous,** or **milk teeth** which consist of two incisors, one canine, and two molars in each quadrant. As illustrated in Fig. 21-1, there are 20 primary teeth. These teeth begin to erupt into the mouth at about the sixth or seventh month and by the end of the second year are usually all present. Then, about the fifth or sixth year, the second set, the **permanent teeth,** begin to make their appearance and, in so doing, in the main replace the primary ones. Usually, by the time the individual is in his early twenties, all the permanent teeth are in place.

ANATOMY OF THE TEETH

Number Each quadrant of the adult mouth normally contains eight teeth: two incisors, one canine, two premolars, and three molars. In many individuals, some or all of the last molars (the so-called wisdom teeth) fail to erupt (Fig. 21-2).

Structure The **anterior** teeth, the incisors and canines, possess a sharp edge and serve to cut and divide food. The **posterior** teeth, the premolars and molars, have a relatively flat surface. In chewing, these surfaces rub across one another and grind the food.

Figure 21-3 shows a longitudinal section through one of the molars. Grossly, the tooth is divided into two parts: (1) the **crown** and (2) the **root.** The crown is the part of the tooth which is seen in the mouth. The root lies beneath the gum and is buried in the bone of the jaw. The point of junction of the crown and the root is termed the **neck.**

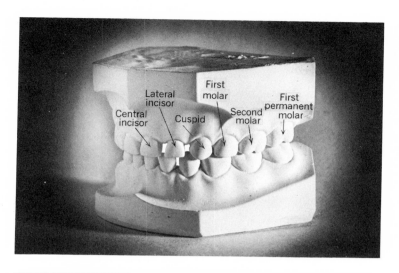

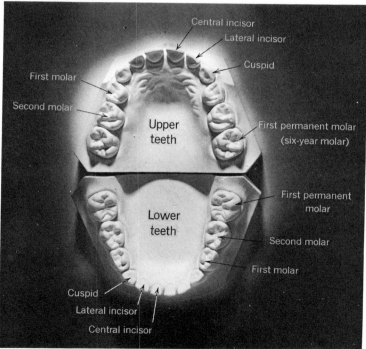

FIG. 21-1   The primary dentition. In addition to the 20 primary teeth, the first permanent molar is shown.

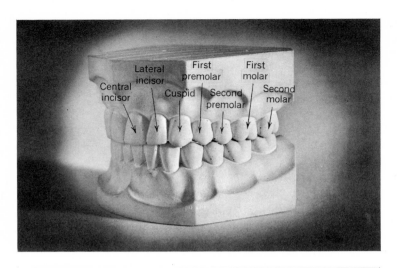

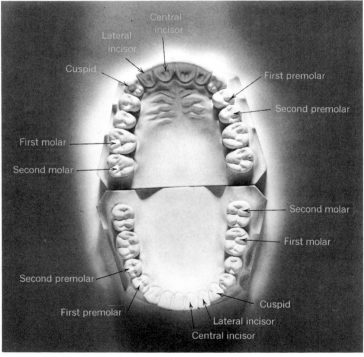

FIG. 21-2   The permanent dentition.

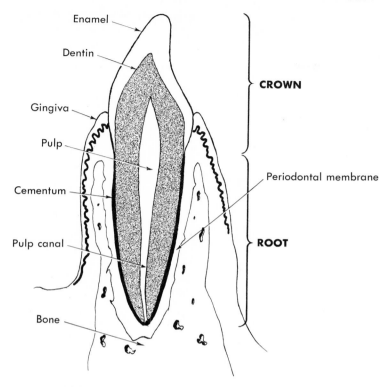

FIG. 21-3   Anatomy of a tooth and the related structures.

The outer surface of the crown is covered by the hardest tissue in the body, called **enamel.** It is composed primarily of calcium and phosphate salts which make it particularly resistant to mechanical and chemical assault. The enamel thus serves not only to make the teeth appear relatively white and therefore attractive but, more importantly, it protects them.

The outer surface of the root is enveloped by a layer, thinner and not so dense as enamel, known as **cementum.** In Fig. 21-3 it can be seen that the bulk of the interior of the tooth is composed of a substance called **dentin.** The composition of dentin and cementum is very much the same. and they resemble bone very closely. Finally, the tooth possesses the **pulp,** which may be divided into a pulp chamber, found in the innermost part of the crown, and pulp canal, which is part of the innermost part of the root. The pulp contains the blood and lymph vessels as well as the nerves of the tooth.

FUNCTION OF THE TEETH

Many animals employ their teeth not only for digestive purposes but for protection as well. For example, in some of the dangerous snakes, there is a canal in the tooth connected to a gland which elaborates a poison. Thus, the snake can bite and allow the poison to pass down through the tooth and into the victim. Interestingly enough, it is this arrangement which precipitated the invention and design of the hypodermic needle. Man, being somewhat more civilized, has found better protective means, and the teeth are now seldom used for this purpose. The teeth are also essential to intelligible speech, a subject alluded to in Chap. 10. Here we shall consider only the digestive function of dentition.

Prehension and Division   The word prehension implies to grasp or take hold of. Division means simply to separate a part from the whole. For these functions the sharp-edged anterior teeth are admirably suited. For example, when an individual eats a sandwich, he grasps it with his anterior teeth and succeeds in dividing a part from the whole. Obviously, if the anterior teeth are lacking or ineffective because of malposition or other reasons, it is not possible to do this. The individual then must cut or tear the sandwich into bits before placing it in his mouth.

Mastication   Masticatory efficiency under a variety of circumstances has been determined. By masticatory efficiency is meant the ability to reduce large particles to smaller size with a standard number of chews. Using this technique it has been possible to show that the absence of but one tooth, even a wisdom tooth, definitely reduces masticatory efficiency. However, although this is undoubtedly true and although it is clear that people with few or defective teeth cannot reduce the size of food particles efficiently, this deficit does not seem to handicap the individual appreciably. Apparently, in so far as digestion is concerned, if the bulk of the food particle is reduced to a size compatible with swallowing, that is sufficient. Periodically, fads have arisen which encourage people to go to extremes in their chewing habits. Children are incessantly admonished to chew their food and are forever reprimanded if they fail to heed this command. But there seems to be little real value in taking such exaggerated pains. As will be seen in the ensuing chapters, there is not much to be gained from prolonged masticatory efforts. To be sure, the enjoyment of food is derived from sense organs in the mouth. Therefore the gourmet carefully and slowly works over a delectable morsel so as to savor all its delicacies. But from a purely physiological standpoint, it is safe to conclude that if the teeth are used to reduce the food particle to a size convenient for swallowing, they have accomplished their purpose.

ABNORMALITIES OF THE TEETH

Caries There has been more research conducted in an attempt to discover the mechanisms of caries formation in teeth than in any other aspect of dentistry. The term **caries** means literally "to rot." It is a word which is applied to the disintegration of teeth and refers to dental cavities (Fig. 21-4).

Caries develop in the permanent dentition, in the average person, at a very early age. We have already seen that the permanent teeth do not usually appear in the mouth until the sixth year of life; yet the average child of seven has at least one cavity. The startling and lamentable fact is that in the United States *the average thirty-year-old person has at least one-half of his teeth either missing, filled, or defective.* It is true that other dental conditions are included in these statistical compilations, but caries is overwhelmingly the major contributor.

The present status of our knowledge of the genesis of dental caries can be summarized by saying that at least three factors play major roles. They are (1) the presence of fermentable carbohydrates, (2) bacteria in the mouth, and (3) the physicochemical characteristics of enamel. It is currently held that fermentable carbohydrates are acted upon by oral bacterial enzyme systems, so that organic acids are produced. These in turn

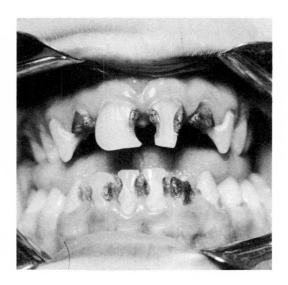

FIG. 21-4 Dental caries. This extensive decay was seen in a 12-year-old child.

destroy the teeth. All of us have bacteria in the mouth, and there is no practical way of reducing this flora. The numerous available mouthwashes possess a pleasant or hygienic taste, but they have scarcely any influence upon the oral bacterial population. Since we consume daily a large amount of carbohydrate, it is obvious that this substance will usually be present in the mouth, particularly right after meals. However, it is possible to limit the time during which fermentable carbohydrates are in a position to react with the bacteria to produce acids which destroy the teeth. It has been shown that, if one will effectively rinse the mouth soon after eating, the concentration of carbohydrate about the teeth is strikingly reduced, and the incidence of dental caries is diminished.

But it is the third factor, the physicochemical characteristics of enamel, which offers the greatest possibilities for reducing caries. Clearly, if the enamel can be hardened to the extent that it successfully resists the acid formed from the combination of fermentable carbohydrates and bacteria, dental caries will not develop. Although the mechanism of the action of fluorine and the fluorides upon the teeth is still not definitely known, there is excellent evidence which shows that small amounts of this substance render the teeth remarkably resistant to caries formation.

The teeth in the developing child can be periodically painted with a weak solution of a fluoride salt with notable success. But by far the more acceptable procedure is to incorporate minute quantities, of the magnitude of 1 part per million, of this chemical in the public drinking water. In communities where this has been done, the incidence of dental caries has been reduced remarkably.

Malocclusion   No doubt most of us at one time or another have chanced across a child who looks like Popeye or Andy Gump. Most such individuals acquire these profiles because of the malpositioning of the teeth in the jaws. Great strides have been made in the prevention and treatment of such cases of malocclusion. Today, the science of orthodontics, which is chiefly concerned with the study of the arrangement of the teeth in the jaws and their effect upon dentofacial growth, has developed complicated wires and bands and bars which can be fixed to the teeth and with appropriate forces cause the teeth to shift about so that a correct alignment is encouraged.

SALIVA

Saliva serves many functions. It is, as we shall learn, most important for swallowing; it cleans the teeth, lubricates the oral mucous membranes; and serves many other uses. But before these activities are studied, it is necessary to learn how saliva is manufactured.

PRODUCTION OF SALIVA

Salivary Glands   There are six large clusters of cells, or glands, three on each side of the mouth, which produce most of the saliva. These are collectively referred to as the **major salivary glands.** Figure 21-5 shows the location of the **parotid, submaxillary,** and **sublingual glands.** The salivary glands are innervated by both branches of the autonomic nervous system (Fig. 8-2). The parasympathetic innervation to the sublingual and submaxillary glands is carried in the **facial nerve (VII);** that to the parotid gland in the **glossopharyngeal nerve (IX).**

The salivary glands are made up of two different types of cells, **serous** and **mucous cells.** Serous cells produce a thin, watery solution, whereas the mucous cells, as the name suggests, elaborate a thick substance. The salivary glands differ in their distribution of these two cell types. For example, the parotid gland possesses only serous cells, the sublingual gland mostly mucous cells, and the submaxillary gland both types. It can be seen, therefore, that the viscosity of the saliva produced will depend upon the relative contribution of these different glands.

Quantity of Saliva   On the average, over a liter of saliva is produced per day. This quantity varies greatly, of course, with climatic conditions, fluid intake, and oral activity. If one chews gum all day, for instance, the saliva production will be greater than the normal amount.

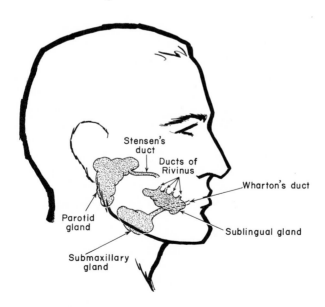

FIG. 21-5   Location of the salivary glands.

MECHANISM OF SALIVATION

Saliva can be secreted against a considerable head of pressure, higher in fact than arterial blood pressure. Thus, there is general agreement that the formation of saliva is an active process. Study of oxygen consumption, in which the quantity of oxygen used increased about fivefold with activity, supports this contention. A hypothesis has been proposed which states that a precursor solution is formed by the acinar cells and then, as it passes through the ducts, it is modified by the absorption of some ions, and the active secretion of others. The results of radioisotope studies, however, suggest that all the ions that appear in the saliva are selectively secreted into it by the duct cells. The acinar cells probably function to contribute fluid, mucus, and ptyalin. The enzyme is secreted by the acinar cells in so-called **secretory granules.** They are also referred to as zymogen granules because zymogen is the name given to the precursor of an enzyme.

Composition of Saliva   The saliva is not simply an ultrafiltrate of the plasma. Its actual composition varies under many conditions, and it can differ markedly from the composition of the plasma. However, many of the substances which are found in the plasma are also present in the saliva. In addition, saliva contains enzymes, mucin, epithelial cells from the oral mucosa, and bacteria. In general, saliva may be said to contain the following:

1. About 98 per cent water.
2. Most of the salts found in the plasma.
3. The enzyme ptyalin and, in some cases, maltase.
4. Carbon dioxide which diffuses out and leaves calcium carbonate, an insoluble substance which precipitates with phosphates to form the tartar of the teeth. This reaction is $Ca(HCO_3)_2 = CO_2 + CaCO_3 + H_2O$.
5. Mucin.
6. Epithelial cells and bacteria.

The reaction of saliva is usually slightly on the acid side.

THE FUNCTION OF SALIVA

Digestion   When food is taken into the mouth, it is cut and ground by the teeth and thoroughly mixed with saliva. The saliva performs three functions: (1) it dissolves some substances, thus making taste possible; (2) the enzyme it contains begins to act; (3) it lubricates the food so that it can be swallowed.

In Chap. 7, the anatomy and physiology of taste were studied. It has been learned that the taste buds can be stimulated only by substances which are in solution. If salt, for example, is placed upon the dried tongue, there is no sensation of taste. As soon as the saliva dissolves some of the salt, a very definite sensation results. Therefore, saliva contributes to our enjoyment of eating by dissolving food substances and making it possible to taste them.

Saliva contains an enzyme called **ptyalin.** An enzyme, it should be recalled, is a substance produced by the body which acts as a catalyst. An enzyme speeds a chemical reaction but takes no part in it itself. Ptyalin is an enzyme which hurries the reaction by which the higher, or more complex, carbohydrates are reduced to simpler sugars. There are many intermediate steps between a substance such as starch and the end product glucose. Ptyalin does not ordinarily complete this breakdown but merely initiates it. In this way, less complex carbohydrates result, and these are subsequently acted upon by other enzymes in the gastrointestinal tract. In some cases saliva also contains another enzyme, **maltase,** which also acts upon carbohydrates, specifically upon maltose to hydrolyze it to glucose. Since there is at best very little of this enzyme present, very little glucose is actually formed in the mouth.

To convince oneself that saliva is important in deglutition, the student should voluntarily swallow several times so as to reduce the amount of saliva in the mouth. If he now places a piece of dry bread in the back of the mouth he will experience great difficulty in swallowing it. As a matter of fact, even without the bread, if he simply attempts to swallow repeatedly he will find that after a while it becomes extremely difficult, if not impossible.

Lubrication Saliva flows even when there is no food in the mouth. It serves to lubricate the mouth and lips. This has two purposes: (1) it prevents the mucous membranes from drying and cracking, and (2) it aids in speaking.

In very dry climates, the quantity of saliva produced is low, and the rapid evaporation of that which does appear causes excessive drying of the lips. Therefore, in these cases the saliva may fail to protect the mucous membranes; if other measures are not instituted, the lips may dry and fissure. Under normal conditions, however, the saliva suffices to maintain these structures soft and pliable.

For normal speech, the quantity of saliva produced usually suffices to keep the mouth and lips moist. But when a long lecture is being delivered, the constant flow of hot air evaporates the saliva faster than it is produced and the mouth becomes dry. As a result, the tongue and lips stick, they lose their mobility, and speech becomes extremely difficult. It is for this reason that lecture stands are often equipped with a pitcher or glass of water.

Cleansing Action   In discussing dental caries it was stated that the length of time that fermentable carbohydrates reside in the mouth is an important factor. There is, of course, no better way of decreasing this time than by vigorous rinsing, but the steady flow of saliva assists immeasurably. The value of saliva is clearly shown in cases where salivation is deficient on one side. In such instances food accumulates about the teeth on that side and the incidence of unilateral caries is much higher than it is normally.

Thirst   The quantity of fluid ingested daily is determined, to a great extent, by what is known as **thirst.** The term means an eager desire, a craving. In its usual connotation it implies a craving for fluid. The mechanism of thirst remains debatable. Some investigators insist that the drying of the mucous membranes of the throat contributes to the typical sensation of thirst. According to this theory, when one becomes dehydrated, the quantity of saliva produced is lessened. Consequently, the mucous membranes dry, and the individual has the sensation of thirst and takes in more fluids.

Protection   Saliva also has an important protective function. There are many substances in the saliva which give to it a fairly potent buffering capacity. Thus, if acids or bases are inadvertently or otherwise introduced into the mouth, the oral structures are protected by the saliva which quickly neutralizes these noxious substances.

Saliva has also been shown to have a bacteriocidal effect upon many organisms. This protective function is of value, since many microorganisms are constantly being introduced into the mouth with food.

Finally, saliva aids in ridding the mouth of foreign objects which may appear there. For example, if a worm residing in an apple should get into the mouth, the individual would quickly expectorate (spit) and thereby rid himself of this undesirable rascal.

REGULATION OF SALIVATION

Psychic Stimulation   The very thought of food is said to evoke a copious flow of saliva. Most everyone believes that when he thinks of food, sees it, or smells delectable aromas, his mouth "waters." Careful measurements, however, have failed to show any significant increase in the rate of salivation as the result of such stimulation. It is interesting that the subjects being tested thought they were salivating excessively. Thus, it is concluded that the thought of food makes one conscious of the saliva already in the mouth, but it does not increase the amount of saliva formed.

Chemical Stimulation   A thick, succulent steak while being chewed gives off juices which chemically stimulate the taste buds. Impulses are then initiated by these taste buds and conducted to the brain stem to set off reflex secretion of saliva. It is interesting to note that the composition of the food eaten determines, to a large extent, the quantity and quality of the saliva. If starchy foods, such as bread, are chewed, there is a very copious secretion of a serous saliva. On the other hand, protein such as meat brings forth a smaller amount of thick mucous saliva. The precise mechanisms which account for these differences are not entirely clear, but whatever the explanation the results prove admirable. This is so because in the case of starch a large quantity of ptyalin serves to begin the digestion of that type of carbohydrate. But there is no enzyme in the saliva which breaks down protein. Therefore, the saliva serves only a lubricative function.

Mechanical Stimulation   If one chews a piece of tasteless paraffin which therefore does not evoke the salivary secretions by chemical means, saliva nonetheless pours forth. In this case it is mechanical stimulation which also initiates a reflex response. When one first begins to chew gum, the flavoring agents produce a chemical result. However, after prolonged chewing, there is little flavor left. The copious flow of saliva is now a result of mechanical reflexes. For the same reason, when the dentist is filling a tooth or cleaning the teeth, there is usually a profuse salivary flow.

SWALLOWING

After the food has been grasped and divided by the anterior teeth, it is ground into fine particles by the posterior dentition. At the same time it is tossed about by the tongue and thoroughly mixed with saliva. As noted previously, the saliva not only, through the action of ptyalin, initiates the digestive processes but also makes it possible to swallow the mass of food which is now termed the **bolus,** a term which literally means a very large pill. But its similarity to a pill ceases here, since the swallowing of food is usually far more pleasant and less difficult than ingesting a large pill.

MECHANISM OF SWALLOWING

The act of swallowing is very complex. It involves both voluntary and reflex mechanisms. In order to analyze this act we shall break down the complex pattern into three stages.

First Stage   It has already been pointed out that the food is ground and rolled in to a bolus which has been thoroughly soaked with saliva. The tongue then directs the bolus to the back of the mouth and forces it to enter the pharynx. All these acts are purely voluntary. The individual can chew the food as long or as briefly as he desires. He may roll the bolus about in his mouth indefinitely, but once he forces it into the pharynx, the voluntary phase of swallowing has ended. From now on, all the mechanisms are purely reflex. The reflex control of the second and third stages is initiated by the voluntary act of the first stage.

Second Stage   During this phase of swallowing, the bolus passes through the pharynx to enter the **esophagus.** This term is most descriptive, since it means "I carry food," which is precisely what the esophagus does. It is a tube which connects the throat (pharynx) with the stomach. It serves to conduct the food into the stomach.

The passage of the food through the pharynx is, in reality, rather precarious. There are many openings into and out of the throat. There is the opening of the trachea (the windpipe), through which air, but not food, must pass. There are the orifices of the eustachian tubes, which connect the middle ear and the pharynx. Finally, there are the openings into the mouth and nasal passageways. But the bolus of food must be directed into the esophageal opening and into none of the others. In order to accomplish this feat, a series of reflex muscular responses seal off, as it were, all the other openings while leaving the esophagus free to receive the bolus.

The bolus is prevented from reentering the mouth by the tongue and neighboring structures. The soft palate is raised to bar the bolus from the nasal passages. The entrance to the eustachian tubes is guarded by muscles which prevent food from entering. The trachea is protected by elevation of the larynx and the closing of a cartilaginous cap, the epiglottis. All these muscular actions must take place synchronously with the contractions which are responsible for propelling the food through the pharynx.

If one will hold his fingers on his Adam's apple and then swallow, he will be able to feel many of these responses. They take place rapidly. The entire second stage of swallowing occupies but a fraction of a second.

Third Stage   Finally, the food traverses the esophagus to enter the stomach. Man usually eats in the upright position, therefore, the force of gravity assists in transporting the bolus through the esophagus. However, one need not rely upon gravity. As a matter of fact, it is possible to swallow and pass the bolus, or even liquids, through the esophagus while being held upside down.

The esophagus is made up chiefly of smooth muscle. The muscles contract in wavelike fashion along the length of the tube. These are called **peristaltic waves** or **movements.** The term **peristalsis** means "to contract around" and describes the contraction of one part, then contraction below it and relaxation of the originally contracted segment—progressing in that way along the tube.

Peristalsis is a reflex mechanism. Smooth muscle, it should be recalled, cannot be contracted voluntarily. It is innervated by the autonomic nervous system. As a result of impulses set up by the previous stages of swallowing, these smooth muscles are caused to contract as described.

THE CARDIA

Where the esophagus joins the stomach, there is a sphincter termed the **cardia.** Contraction closes the opening. But this contraction is never vigorous and is easily overwhelmed by very low pressures. Yet the cardia suffices, under normal conditions, to prevent regurgitation of food from the stomach into the esophagus. Eructation of gas (belching) from the stomach requires sufficient pressure to open the sphincter. Cardiospasm, forceful enough to prevent the passage of food from the esophagus into the stomach, sometimes occurs.

ABNORMALITIES OF SWALLOWING

An impairment in swallowing is termed **dysphagia.** *Phagia* means "to eat," and the prefix *dys-* means "with difficulty." Thus the term simply implies that there is difficulty in eating because of some abnormality in the swallowing mechanism.

From this analysis of swallowing it is obvious that the impairment may involve any or all stages. Thus, it is common to speak of dysphagia of the first stage, of the second stage, or of the third stage. It is not necessary here to delve into all the possibilities, but it should be understood that if the tongue is paralyzed, for example, it will be difficult or impossible to force the bolus into the pharynx. There would then be dysphagia of the first stage. If, through a nervous-system disorder, reflex mechanisms are interfered with or if muscular coordination is lost, then clearly the second stage of swallowing may be seriously impaired. Finally, if the esophagus is damaged, as often happens when one inadvertently or otherwise swallows strong acids, it may not be possible to pass food through the tube. This illustrates dysphagia of the third stage.

SUMMARY

Man develops two sets of teeth: (1) the 20 **primary teeth** and later (2) the 32 **permanent teeth.** The first set begins to appear during the sixth month and is usually completed during the second year of life. The permanent dentition makes its debut about the sixth year and is complete in the latter part of the second decade. A tooth consists of a **crown** and a **root** joined at the **neck.** The outer surface of the crown is covered by **enamel,** the root by **cementum.** There is a large **pulp chamber** and **canal** within the tooth covered by **dentin.**

The anterior teeth serve to grasp and divide food. The posterior teeth possess broad occlusal surfaces which serve to grind substances. The consensus today is that **dental caries** is caused by the action of various oral bacterial enzyme systems upon specific fermentable carbohydrates so that the end result is acid formation which, in turn, acts to dissolve the outer surfaces of the teeth. Effective rinsing following meals and the addition of fluoride salts to the drinking water or locally to the teeth strikingly reduce the incidence of caries formation.

There are three major pairs of salivary glands, **parotid, submaxillary,** and **sublingual glands.** These glands are composed of **serous** and **mucous** cells. Over a quart of **saliva** is produced per day. It contains mostly water, the salts common to the blood plasma, the enzyme ptyalin, carbon dioxide, mucin, epithelial cells, and bacteria. Saliva assists digestion by dissolving food substances, contributing a digestive enzyme, and lubricating the food. **Ptyalin** speeds the conversion of starch and other complex carbohydrate molecules to the simpler sugars. Saliva lubricates the mucous membranes, keeps them from drying, and thus aids in speaking. It also cleanses the teeth, plays a role in the thirst mechanism, and protects man against foreign objects introduced into the mouth.

The production and composition of saliva are under autonomic nervous control. The presence of food or other substances in the mouth increases salivation through chemical and mechanical reflex pathways.

After the food is macerated and insalivated and rolled into a **bolus,** it is forced into the **pharynx.** This is the **first stage of swallowing.** Through a series of reflex connections, the bolus is shot through the pharynx to enter the esophagus. At the same time the openings into the nose, mouth, trachea, and ears are closed. All these reflex acts compose the **second stage of swallowing.** The **third stage** sees the food being passed through the esophagus to enter the stomach. Any impairment of swallowing is termed **dysphagia.**

QUESTIONS

1. How do the primary and permanent teeth differ?
2. In the light of current theories, how may dental caries be prevented?
3. Outline the functions of saliva.
4. How does chewed food evoke the secretion of saliva?
5. Discuss the sequence of events by which the bolus is swallowed.
6. What digestive processes occur in the mouth?

SUGGESTED READING

Dixon, A. D., "Sensory Nerve Terminations in the Oral Mucosa," *Arch. Oral Biol.,* 5:#2, 105–114, November 1961.

"Fluoride and the Teeth," *Therapeutic Notes,* 71:#2, 42–46, February 1964.

Hartles, R. L., "Metabolic Factors in Saliva," *J. D. Res.,* 42:#1 (Part 2), 553–558, January-February 1963.

Walker, R. O., "The Oral Mucosa as an Index of Health," *Brit. J. Clin. Pract.,* 16:#11, 699–704, November 1962.

22 Gastrointestinal Tract

THE TERM **gastrointestinal tract** embraces the stomach (*gaster*) and the intestine. The latter is anatomically further divided into the **small intestine** and the **large intestine.** As portrayed in Fig. 22-1, the upper part of the large intestine is usually referred to as the **colon.**

The food, after being grasped and divided, is ground and mixed with saliva. The saliva, as has been pointed out, contains ptyalin which initiates the digestion of carbohydrates. The moist bolus is then swallowed and passes through the esophagus to enter the stomach. A series of reactions take place here and in the intestine which complete the digestion of the three basic foodstuffs. The end products of digestion are then absorbed from the intestinal tract into the blood stream, while undigested substances are eliminated in the feces. In this chapter, the major reactions responsible for the reduction and simplification of foods to their basic components ready for absorption will be considered.

THE STOMACH

Figure 22-1 shows that the stomach is a greatly expanded part of the digestive tract. The volume of this organ varies considerably from person to person, but its capacity may be as much as 4 liters. Because of its relatively large size, the stomach functions as a reservoir, a place where a great mass of food may be received to be fed slowly into the intestine. It is therefore possible for man to take in all the food he requires per day in one or two meals. Were it not for the stomach, it would be necessary to eat far more frequently, and considerably less could be consumed at each meal. This fact is demonstrated well in an individual who has had his stomach surgically removed.

But the stomach serves the body other than as a reservoir. As will be seen presently, it also possesses an important digestive function.

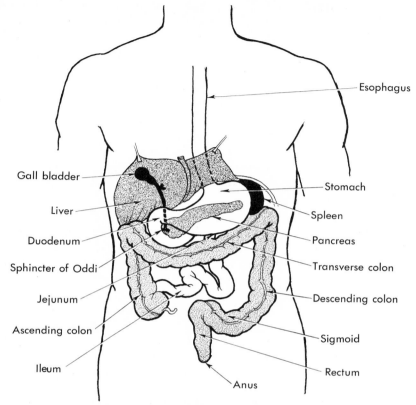

Esophagus

Gall bladder

Liver

Duodenum

Sphincter of Oddi

Jejunum

Ascending colon

Ileum

Stomach

Spleen

Pancreas

Transverse colon

Descending colon

Sigmoid

Rectum

Anus

FIG. 22-1 Diagrammatic representation of the gastrointestinal tract and related structures.

GASTRIC JUICE

Gastric Glands The wall of the stomach is replete with glands. It has been estimated that there are about 35,000,000 such glands. The ducts of these gastric glands open into the stomach cavity, so that as the gastric juice is produced it pours directly into the stomach cavity.

Three types of cells have been described in the gastric glands. They are (1) **mucous neck cells,** (2) **zymogenic, or chief, cells,** and (3) **parietal cells.** Each of these cells elaborates a different substance. Mucus is derived from the first. The precursor of **pepsin,** a very important enzyme, is manufactured by the zymogenic cells. This precursor, that is, a substance which gives rise to another compound, is called **zymogen.** The parietal cells liberate **hydrochloric acid.**

Not all the gastric glands possess the three types of cells. Some have only one, while others have a mixture. By this arrangement the composition of the gastric juice may be varied. As a matter of fact, it is altered remarkably, in a way that permits maximal digestive function whatever the character of the bolus.

Composition of Gastric Juice   We have just mentioned that the gastric glands contain three different types of cells. The gastric juice consists of a mixture of the products of these cells. Thus, the gastric juice is composed of **water, mucin, pepsin, HCl, rennin,** and a **gastric lipase.**

Perhaps the most unusual component of the gastric secretion is the hydrochloric acid. This substance appears in such high concentrations that the gastric juice has a pH very close to 1. It will be recalled that the acidity of any solution may be expressed in pH units ranging up to 14. The symbol, pH, is the designation of the hydrogen-ion concentration in a solution. Acids are characterized by their ability to liberate hydrogen ions when in aqueous solution; bases are acceptors of hydrogen ions. The pH of a solution may be measured with an electrical instrument which transforms a meter reading of electrical dissociation directly into pH units by the use of electrodes immersed in the solution, or with indicators having the properties of changing color in accordance with a scale calibrated in pH units. A neutral solution is assigned a pH of 7. The higher the number, the more basic or alkaline is the solution; the lower, the more acid. Thus it can be seen that the gastric juice with a pH value of 1 is very acid indeed. So acid, in fact, is this secretion that if an individual should be seized with a spell of vomiting the loss of acid by this route would usually cause widespread alterations because of the deranged acid-base balance. Likewise, although the urine is normally slightly acid, after a meal it becomes alkaline. This is referred to as the **alkaline tide** of the urine.

A vivid idea of just how remarkable the acid concentration of the gastric juice is may be obtained from the fact that the hydrogen ion concentration of the plasma is about 0.00005 mEq/L whereas in the gastric juice it is 150 mEq/L! Quite clearly the secretion of hydrogen ions in the gastric juice is an active process. It has been calculated that at least 1,500 calories are required to produce a liter of juice with this acidity.

As yet there is not complete agreement as to the mechanism responsible for the secretion of hydrogen ions in the gastric juice. It is thought that the primary source of the hydrogen ion is intracellular water. Following ionization of the water, the hydrogen ion is secreted from the cell. This will leave the OH ion which must be neutralized. Carbon dioxide enters the cell (Fig. 22-2) where it reacts with H_2O. The reaction is catalyzed by carbonic anhydrase to form H_2CO_3. H_2CO_3 dissociates to HCO_3^-

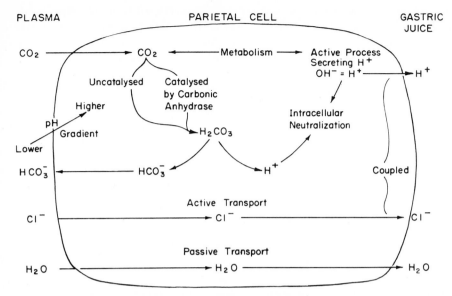

PLASMA   PARIETAL CELL   GASTRIC
                                                                          JUICE

FIG. 22-2   Secretion of HCl by the gastric parietal cells. Note that these cells take up CO_2 from the plasma. The CO_2 serves to neutralize the cell by forming H_2CO_3 which gives rise to H+. The H+ then reacts with OH−. (Reproduced, with permission, from H. W. Davenport, "Physiology of the Digestive Tract," Year Book Medical Publishers, Chicago, 1961.)

and H+. The hydrogen ion neutralizes the OH−, and the HCO_3^- moves from the cell into the plasma.

Even less is known about the mechanism for the secretion of Cl−. It must be an active process because the Cl− is secreted against both an electrical and a concentration gradient.

There are several consequences of this secretion of HCl. In the first place, the parietal cells take up CO_2 rather than excrete it. This means that the arterial blood has a higher CO_2, in the stomach, than does the venous blood. Secondly, while CO_2 molecules have been removed from the blood, they have been replaced by HCO_3 ions. CO_2 molecules are potentially acid; HCO_3 ions are alkaline. Thus, the pH of the venous blood is markedly higher than elsewhere in the body. As a result, as already mentioned, the pH of the urine rises whenever the gastric glands are sufficiently stimulated as they are following a meal.

The unusual acidity of the gastric cavity is essential for digestive purposes. The gastric juice contains pepsin. This is a **proteolytic enzyme;** that is, it catalyzes the reaction by which proteins are reduced to smaller molecules such as the peptones and proteoses. Pepsin functions optimally in a highly acid medium; its efficiency in a less acid environment is seriously impaired. Thus, for protein digestion in the stomach, it is vital that the gastric juice be highly acid. The HCl takes care of that.

Pepsin, as noted above, is not secreted as such by the zymogenic cells. Rather a substance called **zymogen** is elaborated. Strictly speaking, the term zymogen may be applied to the inactive form of any enzyme. In this particular case, the active enzyme is pepsin. When this zymogen, or **pepsinogen,** as it is also called, comes into contact with the existing pepsin in the acid medium of the stomach, it is activated, resulting in more pepsin. In other words, it is the pepsin itself which is primarily responsible for the activation of the gastric zymogen. Pepsin, a potent proteolytic enzyme, now sets to work upon the protein present in the bolus.

Mucin is secreted in varying quantities and apparently serves to buffer the strong acid, or at least to form a protective barrier between it and the stomach mucous membrane. It is obvious that such protection is needed, for if pepsin is capable of digesting protein, it is also capable of digesting the protein in the stomach wall. Of course, in some cases, this is precisely what occurs, and thus one finds a so-called **peptic ulcer.** But in the normal stomach the mucin proves adequate to prevent the pepsin from acting so deleteriously.

It has been shown that gastric juice also contains **rennin.** Rennin is an enzyme which acts specifically upon the casein in milk to cause the formation of curds. A curd is a coagulated semiliquid glob of milk. One may wonder how the formation of such curds assists in the digestion of milk. The explanation probably lies in the fact that fluids do not linger in the stomach. It has been shown that under normal conditions fluid moves, without pausing, through the stomach into the duodenum. Clearly, very little digestion can occur during such hasty passage. Rennin assists in the digestion of milk by transforming it into these semifluid curds which are retained in the stomach long enough for digestion to occur. It has been shown that very little rennin is secreted by the adult stomach. In addition, this enzyme does not function very well in a highly acid medium. It is for these reasons that one may well question the value of adults drinking large quantities of milk. The infant stomach elaborates considerable rennin, and the stomach contents are not nearly so acid as they are in the adult. Accordingly, during the formative years milk is undoubtedly well digested.

The gastric juice also contains a **lipase,** that is, a substance which catalyzes the conversion of the complex fat molecule into its simpler constituents. But it seems probable that very little fat is actually digested in the stomach despite the presence of this enzyme. In the first place, the acidity is too great, and secondly, efficient fat digestion demands bile which is present only in the small intestine.

The gastric juice probably also has a protective function. The high acidity is capable of killing many types of bacteria. This is rather convenient, since it should be evident that the food ingested is far from sterile; millions of microorganisms enter the stomach daily. Unquestionably, the extraordinary acidity acts as a barrier against bacterial invasion by destroying many of these microbes.

In short, the gastric juice acts on the bolus to initiate the digestion of protein. The high acidity stops the action of ptyalin, and since there is no gastric enzyme which acts upon carbohydrates, the breakdown of these foods is temporarily halted. The gastric juice also digests the milk protein casein most efficiently in the infant and in general exerts a convenient protective action. It is doubtful if much fat is digested by the gastric lipase present.

Regulation of Gastric Secretion The quantity of gastric juice formed per day varies, of course, depending upon the type and amount of food ingested. But on the average diet, about 2 liters of gastric juice are produced in a 24-hour period. Not only does the quantity vary, but so does the composition of the juice. Apparently both quantity and quality are regulated in such a way as to handle best the task at hand. Precisely how this is accomplished is not clearly understood, but many regulatory mechanisms have been described.

When one is hungry and sees some appetizing food, or smells it, or simply thinks about it, the saliva begins to flow and so does the gastric juice. In a sense, one drools, inwardly and outwardly. This liberation of gastric juice is brought about by nervous impulses which originate in the cerebral cortex and are conducted to the gastric glands by the vagus nerves to incite higher production. Accordingly, it is known as the **cephalic phase** of gastric secretion.

When food actually reaches the stomach, the flow of gastric juice becomes greater than ever. Meat extracts, as well as other protein products, are most effective in calling forth the gastric juice. Thus it is that soups are frequently the first course of a meal, because they excite the flow of gastric secretions. This effect is not the direct result of the substance upon the gastric glands. It is more complex than that. The protein substance acts upon the stomach wall, provoking it into secreting a chemical substance which is a **hormone.** The term hormone means "to excite," and that is exactly what it does in this instance. The hormone produced by the stomach wall is called **gastrin.** Gastrin is then carried by the blood stream to the gastric glands which it excites to greater activity. This so-called **gastric phase** of stomach secretion results from other stimuli as well. It has been shown that direct mechanical stimulation of the stomach mucosa evokes a juice which is highly mucous in quality. There is also some evidence to indicate that stimulation of the lining of the stomach by the presence of food initiates impulses which are conducted to the central nervous system and then back to the stomach via the vagus nerves to evoke gastric-juice secretion.

Finally, when the food to be digested leaves the stomach and passes into the small intestine, a hormone is produced by the intestinal mucosa which is carried by the blood stream to the stomach and which further encourages gastric-juice secretion. This hormone may be identical with gastrin, but the evidence on this point is not clear. Of perhaps more importance is the liberation of **enterogastrone** by the intestinal wall in response to the presence of fats. Enterogastrone inhibits gastric-juice production. It is a hormone, even though its action is inhibitory rather than excitatory. It can be seen that there are many interrelated mechanisms for the control of gastric secretion. Normally the flow begins before the food is swallowed, reaches its peak while the food is in the stomach, and then when the fats come into contact with the intestinal wall, the gastric secretion is inhibited. This is truly an efficient regulatory mechanism, but there are many factors which may interfere with it.

It is well known that emotional forces may influence digestion. Psychic distress may precipitate the production of gastric juice in the absence of food and thus contribute to ulcer formation, or the production of gastric juice during digestion may be inhibited so that the food is incompletely digested, resulting in excessive gas production as well as other undesirable symptoms and signs.

It has been claimed that the drinking of large quantities of water (particularly ice water) while eating, is detrimental from a physiological standpoint. There is little evidence for this claim. On the contrary, carefully controlled experiments failed to reveal any impairment in digestion even when very great quantities of water were consumed.

It is true that smoking during or immediately following a meal decreases the output of gastric juice, but whether or not the reduction is adequate to interfere significantly with digestion has not been established.

GASTRIC MOVEMENTS

The stomach is chiefly composed of smooth muscle. This type of muscle, as noted many times already, cannot be voluntarily contracted. But it does contract automatically in response to inherent properties within the muscle as well as to stimulation via the autonomic nervous system. The resulting gastric activity serves several functions.

Hunger Contractions If food has not been eaten for about 5 hours (the usual elapsed time between meals), the stomach will be empty and collapsed, so that the walls are loosely together as in a deflated balloon. If the stomach is observed at this time it will be seen to undergo periodic movements. These movements progressively become more frequent and of greater intensity. The individual soon becomes aware of gastric "growling" or "grumbling," and interprets the movement as hunger pains or contractions.

Hunger contractions are, for the most part, controlled by the concentration of blood sugar. Between meals the blood sugar progressively falls, finally reaching a low point at which stomach movements are stimulated. The lower the sugar level, the more frequent and vigorous these movements. Hunger contractions are also associated with a conditioned reflex. By that is meant that, if food is regularly ingested at a particular time each day, hunger contractions will occur at that time, if the meal should be omitted. However, it is important to note that these contractions occur at that time regardless of the blood-sugar concentration. This is important to recognize, because people who are overweight overeat (and vice versa). If they are placed on a diet, or if they are accustomed to eating four or five times a day and are now reduced to two or three, they will complain bitterly of uncontrollable hunger. However, if they refrain from eating those extra meals, then the associated hunger contractions will eventually vanish at that time. People who have successfully dieted agree that the first few days of the regime are the most trying.

Filling A large volume of food can be taken in within a short period of time. Those of us who have experienced the joys of a boardinghouse can attest to that. This large volume causes the stomach to expand. But the stomach-wall muscle progressively relaxes as filling continues. The result of such relaxation is that the pressure within the stomach when empty is not very much lower than it is when normally filled. This is a property common to many of the smooth-muscle viscera. For example, the urinary bladder, as it fills with urine, undergoes very little change in internal pressure. This ability to fill without increasing pressure is of great value. Without it, the augmented pressure might seriously interfere with the circulation of blood through the wall of the organ.

We have seen that the stomach wall moves when empty in the form of hunger contractions. Vigorous movements also occur when the stomach is filled. This activity serves to move the food about, to break it up, thus aiding in its digestion.

Emptying Gastric motility propels the food, as it is acted upon by the gastric juice, toward the opening into the small intestine. Fluids are evacuated from the stomach very quickly. They invariably pass through that organ in less than 20 minutes and in most cases very much more rapidly. But the more solid substances remain longer. The rate of emptying depends upon (1) the relative pressures in the stomach and duodenum, (2) the state of contraction or relaxation of the pyloric sphincter, and (3) the fluidity of the gastric contents.

As has been emphasized many times already, the movement of gases and fluids depends upon a pressure gradient. The same is true of food within the gastrointestinal tract. Accordingly, the greater the pressure in the stomach in relation to the duodenum, the faster will be the movement of food in that direction. Although it is true that the stomach distends to accommodate greater volumes, nonetheless there is, eventually, an increase in pressure which forces the food into the small intestine. Conversely, a filled duodenum will tend to keep the food in the stomach. These relationships hold, of course, only so long as the pyloric sphincter is open. Pyloric constriction will slow or completely halt the passage of food. Just what controls the pyloric sphincter is not completely clear. The autonomic nervous system is known to play a role, and there is good evidence that the presence of acid in the duodenum causes the sphincter to constrict. This, then, would be a protective measure. Finally, as already mentioned, the more fluid the gastric contents, the more rapid is the passage. Water, for example, flows without hesitation through the stomach and into the duodenum.

GASTRIC ABNORMALITIES

Ulceration   An ulcer is a cavity, an area that is unduly worn or which has disintegrated. The enzyme pepsin is capable of digesting protein; therefore, if the wall of the gastrointestinal tract is not protected, there will be digestion or destruction of the wall itself, with the production of a **peptic ulcer.** These ulcers occur in the stomach but most commonly are found in the duodenum just beyond the pyloric sphincter. The stomach is protected by mucin, but the duodenum is not. Accordingly, if large quantities of acid pepsin fail to be sufficiently destroyed or buffered, ulceration of the duodenum occurs.

Most cases of peptic ulcer result from hypersecretion of gastric juice. It has been mentioned that the production of this juice is under the control, to a great extent, of higher brain centers. It is undoubtedly for this reason that abnormal emotional states often result in peptic ulcer. Normally not only mucin but the presence of foods protects the wall. However, it can easily be appreciated that if the gastric juice is secreted between meals damage is bound to occur. Such cases are treated either psychiatrically or by section of the vagus nerve. In the latter procedure great care must be taken to avoid regeneration of the vagus.

Gastritis Simple inflammation of the gastric mucosa may result from a number of causes. Among the more common are vitamin deficiency, especially of the vitamin B complex. Gastritis may also be caused by the excessive ingestion of alcohol or simply by overeating.

THE SMALL INTESTINE

The bolus of food, well mixed with saliva, passes through the esophagus to reach the stomach. The saliva contains ptyalin which initiates the digestion of carbohydrate but does not alter protein or fat. When the bolus comes into contact with the gastric juice, the high acidity, as it works its way into the bolus, halts the digestive action of ptyalin. The gastric juice contains enzymes which begin the digestion of protein, reducing them to peptones and proteoses. Then, by the peristaltic action of the stomach, the now semifluid food termed **chyme** (meaning juice) is moved into the small intestine.

PANCREATIC JUICE

The Pancreas The pancreas is an elongated (about 6 in.) organ lying within the curvature of the small intestine (Fig. 22-1). This organ serves two functions: (1) to secrete the pancreatic juice for digestive purposes and (2) to elaborate a hormone **insulin,** which is essential to normal carbohydrate metabolism. These two substances are formed by different cells. Insulin is poured directly into the blood stream, while the pancreatic juice is collected by a series of ducts and carried by one or two major ducts into the small intestine. Before the pancreatic duct reaches the small intestine, it joins the common bile duct.

Composition of Pancreatic Juice The pancreatic juice contains three important enzymes. They are (1) **trypsin,** (2) **amylase,** and (3) **lipase.** In addition, the pancreatic secretion contains a considerable quantity of the bicarbonate ion which is important for the neutralization of the highly acid gastric juice.

Sodium, potassium, calcium, and magnesium concentrations in the pancreatic juice reflect the concentrations of these cations in the plasma. This is in striking contrast to saliva in which the electrolyte concentrations in the secretion are quite different. Pancreatic juice is isotonic with plasma; saliva is hypotonic.

Just as the mechanism for the remarkable secretion of H^+ in gastric juice continues to concern investigators, so does the mechanism responsible for the secretion of a high concentration of HCO_3^- in pancreatic juice. As a matter of fact, the two mechanisms seem to be the same, but to be operating in reverse directions. The gastric parietal cells secrete

HCl in the juice and sodium bicarbonate into the venous plasma. The pancreatic cells secrete sodium bicarbonate in the juice; therefore, they must put an equivalent amount of acid into the venous plasma.

The pancreatic cells secrete a juice containing the various enzymes and an aqueous juice containing the electrolytes. These two secretions are then mixed to make up the final product that enters the duodenum.

The pancreas secretes **trypsinogen,** which is a precursor of trypsin. When trypsinogen reaches the intestinal tract, it is converted into the active form, trypsin, by two enzymes. They are (1) **enterokinase** and (2) **trypsin.** Enterokinase is produced by the intestinal mucosa. Like trypsin, it is a proteolytic enzyme. Thus we find that as soon as trypsinogen reaches the intestine the enterokinase present there converts it to trypsin. This trypsin now activates more trypsinogen.

Trypsin, like pepsin in the gastric juice, is a proteolytic enzyme and thus acts upon protein and protein derivatives. Some protein reaches the small intestine, having escaped digestion by pepsin. But for the most part, the chyme contains peptones and proteoses. Trypsin acts upon these pro-

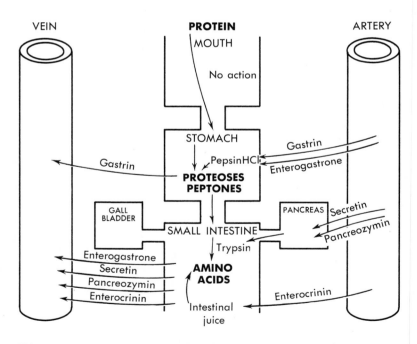

FIG. 22-3   Protein digestion. The hormones formed in the gastrointestinal tract are secreted into the venous blood, then circulate back to various organs to evoke appropriate secretions.

tein derivatives and mostly succeeds in reducing them to the end products of protein digestion, the **amino acids** (Fig. 22-3).

The pancreatic juice also contains an amylase. An amylase is an enzyme which speeds the conversion of carbohydrates to the simple sugars. It will be recalled that some carbohydrate is reduced to intermediary sugars by the salivary ptyalin. The pancreatic amylase proceeds to work on the carbohydrate which has escaped the action of ptyalin, as well as the intermediary sugar forms. **Maltose, sucrose,** and **lactose** are formed as a result of these reactions. They are only one step removed from the simple end-product sugars.

The pancreatic juice also contains other amylases which act specifically upon maltose, sucrose, and lactose and convert them to the simple sugars **glucose, fructose,** and **galactose.** Thus, by mean of the combined activity of salivary ptyalin and pancreatic amylases, the complex carbohydrate compounds are converted into readily digestible simple sugars suitable for absorption (Fig. 22-4).

The pancreatic lipase acts on fats. The fat molecule is converted into its components, fatty acids and glycerol (Fig. 22-5). But for most efficient operation, bile salts must be present. The bile salts, as will be discussed

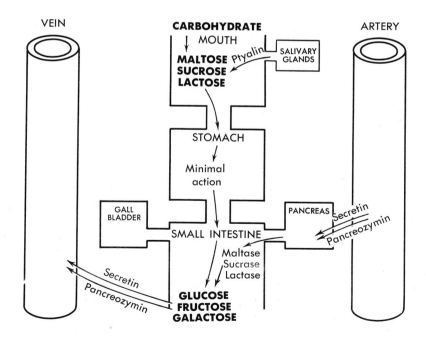

FIG. 22-4   Carbohydrate digestion.

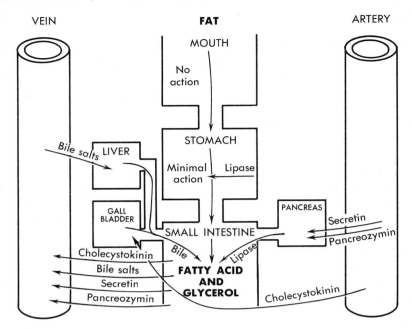

FIG. 22-5   Fat digestion. Bile is essential both for fat digestion and the absorption of the end products.

in detail, make it possible for the lipase to act upon fat and bring about this necessary conversion.

Regulation of Pancreatic Juice   The quantity and quality of the pancreatic juice, as of the gastric juice, vary with the diet. On the average, about 750 ml (about three glasses) of pancreatic juice per day is formed. It possesses a slightly alkaline reaction and is strongly buffered, thus effectively neutralizing the highly acid gastric juice.

The pancreas is innervated by the autonomic nervous system, specifically, the vagus nerve. Stimulation of vagal fibers does not increase the amount of pancreatic juice secreted, but the juice does become more highly concentrated with enzymes. Accordingly, there must be some other mechanism responsible for the elaboration of pancreatic fluid. One of the most potent pancreatic stimulants is **secretin,** a hormone produced by the intestinal wall. Secretin, in turn, seems to be controlled by the degree of acidity of the intestinal contents. It will be recalled that the chyme, as it leaves the stomach, is highly acid. As soon as this mass comes into contact with the intestinal mucosa, secretin is liberated which is quickly absorbed and carried by the blood to the pancreas where it evokes a copious secretion of pancreatic juice (Fig. 22-5).

The acid chyme apparently causes the liberation of still another hormone, this one termed **pancreozymin** which, like vagal stimulation, induces the release of large quantities of enzymes. It can be appreciated, then, that the composition and volume of the pancreatic juice depend upon the relative activity of vagal stimulation and the secretion of pancreozymin, both of which cause enzyme production, and the secretion of secretin which controls the volume of the pancreatic juice.

BILE

Bile is produced in the **liver.** The liver is a large organ which weighs about 1500 gm in man. It lies just under the diaphragm on the right side of the abdominal cavity. The bile is transported by the **hepatic duct** from the liver to the point where the hepatic duct and **cystic duct** join to form the **common bile duct.** The common bile duct unites with the pancreatic duct before entering the intestinal tract. The opening of the common bile duct is guarded by the **sphincter of Oddi.** When this sphincter is closed, the bile formed by the liver flows down the hepatic duct and then backs up the cystic duct to reach the **gallbladder.**

Composition of Bile   Bile is a thick yellow-green fluid of slightly alkaline reaction. It is not believed to possess enzymes; yet it aids in the digestion of fat. Bile contains, in addition to water, many **inorganic salts,** which probably exert a buffering function to neutralize the acid chyme. There is also present a **nucleoprotein,** which accounts for the high viscosity. But the most important constituents are the **bile salts** and the **bile pigments.**

The bile salts play a major role in the digestion and absorption of fat and fat-soluble vitamins. They also serve to regulate the flow of bile. The lipase which is present in the pancreatic juice cannot exert its influence upon fat unless the bile salts are present to lower the surface tension. This enables the water-soluble lipase to come into more intimate contact with the fat molecule. The fatty acids and glycerol which result from fat digestion can be adequately absorbed only by the intestinal wall in the presence of the bile salts. If the common bile duct is tied so as to prevent the bile from entering the intestinal lumen, about one-half of the ingested fat will appear in the feces, a condition known as **steatorrhea.** In other words, this quantity of fat fails to be absorbed because of the absence of the bile salts.

Many of the vitamins are fat-soluble, notably A, D, E, and K. If bile is not present in the intestine, these vitamins are poorly absorbed. As a result, the individual may suffer from a vitamin deficiency.

The bile pigments **bilirubin** and **biliverdin** are derived from the red blood cells. They represent one of the end products of red-cell disintegration and are excreted from the body in the bile. If there is malfunction of the liver so that the bile pigments are not eliminated as rapidly as they are formed, or if the bile system is blocked, the pigments accumulate in the blood and dam back into the skin and other systems. This gives rise to a yellow appearance, a condition termed **jaundice,** derived from a French word meaning yellow.

Regulation of Bile   Between meals, bile is formed at a relatively slow rate. It passes down the hepatic duct and then backs up the cystic duct into the gallbladder. The gallbladder has a capacity of about 50 ml. Much of the water and electrolytes contained in the bile are absorbed by the gallbladder, so that bile salt, bile pigment, and cholesterol are concentrated during its storage there. On the average, 600 to 800 ml of bile are secreted by the liver each day.

Bile, like the pancreatic juice, has a high bicarbonate concentration which becomes even higher as the flow rate increases. The electrolyte composition of bile is very similar to that of pancreatic juice.

The secretion of bile is an active process. The best evidence for active secretion is the secretion pressure which, in the case of bile can reach 20 mm Hg. The pressure within the liver blood vessels is less than 5 mm Hg; thus bile can hardly represent simply a filtration product.

The regulation of bile embraces two problems: (1) the mechanisms which control the rate of production in the liver and (2) the means by which the gallbladder contracts and the sphincter of Oddi relaxes. The most potent stimulus for the production of bile has been found to be the bile salts themselves. A great fraction, over 80 per cent, of the bile salts which reach the intestine in the bile are reabsorbed and pass into the blood stream. They thus are carried back to the liver and here excite the production of bile. For this reason, bile salts are prescribed to stimulate liver function.

The contraction of the gallbladder and the relaxation of the sphincter of Oddi are regulated by a hormone. We have seen that the presence of chyme in the small intestine calls forth two hormones: (1) secretin and (2) pancreozymin. Both of these hormones stimulate the production of pancreatic juice. The chyme, especially in fat content, apparently also is responsible for evoking still another hormone from the intestinal wall. This hormone is called **cholecystokinin.** Cholecystokinin reaches the gallbladder and the sphincter of Oddi via the blood and is believed to cause contraction of the gallbladder and relaxation of the sphincter. As a result, bile is forced from the gallbladder into the intestine.

There is thus a very effective mechanism for delivering an adequate quantity of bile to the small intestine where it is needed. We find that between meals the gallbladder slowly fills with bile. There, many substances in the bile, especially water, are reabsorbed. Now when the chyme reaches the intestine a hormone, cholecystokinin, is produced by the intestinal mucosa. This hormone causes the gallbladder to contract and the sphincter to relax. Consequently, bile is delivered to the small intestine to aid in fat digestion and absorption. But the bile salts, at the same time, are being reabsorbed and carried back to the liver (Fig. 22-6). Here they activate a greater and faster production of bile which now flows directly down the hepatic and common bile ducts to the intestine. Thus, while the food is in the small intestine, there is a steady supply of bile. After the food leaves the intestine, no more cholecystokinin is produced. The gallbladder relaxes, and the sphincter constricts. No more bile is de-

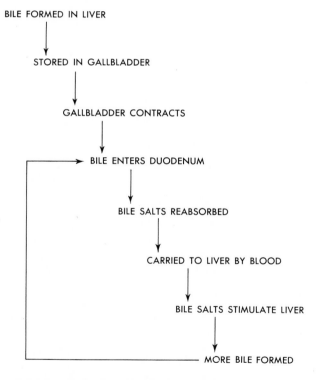

BILE FORMED IN LIVER

STORED IN GALLBLADDER

GALLBLADDER CONTRACTS

BILE ENTERS DUODENUM

BILE SALTS REABSORBED

CARRIED TO LIVER BY BLOOD

BILE SALTS STIMULATE LIVER

MORE BILE FORMED

FIG. 22-6 Bile circulation. The presence of food in the intestine evokes the secretion of cholecystokinin which causes the gallbladder to contract. As a result the recirculation of bile, depicted above, occurs.

livered to the intestinal tract, and therefore the reabsorption of bile salts ceases. Consequently, the production of bile is reduced to its basal level. Once again the gallbladder slowly fills. The cycle is complete.

Abnormalities of the Biliary System   Quite often cholesterol crystals settle out of the bile to form particles or stones of varying sizes. **Gallstones** results when the bile becomes unduly concentrated with cholesterol or when there is an infectious process under way in the biliary system. If no steps are taken to halt the formation of gallstones, they may actually fill the entire gallbladder and destroy its function. They can also lodge in the ducts to obstruct the flow. In either case, the treatment is surgical removal of the offending part. An individual can survive without a gall-bladder, but because of the limited storage of bile it is usually necessary for such patients to subsist on a low-fat diet.

Liver damage in which the destroyed areas are replaced by fibrous tissue is known as **cirrhosis.** In most such cases there will be a reduced production of bile. Further, the limited liver function may prevent adequate excretion of bilirubin. Jaundice results.

INTESTINAL JUICE

It has been seen that considerable digestion takes place in the small intestine as a result of the pancreatic juice in conjunction with bile. However, digestion is not always complete, and therefore, typical of the physiology of man, there is still another line of defense in the form of the intestinal juice.

Composition of Intestinal Juice   It is extremely difficult to determine the exact nature of the intestinal juice. No way has yet been devised for collecting this juice uncontaminated by substances elaborated elsewhere in the gastrointestinal system. There is general agreement, nonetheless, that approximately 3 liters a day of intestinal juices are produced by clusters of cells found in the intestinal mucosa. This juice, also known as **succus entericus,** is said to contain (1) **proteolytic enzymes,** (2) **amylases,** and (3) **lipases.** In other words, if any of the three foodstuffs should have escaped complete digestion, enzymes are present in the intestinal juice which are capable of finishing the task.

The proteolytic enzymes have not all been identified. One of them, however, is now definitely known to be **enterokinase.** It has been mentioned that this enzyme converts trypsinogen into trypsin. All the intestinal proteolytic enzymes or **peptidases** are by some collectively termed **erepsin.** Most serve to complete the conversion of protein products to amino acids (Fig. 22-3).

The lipase and amylase complete the simplification of fat to fatty acids and glycerol and carbohydrates to glucose, galactose, and fructose.

Regulation of Intestinal Juice   The quantity of intestinal juice produced varies, depending upon the type and quantity of food ingested. It has been established that the presence of chyme in the small intestine calls forth still another hormone, the eighth to be mentioned. This one has been labeled **enterocrinin,** and it is thought to be a potent stimulator of the cells which manufacture the intestinal juice. In addition to this rather general stimulation, there is thought to be limited local liberation of the juice in response to direct mechanical or chemical irritation of the intestinal mucosa. Thus, if part of the chyme should escape complete digestion, its very presence in the small intestine will call forth an immediate secretion of enzymes from the surrounding wall to finish the digestive processes.

INTESTINAL MOVEMENTS

Propulsion and Mixing of Chyme   The main force that propels the chyme through the small intestine is provided by **peristaltic movements,** that is, a progressive wave of contraction and then relaxation from one end of the intestine to the other. This is similar to squeezing a rubber tube at one end and then running one's fingers along the length of the tube. Clearly, anything contained within the tube will be moved through it. In the intestine such peristaltic waves move at a rate of 10 to 30 cm per minute. The intensity of the wave of contraction seems to depend upon local reflex action controlled by the degree of distention of the gut. The greater the distention, the more vigorous the peristaltic contractions. Parasympathetic stimulation also increases peristalsis.

In addition to the movements that propel the chyme, there are other intestinal activities which serve to mix the contents. When the chyme is being digested, it can be observed that a large section of the gut will contract as a unit and then two waves start, one from either end of the contracted segment, running toward one another. These fade before coming into contact but effectively mix the intestinal contents.

Emptying   Just as the pyloric sphincter guards the exit of the stomach, the **ileocecal valve** controls the outlet of the small intestine. Again it is found that there are three factors which determine the rate of intestinal emptying. They are (1) the pressure gradient between the small and large intestine, (2) the state of the ileocecal valve, and (3) the fluidity of the intestinal contents.

Vomiting   The propulsion of the gastrointestinal contents in the reverse direction, up through the esophagus and mouth, is known as **vomiting.** This act results from vigorous reverse peristalsis, with a strong assist from the abdominal muscles. Vomiting is initiated by an irritation of the gastrointestinal mucosa which sends impulses to a center in the medulla. As a result, the following sequence occurs: first the individual takes a deep breath, then he closes his glottis, next there is violent contraction of abdominal muscles, and finally, in collaboration with reverse intestinal peristaltic movements and simultaneous opening of the pathway from the stomach to the mouth, the offending material is ejected.

THE LARGE INTESTINE

Digestion, as already outlined, is so efficient that practically no usable food reaches the large intestine. The remains of intestinal digestion, the waste products, are moved into the large intestine as a result of intestinal peristalsis.

THE INTESTINAL FLORA

It has already been noted that many microorganisms are ingested with the food. Many of these bacteria succumb to the strong acid of the stomach, but some survive and are swept into the intestine; others are introduced via the rectum. In the large intestine they find the environment most favorable for action—action of two kinds: (1) **fermentation** and (2) **putrefaction.**

Fermentation   The term fermentation is here used to signify the action of a living organism in causing the split of a complex substance into simpler components. Usually, as a result of bacterial fermentation, various gases are produced. Some foods are more readily fermented in this way than others. Thus, it is common experience that the ingestion of certain foods, such as beans, is associated with the production of excessive gas. This gas formation may be so great that it becomes painful because of intestinal distention.

Putrefaction   Putrefaction is a process similar in many ways to fermentation. Specifically, it refers to the conversion of protein substances into smaller molecules, again with the liberation of various compounds. Among them are **indol, skatol, phenol, hydrogen sulfide,** and **ammonia.** All are characterized by a pungent odor—thus the term **putrefaction,** which means "to make rotten."

The action of bacteria in converting the large molecules is not unlike that of the digestive enzymes. Therefore, the intestinal bacteria must be considered to serve an important function. By the time the digestive enzymes and the bacteria of the large intestine have worked over the food, there is nothing left but undigestible waste.

It is of interest that some of the bacteria in the large intestine actually synthesize vitamin K and many of the components of the vitamin B complex. Generally these vitamins are supplied in adequate quantities in the average diet. However, it can be seen that here again is an emergency mechanism available to the body in case of need.

COLONIC SECRETION

The colon secretes a juice that has a pH of about 8 and this alkalinity serves to neutralize the acid end products of fermentation. Actually the fecal mass is not neutralized in its entirety. It is found that while the surface is neutral, the center is acid, having a pH of about 5.

The colonic secretion has a bicarbonate and potassium content higher than in the plasma. There are few enzymes present with the exception of lysozyme and a trace of amylase.

Secretion in the colon is under parasympathetic control. As yet there is no evidence of hormonal regulation.

APPENDICAL SECRETION

The appendix secretes a large volume of fluid, apparently spontaneously. This large volume normally drains from the appendix, but if the opening is obstructed, the pressure within the appendix can rise to over 120 mm Hg. The high pressure acting on the walls of the appendix impairs circulation so that necrosis results. The wall becomes weakened and ruptures.

COLONIC MOVEMENTS

Movements in the colon are similar to those in the small intestine. There are contractions which do not move the contents through the colon, but instead serve to mix it. In addition, there are so-called **mass movements,** vigorous peristalis, which do drive the contents to lower segments. Mass movements take place two or three times a day.

The residue of a meal is generally turned into feces and is ready for expulsion within 12 hours after ingestion. This figure varies greatly, however. Fluids move through the stomach rapidly, carbohydrates more slowly, proteins even slower, and fatty foods may linger for hours. It may take about 6 hours for the chyme to traverse the small intestine, and another 3 or 4 hours may be spent in the colon. It should be understood that these are minimal times and in some cases may be very much longer. Further, not all of the residue in any one meal is excreted at the same time. Part of the residue remains to be mixed with that of subsequent meals so that it is possible to find residue in the feces from a meal that may have been eaten several days before.

FECES

The term **feces** is derived from the Latin and literally means "dregs" or a worthless residue. We have seen that through the action of the digestive enzymes and perhaps with some aid from the intestinal flora every last bit of nutritive value is extracted from the mass of ingested material. What passes into the lower colon, the **rectum,** is truly a worthless residue and is aptly termed.

The quantity of feces formed per day varies with the quality and quantity of food ingested. On the average diet, it amounts to about 300 gm per day. However, even during complete starvation, some fecal material is formed. This indicates that a part of the feces represents a contribution by the large intestine, plus bacteria and worn-out epithelial cells.

Feces contain close to 75 per cent water; yet the amount of fluid imbibed has very little influence over its composition. Certainly, if one becomes grossly dehydrated, the fecal water content will diminish, but within a wide range of drinking habits the feces remain remarkably constant. The maintenance of this constancy is a function of the large intestine. The evidence indicates that the colon can either add water to, or subtract water from, the feces and in this way keep the composition constant.

The color of the feces is determined by its content of bilirubin. It will be remembered that bilirubin is released by disintegrating red blood cells and is then placed in the bile by the liver. In this way it enters the small intestine, after which it is carried into the large intestine. Here the bacteria converts it into **urobilinogen** which is then oxidized to **urobilin.** These are all pigments which color the feces. If the feces appear white, clay-colored, or gray, a disorder of the biliary system must be suspected, since it is obvious that little or no bilirubin is being excreted.

The fecal material is collected in the rectum, the lower 4 in. of the intestinal tract. There it awaits expulsion.

SUMMARY

In its broadest sense, the gastrointestinal tract extends from the mouth to the anus. In this long tube, which in man measures some 30 ft, the **proteins** are reduced to **animo acids, fat** to **fatty acids** and **glycerol,** and **carbohydrate** to the **simple sugars.** The remainder in combination with water, bacteria, and intestinal debris accumulates as **feces** in the rectum.

The **gastric glands** are made up of **mucous neck cells, zymogenic cells,** and **parietal cells.** They produce about 2 liters of gastric juice per day. It contains **water, mucin, pepsin, HCl, rennin,** and a **lipase.** The gastric juice, because of the HCl, is a very acid medium in which pepsin works to reduce protein. Because of the withdrawal of acid ions from the blood to form HCl, there is a shift of the blood to a more alkaline reaction, and this is reflected in an increase of alkalinity of the urine which is termed the **akaline tide of the urine.** Gastric juice is regulated by nervous impulses and the hormones **gastrin** and **enterogastrone.** The very thought of food initates the flow of gastric juice. Gastric movements of the empty stomach give rise to a sensation of hunger. These movements, when the stomach is filled, serve to macerate and move the food. Within about 3 hours after eating, the stomach is almost completely evacuated.

The semiliquid mass which leaves the stomach to enter the small intestine is termed **chyme.** It has an acid reaction, and when this acid comes into contact with the intestinal mucosa, at least five hormones are liberated. They are (1) **secretin,** which encourages pancreatic secretion; (2) **pancreozymin,** which stimulates the production of the pancreatic enzymes; (3) **cholecystokinin,** which causes contraction of the **gallbladder** and relaxation of the **sphincter of Oddi;** (4) **enterocrinin,** which calls forth the intestinal juice; and (5) **enterogastrone,** which controls gastric secretion.

Pancreatic juice contains **trypsin, amylases,** and **lipase.** Trypsin is a proteolytic enzyme. The amylases succeed in reducing carbohydrate to glucose, fructose, and galactose. Lipase acts on fat with the aid of bile. About 750 ml of pancreatic juice are formed per day.

Bile is formed in the liver and flows down the **hepatic duct** and back up the **cystic duct** to enter the gallbladder, where it is concentrated and stored. When food reaches the intestine, cholecystokinin causes the bladder to contract and the sphincter of Oddi to relax. Bile contains **water, inorganic salts, nucleoprotein, bile pigments,** and **bile salts.** The bile salts are reabsorbed by the intestine and carried to the liver where they greatly increase the production of bile. In the intestine, the bile salts lower surface tension so that the enzyme lipase may come into more intimate contact with the fat substances. They are also essential to the absorption of the products of fat digestion. The bile pigments are **bilirubin** and **biliverdin.** They represent the products of disintegrated red blood cells and are excreted in the bile. If for any reason they accumulate in the blood and tissues, **jaundice** results.

The intestinal juice, called **succus entericus,** contains enzymes which can digest all three foodstuffs. Thus, if any remain incompletely digested, the intestinal juice completes the task. Its proteolytic enzymes are termed **erepsin.** The most important one is **enterokinase.**

Any remaining foodstuffs which reach the large intestine are fermented or undergo putrefaction by the bacteria which reside there. These processes are very similar to enzymatic digestion and probably represent the final line of digestive defense. The irreducible remainder amounts to about 300 gm, on the average diet. The feces are composed of about 75 per cent water, a composition which is carefully controlled by secretion or absorption of water in the large intestine. The fecal matter accumulates in the **rectum.**

QUESTIONS

1. What mechanisms control the secretion of gastric juice?
2. What mechanisms govern the secretion of pancreatic juice?
3. Discuss the formation, storage, and expulsion of bile.
4. Make a chart listing the gastrointestinal enzymes and hormones, showing their origin and action.
5. What factors control the rate of gastric emptying?
6. How is chyme mixed and moved in the small intestine?

SUGGESTED READING

Bachrach, W. H., "Physiology and Pathologic Physiology of the Stomach," *Clin. Symposia,* 11:#1, 3–28, January-February 1959.

Davenport, H. W., "Physiology of the Digestive Tract," Year Book Medical Publishers, Chicago, 1961.

Hogben, C. A. M., "Formation of Hydrochloric Acid by the Stomach. The Current Status," *Am. J. Med.,* 29:#5, 726–731, November 1960.

Hunt, J. N., "Gastric Emptying and Secretion in Man," *Physiol. Rev.,* 39:#3, 491–533, July 1959.

Menguy, R., "Motor Function of the Alimentary Tract," *Ann. Rev. Physiol.,* 26: 227–248, 1964.

"The Gallbladder," *Spectrum,* 5:#16, 462–463, September 15, 1957.

Absorption and Utilization

WE HAVE seen that, through a chain of complex processes, the basic foodstuffs are effectively transformed into their elemental components. Carbohydrates are reduced to the simple sugars, proteins to amino acids, and fats to glycerol and fatty acids. These substances must move from the lumen of the gastrointestinal tract into the blood. The blood then carries the products of digestion to various parts of the body where they may be stored unchanged, transformed into other compounds, or oxidized for the production of energy. Other substances than those just mentioned are transported from the intestinal lumen to the blood stream. These include inorganic salts as well as the vitamins. In short, from the ingested food a wide variety of compounds enters the blood. These must now be stored, utilized for energy, or eliminated in one form or another by the kidneys, the lungs, or the skin. A consideration of the fate of the foodstuffs must embrace (1) **absorption,** (2) **intermediary metabolism,** and (3) **excretion.**

ABSORPTION

Absorption is not a simple process of diffusion. The rate and effectiveness of absorption vary in different parts of the alimentary canal. Some substances are readily absorbed whereas others are not. But first let us examine the absorptive mechanisms.

MECHANISM OF ABSORPTION

Villi Figure 23-1 shows the design of the wall of the small intestine. It is seen to be roughened by a series of mucosal folds. If these folds are examined under the microscope they will be found to contain millions of fingerlike projections. These projections are called **villi.** Figure 23-1 also shows an enlarged longitudinal section of a villus. Each villus contains an artery, a vein, and a lymph vessel. By virtue of this arrangement the villus is capable of taking up or absorbing the contents of the small

455

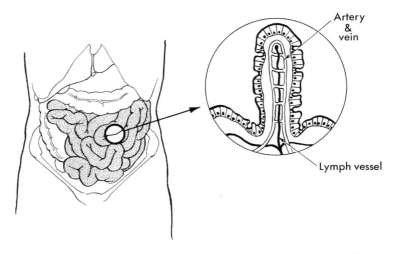

FIG. 23-1 Intestinal villi. The villi are found only in the small in-testine. They are minute projections of the mucosa. As shown on the right, each is supplied with blood and lymph vessels.

intestine. As a matter of fact, absorption is the cardinal function of the villi.

It has been calculated that in the small intestine of man there are some 5,000,000 such villi. Further calculations reveal that these 5,000,000 villi present a total surface area of approximately 10 sq m. This huge area, which is as large as the floor space of a large room, of course facilitates absorption.

The villi have a role other than to increase the surface area. They are capable of vigorous movements. Such movements create pressures which aid absorption. This has been termed the **villous pump.** The movement of the millions of villi also serves to stir the food lying next to the intes-tinal mucosa. In this way new surfaces are constantly presented to the mucosa to facilitate absorption. A hormone, **villikinin,** purported to be released by the presence of chyme, greatly augments villi movements.

Absorption Theories There is no doubt that some substances are ab-sorbed from the intestine in accordance with physicochemical laws. By that we mean that the passage of a particular substance from the intestinal lumen into the blood stream or into the lymph system is a function of concentration gradients. Thus, if one eats much carbohydrate, the con-centration of glucose in the intestine will probably be higher than in the blood. Therefore, glucose will diffuse into the blood and thus establish equilibrium. Likewise, it has been shown that a high pressure within the intestinal tract speeds the absorptive processes.

Although the concentration and pressure gradients are undoubtedly important, it is impossible to explain all absorption on this basis alone. It is necessary to postulate that there are active secretory mechanisms capable of conveying substances from the intestine into the blood or lymph regardless of concentration or pressure. In other words, the intestinal wall is capable of doing work. This is clearly shown by the fact that, when absorption is going on, the intestine uses more oxygen than when it is dormant. In addition, substances can be absorbed even from hypotonic solutions, that is, when the concentration is lower in the intestine than in the blood. Finally, the rate of absorption of very similar substances, such as glucose and fructose, varies significantly.

In short, absorption depends upon two groups of factors: (1) **physicochemical laws** and (2) **secretory processes.**

SITE OF ABSORPTION

The small intestine is the main site of absorption but some absorption does occur in the stomach. Water moves freely in both directions through the gastric mucosa. Usually, more water is absorbed than moves in the opposite direction. Glucose, most electrolytes, and amino acids will diffuse slowly out of the stomach if the concentration in the stomach is high enough. Fat soluble substances readily diffuse down a concentration gradient. In short, the stomach mucosa does not actively absorb any of the solutes, but if the concentration gradient is great enough, the stomach will permit them to pass. The fat-soluble substances diffuse most readily because the stomach mucosa, like most living membranes, is composed of fat. For the same reason, the alcohols and other fat soluble compounds are absorbed.

Anatomical and physiological evidence points irrefutably to the small intestine as the principal site of absorption. Absorption is so efficient in the small intestine that very little absorbable substance reaches the large intestine.

The large intestine, like the stomach, is completely devoid of villi. But, if the concentration and pressure gradients are favorable, absorption, purely by diffusion, will take place from the lumen of the large intestine. Under normal conditions, however, most of the end products of digestion are absorbed by the small intestine. In addition, practically all of the digestible material has been converted to absorbable end products before the substance reaches the large intestine. Thus, it is extremely doubtful if any significant absorption takes place in the large intestine.

It does, as already mentioned, regulate the concentration of water in the feces. Water, for this purpose, moves in either direction.

CARBOHYDRATE ABSORPTION

The normal end products of carbohydrate digestion are the monosaccharides. If a large quantity of the disaccharide, sucrose, is ingested, some of it will fail to be converted to monosaccharides and will be absorbed as unchanged sucrose. It is interesting, however, that such absorbed sucrose undergoes no metabolic alteration and is simply excreted unchanged in the urine. In short, it may be concluded that for metabolic needs, the monosaccharides must be absorbed from the intestinal tract.

It has been thoroughly demonstrated that the absorption of the hexoses involves active transport. This is made clear by the observation that sugars which have the same physical diffusion rate are absorbed by the intestine at very different rates. Further, pentoses, which are smaller molecules and therefore diffuse more rapidy than hexoses, are actually absorbed by the intestine more slowly. In so far as the end products of digestion are concerned, it has been found that galactose is absorbed more rapidly than glucose, which is absorbed more rapidly than fructose. If glucose is given an arbitrary absorption rate of 100, then galactose equals 110 and fructose 43.

AMINO ACID ABSORPTION

The end products of protein digestion are the amino acids. These are rapidly absorbed by the small intestine, again, by an unknown mechanism. Energy studies have shown that the oxygen utilization of the intestine increases during amino acid absorption and that if the mucosa is deprived of oxygen, the rate of absorption is reduced. In addition, the rate of absorption of different amino acids varies. Accordingly, such uptake is considered to be the result of active processes. Besides the amino acids, the intestine is capable of absorbing peptides, and even some undigested protein. The absorption of protein is thought to underlie the development of allergy, that is, immunological sensitization that some individuals show to certain foods.

LIPID ABSORPTION

Fats are digested to glycerol and fatty acids. These end products of lipid digestion are then absorbed by the intestinal cells and within the cells reconverted to the triglyceride fat molecule. Fats that contain fatty acids with long chains (over 12 carbon atoms) enter the lymph vessels of the villi. As a result, these lymph vessels assume a milky appearance which, because of their appearance, are termed **lacteals.** The lymph then carries the fat, in droplets called **chylomicrons,** through the lymphatics to enter the venous blood via the thoracic duct. A diet high in fats containing long-chain fatty acids so elevates the fat content of the plasma that it has a milky color. Fats that contain fatty acids with chains less than 12 carbon atoms long enter the portal blood stream. The liver quickly removes much of this fat so that the diet high in fats containing short-chain fatty acids does not result in milky colored plasma.

Electromicrograph studies indicate that large fat molecules can be absorbed by pinocytosis without first undergoing digestion and resynthesis.

Fatty digestion and absorption is normally so complete that none of the ingested fat reaches the feces directly. There is, however, about 8 per cent of the ingested fat in the stool. But this comes from bile fats and intestinal secretions. That is to say, the fat is first absorbed completely; part of it is then converted into bile fats and intestinal secretions which end up in the stool.

Impairment of digestion or absorption results in a high fat content in the feces (**steatorrhea**). This may be due to an inadequate secretion of lipases or of bile.

There is a simple clinical test for determining whether steatorrhea is due to impairment of digestion or absorption. The fat, **triolein,** labelled with I^{131}, is given orally. The blood and stool are then checked for radioactivity. In the normal patient, the blood activity rises rapidly, reaching a peak in about 3 or 4 hours (Fig. 23-2). The peak level reaches at least 8 per cent of the dose. In the stool not over 2 per cent is found at 24 or 48 hours. But if too much activity is found in the stool and too little in the blood, obviously there is either inadequate digestion or absorption. The fatty acid, **oleic acid,** labelled with I^{131}, is then given in the same way and the blood and stool once again checked. If fatty acid values are normal while the whole fat values are abnormal, the defect must be in digestion. If both are abnormal, there is malabsorption.

VITAMIN ABSORPTION

Some of the vitamins are water-soluble, others are fat-soluble. The water-soluble vitamins are quickly absorbed. But if there is fat malabsorption, there will be decreased absorption of the fat-soluble vitamins A, D, E, and K.

The absorption of vitamin B_{12} is unique. It is a water-soluble vitamin, but it has a large molecule, probably too large for simple diffusion. For absorption to take place, a mucoprotein, called **intrinsic factor,** is required. Intrinsic factor is secreted by the stomach, but the responsible cells have not been identified nor has the structure of the factor. Although the intrinsic factor is secreted in the stomach, no absorption of vitamin

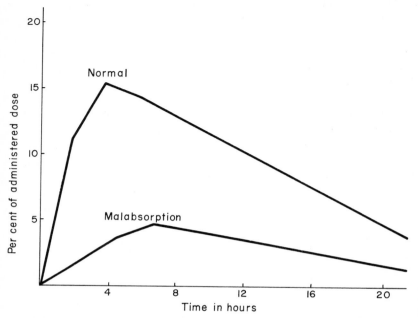

FIG. 23-2   Fat absorption. Triolein labelled with I^{131} is rapidly absorbed by the normal gut so that the plasma level, expressed as per cent of the administered dose, reaches about 15 per cent in 4 to 6 hours. Subjects with malabsorption show a peak plasma level of less than 8 per cent.

B_{12} takes place there. The site of absorption is the lower half of the small intestine. There appears to be binding of intrinsic factor and the vitamin. Then, if adequate calcium is present, the bound vitamin is absorbed. Once absorbed, the vitamin is released from the intrinsic factor and enters the portal blood stream.

If there is dietary deficiency of vitamin B_{12} or if there is inadequate absorption, **pernicious anemia** results because this vitamin is essential for erythrocytic maturation. Vitamin B_{12}, labelled with radioactive cobalt, is now available. As a diagnostic test, it is given orally and then the urine checked for radioactivity. Normally, the 24-hour urine will contain at least 10 per cent of the dose of the radioactivity. If there is less than 10 per cent, another dose is given along with intrinsic factor. Should normal values now result, there is evidence for inadequate production of intrinsic factor.

WATER ABSORPTION

As already mentioned, water can be absorbed by the stomach, but the major water absorption takes place in the small intestine. In the small intestine over 5 liters of water are absorbed per day, and this can be markedly increased. It has been calculated that the small intestine can easily absorb water at a rate of at least 1 liter per hour. In fact, water can be absorbed so fast that if sufficient amounts are presented to the intestine there will be such dilution of the blood that hemolysis will occur. The colon is also capable of water absorption but not to the extent of the small intestine.

Actually, water moves in both directions in all parts of the intestine and stomach, but under normal conditions, the movement out of the lumen exceeds movement into it. The mechanism involved in the movement of water is not known. Most likely water moves according to the osmotic gradient. Thus, as solutes are actively absorbed, there is created an osmotic gradient favorable for the movement of water in the same direction. When the fluid content of the food is very low or when solute absorption is impaired, there will be net movement of water into the intestine because the osmotic gradient is in that direction.

INTERMEDIARY METABOLISM

The three basic foodstuffs, protein, carbohydrate, and fat, are reduced by the digestive processes in the intestinal tract to elemental substances which are then absorbed into the blood stream. What becomes of them then? The subject embraced by the term **intermediary metabolism** includes all the processes by which these basic substances are either utilized for energy or stored.

PROTEIN

The main source of protein in the diet is meat, dairy products, chicken, fish, and vegetables. These very intricate molecules are acted upon by pepsin in the stomach and by trypsin and enterokinase in the small intestine so that the basic amino acids are liberated. The amino acids are then absorbed into the blood stream by the intestinal villi. The average concentration of amino acids in the blood is about 30 mg per cent. These amino acids may now be (1) oxidized for energy, (2) used to create body proteins, (3) converted to carbohydrate, (4) transformed into fat, (5) excreted, or (6) stored in the liver.

Oxidation   There is general agreement that most of the amino acids, soon after they enter the blood stream and probably when they arrive in the liver, are quickly deaminated. That means that the amino group, $-NH_2$, is removed from the molecule. What remains is a simple carbon-hydrogen-oxygen chain. As will be seen, this simple chain is then available for many purposes. One avenue is oxidation. The end products of this oxidative process are CO_2, H_2O, and energy. Sensitive homeostatic mechanisms quickly rid the body of the CO_2 and H_2O, whereas the energy is utilized for all the body needs. The body requires energy not only for muscular contraction but for such processes as absorption by the intestinal tract and elimination of waste substances by the kidney.

Protein Formation   The long, complex protein molecules are not absorbed, as such, to any great extent. Yet protein is required for many purposes. For example, when a person cuts himself, the reparative process demands protein. Many of the enzymes and hormones are proteins. These two examples suffice to indicate that the body must have protein. This protein is not simply ingested and then absorbed as such. Rather the basic amino acids, after they are absorbed into the blood stream, are reconverted into the specific proteins demanded by the body.

The proteins formed from the amino acids serve many functions. Perhaps of primary importance is the role played by the proteins in maintaining fluid balance. It will be recalled that it is by virtue of the proteins, which incidentally cannot readily pass through the capillary walls, that fluid is attracted from the tissue spaces into the vascular tree. If an individual should abstain from fluid for a period of time and thus become dehydrated, the blood proteins would become relatively concentrated. Fluid, therefore, would be attracted from the tissue spaces into the vascular tree, thereby maintaining normal circulatory dynamics.

One of the blood proteins is fibrinogen, which is essential to blood clotting. During hemorrhage, fibrinogen is lost and must be replaced. This is accomplished through the new synthesis of fibrinogen from the absorbed amino acids. Many hormones and all enzymes are proteins. They are constantly being degraded, and consequently there must be a steady production. For this purpose, the amino acids are also used.

If the diet should be poor in protein, its is obvious that grave results will ensue. Protein apparently cannot be synthesized from the other foodstuffs. The basic ingredients must be supplied in the diet. We may therefore conclude that protein is an indispensable part of the diet.

Carbohydrate Formation   After amino acids have been deaminated, instead of being oxidized for energy they may be converted into carbohydrate. This formation of new carbohydrate is termed **gluconeogenesis.** The term breaks down into *gluco,* glucose; *neo,* new; and *genesis,* to form. It is the new formation of glucose. It has been calculated that 50 to 60 per cent of the dietary amino acids can be converted by the liver into glycogen.

Fat Formation   It is a simple, if somewhat expensive, matter to prove that one can become obese on a protein diet alone. Protein can be converted to fat as well as to carbohydrate, and if excessive quantities of this foodstuff are ingested, fat will be deposited.

Protein, then, is an excellent food; it is essential for the purposes just mentioned as well as for many others. It can be converted to carbohydrate and to fat. It would seem, therefore, that a person can survive on a diet consisting only of protein. Experiments indicate that this assumption is correct. Whether or not there would result any deleterious effects from such an abnormal diet has not been clearly established. But at least on a hypothetical basis, as just outlined, a protein diet should satisfy body needs. However, for many reasons, a well-balanced diet is to be preferred.

Nitrogen Balance We have seen that the amino acids are used for many purposes. For all these processes, with the single exception of the re-formation of protein, nitrogen is liberated. For example, when carbohydrate is formed, that is, when gluconeogenesis occurs, nitrogen must be eliminated because carbohydrate contains no nitrogen. The same is true of fat formation. Likewise, when the amino acids are used for energy, there are two types of end products, nitrogenous and nonnitrogenous. The nitrogenous substances, such as urea and creatinine, are eliminated in the urine. In short, as a result of the intermediary metabolism of protein, nitrogen appears in the urine. It is therefore possible to determine the quantity of nitrogen ingested and the amount eliminated. Under normal circumstances these two values equal one another. The individual is then said to be in **nitrogen balance.**

There are many circumstances in which this balance is upset so that the output is greater than the intake, or vice versa. If an individual is on a complete protein fast, that is, if he is eating only carbohydrate and fat, he is obviously taking in no nitrogen. Yet, he still eliminates nitrogen. Under these circumstances, the average man daily excretes about 3 gm of nitrogen. Since it takes 6.25 gm of protein to produce a gram of nitrogen, on a protein-free diet, approximately 19 gm of body protein must be catabolized. Carbohydrate and fat cannot be converted to, or substituted for, protein. Therefore, on a protein-free diet, body tissue is consumed to satisfy the various protein needs.

These figures indicate that about 19 gm of protein per day are catabolized. Therefore it might be thought that if an individual ingested this quantity of protein he would be in nitrogen balance. This is not the case. If the individual eats only 19 gm of protein, he will still be in **negative nitrogen balance,** that is, he will excrete more nitrogen than he takes in. As shown in Table 23-1, he must ingest considerably more than 19 gm of protein in order to establish equilibrium. This is explicable on the basis that the body requires specific amino acids. Not all these amino acids are supplied by each gram of protein ingested. A large quantity of protein must therefore be available so that the body can select the amino acids it desires. In Table 23-1, it is seen that ultimately the amount of nitrogen ingested exceeds that eliminated. The individual is now said to be in a **positive nitrogen balance.**

TABLE 23-1   Relation of Nitrogen Ingested to Nitrogen Eliminated

Protein Ingested, gm	Nitrogen Ingested, gm	Nitrogen in Feces, gm	Nitrogen Absorbed, gm	Nitrogen in Urine, gm	Nitrogen Balance, gm
None	None	0.25	None	3.10	−3.10
96.40	15.40	0.75	14.65	14.60	+0.05
131.40	21.00	0.85	20.15	17.90	+2.25

Some nitrogen appears in the feces. This small amount represents the nitrogen content of the undigested residue as well as nitrogen excreted by the large intestine plus the nitrogen residue of the intestinal debris and bacteria. Even during a complete protein fast, there is some nitrogen in the feces.

In the particular experiment from which the data of Table 23-1 were taken, a diet containing about 96 gm of protein sufficed to maintain nitrogen balance. If more carbohydrate is added to the diet, it is possible to lower the amount of ingested protein and still maintain nitrogen balance. This does not mean that the extra carbohydrate supplies nitrogen, but rather that the carbohydrate in this case is being used for energy and thus spares protein from this necessity. For this reason, carbohydrates and also fats are often called **protein sparers.** The body, by using them for energy, spares protein for other purposes. Consequently, less nitrogen is eliminated.

The statement has been made that, in view of the fact that protein can be converted to fat or carbohydrate or used for energy, a diet of protein alone should satisfy body needs. Actual calculations reveal, however, that in order to satisfy all body needs a man would have to eat over 8 lb of meat per day. This is a possible but not very practical feat. Therefore, the ideal diet contains a balanced mixture of all three foodstuffs.

In some cases, there is a **positive nitrogen balance.** This means that more nitrogen is being ingested than is being eliminated. The extra nitrogen must be undergoing utilization in some form. For example, during growth, children always exhibit a positive nitrogen balance. The excess nitrogen is being deposited in new tissue as protein. The same condition prevails as a person recovers from a wasting disease. And, of course, the pregnant woman is in positive balance because she is supplying large amounts of nitrogenous substances to the developing fetus.

CARBOHYDRATE

The average diet, for most people, is made up mainly of carbohydrate. Bread, cake, potatoes, and the like are rich in carbohydrate. Salivary ptyalin begins the digestion, and then the amylases in the pancreatic and intestinal juices finish the conversion of the complex carbohydrate molecules to glucose, fructose, and galactose. These simple sugars are rapidly absorbed from the small intestine into the venous blood which then carries them to the liver. Here the intermediary metabolism of carbohydrate begins.

The absorbed sugar may (1) be converted to glycogen and stored in the liver, (2) be changed to glycogen in the muscles, (3) be transformed to fat and deposited as adipose tissue, (4) circulate as blood sugar, (5) be oxidized for energy, or (6) be excreted.

Liver Glycogen Glycogen is a complex carbohydrate made up of a number of molecules of simple sugars. It is usually represented by the formula $n(C_6H_{10}O_5)$. This is because the exact structural formula is not known.

Glycogen is principally formed and stored in the liver. The amount of glycogen in the liver varies with the diet. The liver of an animal immediately after eating contains about 4 to 5 per cent glycogen. After a 24-hour fast the liver is practically devoid of the substance. It thus seems evident that the liver is the principal storehouse of carbohydrate. Some tissues of the body, especially brain and cardiac muscle, can survive only so long as they are delivered an adequate supply of carbohydrate. If this supply depended entirely upon ingestion, we would all be living under very precarious circumstances. However, it is a well-known fact that man can fast for many days without ill effects. There must be endogenous sources of carbohydrate. One such reservoir is liver glycogen. But after 24 hours the liver glycogen is exhausted. Now the organism must convert protein to carbohydrate by the process labeled gluconeogenesis.

Liver glycogen is formed not only from the simple sugars which are absorbed from the intestinal tract but also from lactic acid. Lactic acid is produced by the muscles when they perform work. This lactic acid is carried by the venous blood to the liver where most of it is converted into liver glycogen.

We have noted that the liver performs many essential functions. In the previous chapter it was noted that the liver removes disintegrated red cells from the blood and excretes some of their products in the bile. It also produces the very important bile salts. Now we learn that the liver functions to synthesize and store glycogen and to hold it ready in case of need.

Muscle Glycogen   By a series of chemical reactions, energy is provided for muscular contraction. In order for muscular activity to continue, the essential substances which provide the energy must be resynthesized. Resynthesis requires energy, and the energy for this process is provided by the conversion of glycogen to lactic acid. During exercise lactic acid escapes into the blood and is carried to the liver. As already pointed out, this lactic acid is converted into liver glycogen which can then be reduced to blood sugar. The sugar is carried by the blood back to the muscle for storage as liver glycogen. This closed circuit is known as the **Cori cycle** (Fig. 23-3).

From what has been said, it is evident that there is a steady formation and a comparable breakdown of glycogen. These processes are termed, respectively, **glycogenesis** and **glycogenolysis.** The prefix *glyco-* refers to glycogen. *Genesis* means "to form," whereas *lysis* means "to break down." Thus the process of converting the simple sugars and lactic acid to glycogen is termed glycogenesis; that by which glycogen is converted into the simple sugars is glycogenolysis.

Blood Sugar   The sugar of the blood is mostly in the form of glucose, although fructose and galactose are also present. Figure 23-4 shows the source and fate of blood sugar. As we have already noted, even in the absence of carbohydrate in the diet there is a potential source of carbohydrate in protein. However, under normal circumstances, the ingested carbohydrate satisfies body needs for that substance. Soon after a meal the blood-sugar concentration increases, but at the same time more liver glycogen is formed. Thus the blood sugar is kept within a fairly narrow range despite the large quantities being absorbed from the intestinal tract. Between meals the liver glycogen is reconverted to glucose, thus serving to maintain the blood-sugar level.

There are many delicate mechanisms which function to control the level of blood sugar. Since these processes involve several of the hormones

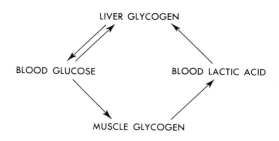

FIG. 23-3   The Cori cycle.

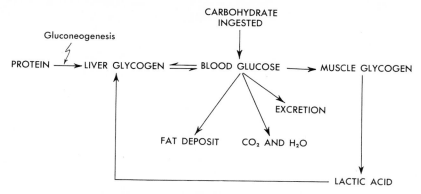

FIG. 23-4   Source and fate of blood glucose.

produced by the endocrine glands, this aspect of carbohydrate metabolism will be deferred until endocrinology is studied. In the postabsorptive state, that is, after all the foodstuffs have been taken out of the digestive tract and distributed, the concentration of sugar in the blood is about 80 mg per 100 ml of blood. The blood glucose is steadily oxidized for energy. But as the glucose is removed from the blood by this process, the liver at the same rate adds glucose to the circulation. In this manner the blood concentration is maintained.

Fat   Everyone knows that to eat a lot of cake and potatoes and bread means inevitable weight gain and that excess weight will be very obviously fat. There is no question but that carbohydrate can be converted to fat. The normal store of carbohydrate is liver glycogen. The excessive storage of carbohydrate as fat is abnormal.

Carbohydrate will be deposited as fat only when large quantities are ingested. On the normal diet, the absorbed sugar is converted to liver glycogen and then reconverted to glucose between meals. Thus, when the individual eats again, the liver-glycogen store is low and ready to be replenished. But if he eats so much and so frequently that the liver-glycogen store is filled, there is no place for the excess carbohydrate to go but into fat. This process may be considered as an abnormal defense mechanism to protect the blood from becoming overloaded with sugar.

Energy Production   All three of the basic foodstuffs can be oxidized for the production of energy. And, on the average mixed diet, the energy provided comes from the simultaneous oxidation of all three.

It has already been noted that the amount of oxygen taken up by the body is not always the same as the quantity of carbon dioxide produced.

The ratio between these two values is termed the **respiratory quotient** (RQ) and depends upon the type of foodstuff being oxidized. For example, from the reaction

$$\text{Glucose} + \text{oxygen} = \text{carbon dioxide} + \text{water}$$
$$C_6H_{12}O_6 + 6O_2 = 6CO_2 + 6H_2O$$

it can be seen that six molecules of oxygen are utilized and the same number of molecules of CO_2 are produced. Thus, if only carbohydrate is being burned, the RQ must be 1. When protein is oxidized, the RQ is about 0.8, and for fat it is close to 0.7. Therefore by determining the RQ of man as a whole, or of individual tissues, one can tell what type of food is being utilized. By such a procedure it has been shown that the brain utilizes carbohydrate almost exclusively. The dependence of brain tissue upon glucose is well illustrated by the observation that when the blood sugar falls below a critical point, about 50 mg per cent, mental confusion, convulsions, and even loss of consciousness may occur.

Heart muscle also relies upon carbohydrate, perhaps not to the extent that brain tissue does, but when there is an adequate supply of glucose the RQ of cardiac muscle approaches 1. It is true that the heart can utilize other substances, especially fat for energy, but it obviously prefers carbohydrate.

The RQ of most other tissues of the body is about 0.82, which indicates that all three substances are being burned. Likewise it can be demonstrated that most tissues can utilize any one of the foodstuffs with equal facility. Apparently, only brain and heart tissue demand carbohydrate.

Excretion   Normally, the urine does not contain glucose to any appreciable degree. However, if the blood sugar rises high enough, glucose can be detected in the urine. On the average, when the blood sugar exceeds a level of approximately 160 mg per cent, glucose begins to appear in the urine.

FAT

Fat passes through the oral cavity and the stomach practically unmolested. But in the small intestine the lipases of the pancreatic and intestinal juices, with the aid of the bile salts, succeed in reducing the fat molecule to glycerol and the fatty acids. Then, again with the help of the bile salts, these substances are absorbed. Once in the blood, the fatty substances may be (1) stored or (2) oxidized. Under specific conditions fat may be converted to carbohydrate, but it is doubtful if this is a significant mechanism under normal circumstances.

Blood plasma normally contains about 500 mg per cent of total lipid. This includes: triglyceride, 165 mg per cent; cholesterol, 170 mg per cent;

and phosphatides, 165 mg per cent. In the body as a whole, approximately 10 per cent of the total weight is lipid. This, however, varies greatly.

Storage of Fat   The *distribution* of fat is, to a limited extent, determined by (1) the type of work or exercise a person does and (2) the hormonal pattern. For example, under the influence of the female sex hormones, mature women have typical fat deposits in the breasts and hips. But the *amount* of fat carried by an individual is controlled exclusively by the diet.

A definite amount of fat is beneficial for protection as well as for cosmetic purposes. But the excessive accumulation of fat is pathological. It has long been maintained, mostly by obese people, that fat deposition represents a store of energy. The grossly buxom opera stars of yesteryear vigorously protested that were they to give up any of that fat they would not have the strength to go on. All such notions have now been exploded. It is well established that fat not only does not give a person strength but, on the contrary, represents an excess load which saps one's energy and shortens one's life. Without delving into the statistics and the physiological explanation of those statements, we may state simply that obesity is a pathological condition which should be treated as promptly and as effectively as any other disease. Obesity means a weight in excess of 15 per cent above normal.

Oxidation of Fat   Fat is an excellent source of energy. It provides about twice as much energy as carbohydrate or protein. For this reason the diet should contain some fat.

By very complex and not completely understood processes, fatty acids and glycerol are converted into **ketone bodies,** and the ketone bodies are further broken down to liberate energy, with the production of CO_2 and H_2O. If man is capable of utilizing all three foodstuffs, there is a balance between the quantity of ketone bodies formed and those oxidized. Consequently, ketone bodies do not ordinarily accumulate in significant amounts in the blood. But when carbohydrate metabolism is impaired, as in diabetes mellitus, fat oxidation must take its place. However, ketone oxidation does not keep pace with the accelerated ketone-body formation. As a result, ketone bodies accumulate in the blood and spill over into the urine, giving to it a characteristic acetone smell.

We have seen that both protein and carbohydrate are stored only to a very limited extent. Thus, during a prolonged fast, fat is called upon more and more to supply the body's energy needs. Here again, as in diabetes mellitus, the accelerated ketone formation outruns the oxidation of those substances, with the result that ketone bodies accumulate, cause the blood to become acid, and if unchecked, constitute one of the contributory causes of death.

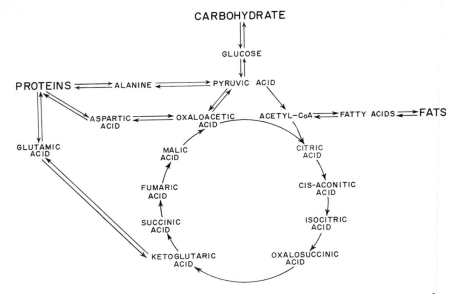

FIG. 23-5 Metabolic interrelationships. Ultimately the products of protein, carbohydrate, and fat metabolism enter the citric acid cycle for final oxidation.

METABOLIC INTERRELATIONSHIPS

The intermediary metabolism of protein, carbohydrate, and fat has been discussed, but it is important to emphasize that the involved reactions are interrelated and, as can be seen in Fig. 23-5, there is a final common pathway in the so-called **citric acid cycle.** It should be noted that ultimately the end products of the metabolism of all three basic foodstuffs enter the citric acid cycle. In this cycle oxygen is utilized; carbon dioxide and water are produced. The citric acid cycle generates a total of 15 ATP molecules. ATP, as already mentioned, is the cell's major source of energy.

It should be noted (Fig. 23-5) that the reaction by which pyruvic acid is converted to acetyl-Co is not reversible. Accordingly, fat cannot be converted to carbohydrate through this route. Carbohydrate, however, is readily converted to fat.

CALORIMETRY

The term **metabolism** is applied to the various transformations—energy transformations—which go on continuously in all living forms. It has been pointed out that living things can move, grow, and reproduce themselves. All these activities require energy. That energy is not created by man, for energy can be neither created nor destroyed. It must be derived from the ingested food. The food contains the energy; man simply transforms that energy to satisfy his particular needs.

It has been noted that each of the three foodstuffs can be oxidized for the production of energy. In each case, carbon dioxide and water result. It seems clear that man can derive energy only from substances containing carbon and hydrogen. Consequently, throughout life there must be a steady and adequate supply of compounds containing these elements. However, man cannot make use of these elements unless they are in a particular form; only carbohydrates, proteins, and fats satisfy this requirement.

The energy provided by these metabolic processes is utilized for work. By work we mean not only lifting a weight or even necessarily contracting muscles. When a substance is transported across a membrane in opposition to pressure and concentration gradients, work is done. For example, it has been seen that the small intestine is capable of absorbing glucose even though the concentration of that substance in the intestine is less than in the blood. Clearly, in such a case the tendency is for the glucose to pass in the opposite direction, but by specific metabolic processes the glucose is transferred into the blood. Thus work has been accomplished. Similarly, when kidney function is studied, it will be learned that a hypertonic urine is produced. To accomplish this feat work must be done, work which requires energy. In short, every living process demands energy, accomplishes work, and in so doing, generates heat.

We speak of the foodstuffs as being "burned." It is a well-chosen expression, because if food is placed in an atmosphere of oxygen within a metal chamber and then ignited, approximately the same quantity of heat is produced as when the same amount of food is burned in the body. Not only is the heat production comparable, but the end products of this combustive process are identical.

Simple but ingenious experiments carried out over a century ago established the fact that the heat produced by the three types of food when burned outside the body is practically the same as that produced within the body. Only the combustion of protein gives different values. This is because the body does not completely oxidize protein but rather excretes energy-containing residues in the urine. However, if corrections for this incomplete combustion are made, the figures are found to be remarkably similar.

THE CALORIE

In view of the fact that animal energy is derived only from the combustion of these foodstuffs, a process which produces heat, energy in the living form is expressed in **calories.**

Small Calorie   There are two units of heat, the small and the large Calorie. The small calorie is defined as the amount of heat necessary to raise the temperature of 1 gm of water from 14.5 to 15.5°C.

Large Calorie   The large Calorie is simply one thousand times greater than the small calorie. By definition, it is the amount of heat necessary to raise the temperature of 1 kg of water from 14.5 to 15.5°C. The large Calorie is always written with a capital C, and it is most commonly used to express food values.

Food Values   As already mentioned, when the various foodstuffs are burned in an atmosphere of oxygen, heat is produced. If 1 gm of each of the three foods is placed in a carefully regulated chamber (Fig. 23-6) and ignited, the following values are obtained:

Protein	5.3 Calories
Carbohydrate	4.3 Calories
Fat	9.5 Calories

When 1 gm of each of these same substances is burned in the body, the following values are noted:

Protein	4.1 Calories
Carbohydrate	4.1 Calories
Fat	9.3 Calories

It is seen that the values for fat and carbohydrate are practically the same whether burned in a calorimeter or in the body. The slight difference is probably due to failure of absorption plus a small experimental error. The large discrepancy in the protein values, as already explained, is a result of the fact that protein is not completely oxidized in man.

CALORIC PRODUCTION IN MAN

Since all metabolic processes ultimately produce CO_2 and H_2O and utilize oxygen, heat is produced in accordance with the values just listed for the major foodstuffs. The quantity of heat produced by these processes is, then, a measure of the amount of food being burned. When work is done, more of these metabolic processes swing into action and others proceed at a more rapid rate. The net result is that the total heat production increases. It is obviously of value, therefore, to be able to determine the quantity of heat produced by the body under various circumstances. These determinations may be made either directly or indirectly.

Direct Method   It has been mentioned that a **calorimeter** is used to determine the caloric value of food. The type of calorimeter most widely employed is shown in Fig. 23-6. It is the so-called **bomb calorimeter.** The food to be analyzed is dried and a carefully weighed quantity placed

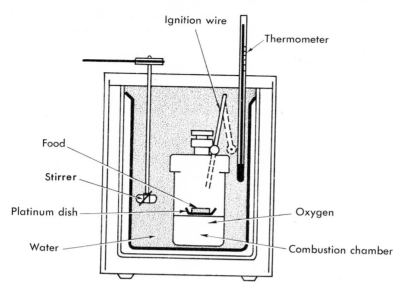

FIG. 23-6   The bomb calorimeter. A weighed sample of food is ignited. The resulting heat elevates the temperature of the surrounding water. The temperature change indicates the caloric value of the substance burned.

within the bomb. The inside of the bomb is lined with platinum; the outside is steel. Besides the food, there is only pure oxygen in the bomb. The entire chamber is then submerged in water, and the food is electrically ignited. As a result of the heat of combustion, the temperature of the water is elevated and determined. By making suitable calculations for the quantity of water, the caloric value of the food may be easily computed.

Essentially the same principle is used to ascertain the amount of heat produced by man by the direct method. The subject is placed in a chamber through which water circulates. If the temperature of the water entering and leaving is measured and if the total quantity of water which passes through the chamber is known, it is then possible to determine the amount of heat taken up by that quantity of water. Again, appropriate calculations disclose the number of Calories produced by the subject in a particular period of time. In actual practice, it is also necessary to collect the water vapor given off by the subject from his lungs and skin. The latent heat of this quantity of water must then be added to the total Calories calculated from the rise in circulating-water temperature.

The direct method is a very useful procedure for making highly accurate studies. However, as may be quickly surmised, the equipment is so large and so expensive that this method is usually not feasible. In the clinic, the overwhelming majority of determinations are made by means of the indirect method.

Indirect Method There are many types of machines designed to determine heat production by the indirect method. All of them are made so that the quantity of oxygen used, or carbon dioxide produced, or both, can be determined. From this information, as we shall see, it is possible to determine the amount of heat produced by the body in a specified period of time. Results obtained by indirect methods agree usually within 1 per cent with results derived by the direct method. And, since the apparatus is so much simpler and easier to use, it is the method of choice.

Of all the ways that have been designed to determine heat production by the indirect method, the Benedict-Roth apparatus, shown in Fig. 23-7,

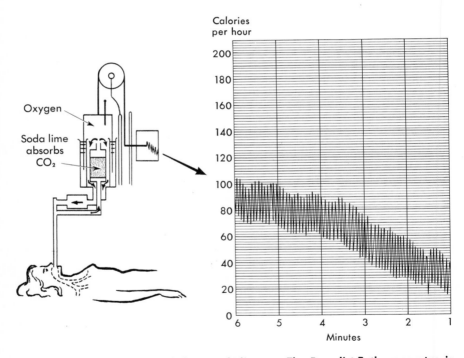

FIG. 23-7 Determination of the metabolic rate. The Benedict-Roth apparatus is depicted on the left. The chart on the right is used to determine the amount of oxygen utilized by the subject. The chart is calibrated both in ml of oxygen per minute and Calories per hour, as shown above.

remains the most popular model. The heat production is calculated from the quantity of oxygen utilized during a test period of 6 minutes.

It can be seen that the apparatus consists simply of a spirometer filled with oxygen. Within the spirometer is a canister of soda lime. When the subject inspires, he takes in pure oxygen. When he expires, the carbon dioxide is quickly and completely removed by the soda lime. Since the subject withdraws about 500 ml of oxygen from the spirometer when he inspires, the bell of the spirometer falls. There is a pen attached to the bell which writes on a slowly moving sheet of paper. During inspiration there is an upward stroke. When the subject expires, the bell rises and makes a downstroke on the moving paper. However, as shown in Fig. 23-7, the crest of each stroke is higher than that of the previous one so that there is a fairly even slope drawn over the 6-minute period. The paper is ruled and calibrated so that the actual quantity of oxygen used by the subject per minute can be easily determined from the slope of the curve. The average subject will consume about 250 ml of oxygen per minute. At the end of the 6-minute period, therefore, the spirometer will contain about 1,500 ml less oxygen than at the beginning of the test.

After the volume of oxygen utilized per minute is ascertained, it must then be corrected to standard conditions of 760 mm Hg pressure and 0°C. This can be done by using the equations combining Boyle's and Charles' laws, or prepared tables may be consulted. Having the corrected volume, the operator simply consults another prepared table or multiplies the volume in liters by 4.825. This figure represents the caloric equivalent of 1 liter of oxygen. To clarify this, let us assume that the corrected volume of oxygen used for the 6-minute period was 1.5 liters. Using the factor 4.825, we see that in 6 minutes 7.24 Calories were produced. In 1 hour that would be 72.4 Calories.

The above information will make it possible for the reader to operate the Benedict-Roth metabolism apparatus and to determine the heat production of the subject. But the student should be able to do more than that. He should be able to explain the physiological basis of these calculations.

We have seen that all metabolic processes consume oxygen and that each of the foodstuffs liberates a specific number of Calories when burned in oxygen or in the body. Let us turn once again to the reaction of carbohydrate with oxygen:

$$C_6H_{12}O_6 + 6O_2 = 6CO_2 + 6H_2O$$

One gm-mole weight of glucose is 180 gm. According to the equation, this quantity must react with 192 gm of O_2. Avogadro's principle states that

1 gm-mole of any gas has a volume of 22.4 liters. Therefore 6 gm-moles will occupy 134.4 liters (6 × 22.4). In other words, 134.4 liters of oxygen react with 180 gm of glucose. Therefore, 0.75 liter of O_2 must react with each gram of glucose (134.4/180).

We know from direct experiments that each gram of glucose burned in the body liberates 4.1 Calories. We now see that that gram of glucose while being burned utilizes 0.75 liter of O_2. One liter of oxygen then, in reacting with carbohydrate, must produce 5.47 Calories (4.1/.75).

If Table 23-2 is consulted, it will be seen that 2.03 liters of oxygen react with each gram of fat. Since each gram of fat, upon oxidation, liberates 9.3 Calories, 1 liter of oxygen in burning fat would produce only about

TABLE 23-2   Energy Relationships

	Carbohydrate	Fat	Protein
Liters of O_2 per gram utilized	0.75	2.03	0.97
Liters of CO_2 per gram utilized	0.75	1.43	0.78
RQ	1.00	0.70	0.80
Calories per gram produced	4.10	9.30	4.10
Caloric equivalent of 1 liter O_2	5.47	4.65	4.23

4.65 Calories. For protein, the figure would be 4.23 Calories; for carbohydrate, 5.47 Calories. Thus, when the amount of oxygen is determined, using the Benedict-Roth apparatus, how do we know which figure to use? The assumption is made that the subject is burning a mixture of the three foodstuffs. As a matter of fact, if the CO_2 is determined at the same time, the RQ will be found to be about 0.82. At that RQ, the caloric equivalent of a liter of oxygen is found to be 4.825. Since the Benedict-Roth method measures only the volume of oxygen utilized, the RQ cannot be determined and is assumed to be 0.82. For more accurate indirect metabolic studies, both oxygen utilization and carbon dioxide production are measured, the RQ is calculated, and the appropriate factor is then employed.

BASAL METABOLIC RATE

The methods by which the amount of heat produced by a subject may be determined have been explained. In view of the fact that heat production depends upon the metabolic processes, and these processes vary with the subject's activities, it is clear that studies of heat production would be relatively meaningless unless these determinations were made under well-defined and rigid conditions.

STANDARD CONDITIONS

Since the heat is produced by the metabolic processes and the quantity of heat liberated varies directly with the rate at which these processes proceed, the determinations accurately reflect the metabolic rate. We therefore speak of the metabolic rate rather than of heat production.

Determination of Basal Metabolic Rate   The more active an individual, the faster is his metabolic rate. Conversely, this rate falls to its lowest ebb during sleep. This is the true basal level, but since it is difficult to induce sleep whenever one desires to measure the metabolic rate, the basal level is calculated while the subject is awake but at rest and in the postabsorptive state. In actual practice, the subject is instructed to eat a light meal the night before the determination, to retire early so as to get about 8 hours sleep, to refrain from excessive exercise for at least 24 hours, and to omit breakfast before the test is conducted. Most metabolic tests are performed early in the morning after the subject has reclined in a quiet, semidark room for about 30 minutes. The equipment is then attached to the subject, and he is instructed to breathe normally.

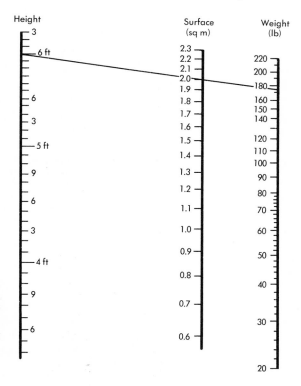

FIG. 23-8   A nomogram. To determine the subject's surface area, the weight and height must be known. From these two values, the surface area is obtained as shown.

Surface Area   Using these standard conditions for the determination of the Calories produced, it is now necessary to interpret the results. It has been found from comparing large numbers of such determinations that the best agreement among individuals is had when the heat production is expressed in terms of surface area. Very complicated formulas are required to calculate the surface areas, but tables and other aids, such as the nomogram shown in Fig. 23-8, simplify the task. If the individual's weight and height are known, the surface area may be easily ascertained. The average surface area in the United States is about 1.6 sq m for women and 1.8 for men.

The total heat production per hour is then divided by the surface area. The final figure for comparison is expressed in **Calories per hour per square meter.** In our illustration, we calculated that the subject produced 72.4 Calories per hour. Let us assume that he is a man 6 ft tall and weighs 175 lb. Using the nomogram, we find that he has a surface area of 2 sq m. Dividing this into 72.4, we conclude that this subject produces 36.2 Calories per hour per square meter.

NORMAL VALUES

The basal metabolic rate (BMR) is commonly expressed as a percentage of normal. A person is said to have, for example, a BMR of +20, or of −15. These figures mean that the first person's metabolic rate is 20 per cent above normal, while the second person is 15 per cent below normal. But what is normal?

The normal figures are obtained from determining the heat production of great numbers of people. After this is done, the figures are averaged and then grouped according to age and sex. Table 23-3 gives some repre-

TABLE 23-3   Heat Production per Hour per Square Meter

Age, years	Males, Calories	Females, Calories
10–12	49.5	45.8
12–14	47.8	43.4
14–16	46.0	41.0
16–18	43.0	38.5
18–20	41.0	37.6
20–30	40.5	36.8
30–40	39.5	36.5
40–50	38.0	35.3
50–60	36.9	34.4
60–70	35.8	33.6
70–80	34.5	32.6

sentative values. Let us assume that our 6-ft man is thirty-five years old. Using the table, we find that such a man should produce about 39.5 Calories per hour per square meter. Our subject generated only 36.2 Calories, which is approximately 8 per cent below the average. We say therefore that he has a BMR of −8. Is this normal? Actually, a variation of only 8 per cent is not considered abnormal. Speaking generally, a metabolic rate which is within 15 per cent of normal is not considered pathological. A deviation greater than 15 per cent, however, may signify some abnormality.

Age and Sex A glance at Table 23-3 suffices to convince one that the BMR varies with age and sex. Why the metabolic processes should progressively slow as one grows older and why there should be such a consistent and striking difference between the sexes remains unexplained. But whatever the explanation, it is necessary to compare the determined BMR with the norms for the proper groups.

Climate It has been found that the average BMR of people living in tropical climates is significantly lower than that of those residing in the more temperate latitudes. These differences are seen in various parts of the United States. The average BMR of residents of the southern states is some 8 per cent lower than that of the country taken as a whole.

ABNORMAL VALUES

Thyroid Disorders As has been noted, values which vary from the norm by more than 15 per cent are considered abnormal. As will be discussed in detail later, the thyroid gland controls the metabolic rate. Therefore malfunction of this gland usually results in marked alterations in the BMR. Thus we find that **hypothyroidism** is associated with basal metabolic rates as low as 30 to 40 per cent below normal. **Hyperthyroidism** produces a comparable increase in the rate.

Fever The metabolic rate determined while an individual has a fever will be above the true basal level. Roughly, for each degree of fever the metabolic rate is increased about 7 per cent. For this reason, the temperature of the subject is routinely taken before the BMR is ascertained.

Other Disorders Many disorders such as **diabetes insipidus** (page 639), **Addison's disease** (page 621), **malnutrition,** and **leukemia** are associated with abnormal basal metabolic rates.

METABOLIC RATE UNDER VARYING CONDITIONS

If the standard conditions are not obeyed, the amount of heat production will usually be significantly above normal. The use of drugs, the digestion of food, and exercise all vary the metabolic rate.

Exercise   The more strenuous the exercise or work, the higher will be the heat production. During very heavy activity, it is possible to increase the metabolic rate some ten times above the basal level.

Mental Work   It will come as something of a shock and a disappointment to the student to learn that mental work requires little or no energy. Benedict, to whom we owe much of our knowledge concerning metabolism, carried out an experiment in which he determined the metabolic rate of students while they were engaged in solving very difficult mathematical problems. He found that the metabolic rate under these conditions increased only 3 to 4 per cent. In discussing these findings, Benedict said, "The cloistered scholar at his books may be surprised to learn that the extra Calories needed for one hour of intense mental effort would be completely met by the eating of one oyster cracker or one-half of a salted peanut."

Specific Dynamic Action of Food   One of the conditions required for determining the BMR is that the subject should not have eaten for 10 or 12 hours. This stipulation is included because the ingestion of food elevates the heat production. This rise in metabolism above the basal level is due to the **specific dynamic action of food.**

Protein has a greater specific dynamic action, by far, than either fat or carbohydrate. If a man who produces, say, 75 Calories per hour is fed protein with a caloric value of 75, his heat production will be found to be not 75 but about 96 or 97 Calories. In other words, there has been an increase of about 30 per cent. This increment represents the specific dynamic action of protein. For carbohydrate it is only 6 per cent, and for fat, 4 per cent. The student can see the implication of these findings. One must actually eat more than his basal caloric output if he is not to lose weight. In the illustration just cited, although the basal rate was about 75 Calories per hour, this individual must eat protein with a caloric value of about 97 Calories. This demonstrates why protein alone is an extravagant way of satisfying bodily needs.

The increase in metabolism caused by the ingestion of food cannot be ascribed to the alimentary processes such as the work entailed in secreting the digestive juices and in absorption. This has been clearly proved. The increased metabolism involves work done in "processing" the ingested food, such as in converting glucose to liver glycogen and in deaminating protein. All these complex transformations previously discussed require energy which is reflected in a greater heat production.

The question is raised immediately, however, as to why the utilization of the protein, carbohydrate, and fat stores of the body does not require as much energy as the utilization of ingested foodstuffs. About all that can be said is that the body utilizes its own substance more efficiently than ingested food. This is clearly an inadequate explanation which awaits further research.

SUMMARY

The wall of the **small intestine** is thrown into folds, each of which is replete with microscopic fingerlike projections called **villi.** The 5,000,000 villi present a great surface area which facilitates absorption. Although physicochemical factors play a role in absorption, there are also active secretory processes which transfer the digested substances from the lumen of the intestine to the blood or lymph system. During the absorption of fat, .the lymph vessels appear milky and are therefore termed **lacteals.**

The **amino acids** resulting from **protein** digestion are absorbed into the blood stream. They may then be (1) oxidized for energy, (2) used to build body protein, (3) converted to carbohydrate, (4) transformed into fat, (5) excreted, or (6) stored in the liver. The process by which protein is converted to carbohydrate is termed **gluconeogenesis.** The nitrogen which appears in the urine is derived from protein catabolism. Since the body demands specific amino acids, considerable protein must be ingested in order to establish **nitrogen balance.**

The end products of **carbohydrate** digestion—**glucose, fructose,** and **galactose**—are absorbed into the blood stream. They may then (1) be converted to glycogen and stored in the liver, (2) be deposited in the muscles, (3) be transformed to fat and stored as adipose tissue, (4) circulate as blood sugar, (5) be oxidized for energy, or (6) be excreted. During exercise, lactic acid enters the blood from the active muscles. The liver converts this to glycogen and then to blood sugar which is carried back to the muscles. This is the **Cori cycle.** The formation of glycogen is termed **glycogenesis;** the breakdown of glycogen is called **glycogenolysis.** The normal fasting blood-sugar ranges from 70 to 90 mg per cent.

The end products of **fat** digestion, **glycerol** and the **fatty acids,** are absorbed into the blood stream and may be (1) stored in the body-fat deposits or (2) oxidized for energy. The final common pathway for the oxidation of all foodstuffs is the **citric acid cycle.**

Metabolism is the term applied to the various energy transformations which go on continuously in all living forms. Heat is measured in Calories. The **large Calorie** is the amount of heat necessary to raise the temperature of 1 kg of water from 14.5 to 15.5°C. It is one thousand times greater than the **small calorie.** The faster the metabolic process proceeds, the greater will be the heat production. The heat production in man can be calculated by either the **direct** or **indirect method.**

The **basal metabolic rate (BMR)** refers to the heat production of a subject at rest but awake in the postabsorptive state. For comparison, the BMR is calculated in terms of **surface area** of the subject. The average heat production **per hour per square meter** of a large group of people is used as the norm. The BMR of any particular person is expressed as a percentage of that norm. If the BMR varies more than 15 per cent from the normal, it is considered abnormal. Thyroid disorders, fever, as well as many other diseases are associated with abnormal basal metabolic rates.

QUESTIONS

1. What role do the villi play in absorption?
2. What use may the body make of the amino acids absorbed into the blood stream?
3. Discuss the mechanisms which maintain the blood sugar relatively constant.
4. How do the end products of fat digestion reach the blood stream?
5. Outline the steps for determining the basal metabolic rate by the indirect method.
6. What factors alter the metabolic rate?

SUGGESTED READING

Allfrey, V. G., and Mirsky, A. E., "How Cells Make Molecules," *Sci. American,* **205:**#3, 74–82, September 1961.

Cabib, E., "Carbohydrate Metabolism," *Ann. Rev. Biochem.,* **32:** 321–354, 1963.

Green, D. E., "Biological Oxidation," *Sci. American,* **199:**#1, 56–62, July 1958.

Kleiber, M., and Rogers, T. A., "Energy Metabolism," *Ann. Rev. Physiol.,* **23:** 15–36, 1961.

Lehninger, A. L., "Energy Transformation in the Cell," *Sci. American,* **202:**#5, 102–114, May 1960.

Watson, J. D., "Involvement of RNA in the Synthesis of Proteins," *Science,* **140:** #3562, 17–26, April 5, 1963.

Elimination

24

THE TERM **homeostasis** has been used several times in this book. It refers to the constancy of the internal environment. In Part 3, on circulation, we studied the homeostatic mechanisms which keep the pressure of the blood within a narrow range regardless of changing external conditions. The consideration of respiration emphasized the point that, despite one's activity, the carbon dioxide and oxygen content of the arterial blood are kept constant. That is to say, even though large quantities of carbon dioxide are poured into the venous blood stream, the concentration of that substance in the arterial blood does not materially vary because of the exquisitely attuned respiratory mechanisms. The more CO_2 produced, the more eliminated. Consequently, the quantity which remains in the arterial blood is always about the same.

Obviously, similar homeostatic mechanisms are required for alimentation. Our diet varies. We may ingest a box of candy at one sitting and then take in very little carbohydrate for many hours thereafter. Yet the blood sugar is held remarkably steady. We may eat a 2-lb steak one day and then very little protein for days to follow. Still, the living processes go on, protein is utilized at a constant rate, and the consistency of the internal environment is safeguarded. Likewise, we may greatly vary the quantity of salt we consume from meal to meal. But even so the concentration of sodium, for example, in the blood does not change significantly. In short, despite our changing habits, regardless of the wide variations in our diet, the concentration of the various ingested substances remains constant. There is only one way that this can be accomplished, and that is by varying elimination in step with ingestion. In this chapter we shall study the various routes of elimination from the body and then attempt to explain how the excretory mechanisms are regulated so as to maintain the constancy of the internal environment.

DEFECATION

The gastrointestinal tract is a continuous tube extending from the mouth to the anus. The residuum of the ingested food is expelled through the anal opening. This elimination differs markedly from that via the lungs, kidneys, or skin. It differs because the substances expelled have never really entered the blood stream, have never actually become a part of the body. They simply traverse a tube which happens to pass through the body. Nonetheless, it is essential to include the elimination of fecal material in this discussion of the fate of the foodstuffs for two reasons: (1) a part of the ingested material does end up in the feces; (2) abnormalities of fecal elimination may markedly influence the body.

THE RECTUM

The **rectum** and **anus** represent the terminal parts of the large intestine. The rectum in man is not straight; its 12 cm length is twisted backward and forward and from side to side (Fig. 22-1). Like the rest of the gastrointestinal tract, the rectum is lined with mucous membrane. However, unlike the other parts of the intestinal system, the mucosa and underlying circular bands of muscle are arranged in folds, or sleeves. Finally, the rectum makes a short right-angle bend. The remaining 2 or 3 cm of the intestinal tract is referred to as the **anal canal** and ends at the surface as the anus.

Of great physiological importance are two sets of muscular valves, the **external** and **internal sphincters,** which control the passage of feces.

The rectum and anal canal are richly supplied with arteries and veins. Of particular interest are the veins. The fact that man has learned to walk upright means that gravity plays a role in slowing venous drainage. In addition, the social structure in which man lives makes it necessary that he control defecation sometimes for hours. Thus the pressure of the feces also tends to discourage venous drainage. All in all, it is therefore not surprising that the rectal veins frequently enlarge and become tortuous. This condition is referred to as **hemorrhoids** or **piles.**

FORMATION OF FECES

We have already seen that, by virtue of the digestive juices and the intestinal flora, very little if any digestible food remains in the residue. The large intestine normally removes a considerable quantity of water from this residue as it moves through the intestine and comes to rest in the rectum. The residue moves for two reasons: (1) strong peristaltic contraction and (2) overloading of the intestine so that the fecal material is simply pushed along by the material above.

The rate of movement through the intestinal tract depends upon the substances ingested. The usual meal takes 12 to 14 hours to pass from the stomach to the rectum. However, after the residue reaches the rectum, it remains there for a variable length of time, so that the substances eaten one day do not usually appear in the stool until the next day. As a matter of fact, there may be traces of a meal still appearing in the stool two or three days later.

These figures are very vague because they vary so considerably from person to person. The fluidity of the meal makes a big difference in the rate of progress through the intestinal tract. The quantity of food is also a factor. The more one eats, of course, the faster it will be moved along. Finally, emotional states and exercise must be taken into consideration, because they are found to modify intestinal peristalsis.

ELIMINATION OF FECES

The elimination of feces or, as the act is termed, **defecation** is fundamentally a reflex mechanism, but it is a reflex which can be controlled voluntarily under most circumstances.

Defecation Reflex As fecal material accumulates in the rectum, the rectum becomes distended and the intrarectal pressure steadily increases. The distention, or stretch, of the rectum stimulates proprioceptors which reside in the rectal wall. The greater the stretch, the greater will be the the number of receptors which fire. Finally, when the intrarectal pressure exceeds about 40 mm Hg, enough impulses reach the spinal cord via nerves from the rectum to fire the motor nerves which course from the spinal cord to the rectum. As a result, the muscle in the rectal wall contracts, thereby expelling the feces. The defecation reflex includes receptors in the rectal wall, afferent sensory nerves which conduct impulses to the spinal cord, and efferent motor nerves which bring the impulses back to the rectum, to the muscle which now contracts (Fig. 24-1). The effective stimulus for the reflex is stretch of the rectum. The response to this stimulus is rectal contraction, removing the feces and thereby eliminating the stretch.

Control of Defecation If a man's spinal cord is completely severed, impulses from the brain cannot cross the gap; therefore, all reflex action below the level of injury now proceeds free of higher-center censorship. In such cases, the rectum empties automatically whenever the intrarectal pressure exceeds about 40 mm Hg. But the normal individual can prevent defecation from occurring even though the rectum is stretched past the critical point, and he can usually encourage defecation even though the intrarectal pressure is below the point necessary to fire the reflex.

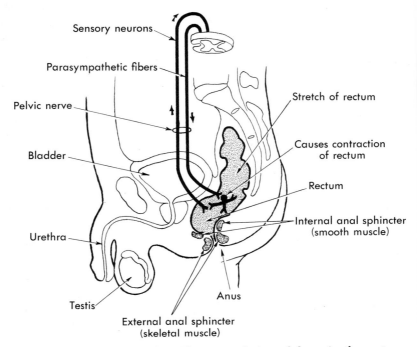

Sensory neurons

Parasympathetic fibers

Pelvic nerve

Bladder

Urethra

Testis

Stretch of rectum

Causes contraction of rectum

Rectum

Internal anal sphincter (smooth muscle)

Anus

External anal sphincter (skeletal muscle)

FIG. 24-1   Defecation reflex. The accumulation of feces in the rectum causes stretch which initiates impulses resulting in rectal contraction and expulsion of the fecal material.

The whole subject of inhibition of reflex activity is poorly understood. Most reflexes involving the autonomic nervous system cannot be voluntarily altered. For example, we are quite powerless to slow heart action at will, to augment blood pressure, or to change the peristaltic movements of the intestine. Yet, in some manner, we do develop the capacity to inhibit the defecatory reflex. A part of this control is exercised by vigorously contracting the anal-sphincter muscles. These are skeletal muscles and are therefore under voluntary control. Thus, even though the defecation reflex threatens to evacuate the rectum, it is possible to frustrate this attempt by closing the anal opening.

The defecation reflex may be initiated and assisted through voluntary efforts. This is accomplished by contracting the abdominal muscles, which results in an increase of intra-abdominal pressure. At the same time, the epiglottis is closed and the thoracic muscles are contracted. This greatly increases intrapleural pressure, forcing the dome of the diaphragm to descend into the abdominal cavity. Since the abdominal muscles are rigid, the viscera must be squeezed by the descent of the diaphragm. The intra-abdominal pressure accordingly rises. Consequently, the intestinal tract is squeezed. If the rectum contains any fecal material, the squeezing action will cause a rise in the intrarectal pressure. It is just as though one were to press upon a partially filled balloon. The pressure within the balloon would increase proportionally with the force applied on the outside.

It can be seen that this external force applied to the rectum in the form of intra-abdominal pressure will serve to initiate and augment the defecation reflex, and, at the same time, to aid in evacuating the rectum.

When an individual stands, the abdominal viscera press down upon the rectum and exert a pressure amounting to some 20 mm Hg. But when he strains, as just described, he can increase the pressure on the rectum to well over 100 mm Hg. This is a considerable force and usually suffices to empty the rectum.

CONSTIPATION

The term **constipation** is derived from *constipare,* a Latin word meaning "to press together." It is a condition in which the evacuations from the rectum are infrequent or incomplete, so that considerable fecal matter is retained.

Regularity The rectum will evacuate itself automatically if it is not inhibited by the higher centers. Since our modern living demands that the defecation reflex be controlled, it is necessary to establish definite regularity for this function. The frequency depends upon the quantity of food ingested, but whatever the needs, the act should be undertaken at the same time, or times, each day.

If regular habits in this respect are not established, the rectal reflex is inhibited and the rectum becomes distended. Because of the voluntary inhibition, however, the receptors quickly adapt, and therefore the urge to defecate soon passes. Thus, the fecal matter is retained for an undue length of time. In most cases there is excessive absorption of water from the feces due to its long stay in the rectum and lower large intestine. The feces become dry, hard, and difficult to expel. The individual is now constipated.

The above is not to be construed as meaning that, if it is necessary to miss a usual bowel movement or if it is essential for some reason to inhibit defecation, one will immediately become constipated. Not at all. Constipation from a lack of regularity results only after a long period of time during which the defecation reflex is repeatedly frustrated.

Diet The composition of the ingested food may be such as to be conducive to constipation. Without engaging in an extended discussion of nutrition, it is enough to remind the reader that if the food contains too little residue or too little fluid there will be only a small amount of fecal material formed and it will be dry and hard. The diet should thus contain what is known as "roughage," to make up sufficient bulk in the rectum, thereby stimulating the defecation reflexes.

Abnormal Intestinal Function If the large intestine absorbs too much water, if it is thrown into spastic contractions, or if the peristalsis is too weak to move the food residue, constipation may result. Such conditions are extremely difficult to correct, and the individual should consult a physician rather than attempt self-medication. This statement is applicable to all cases of chronic constipation.

DIARRHEA

Generally speaking, we can say that constipation is a digestive disorder of civilized city dwellers, especially in the temperate zones, whereas diarrhea is more commonly found among primitive people living in the tropics. Although these generalities contain a strong element of fact, it is still true that many of our civilized neighbors are afflicted with diarrhea. Thus this problem is worthy of note here.

Diarrhea is a term which means "a flow," and thus is descriptive of the condition in which the fecal material is unduly fluid and flows out of the rectum instead of being eliminated in solid form.

The cause of diarrhea among primitive people is usually bacterial. Where there is adequate sanitation, diarrhea is most commonly caused by excessive use of cathartics, the ingestion of irritating or spoiled foods, emotional upsets, and fever states. Usually, after the irritation, emotion, or fever has passed, the condition will rectify itself. But should it persist, medication is required to stem the flow and thereby prevent undue generalized dehydration.

CATHARTIC

A **cathartic** is a drug which increases rectal evacuation. The term means "purification." The old medicine men were firmly convinced that the body could be cleansed and thus cured of whatever might ail it if a good bowel movement were to be promoted. There is no question but that several extreme instances demand the use of a cathartic. In general, however, these drugs are fabulously overused, thus resulting in anything but purification.

Cathartics act in many ways. Only a few of the more common ones will be mentioned here in order to emphasize the basic mechanisms of defecation.

Castor Oil This widely used and highly unpopular substance increases fecal evacuation because it irritates the intestinal tract. It causes marked stimulation, by this irritating effect, of the small intestine. Consequently, the food is propelled into the large intestine very rapidly. This serves to increase the fecal content and encourage the reflex. Since the fecal material moves so rapidly, there is hardly enough time for fluid absorption. Therefore the feces remains semifluid, and this too makes for ease of elimination.

Epsom Salts Magnesium sulfate, or epsom salts, as it is popularly called, is one of the most commonly used cathartics. It operates to promote defecation because both the magnesium and sulfate ions are not readily absorbed by the intestine. Therefore there is osmotic retention of fluid in the fecal matter. This increase in bulk stimulates the reflex, and the fluid material is easier to eliminate than dried, hard feces.

Liquid Petrolatum This oil is indigestible and unabsorbable. Consequently, it passes along the intestinal tract with the food residue and serves to lubricate the fecal contents as well as the walls of the tract. By coating the feces with oil, it diminishes the absorption of water. As a result, the feces is more fluid and can move through the rectum with greater ease. Of all the cathartics, it is perhaps the safest, though it too should not be used indiscriminately.

URINE

Urine is normally a clear, transparent, amber-colored liquid which is formed and excreted by the kidneys. It contains most of the substances found in the blood plasma, with the notable exception of protein and glucose. The concentration of the urinary ingredients varies in such a way as to assist in the maintenance of the constancy of the blood composition.

THE KIDNEYS

Structure When the kidneys are examined grossly, they are found to consist of two parts. The inner core is called the **medulla,** and the outer shell is termed the **cortex.** Microscopically, the kidney is seen to contain a mass of tubes which, because of their minuteness, are termed **tubules.** Figure 24-2 shows that the tubules are so arranged that the very important **Bowman's capsule (glomerulus)** lies in the cortex. This leads to the **proximal convoluted part** of the tubule. Next it is seen that the long thin **Henle's loop** dips into the medulla. The **distal convoluted part** of the tubule is found once again in the cortex, and this, finally, empties into a **collecting duct** which conveys the urine to the **renal pelvis.**

In the human kidney, there are approximately 1,000,000 **nephrons.** The nephron includes Bowman's capsule, with the various parts of the tubule just described. The nephron is the structural unit of the kidney.

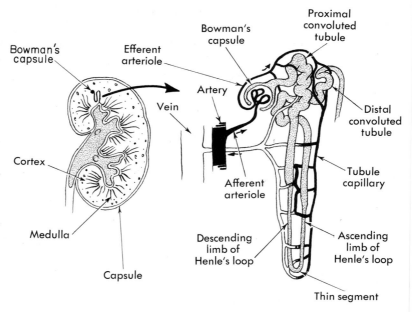

FIG. 24-2 Diagrammatic representation of the anatomy of the kidney. Not all nephrons dip deeply into the medulla. The peritubular capillaries surrounding the juxtamedullary nephron, depicted on the right, form the vasa recta.

It is important to differentiate two types of nephrons. The **cortical nephron** is situated almost completely in the cortex of the kidney. It is characterized by having a very short thin loop of Henle. The second type, the **juxtamedullary nephron,** has its glomerulus in the cortex close to the medulla. The tubule then sweeps down deep into the medullary tissue. These nephrons are characterized by having long thin loops of Henle. In man, cortical nephrons outnumber juxtamedullary nephrons 7 to 1.

Blood Supply The **renal artery** leaves the descending aorta to enter the kidney. It quickly breaks up into numerous smaller arteries. These small arteries pass to all parts of the kidney and give off individual branches to each Bowman's capsule. Each branch is called an **afferent arteriole.** As soon as it enters the capsule, it breaks up into a capillary tuft. The capillaries then re-form to empty *not* into a vein, as one would expect, but into another arteriole, the **efferent arteriole.** This is the only place in the body where there exists a capillary network between two arterioles. Ordinarily, the capillaries are supplied by an arteriole and drained by a venule.

The efferent arteriole then turns down toward the tubule. Once again the arteriole arborizes into a capillary network, this time to supply the tubule cells. This capillary *does* drain into a venule which leads ultimately to the renal vein which leaves the kidney to carry the blood to the inferior vena cava.

The juxtamedullary nephrons have long vessels which follow the tubules deep into the medulla. These long vessels form a series of hairpin loops, called **vasa recta**. This arrangement, as will be discussed below, is extremely important to renal function.

By virtue of the fact that there are two arterioles in series, the pressure drop in the renal circulation has two points of sharp decrease (Fig. 24-3). It should be noted that the afferent arterioles lower the mean pressure from about 100 to close to 60 mm Hg. This represents the hydrostatic pressure in the glomeruli. The efferent arterioles lower the pressure still further, to about 15 mm Hg. Thus, the hydrostatic pressure in the peritubular capillaries is very low and, accordingly, favors movement of fluid into the capillaries from the interstitial spaces.

By the arrangement just described in Bowman's capsule, it should be understood that the blood is separated from the cavity of this capsule only by two very thin membranes: (1) the **membrane of the capillary** and (2) the **membrane of Bowman's capsule.** It is across these very thin barriers that the various filtrable substances of the blood pass to enter the tubule.

Nerve Supply   The kidneys are liberally supplied by both branches of the autonomic nervous system. These fibers control the renal arterioles and thus can markedly alter kidney function.

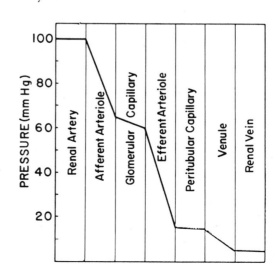

FIG. 24-3   Pressure in various parts of the renal circulation. Note the high capillary pressure in the glomerulus. (Reproduced, with permission, from R. F. Pitts, "Physiology of the Kidney and Body Fluids," Year Book Medical Publishers, Chicago, 1963.)

FORMATION OF URINE

As the blood passes through Bowman's capsule, all the substances contained in the plasma of small enough molecular size filter through the membranes to enter the cavity of the capsule which is continuous with the tubule. Only the proteins, of all the plasma constituents, fail to be filtered in this manner. Then, as the filtrate flows through the tubule, water and many of the other constituents are reabsorbed by the tubular cells. In some cases the tubules, instead of absorbing a particular substance, actually excrete more of that substance into the filtrate. The urine now flows into the collecting ducts and ultimately enters the ureters to be conducted to the urinary bladder. The formation of urine, then, is seen

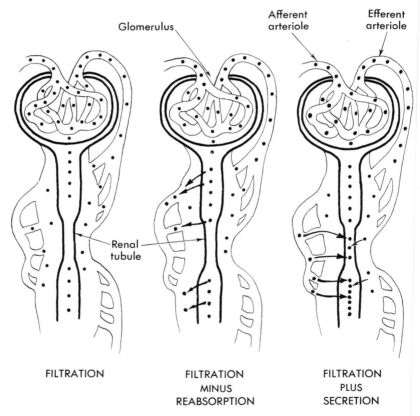

FILTRATION

FILTRATION
MINUS
REABSORPTION

FILTRATION
PLUS
SECRETION

FIG. 24-4   Formation of urine. The dots represent solutes. In every case there is filtration of the solute through the glomerulus. In the second example, some of the solute is then reabsorbed by the tubules. In the last example, additional solute is added to the filtrate by the tubules.

to involve (1) *filtration through Bowman's capsule,* and (2) *reabsorption by the tubules* or (3) *tubular secretion* (Fig. 24-4).

Filtration   The hydrostatic pressure of the blood tends to drive the fluid through the membranes. It amounts to about 60 mm Hg. This pressure is opposed by two forces: (1) the osmotic attraction of the blood proteins, which is about 25 mm Hg, and (2) the capsular pressure, which is approximately 10 mm Hg. In other words, there is a resulting force of about 25 mm Hg, i.e., [60 − (25 + 10)], which drives the fluid portion of the blood through the membranes and into the tubules. It is for this reason that in cases of shock, when the blood pressure falls, urine formation ceases.

Tubular Reabsorption   The evidence that the filtrate as it enters the tubules is an ultrafiltrate of the plasma is strong and generally accepted. Yet, when bladder urine is analyzed, it is found to have a very different composition from that of plasma. There is no question that some very drastic changes must take place as the filtrate passes through the tubules and collecting ducts. Much of the water of the filtrate is removed so that urine is normally hypertonic (more concentrated than plasma). The tubules also selectively reabsorb various filtrate constituents. Some components, such as glucose, are completely reabsorbed; thus none appears in the urine. Others, such as urea, are only partially reabsorbed. It can be seen that the activity of the tubule and collecting duct cells actually control the composition of the urine. They are presented with an ultra-filrate of the plasma. By selective reabsorption, they regulate the quantity of each substance eliminated from the body.

Tubular Secretion   In so far as the normally appearing constituents of the blood are concerned, none is secreted by the tubules. But such substances as phenol red, Diodrast, and the very useful drug penicillin appear in the urine not only by virtue of their fitration through the capsule, but a considerable percentage is contributed by tubular secretion. Whether or not this mechanism represents a defense means of the body for quickly getting rid of noxious substances can only be surmised.

Renal Clearance   In certain organisms it is possible to introduce small needles into the cavity of Bowman's capsule and withdraw samples of the filtrate for analysis. However, in man this is clearly impractical. Therefore other methods have had to be devised to study kidney function. A truly ingenious procedure has been developed. Those readers who are mathematically minded will quickly see that if we know the concentration of any substance in the blood and in the urine, and if we know the volume of urine formed in a specific period of time, then by means of a simple equation considerable knowledge of the manner in which the kidneys handle that substance can be gained. The equation is $C = UV/P$, where C is **clearance** in milliliters per minute, U the concentration of the substance in the urine, V the volume of urine per minute, and P the concentration of that substance in the plasma.

To illustrate these relationships, let us assume that we have a substance which is freely filtered in the capsule but is neither reabsorbed nor secreted by the tubules. If the concentration in the plasma is 1 mg per milliliter, the concentration in the urine 125 mg per milliliter, and the urine flow 1 ml per minute, using the given equation, C is seen to be equal to 125 ml per minute. What does this figure mean? Since this substance was neither reabsorbed nor secreted by the tubules, it entered the urine purely as the result of filtration. In view of the fact that the plasma contained only 1 mg per milliliter, 125 ml of plasma had to be filtered to supply this quantity. In other words, the renal clearance of this substance gives us a measure of the rate of filtration in Bowman's capsule. Such a compound is **inulin,** a carbohydrate which can be administered intravenously. It affords a means of determining the quantity of filtrate formed per minute. In man this quantity is about 125 ml per minute.

A little study will convince one that if the renal clearance for any compound is lower than that for inulin, some of that substance must be reabsorbed by the tubules. The renal clearance of glucose under normal conditions is zero. This means that all the glucose which freely enters the filtrate is reabsorbed by the tubules, so that none appears in the urine. The renal clearance of urea is about 70 ml per minute. This means that some of the filtered urea is reabsorbed.

Finally, if the renal clearance of any substance is higher than that of inulin, one must conclude that some of that substance is being contributed to the urine by tubular secretion. Carrying this concept one step further, it will be appreciated that if the secretion process is so effective that none of the substance appears in the renal venous blood then the clearance value for this substance is a measure of the total renal plasma flow. **Diodrast,** an iodine compound, is a substance which almost fits this description. About 90% of Diodrast is removed in one circulation through the kidneys. The renal clearance of Diodrast in man is about 600 ml per minute. This means that approximately 667 ml of plasma pass through both kidneys per minute (600/.90).

Enough has been said to demonstrate that the concept of renal clearance is important to any study of renal function. Its use has contributed tremendously to our knowledge of kidney physiology.

Counter-current Mechanism   According to the classic concept purporting to explain the formation of urine, from the time the filtrate enters the proximal tubule until it reaches the collecting duct there is a progressive concentration, thus resulting in the final, hypertonic urine. To satisfy this concept, water has to be actively transported. Secondly, the tubular cells have to create and maintain a gradient of about 900 mOsm/L. There is no evidence anywhere else in the body for active water transport, nor is there evidence that any cell can maintain such a gradient. In addition, micropuncture studies reveal that the filtrate as it enters the proximal tubule is isotonic. In the thin loop of Henle it is highly hypertonic, but then it progressively becomes isotonic once again in the ascending tubule (Fig. 24-5). These findings require modification of the classic concept of urine formation.

The counter-current hypothesis explains the observed data satisfactorily. This hypothesis does not require active transport of water and nowhere is there a gradient over about 200 mOsm/L. Finally, there is good evidence to support this viewpoint.

Anatomically, the descending, ascending, and collecting tubules are found to lie very close to one another. In them the filtrate circulates in such a way that the current in the ascending tubule is counter to that in the descending tubule as well as to that in the collecting duct. Thus, it has been proposed that in the proximal tubule many substances, including sodium, are actively transported out of the filtrate. Because of the osmotic gradient so established, water moves out also. This transport is so great that about 80 per cent of the total filtrate has left the tubule by the time it reaches the thin loop of Henle. To this point, then, the filtrate, although markedly decreased in volume, is still isotonic (Fig. 24-5).

In the descending part of the thin loop of Henle, sodium passively diffuses into the filtrate and water passively diffuses out. As a result, the filtrate becomes greatly concentrated, reaching a maximum at the bottom of the loop (Fig. 24-5). Another 5 per cent of the filtrate is removed, making a total of 85 per cent to this point.

Throughout the entire ascending limb, which includes the distal tubule, as well as the loop of Henle, there is active transport of sodium out of the filtrate but no movement of water throughout most of that length. Consequently, the filtrate becomes less concentrated and, in the distal convoluted tubule it actually becomes hypotonic until the subsequent movement of water makes it isotonic. The ascending tubule, over most of its length, is impermeable to water. In the last part of the distal convoluted tubule another 10 per cent of the filtrate is removed.

When the filtrate enters the collecting duct, it is isotonic. There is additional active transport of sodium from the collecting duct, but because the interstitial fluid is hyperosmotic, water diffuses out of the filtrate even faster, thus concentrating it. By the time the filtrate reaches the end of the collecting duct, over 95.5 per cent of the fluid has been reabsorbed.

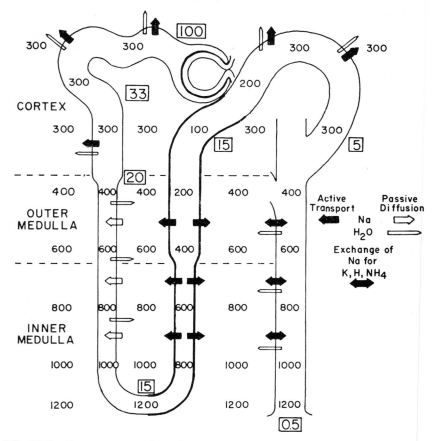

FIG. 24-5 Counter-current hypothesis. The movement of sodium and water are indicated. Concentrations of tubular urine and peritubular fluid are expressed in mOsm/L. The large, boxed numbers indicate the estimated per cent of glomerular filtrate remaining within the tubule at each level. (Reproduced, with permission, from R. F. Pitts, "Physiology of the Kidney and Body Fluids," Year Book Medical Publishers, Chicago, 1963.)

It will be noted that the interstitial fluid in the medullary tissue becomes more and more concentrated, reaching a maximum in the innermost portion (Fig. 24-5). It will be recalled that the tubules of the juxtamedullary nephrons dip down into this medullary tissue. It is the active transport of sodium from the ascending tubules that accounts for the progressive increase in concentration of the medullary interstitial fluid. Because the ascending tubules are impermeable to water, water cannot move with the sodium. But the collecting duct is permeable to water. Now, because of the highly concentrated interstitial fluid surrounding that duct, water moves down its osmotic gradient, thus resulting in a concentrated urine.

Not only does this counter-current concept explain the movement of water without postulating active water transport, but a final examination of Fig. 24-5 will disclose that nowhere along the system is there a concentration gradient greater than 200 mOsm/L, yet the concentration of the filtrate increases from about 300 mOsm/L to 1200 mOsm/L by the time it passes through the collecting duct.

It is extremely important to understand that this counter-current mechanism could not operate for long unless the concentration of the medullary interstitial fluid was maintained. It is maintained by the vasa recta. The vasa recta acts as another counter-current system. In this case it is the current of blood flowing through the vessels that is counter. The blood flows down into the medullary tissue and then up toward the cortex (Fig. 24-6). As it flows down into the medulla, water diffuses out and sodium diffuses in. But as the blood flows up toward the cortex, sodium diffuses out and water moves in. The net result is that the blood carries away water but leaves most of the sodium to recirculate through the medullary interstitial fluid.

The vasa recta maintains the high concentration of sodium and other solutes in the medullary interstitial fluid because of its configuration as a counter-current system, but also because the blood flow in it is very scanty and slow. The faster the flow, the more inefficient it becomes. Measurements show that the blood transit time in the cortex is 2 or 3 seconds. In the medullary tissue it is about 30 seconds. In the dog the

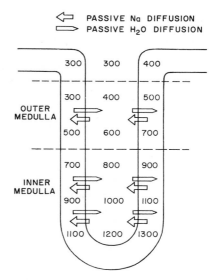

FIG. 24-6   Concentration gradients in the vasa recta and the medullary interstitial fluid. This circulatory system maintains the concentration in the interstitial fluid while removing water.

medulla composes about 10 per cent of the total kidney tissue, but it receives only approximately 1 per cent of the total blood flow.

In the interstitial fluid of the cortex there is no concentration gradient. It appears, then, that the cortical nephrons do not operate in this manner and probably do not form a hypertonic urine. If this is true then the juxtamedullary nephrons must concentrate the filtrate even more than the figures given above would indicate. Since it has been estimated in man that only one-seventh of all nephrons are of the juxtamedullary type, these units must bear the burden of concentrating the filtrate to such an extent that when it is mixed with the isotonic fluid from the cortical nephrons the characteristic hypertonic urine results. It is interesting to note that animals native to the desert have kidneys with a much higher percentage of juxtamedullary nephrons, and they can concentrate their urine far more than can man.

QUANTITY AND COMPOSITION OF URINE

The amount of urine eliminated each day is highly variable. It depends upon many factors such as fluid intake, the amount of salt ingested, the climate, and the individual's activities. But it is a fair approximation to state that the average person excretes between 1 and 2 liters of urine a day. This is roughly 1 ml per minute.

The composition of the urine likewise varies markedly. It must be borne in mind that, by this great sensitivity and flexibility in quantity and composition of the urine, the quality and volume of the blood are maintained constant. Again, speaking generally, we can list the principal constituents of the urine as in Table 24-1.

Specific Gravity   The specific gravity of a substance refers simply to its weight as compared to distilled water. Water possesses a specific gravity

TABLE 24-1   Composition of Urine

Constituent	Grams per Day
Water	1,500.0
Urea	30.0
Chloride	6.0
Sodium	4.0
Potassium	2.0
Phosphorus	1.0
Creatinine	1.0
Sulfur	1.0
Ammonia	0.6
Calcium	0.2
Iron	0.003

of 1. The specific gravity of the urine, under ordinary conditions, varies between 1.015 and 1.025. Usually, the greater the urine volume, the lower the specific gravity. After a heavy beer party, the urine output may increase to over 10 ml per minute. At this rate the specific gravity may approach that of water and be about 1.001.

In many pathological conditions this inverse relationship between specific gravity and volume does not hold. In severe **diabetes mellitus** (page 611), the high sugar content of the urine will keep the specific gravity up to about 1.040 even though the urine output is very high. On the other hand, a damaged kidney may be unable to concentrate urine even at low production rates.

Water The excretion of water is under the control of the **antidiuretic hormone (ADH)** secreted by the posterior lobe of the hypophysis. Under the influence of this hormone the reabsorption of water may be so great as to reduce the urine output to about 0.35 ml per minute. In the complete absence of the hormone, about 15 to 18 ml of urine per minute are excreted with a specific gravity practically the same as that of blood.

ADH is thought to control water movement by increasing the permeability of the collecting duct. There is good evidence that ADH can increase membrane permeability. According to the counter-current hypothesis, water moves out of the collecting duct because of an osmotic gradient. The rate at which it moves, for any gradient, is a function of the duct membrane permeability. Under the influence of ADH, permeability increases; thus water moves more rapidly out of the filtrate, thereby decreasing the urine output.

It has long been known that ADH has a pressor effect, that is, in adequate doses it evokes vasoconstriction. The suggestion has been made that ADH, in addition to altering permeability, also constricts the vasa recta, thus decreasing blood flow through this counter-current system. The slower the blood flow in the vasa recta the greater will be the concentration of sodium and other solutes in the medullary interstitial fluid and, therefore, the greater will be the water reabsorption.

It should be understood that a small change in reabsorption of water can make a big difference in the urine flow rate. Approximately 5 per cent of the filtrate enters the duct. If the glomerular filtration rate is 125 ml per minute about 6.25 ml per minute of the filtrate enter the duct. Normally some 5.25 ml per minute are reabsorbed in the duct so that the urine flow is 1 ml per minute. If 4.25 instead of 5.25 ml per minute were reabsorbed, the urine flow would double.

Electrolytes The kidneys are capable of selectively excreting various electrolytes. It should be remembered that the filtrate contains the same make-up as the plasma, but the tubules apparently have individual mechanisms for the reabsorption of the various ions. Therefore, the kidney can control their concentration in the blood despite varied ingestion and altered body functions. The specific metabolism of such ions as calcium, phosphorus, sodium, and potassium will be considered later.

Acidity   Normal urine is very slightly acid. In pH units, 7 is neutral. Using these units, the normal urine is found to vary between 5 and 7, with an average close to 6, or slightly acid. The reaction of the blood expressed in these same units is 7.4. Obviously, therefore, the urine must conserve base and eliminate acid metabolites.

The reaction of the urine is controlled by the selective tubular reabsorption of various ions. Thus, if one exercises heavily, a large quantity of acid metabolites is liberated into the blood. In order to maintain the reaction of the blood constant, the kidneys must increase the elimination of these metabolites. Consequently, the urine reaction becomes more acid. On the other hand, after a large meal, because of the withdrawal from the blood of hydrogen and chloride ions to make the HCl of the stomach, the blood reaction tends to become alkaline. To prevent this, the kidneys now decrease the elimination of acid products and may even expel fixed base. The urine becomes alkaline, and this is called the **alkaline tide of the urine.**

DIURETICS

Some substances have a potent influence on the quantity of urine formed. An agent which increases the flow of urine is termed a **diuretic.** In many pathological conditions, such as heart failure associated with swelling of the ankles, it is desirable to decrease the water content of the body. An appropriate diuretic may be administered.

Coffee   Coffee contains **caffeine,** which has many physiological effects, one of them being to increase the production of urine. It accomplishes this, apparently, by decreasing the amount of water reabsorbed. Some investigators hold that this drug causes vasodilatation of the renal arterioles and, as a result, augmented filtration in Bowman's capsule. However, this interpretation is now being questioned.

Water   It is an easily verifiable fact that the more water one consumes, the more one urinates. The increased water intake dilutes the plasma; consequently, the secretion of the so-called antidiuretic hormone of the posterior lobe of the pituitary gland is decreased. Therefore, the ducts do not reabsorb as much water and the urine production increases.

Alcohol   Alcohol is a potent diuretic. However, it must be kept in mind that the diuresis which results from beer drinking is caused as much by the volume of the fluid intake as by the alcoholic content of the beverage.

It is interesting to note that if one group of people drinks beer while another group consumes the same quantity of water or milk, the urine output of the two groups is not significantly different. Harder drinks, however, which contain a greater percentage of alcohol exert their diuretic effect principally because of the alcohol, not the volume.

BODY FLUIDS

The human body contains, by weight, 50 to 70 per cent fluid. One may wonder why there is such a great variation between these values. The answer lies in the adipose tissue, which is highly variable from one individual to another and which contains very little water. When fluid content is expressed on the basis of fat-free tissue, there is much less variation. Calculated in this manner the fat-free body is found to contain about 70 per cent fluid.

Distribution It is convenient to think of this mass of fluid as being contained in three compartments within the body: (1) within the cells, (2) within the blood vessels, and (3) within the tissue spaces, that is, surrounding the cells. Thus, the terms **intracellular** fluid and **extracellular** fluid are used. The latter expression includes both the blood and the so-called **interstitial** fluid. Table 24-2 shows average values expressed in per cent of body weight for the distribution of fluid in the various compartments.

TABLE 24-2 Distribution of Body Fluid (Normal Adiposity)

	Percentage of Body Wt
Total body fluid	58
Intracellular fluid	41
Extracellular fluid	17
Interstitial fluid	13
Plasma	4

Maintenance of Fluid Balance Table 24-3 lists the sites of fluid loss. It can be seen that about 3 liters of fluid are lost every day under normal conditions. But in hot, humid climates this figure may be strikingly increased. The fluids expelled in the feces and in the expired air remain relatively constant. Perspiration, on the other hand, varies markedly. Even in a cool, dry environment there is a steady loss of water by evaporation from the skin. This is termed **insensible perspiration**. As already discussed, fluid loss via the urine is the most important homeostatic mechanism for balance maintenance.

TABLE 24-3   Sites of Fluid Loss

Site	Amount, Ml
Skin	1,000
Expired air	350
Urine	1,500
Feces	150
Total	3,000

It is seen that man possesses several routes for fluid loss, but fluid is gained only through the gastrointestinal tract. Food contains a large volume of water but, in view of the fact that food intake is controlled by factors other than body fluid needs, another mechanism is indicated to control fluid gain. When one works in a warm, humid climate, the intake may exceed 10 liters per day. For the most part, the volume imbibed is determined by **thirst**.

The mechanism of thirst has been investigated for many years, yet it is still poorly understood. There is general agreement that at least part of thirst is a local phenomenon, that is, drying of the tissues of the oral cavity. A reduced salivary flow always gives rise to a sensation of thirst. There is ample evidence that changes in circulation, or alterations in the osmotic state of the blood, influence the rate of salivary secretion. There is also recent evidence that the antidiuretic hormone of the posterior lobe of the hypophysis diminishes blood flow through the salivary glands and thus decreases salivation. Therefore, it seems established that dehydration evokes circulatory changes which are reflected in the rate of salivation. The consequent drying of the mouth and pharynx produce thirst.

Oral and pharyngeal drying, however, cannot be the entire story. The hypothalamus is apparently also involved. Stimulation of dorsal hypothalamic nuclei in the dog results in drinking. Lesions in the area abolish fluid intake. And these actions appear to be independent of salivation. It would seem that activation of the appropriate hypothalamic nuclei gives rise, in the animal, to the sensation of thirst—a sensation that cannot be evoked when those nuclei are destroyed.

The cells that make up these so-called **thirst centers** are said to be **osmoreceptors,** that is, they respond to variations in the osmotic state of the blood. When dehydration occurs, there is increased osmotic pressure of the body fluids; the osmoreceptors of the hypothalamus respond, thereby evoking a sensation of thirst.

It is interesting that if an animal is dehydrated and then permitted to drink water freely, the body will take in an amount remarkably adjusted to return the osmotic pressure of the blood exactly to normal. This would seem to support the theory of osmotic control of thirst; however, the animal stops drinking before the water has had time to be absorbed and alter the osmotic state of the blood. In short, the mechanism responsible for the satiation of thirst has not yet been clarified.

URINATION

Urine is formed at a fairly steady rate by the kidneys. It then passes down the **ureters** (Fig. 24-7) to accumulate in the **urinary bladder.** It is periodi-

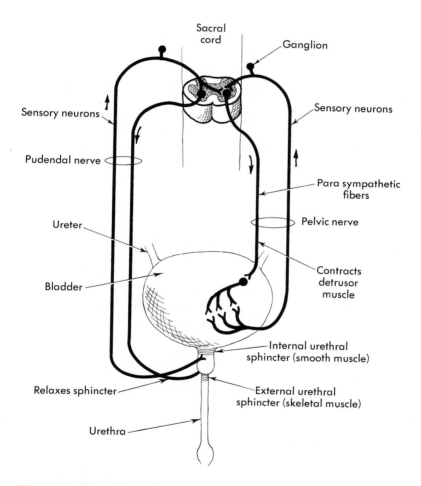

FIG. 24-7 Micturition reflex. As the bladder fills with urine, the wall stretches, impulses are initiated, and, as a result, the bladder contracts.

cally expelled from the bladder through the **urethra.** The act of expelling urine from the bladder is termed **urination** or **micturition.**

URINATION MECHANISM

The Bladder   The urinary bladder, which is located low in the abdominal cavity, is a hollow, pear-shaped muscular organ. Smooth muscle makes up the bladder wall and is called the **detrusor muscle.** The organ is innervated by both divisions of the autonomic nervous system. Parasympathetic fibers reach the bladder via the pelvic nerves, while sympathetic fibers travel in the hypogastric nerve. Sensory fibers are also found in these nerves. They make it possible for the individual to be aware of a sensation of fullness emanating from the bladder.

The Urethra   Figure 24-7 shows that the urethra is attached to the base of the bladder and communicates with the external world. In the male, the tortuous urethra runs the length of the penis, thus its length is quite variable. In the female, the urethra is very short and straight and opens between the labial folds just above the vagina and just below the clitoris. The difference in the length and straightness of the urethra explains, in part, why the female is more prone to bladder infections.

Surrounding the urethral canal are two sets of muscles, an inner longitudinal and outer circular band. At about the junction of the bladder and the urethra, this musculature is modified so that a sphincter, the **internal urethral sphincter,** acts under the supervision of the autonomic nervous system to control the flow of urine. Farther out, in the urethra itself, there is another such arrangement, the **external urethral sphincter,** which can be voluntarily governed and thus controls the release of urine.

ACT OF URINATION

Filling of the Bladder   It has been pointed out that the stomach, as it fills, accommodates for each new load; thus its internal pressure varies very little while being filled. The same is true of the urinary bladder. The smooth muscle which constitutes the bladder wall has the inherent capacity to adapt itself to changing volumes. Thus if a tube is placed in the bladder and the other end connected to a water manometer, it can easily be shown that the internal pressure only slowly increases as the bladder fills.

When more than about 300 ml of urine accumulate in the bladder, there develops a sensation of fullness, a desire to urinate. However, it is possible to suppress this urge and thus permit considerably more urine to pool. But when more than 700 to 800 ml have accumulated, the sensation of fullness may give way to frank pain, and the desire to empty the bladder may be insuppressible.

Emptying of the Bladder A reflex mechanism similar to the one described for defecation controls the bladder. Thus it is that, when approximately 300 ml of urine collect, the stretch of the bladder wall initiates impulses which are conducted by afferent nerves to the spinal cord. These impulses activate the parasympathetic fibers which return to innervate the detrusor muscle. As a result, the bladder contracts and the urine is expelled.

Urination involves more than this one reflex. It has also been shown that the presence of urine in the urethra sets off at least two more reflexes. One results in greater contraction of the bladder. The second causes relaxation of the sphincters (Fig. 24-7).

We know that these reflex mechanisms can be voluntarily regulated. Even though the bladder is filled and the reflex tends to empty it, one can inhibit or block that impulse. On the other hand, it is possible to empty the bladder even when it contains only a few milliliters of urine. This is accomplished by straining, which elevates the intra-abdominal pressure. In this way, the bladder is squeezed and some urine forced into the urethra. The presence of the urine there initiates the reflexes just mentioned, now urination continues, and the straining effort may be discontinued.

The force with which urine is expelled from the bladder depends not only upon the force of contraction of the detrusor muscle but upon other factors as well. At puberty, the prostate gland in man begins to enlarge. Since this organ surrounds the urethra, its enlargement tends to compress the urethra. Also, after puberty, the bladder descends deeper into the pelvic cavity and thus is removed from the direct influence of the abdominal muscles. These two changes account for the well-known fact that young boys can urinate with far more force, vigor, and distance than mature men.

THE SKIN

The body's envelope, the skin, is a fascinating mantle which weighs about 3 kilograms (about twice as much as the liver or brain) and receives approximately one-third of the circulating blood. It serves many useful functions. The more important purposes may be listed as (1) **protection,** (2) **sensation,** (3) **body-temperature regulation,** and (4) **excretion.** In lower animals, the skin also serves a very important respiratory function. In these simple organisms, there is a considerable quantity of gaseous exchange between the blood and the air through the moist skin. In man, such exchange does not occur.

The protective role of the skin is quite apparent. It may be thought of as the first line of defense against mechanical, chemical, and bacterial damage. Everyone knows that though his skin, especially the skin of his hands, comes into contact with millions of bacteria a day, infections seldom develop. When the skin is broken or damaged by burns, cuts, or bruises, bacterial invasion becomes very likely.

The function of the skin in body-temperature regulation was discussed in Chap. 8. In this section, we shall be primarily concerned with the skin as an excretory organ.

ANATOMY OF THE SKIN

Epidermis Figure 24-8 shows a cross section through an area of skin. *Dermis* means "skin." The prefix *epi-* implies "upon." The term **epidermis** means "the skin upon the skin" and that is exactly what it is. The epidermis is a tough outer covering which is constantly worn away and replaced from cells below.

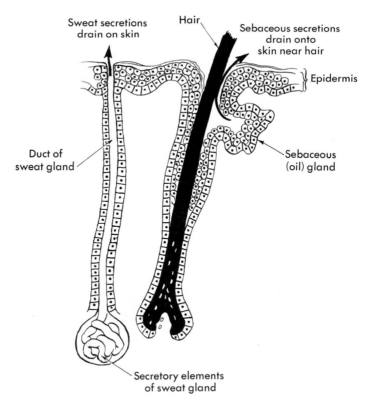

Sweat secretions drain on skin

Hair

Sebaceous secretions drain onto skin near hair

Epidermis

Duct of sweat gland

Sebaceous (oil) gland

Secretory elements of sweat gland

FIG. 24-8   Sweat and sebaceous glands.

The epidermis has no blood supply. The cells as they push outward receive some nourishment from the subjacent capillaries, but as they get farther and farther away, this nourishment proves inadequate and they die. That is to say, the outer layers of the epidermis are composed of a tough, horny mass of cells which no longer possess the essential properties of life. They are dead cells which are soon to be worn off and replaced.

As the cells migrate from the blood supply, the protein which makes up much of these cells undergoes a change. In its new make-up it is called **keratin,** a term derived from *keras,* meaning "horny." It is the same material which is found in the fingernails and toenails. When the skin is irritated by constant rubbing, as in rough manual labor, or such sports as rowing, this epidermal layer of the exposed areas hypertrophies. That is, it thickens into a swelling called a **callus** or **corn.**

Dermis   The dermis is sometimes referred to as the true skin, or **corium.** It is highly vascular and abundantly supplied with sensitive nerve endings. The **hair follicles** are seen to arise deep in the dermis, usually in the underlying fatty tissue, and to push their way up through the dermis and epidermis. The cells of the dermis steadily migrate outward and replace the epidermis as it is worn off.

Sebaceous Glands   The term **sebaceous** comes from *sebum,* which means "tallow," a heavy oil. The sebaceous glands produce an oily secretion which is conducted by the duct of the gland, usually to the hair canal. The secretions then make their way along the hair follicle to the surface of the skin.

Sweat Glands   Figure 24-8 portrays the sweat glands as lying deep in the fatty tissue. A long thin duct traverses the outer layers of the dermis and the epidermis to reach the surface of the skin.

SEBACEOUS SECRETIONS

Although the sebaceous secretions contain fats, proteins, salts, and water, the output of these glands can hardly be considered excretory. It is true that the substances are lost from the body, but the total loss in relation to elimination via other avenues is insignificant. The sebaceous secretions serve to oil the skin and thus protect it from undue drying. There is also evidence to indicate that sebaceous secretions, by covering the skin, prevent excess evaporation of moisture from the body surface.

PERSPIRATION

The quantity of fluid and dissolved substances which may be lost from the body through perspiration is normally surprisingly large and under various conditions may increase so much as to derange seriously the internal environment. For these reasons, perspiration must be taken into account in any comprehensive consideration of elimination.

Composition   Sweat is mostly water, but it does contain sodium and potassium chloride and some urea, usually just a trace. The specific gravity of sweat is normally about 1.005 or lower. This is to be compared with the specific gravity of urine, which usually varies between 1.015 and 1.025. Under abnormal conditions, the sweat glands are utilized by the body to eliminate such substances as poisons, bile pigments, and glucose. Even blood has been reported in the sweat. The acidity of the sweat apparently varies in conformity with changes in the blood. Most often the reaction is close to neutral. Sweat usually has a characteristic odor, and there is evidence to indicate that this odor in some lower animal forms has an important sexual significance. Just what role it plays in human relations is difficult to analyze.

Quantity   Under extreme conditions of heat, humidity, and work, as much as 1500 ml per hour of sweat may be produced. The most sedentary person in a perfectly air-conditioned room still secretes at least 1000 ml of sweat per day.

In view of the fact that so much fluid can be eliminated from the body by these glands, severe dehydration will occur in the absence of compensation by other organs. Thus it may easily be observed that if one has perspired copiously urine output becomes very scant. Still there will be a negative water balance unless great quantities are taken in. The great loss of water by perspiration evokes an insatiable thirst. As a result, fluids are consumed and the body water balance is maintained.

It has been mentioned that sweat contains salt (sodium chloride). When perspiration becomes marked, the quantity of salt lost from the body, if not replaced, causes distressing alterations. **Heat prostration** is characterized by weakness, nausea, vomiting, cramps, and often loss of consciousness. It is caused by the undue loss of salt from the body. For these reasons it is advisable to increase the amount of salt used with food during the hot, humid months, especially if the individual does considerable labor or exercise. As a matter of fact, it is extremely helpful to supplement the salt intake under adverse conditions by taking sodium chloride tablets periodically along with several glasses of water. The problem is so common and can be so serious that many large commercial plants require their personnel who work near open-hearth furnaces and in other places where the heat is intense to take salt tablets routinely. As noted, the great loss of fluid through perspiration evokes the thirst mechanism, but if one simply drinks water while at the same time salt is being lost from the body, it can be seen that the concentration of salt in the blood and body fluids will be markedly diluted. This eventuality must be avoided by the taking of added salt.

Regulation The sweat glands are innervated by the sympathetic nervous system. As is well known, the amount of perspiration cannot be controlled voluntarily. It is purely a reflex mechanism, usually regulated by the needs of the body to maintain the internal temperature constant. Thus in hot weather the quantity of perspiration produced increases. This water as it evaporates on the surface of the body takes up heat and serves to cool the body. In cold climates the loss of water in this way is reduced to a minimum.

But sweating may result from other than temperature-regulating mechanisms. Every student knows that his production of sweat increases noticeably during an examination, especially an oral examination for which he is poorly prepared. During fright or in an emergency situation, the sympathetic nervous system is fired. Consequently, sweating is increased, and the so-called "cold sweat" occurs.

The mechanism by which the quantity of perspiration is controlled to maintain body temperature is fairly well understood, but how the quantity and quality of the perspiration are varied for the purposes of elimination has not been satisfactorily investigated.

SUMMARY

Defecation is a reflex act which, within limits, may be voluntarily regulated. The stretch of the **rectum** caused by the accumulation of feces is the effective stimulus. The smooth muscle of the rectal wall contracts and thereby expels the contents. This reflex may be inhibited voluntarily, and, at the same time, the **anal sphincters** tightly contract to prevent defecation.

The kidneys consist of a **medulla** and the **cortex.** The functional and structural unit of the kidney is the **nephron.** The nephron is made up of **Bowman's capsule,** the **proximal convoluted tubule, Henle's loop,** and the **distal convoluted tubule.** The urine elaborated by the nephrons is collected in a series of ducts which empty into the renal pelvis. The urine then traverses the **ureters** to accumulate in the **urinary bladder.**

As urine collects in the bladder, the internal pressure increases only slightly because the **detrusor muscle** which makes up the bladder wall relaxes and thus accommodates increasing volumes. When approximately 300 ml of urine have accumulated, the stretch of the bladder wall initiates impulses which set off a reflex resulting in contraction of the bladder. The urine is thus forced into the **urethra.** The presence of the urine in the urethra evokes another reflex which reinforces the contraction of the detrusor muscle, and finally a third reflex causes relaxation of the urethral sphincter. Urination, though a reflex act, may be inhibited voluntarily or augmented by straining.

As blood passes through Bowman's capsule, about 125 ml per minute are filtered. This filtrate contains all the substances found in the blood, with the exception of protein. As it passes through the tubule, much of the dissolved material and about 124 ml of water are reabsorbed. Thus, the normal urine output in man approximates 1 ml per minute. **Diuretics** increase the urine flow. The composition of the urine varies widely. The specific gravity is about 1.020, the reaction slightly acid, except during **alkaline tide** which follows a meal.

Urine forms by the process of **filtration** and **tubular reabsorption.** In some cases, substances may be handled by filtration plus tubular secretion. Using the **renal-clearance** method it has been determined that approximately 667 ml of plasma, or about 1300 ml of whole blood, flows through the kidneys each minute.

The **counter-current hypothesis** explains how a hypertonic urine can be formed without postulating active reabsorption of water. The active transport of sodium, and perhaps other solutes, creates osmotic pressure gradients in the interstitial fluid. As a result water moves out of the collecting duct into the interstitial fluid. The **vasa recta** form another counter-current system that functions to maintain the concentration of the medullary interstitial fluid.

Fluid makes up 50 to 70 per cent of the human body. It is distributed as **intracellular, extracellular,** and **interstitial** fluid. The total body water is maintained constant by virtue of fluid intake regulated by **thirst** which balances loss through the skin, in the expired air, urine, and feces.

The skin serves for (1) **protection,** (2) **sensation,** (3) **body-temperature regulation,** and (4) **excretion.** The skin is composed of an outer **epidermis** and the underlying **dermis.** The cells of the epidermis migrate outward, die, and undergo a change in the protein content to become **keratin,** a tough, horny substance. The epidermis is constantly worn away and re-placed. The dermis is highly vascular and contains sensitive nerve endings and the **sweat** and **sebaceous glands,** as well as **hair follicles.**

The sebaceous secretion are oily. They protect the skin and hair from undue drying. Perspiration has two functions: (1) **temperature regulation** and (2) **excretion.** The quantity of sweat varies from the basal amount of about 1000 ml per day, termed **insensible perspiration,** to a maximum of approximately 1500 ml per hour.

QUESTIONS

1. Describe the mechanisms which control defecation.
2. By what sequence of events is urine formed?
3. Describe the mechanisms which control urination.
4. How do the kidneys maintain fluid balance?
5. How may renal blood flow be determined in man?
6. What are the functions of the skin?

SUGGESTED READING

Earle, H., "What You Should Know about Your Kidneys," *Today's Health,* **39:** #6, 52–55, June 1961.

Franklin, S. S., and Merrill, J. P., "The Kidney in Health; the Nephron in Disease," *Am. J. Med.,* **28:** #1, 1–7, January 1960.

Gottschalk, C. W., "Osmotic Concentration and Dilution of the Urine," *Am. J. Med.,* **36:** #5, 670–685, May 1964.

Langley, L. L., and Whiteside, J. A., "Mechanism of Accommodation and Tone of Urinary Bladder," *J. Neurophysiol.,* **14:** 147–152, 1951.

Ratcliff, J. D., "Your Body's Master Chemists," *Today's Health,* **38:** #12, 59, 76–78, December 1960.

Solomon, A. K., "Pumps in the Living Cell," *Sci. American,* **207:** #2, 100–108, August 1962.

25   Diet and Nutrition

WE HAVE NOW JOURNEYED WITH THE THREE MAJOR FOODSTUFFS through the alimentary tract. It has been seen how the various digestive processes simplify the complex molecules which can then be absorbed by the intestinal mucosa. The fate of end products of digestion has also been discussed. Finally, it has been noted that, by variations in the quantity of the substances eliminated, the internal environment is maintained constant.

The term **nutrition** has been defined as *the sum total of those processes by which the living organism receives and utilizes the materials necessary for the maintenance of life.* It should be evident from this definition that many of these processes have already been considered. However, some important aspects of nutrition have not yet been analyzed. For example, little has been said about vitamins. No mention has been made concerning the nutritional requirements for the various minerals, and we have only suggested the optimal ratio of the three foodstuffs in the diet. These matters must now be considered. Then it will prove helpful and interesting to integrate all this material by a study of the problems of dieting—dieting not only to lose weight but to gain weight, as well as to satisfy specific needs in unusual conditions.

VITAMINS

The term **vitamin** implies that the substance so named is essential for life. Although it is true that an individual may survive in the absence of some of the vitamins, grave disturbances usually occur. A normal, healthy life does indeed depend upon an adequate intake of the various vitamins.

Animals in the wilderness rarely if ever suffer from vitamin deficiencies. Such disorders seem part of the heritage of man and man-fed animals. The explanation lies in the mode of preparing food. Eagerness to make

512

food more attractive and more tasteful has resulted in the destruction or loss of many of the essential vitamins. For example, white bread appeals to more people than do the coarse dark breads.

The first notice of a vitamin deficiency was made by a Japanese who observed that a condition called **beriberi** was debilitating Japanese navy personnel. It was ultimately learned that when rice is highly polished it loses some nutritive fractions. Similarly, English scientists noted the great prevalence of **scurvy** among English sailors. They further found that this condition could be avoided if adequate citrus fruit were provided. Thereafter English sailors took to sucking on limes. This habit not only helped to prevent scurvy but also won for them the appellative "Limey."

Following these astute observations, a tremendous concentration of research was conducted in laboratories throughout the world. As a result, a great and accurate body of knowledge has developed concerning the vitamins, most of it only since the early twenties.

VITAMIN A

When the vitamins were first discovered, there was no inkling of their structure. For a long time it was impossible to obtain them in pure form, and thus their true identity remained unknown. For that reason the vitamins were at first designated simply by letters, more or less in the order in which they were discovered. This letter designation has persisted. The vitamins are also often classified according to whether they are water-soluble or fat-soluble. It is interesting to note, and important to remember, that the absorption of the fat-soluble vitamins depends upon an adequate supply of bile salts. Thus, though an individual ingests an adequate amount of these fat-soluble vitamins, if there is a shortage of bile he may suffer a vitamin deficiency.

Source and Requirement The precursor of vitamin A is **carotene,** a substance found widely distributed in nature, especially in carrots and other pigmented vegetables. It is also highly concentrated in spinach, milk, and liver. It is believed that carotene is converted to the active form in the intestine and then is stored in the liver.

Vitamin A is expressed, for nutritional purposes, in **international units (IU).** Actually, 1 IU of vitamin A is equal to 0.0006 mg of pure beta-carotene. But in more meaningful terms, it is found, for example, that a glass of milk contains about 300 IU, while a pound of fresh liver contains over 400,000 IU. The requirement of an adult is said to be about 5,000 IU per day. This is not a difficult quantity to consume in the average diet. For example, a normal diet consisting of the usual amount of butter and vegetables, plus liver periodically, will satisfy vitamin-A requirements. Of course, there is a great difference between minimum requirements and optimal intake. There is now good evidence to indicate that, though no frank abnormalities will develop if one ingests just 5,000 IU of vitamin A per day, an individual's vigor and well-being will be noticeably improved if he takes in three or four times this amount. On the other hand, excessive ingestion of vitamins, particularly vitamin A, does produce deleterious effects.

Fate   As has already been pointed out, vitamin A is fat-soluble, and therefore its absorption depends upon the bile salts. Once absorbed, vitamin A is brought to the liver, where it is stored. Vitamin A is also deposited in other organs, such as the kidneys and lungs, but over 95 per cent of the total vitamin-A content of the body is found in the liver. The livers of individuals killed in accidents assayed over 330 units of vitamin A per gram. In view of the fact that the liver weighs some 1,500 gm, it can be seen that an individual stores about 500,000 IU of vitamin A.

FIG. 25-1   Xerophthalmia caused by vitamin-A deficiency. (Courtesy of the Upjohn Company.)

This amount should suffice for about 100 days. These crude calculations are introduced simply to indicate why an individual can continue for so long on a deficient vitamin-A diet without showing any ill effects. It must be borne in mind that these livers were from healthy individuals. In various diseased states, the content of vitamin A in the liver is strikingly reduced.

Function   Vitamin A has been shown to be necessary to (1) growth, (2) vision, and (3) maintenance of the integrity of the epithelial tissues.

If vitamin A is deficient in the diet of a growing experimental animal, the animal's skeletal development will be retarded. Happily, however, this deficit may be made up before the animal has matured, and the growth will spurt so that normal stature is attained.

The role that vitamin A plays in vision was analyzed in Chap. 6. We need only state here that this vitamin unites with a protein in the retina to form **visual purple,** a substance essential to normal vision under conditions of low illumination. A deficiency of this substance results in **night blindness.** Night blindness is usually the first evidence of a vitamin-A shortage.

It has definitely been established that a deficiency of vitamin A does cause serious changes in the epithelial tissues of the body. Apparently, the normal growth and maintenance of skin, the cornea of the eye, and other protective tissues is regulated, at least in part, by the presence of adequate quantities of vitamin A. In its absence a condition called **xerophthalmia** develops (Fig. 25-1), which means "dry eye." It is also relatively common to find cutaneous keratinization, with a resultant dry skin.

VITAMIN B₁

Since the first substance was identified as vitamin B, so many related compounds have been found that we now speak of the **vitamin-B complex.** This complex is known to contain at least 10 distinct fractions, and there is evidence to indicate that there are others still to be identified. Only a few of the more important constituents of this compex wil be considered here. Some of these vitamins are identified as vitamin B_1, vitamin B_2, and so forth, while others are more commonly referred to according to their chemical names.

Vitamin B_1 is now known to be **thiamine hydrochloride.** It is more often simply called thiamine.

Source and Requirement   Thiamine is distributed widely throughout the animal and vegetable tissues, but the most concentrated source is yeast and cereals. Next in importance are peas, beans, oatmeal, whole wheat, lean pork, and peanuts.

In view of the fact that vitamin B_1 is now available in the pure chemical form, the international unit has been set so that 1 mg of thiamine hydro-chloride equals 333 IU. The minimum daily requirements for this vitamin are determined in relation to the size of the individual and the number of calories utilized per day. Taking these factors into consideration, it can be said that the normal adult's minimal requirement lies between 0.13 and 0.17 mg per 1000 Calories. This simply means that the more active the person is, the more vitamin B_1 he should have. It is recommended that the adult consume at least 0.5 mg of this substance per 1000 Calories. White bread is now strongly enriched with this vitamin. The quantity varies, but on the average, a slice of this bread will contain about 0.1 mg of thiamine.

Fate   This vitamin is readily and rapidly absorbed by the small intestine. Again, the liver is found to be the chief reservoir, although vitamin B_1 is not stored in anywhere near the high concentrations that vitamin A is. If the diet is very rich in thiamine, considerable amounts are stored and can be used to supply body needs during periods of malnutrition. But this supply can last for only a few days, and therefore an adequate quantity of vitamin B_1 should be included in the daily diet. Perhaps one reason why this vitamin is not readily stored is because of the rapid urinary excretion. Renal studies have disclosed that the urinary output keeps pace with the intake; thus the amount stored in the body is kept at a minimum.

Function   Vitamin B_1 plays an essential role, as a coenzyme, in the cellu-lar processes which have to do with internal respiration, that is, the utili-zation of oxygen and the production of carbon dioxide in the cell. It can be seen, therefore, that a shortage of this substance will interfere with one of life's most essential functions.

The first alterations which occur as a result of vitamin-B_1 deficiency are referable to the digestive system. The individual loses his appetite, suffers indigestion, and embarks upon a downward course. Next, the nerv-ous system becomes involved. Actual degeneration of the nerves takes place, so that the individual may first report pain which, if continued unchecked, may result in loss of sensation or function of a part.

The long-continued deficiency of thiamine produces the clinical syn-drome called **beriberi.** The patient usually first complains of easy fatigue. This is followed by pain in the legs, loss of appetite, headache, enlarged heart, and shortness of breath. Beriberi, most prevalent among the poor, can be prevented or cured by the prompt and liberal use of thiamine. In emergencies, the pure crystalline form may be used, but ordinarily it suffices to feed thiamine-rich foods.

It is now fairly well established that thiamine deficiency interferes specifically with the oxidation of carbohydrates. Certainly the inability to utilize carbohydrates would impair nervous function as this is one of the vital foods for the maintenance of the central nervous system. In the absence of this vitamin, striking changes are observed in the nerve cells. Finally, the myelin sheaths degenerate, leaving the nerves exposed and irritable, resulting in the typical pain of polyneuritis.

The cardiac difficulties may also be explained on the same basis. The impairment of nervous function permits the arterioles throughout the body to dilate, and therefore the venous return of blood may increase two- to threefold. This great flow of blood into the right ventricle causes it to dilate and then hypertrophy and ultimately to fail. And finally, the gastrointestinal complaints are also believed to be due to the inadequate nervous control which results in indigestion, constipation, and loss of appetite.

VITAMIN B$_2$

Vitamin B$_2$ is now known to be **riboflavin.** Like all of the B complex vitamins, it is water-soluble.

Source and Requirement   The more common foods which offer a rich source of this vitamin are milk, broccoli, spinach, eggs, and liver. The minimum daily requirement for riboflavin has not been accurately established, but authoritative sources recommend that an adult doing an average amount of work should get 1.5 to 1.8 mg of riboflavin per day. There are bacteria in the intestine of man which are capable of synthesizing this substance. Therefore classic riboflavin deficiency is not very common. A glass of fresh milk contains about 0.34 mg of this substance, while the usual sandwich with two pieces of enriched white bread and a slice of luncheon meat may easily contain 0.5 mg. It can be seen, therefore, that the well balanced diet is well fortified with vitamin B$_2$.

Fate   Very little is known concerning the metabolism of riboflavin. Since it is water-soluble, it is readily absorbed, and as indicated, it may actually by synthesized in the intestine. This vitamin is a normal constituent of the urine, the amount increasing with the intake. On a deficiency diet, the excretion is completely suspended.

Function   Riboflavin is found in all living cells and participates in the oxidation processes. Again, like so many of the other vitamins, although no specific deficits will appear until the intake is reduced to a very low level, increased ingestion far above this minimal requirement results in a very noticeable increase in vigor and well-being.

Generally speaking, this substance is essential for growth during the developmental period and for health and vigor at all ages. A chronic deficiency of riboflavin results in blurred vision, burning and soreness of the eyes and tongue, dermatitis, and cracking and fissuring at the angles of the mouth (Fig. 25-2).

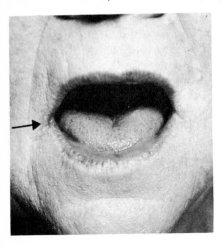

FIG. 25-2 Angular cheilosis due to riboflavin deficiency.

OTHER B-COMPLEX VITAMINS

It is beyond the scope of this text to consider each component of the B complex in detail. The remaining constituents of the B group will be but briefly noted.

Nicotinic acid, or **niacin,** has now been obtained in the pure crystalline form. The recommended daily intake is 12 to 20 mg. This supply is obtained by eating two servings of lean meat or a couple of handfuls of peanuts. Other sources of nicotinic acid are liver, peanut butter, chicken, and yeast.

This substance is also concerned with cellular respiration. When insufficient quantities are ingested, **pellagra** develops (Fig. 25-3). Pellagra has been recognized for centuries. Until recently it was very common in Italy and Spain and other southern European countries, especially among the poorly fed prison populace. At the turn of this century, it was found to be quite prevalent in the southern United States. Pellagra is characterized by skin disorders which appear on all the exposed parts. The skin may crack and become infected. There is usually digestive upset with feelings of weakness, irritability, and anxiety. The condition can usually be successfully prevented or treated by liberal use of nicotinic acid.

Folic acid is actually **pteroylglutamic acid,** but the simpler term has persisted. Folic acid is found in fresh green vegetables, eggs, and liver. In lesser concentrations it also appears in beef, veal, and breakfast cereals. The daily requirement is as yet uncertain.

Folic acid is important for the maintenance of the normal blood pattern. When this substance is deficient, anemia often develops. It apparently operates to stimulate the production of both red and white blood cells.

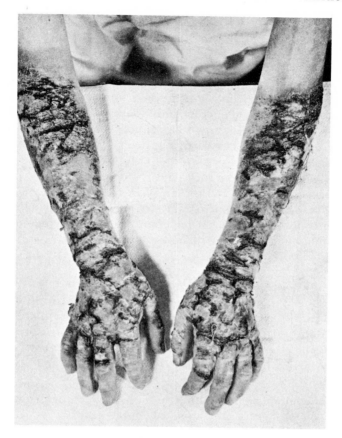

FIG. 25-3 Pellagra due to niacin deficiency. (Reproduced, with permission, from S. Harris, "Clinical Pellagra," C. V. Mosby, 1941.)

Vitamin B$_6$ is now known to be **pyridoxine.** In view of the fact that it prevents dermatitis in many cases, it is also called the **antidermatitic factor.**

Pyridoxine is found most abundantly in liver, yeast, rice, bran, cereals, and milk. The daily requirements have not been set. When the intake is low, characteristic skin lesions result. There is also retardation of growth.

Pantothenic Acid This vitamin is found in many foods. It is doubtful if man, except in very extreme cases, ever suffers frank pantothenic-acid deficiency. It is interesting to note that lack of pantothenic acid produces graying of hair in rats. Much has been made of this finding, but as yet graying in man has not been prevented by the intake of even very large quantities of this substance.

Vitamin B₁₂   The usual active form of vitamin B_{12} is **cyanocobalamin,** which is a porphyrin, similar to hemoglobin. In vitamin B_{12} cobalt occupies similar positions to those occupied by iron in hemoglobin.

Liver, meat, eggs, and milk are the best source of this vitamin. It is interesting to note that soil microorganisms appear to be the prime source of B_{12}. Because this vitamin cannot be synthesized in the organism, it must be provided by the diet. The daily requirement is about 2.8 micrograms per day. Since animal products are the only source, deficiency results in individuals who abstain from such foods.

The concentration of cyanocobalamin in the plasma of normal individuals is 200 to 350 micro-micrograms per ml. Individuals suffering from B_{12} deficiency have blood levels less than 200 micromicrograms per ml. The main finding is pernicious anemia.

VITAMIN C

As has already been pointed out, the history of vitamin C is an extremely interesting one. Vitamin-C deficiency sailed with practically every ship on the seas in the eighteenth century, until it was found that the lack of fresh food deprived the men of a needed nutritional element. It is now known that the essential element is vitamin C.

It has been obtained in the pure crystalline form and identified as **ascorbic acid.**

Source and Requirement   Vitamin C is found in very high concentrations in oranges, lemons, grapefruit, tomatoes, fresh strawberries, cabbage, onions, and potatoes.

The international unit of vitamin C has been set at 0.05 mg of ascorbic acid. An adequate diet should contain at least 75 mg of ascorbic acid per day. Since this is the quantity found in a large glass of orange juice and in view of the fact that potatoes are rich in the substance, there is little cause for frank vitamin-C deficiency. However, for a variety of reasons it seems that the ascorbic-acid intake or utilization of a large percentage of the population is somewhat less than this figure.

Fate   Some species can synthesize vitamin C, but man does not seem able to do this. Therefore the entire requirement must be ingested. Vitamin C is rapidly absorbed from the intestinal tract and is stored in many organs. The largest reservoirs are the adrenal glands, hypophysis, pancreas, and liver. Vitamin C is excreted in variable quantities by the kidneys. Thus, when excessive quantities are ingested, the urine output increases proportionately. For this reason an abnormally high intake probably accomplishes very little of value.

Function Two specific functions have been attributed to vitamin C: (1) a respiratory function in which the vitamin aids in the important intracellular metabolic processes and (2) regulation of the colloidal condition of intercellular substances. But whatever the specific mechanisms, it is important to recognize that deficiency of this substance leads to **scurvy**.

Because of the large reserves of ascorbic acid in the body, it takes 2 to 4 months on a vitamin-C-deficient diet to produce full-blown scurvy in man. It is for this reason that classic cases of scurvy are rare today, although there are many people who manifest subclinical disorders caused by vitamin-C inadequacy.

There is growing evidence that most of the alterations observed in vitamin-C-deficient cases result from a defect in the intercellular substance. For example, in animals deprived of ascorbic acid, even superficial wounds fail to heal. The healing process requires the deposition of collagen fibrils along with intercellular material. It is the lack of the latter that apparently prevents normal healing in these cases. In addition, the walls of the blood vessels are very fragile because of the inadequate cementing together of the endothelial cells. Consequently, there is a tendency for capillaries to rupture, and seemingly spontaneous bleeding is one of the chief findings in vitamin-C deficiency. The slightest blow or pinch leaves a black and blue mark due to rupture of underlying capillaries and the escape of blood

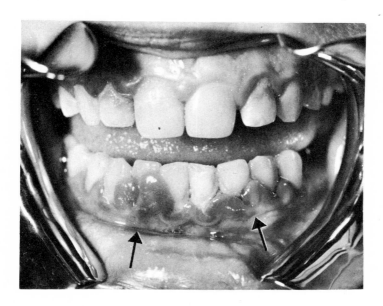

FIG. 25-4 Bleeding and swelling of the gingiva due to vitamin-C deficiency.

into the tissue space. It can be understood, then, why individuals deprived of ascorbic acid complain of bleeding gums (Fig. 25-4), feel weak, and in severe cases there may even be bone alterations and loosening of the teeth.

VITAMIN D

Vitamin D, like vitamin A, is fat-soluble. Pure vitamin D is now considered to be **calciferol**. But, as in the B complex, many closely related compounds have been described. At least 10 chemically distinct forms of this vitamin have been reported.

Source and Requirement   Vitamin D is found principally in fish, especially the oily fish such as salmon, sardines, and herring. Milk is another excellent source, notably milk obtained during the summer. This is so because the cows receive more sunlight during the summer months; therefore their milk possesses a high concentration of vitamin D. Vegetables are practically devoid of this vitamin.

One international unit of vitamin D is equal to 0.025 μg of calciferol. To put it another way, 1 gm of calciferol provides 40,000,000 units. It is difficult to estimate the daily requirement of man, because he manufactures this substance when exposed to sunlight. The need for the vitamin is greatest during the developmental period, when at least 400 units per day should be provided. During pregnancy, a woman requires about 800 units. Since many foods, especially milk, are now fortified with vitamin D, there is little problem in satisfying daily requirements. Fresh milk is usually fortified with about 400 units per quart. It can be seen that if a person is not exposed to sunlight for any significant length of time he must consume foods rich in vitamin D. Therefore, if he is not in the habit of consuming milk and eggs with regularity, he should frequently include the oily fish as part of his diet.

Fate   The absorption of this fat-soluble vitamin depends upon the presence of bile. Therefore, many of the signs and symptoms of vitamin-D deficiency are noted in cases of biliary disturbances. Once the vitamin has been absorbed, it is either utilized or stored. It has been shown that storage is so excellent that if the mother consumes adequate quantities of this vitamin during the gestation period her child will be born with a large reservoir of vitamin D. This supply proves of value in combating rickets during the early days when feeding may be a problem.

Function   Vitamin D plays an important role in the metabolism of calcium and phosphorus. Since these two elements are the major constituents of bone, vitamin-D deficiencies are characterized by bone abnormalities.

Vitamin D apparently aids in the absorption of calcium from the intestinal tract. When this vitamin is lacking, a high concentration of calcium is found in the stool and only an inadequate amount is absorbed. Through

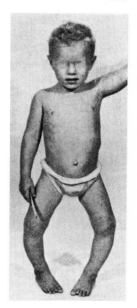

FIG. 25-5   Rickets due to vitamin-D deficiency. (Reproduced, with permission, from R. L. Pullen, "Medical Diagnosis," 2nd ed., Saunders, 1950.)

its influence in assisting the absorption of calcium from the intestinal tract, an adequate supply of vitamin D is usually associated with normal-statured and well-formed individuals. A vitamin-D deficiency, on the other hand, prevents the proper calcification of bone during the developmental period. Consequently, there are skeletal deformities characteristic of **rickets,** a term which means "to twist" (Fig. 25-5).

Rickets is more widespread than is commonly realized. It has been estimated that over 50 per cent of city children are afflicted with this disorder, at least in its milder forms. Babies suffering from vitamin-D deficiency sleep poorly. These children do not begin to walk at the usual age because of weakness of the muscles and bone. Their abdominal muscles are atonic, and so they appear potbellied. In the more severe cases, the thorax becomes deformed into the typical pigeon chest; the legs may become bowed. Clearly, these tragic consequences should be prevented by the early administration of adequate quantities of vitamin D.

VITAMIN E

This vitamin, like so many of the others, was first discovered by astute observation. In 1923 a group of investigators noted that when animals were fed what appeared to be a well-balanced diet they matured, attained normal stature, and appeared well in other respects but consistently failed to reproduce. It was therefore assumed that some nutritional factor was missing in the diet. This assumption has now been proved correct.

Source and Requirement Vitamin E is most concentrated in wheat-germ oil, but it is also found in meat, milk, butter, and some of the vegetables.

Present work indicates that vitamin E is a sterol or an alcohol, and the name **alpha-tocopherol** has been proposed for this substance. But since its actual identity is still a matter of conjecture, the various proposed standards have yet to be agreed upon. In addition, it is impossible even to suggest the requirements in man because most of the work on this vitamin has been done on small rodents, and the application of these results to man has yet to be established.

Function It was early observed in rats that although the female would become pregnant on a vitamin-E-deficient diet, the fetus would soon die and be expelled. Later it was shown that this vitamin is essential for normal sexual function in both sexes. In the male, a shortage of vitamin E leads to changes in the testes which result in loss of fertility and perhaps loss of potency as well.

Other claims for vitamin E have recently been made. In some species, muscular dystrophy results from the lack of this substance. But treatment of this disorder in humans with vitamin E has been completely unsuccessful.

In man, there have been no confirmed reports of vitamin-E deficiency. This is probably because the vitamin is so widespread throughout the common foodstuffs that almost any diet will supply sufficient quantities. Vitamin E has been given to patients with a wide variety of complaints such as menstrual disorders, infertility, impotency, and so forth, but as yet it is impossible to conclude whether or not such treatments have been of value.

VITAMIN K

One of the latest vitamins to be identified is known as **vitamin K.** Because it seems essential to the blood-clotting mechanism, it has been intensely investigated.

Source and Requirement Vitamin K is present everywhere. A list of the vitamin content of the more common foods shows that no matter what one eats he gets a good supply of this vitamin. The leafy vegetables are especially vitamin K rich. Spinach is outstanding in this respect, thus presenting at least one reason for eating that infamous substance.

Vitamin K is fat-soluble and has a complex formula, which has recently been named **menadione.** The minimum requirement is probably very low, about 1 or 2 mg per day. However, it has proved helpful in various blood abnormalities to administer far higher concentrations. Since the vitamin is so widely distributed in nature and in view of the fact that the requirements are low, it seems likely that most cases of deficiency must result from a failure of intestinal absorption rather than an inadequate supply.

Function   If the clotting mechanism will be reviewed (page 223), it will be seen that thrombin occupies a key position. Vitamin K is essential to the formation of prothrombin, the precursor of thrombin. Thus, when there is a shortage of this vitamin there is too little prothrombin formed, and as a result the blood may not clot. This disorder most often appears in newborn babies. They bleed easily, a condition which has been success-fully treated with vitamin K. So effective and dramatic is this treatment that in many hospitals it is now routine to give the expectant mother large doses of vitamin K in an effort to prevent the intracranial hemor-rhages which children sometimes experience in difficult births.

MINERALS

We have seen that the health, well-being, and happiness of the indi-vidual rests upon adequate nutrition. Thus far, it has been emphasized that adequate nutrition includes foods which not only supply sufficient calories and the three major foodstuffs but also provide the various vita-mins. In this section we shall find that even though all these requirements are met, the individual may still suffer if the diet is poor in any of the essential minerals.

The term mineral means "to mine." This name is applicable, because many of these substances, such as iron, cobalt, and copper, man actually obtains by mining. The minerals which appear in the blood are potassium, sodium, phosphorus, calcium, sulfur, magnesium, chlorine, iron, copper, iodine, manganese, cobalt, and zinc. It is true that the last six in this list are found in the body only in very small concentrations; yet apparently they must be present in that concentration.

Throughout this text, reference is made to many of these elements. When the parathyroid gland is reviewed (Chap. 26), calcium and phos-phorus metabolism will be studied. The consideration of dental caries (page 421) included the mention of fluorine. The discussion of hemoglobin involved iron (page 214). Therefore, in this section we shall simply note the source and nutritional requirements of the other important minerals.

SODIUM AND POTASSIUM

In order to provide a diet deficient in either one of these essential min-erals, great pains must be taken. The foods eaten by all groups of people contain completely adequate quantities. Thus these minerals do not pre-sent a serious nutritional problem. It will be recalled, however, that sweat contains sodium chloride. Therefore if one perspires profusely, the diet should be fortified with large amounts of salt. It is essential that the nutritionist take the weather and the individual's activities into consideration and provide salt in one way or another to compensate for undue loss by perspiration.

The hospital nutritionist is often quite concerned with these minerals. There are many disease states which can be assisted by varying the concentration of these substances in the diet. For example, in congestive heart failure, there is usually edema. This excessive fluid in the tissue spaces can often be lessened by restriction of the salt intake. Without going into an extensive discussion of all the ramifications, suffice it to say that sodium and potassium are very important mineral constituents of the body and, under abnormal conditions, it may be necessary to take steps to alter their intake.

CALCIUM

Calcium is one of the most important minerals, and yet, according to some authorities, our diet is more likely to be lacking in this element than in any of the other minerals.

Source and Requirement   Calcium is highly concentrated in milk, broccoli, almonds, turnip greens, and beans. The requirement for calcium is, of course, greatest in growing children and pregnant women. In all cases there should be a large safety factor. That is, one should ingest far more than the minimal values. It is recommended that children should have at least 0.75 gm of calcium per day. A quart of milk satisfies this requirement.

Function   In addition to the obvious role that calcium plays in the development of the skeleton and the teeth, this element is also essential to the coagulation of blood, to normal heart action, and to nerve conduction. It must be kept in mind that vitamin D is essential for the absorption of calcium from the intestinal tract. Therefore the diet must contain adequate quantities of both these substances.

PHOSPHORUS

As will be pointed out in Chap. 26, the metabolism of phosphorus is intimately associated with that of calcium.

Source and Requirement   Phosphorus is found in sufficient amounts in almonds, beans, lean beef, eggs, milk, and wheat. It is recommended that the diet of growing children and pregnant women be equal in calcium and phosphorus. For other adults it is suggested that there be approximately 1.5 times as much phosphorus as calcium.

Function   Aside from the role that this element plays in the formation of bone and teeth, it has been shown to be essential for muscular contraction and other processes requiring the transfer of energy.

IRON

Iron is the essential part of the hemoglobin molecule (Fig. 11-3). This material clearly must be supplied in adequate quantities.

Source and Requirement   Iron is abundant in meat, eggs, beans, peas, whole wheat, spinach, prunes, and molasses. However, the actual iron content of the various foods may prove misleading, because iron is not taken from all foods in the same percentages. For example, it has been shown that in the process of digestion and absorption only 25 per cent of the total iron content will be extracted from some foods whereas up to 85 per cent may be obtained from others.

The minimal requirement is set at about 5 mg of iron per day. To be on the safe side, it is recommended that the adult have at least 12 mg daily.

Function   Iron not only functions as an oxygen carrier but also seems to be intimately associated with the vitamin-B complex. That is to say, many of the disorders characteristic of vitamin-B-complex deficiency are also seen when the intake of iron is inadequate. Not only does the iron-poor diet produce anemia, but there are also digestive disturbances and changes in the epithelium, such as cracking of the corners of the mouth, dryness of the skin, and dullness of the fingernails. Exactly how iron operates in these instances is not clear.

COPPER

There is only a trace of copper in the body, but this small amount is essential. In the lower animals it plays much the same role as iron does in man, and in man copper and iron seem, to some extent, to be interchangeable.

Source and Requirement   Copper is contained in practically everything eaten. It is especially plentiful in nuts, cereals, fruit, poultry, and fish. Since the total body content of copper is small, the daily requirement for this mineral is equally low. Certainly 2 mg per day should suffice. This quantity is available in practically all diets.

Function   Copper, as has been pointed out, supplements iron in the formation of hemoglobin. It apparently acts as a catalyst in the formation of the hemoglobin molecule. Copper also seems to play a vital role in intracellular oxidation reactions, but it is its blood-building power which is of cardinal importance.

IODINE

Iodine is of great nutritional importance in areas where the food and water do not contain adequate concentrations. The farther one lives from the ocean, the poorer the water and food iodine supply becomes. Iodine, as will be discussed in the next chapter, is an essential part of the thyroxin molecule. A shortage of iodine impairs effectiveness of the thyroid-gland hormone; iodine-deficient individuals suffer the characteristics of hypothyroidism. It is for this reason that hypothyroidism was formerly so prevalent in inland and mountain areas. Now, however, various foods, such as table salt, are fortified with minute but adequate quantities of iodine. **Iodized salt** has made this condition all but extinct.

It is recommended that the adult consume about 0.25 mg of iodine daily.

DIET

The term **diet** usually implies a scanty regime designed to cause loss of weight. Actually, the word has a much broader connotation. It refers to any regulated course of eating and drinking, whatever the purpose. It would be clearly impossible here to go into detail concerning specific diets for all conditions in health and disease. Nonetheless, a few of the more general principles will be discussed in order to reemphasize the various important aspects of alimentation.

THE NORMAL DIET

The average person pays very little attention to his diet. To most people, eating is simply a problem of filling the stomach so that the gnawing, uncomfortable, irritating sensation of hunger is replaced by a feeling of plethora, a warm, stuffed state closely bordering upon unconsciousness. It is rather startling, therefore, to find that the great majority of people in the United States satisfy their nutritional needs quite adequately.

Actually, any diet should fulfill the requirements for (1) **calories,** (2) **protein,** (3) **vitamins,** and (4) **minerals.** If there are too few calories, the individual will lose weight. If there are too many, he may gain. Since neither fat nor carbohydrate can be converted to protein, there must be enough of that foodstuff in the diet to satisfy the protein demands of the body. To prevent the various vitamin- and mineral-deficiency disorders, these substances must also be provided in adequate amounts. Finally, for normal defecation, the diet must include adequate roughage to give bulk to the feces and sufficient fluids to prevent a hard, dry stool.

The vitamin and mineral requirements have already been discussed in detail. Whether one is on a normal diet, or one to lose or gain weight, these requirements remain more or less the same. For that reason no more will be added in this section concerning these dietary components. The dietitian should keep in mind that a diet low enough in calories to reduce an obese individual may be inadequate in vitamins and minerals. This eventuality must be guarded against.

Caloric Requirements Table 25-1 gives the approximate Calories required by the average adult in various occupations. Such a chart serves merely as a rough guide. If after the diet has been prepared and used for a period of time the individual is found to be gaining or losing weight,

TABLE 25-1 Caloric Requirements

Occupation	Caloric Requirement per Day
Resting	2000
Sedentary (student)	2500
Light work (scientist)	3000
Moderate work (truck driver)	3500
Heavy work (football player)	4000 +

when no weight change is desired, then the caloric requirements have not been met. For this reason everyone should periodically weigh himself and alter his diet accordingly.

The average person does not actually calculate his caloric requirements but eats according to his tastes. Yet somehow this suffices to maintain his weight constant. It has long been considered normal for an individual to gain weight as he grows older. This is not correct. Health and longevity have been irrefragably demonstrated to be impaired by the accumulation of fat. If anything, a person should lose weight as he grows older because he becomes less active and his muscles atrophy somewhat.

Most books on nutrition offer complete tables illustrating the exact number of Calories in all conceivable types of food. Table 25-2 simply

TABLE 25-2 Caloric Content of the More Common Foods

Foods	Portion	Calories
Apple	large	100
Banana	small	100
Bread	slice	75
Broth, chicken	1 bowl	100
Butter	pat	25
Cake	average slice	250
Candy bar	small	350
Cauliflower	1 helping	25
Cereal, milk and sugar	bowl	150
Chicken, fried	1 piece	200
Chop suey	1 helping	200
Chow mein	1 helping	250
Consommé	1 bowl	25
Corn on cob	1	100
Doughnut	1	200
Egg, fried	1	100

TABLE 25-2 **(Continued)**

Foods	Portion	Calories
Egg, poached	1	75
Egg roll	1	100
Frankfurter, roll	1	300
Ham	slice	150
Ice cream, chocolate	cone	200
Ice cream, vanilla	cone	100
Macaroni	1 helping	250
Meat	slice	200
Olives, black, medium	each	15
Olives, green, medium	each	20
Pancakes, sirup	each	200
Peas	1 helping	100
Pie	average slice	300
Potato, baked, butter	1 average	150
Potato, mashed, butter	1 helping	125
Salad, dressing	average helping	125
Sandwich	average size	300
Shrimp, medium-sized	each	15
Soup, split-pea	1 bowl	300
Spaghetti	1 helping	250
Tomato	medium	25
Turkey	large helping	250

Beverages	Portion	Calories
Beer	bottle	200
Coca-Cola	6 oz.	65
Coffee or tea, no sugar or cream	cup	0
Coffee or tea, sugar	cup	50
Coffee or tea, sugar and cream	cup	100
Juice, orange	glass	100
Juice, tomato	glass	25
Manhattan	average	150
Martini	average	150
Milk	glass	150
Milk, malted	large glass	600
Scotch, bourbon, rye, gin	per ounce	85
Tom Collins	tall	300

lists some of the more common foods for illustrative purposes. The reader can derive a rough estimate of the number of Calories he consumes per day from this table. It should be realized that these are average values. A slice of meat, for example, is listed at 200 Calories, but this figure clearly depends upon the mass of the slice. It seems superfluous to state that a 2-in. steak contains twice as many Calories as a 1-in. steak. But many people, especially those ostensibly trying to lose weight, have inordinate difficulty in grasping this concept. Again, it seems necessary to emphasize that the final judge of one's caloric intake is the bathroom scale.

Protein Requirements Table 25-3 indicates the protein requirements of individuals in various occupations. The carbohydrate and fat composition of the diet are also included. It will be recalled that, because protein can be converted into the other two foodstuffs, it is possible to survive on a pure protein diet. This is, however, an expensive and not a particularly desirable undertaking. Protein is needed for specific functions which the other foodstuffs cannot satisfy. Therefore, when the other substances are present in large enough quantities, protein is spared for its essential tasks. Some fat is included, because it is a high caloric source and aso because it gives a sensation of satiety. In short, the ideal diet from the standpoint of nutrition, economy, and palatability contains all three foodstuffs in approximately the ratio shown in Table 25-3.

TABLE 25-3 Protein, Fat, and Carbohydrate Requirements per Day

Occupation	Protein, gm	Carbohydrate, gm	Fat, gm
Resting	75	250	80
Sedentary	95	325	90
Light work	110	350	100
Moderate work	130	400	120
Heavy work	150	500	140

There are almost 500 gm in a pound. It is not uncommon for a worker in the United States to consume in one meal a steak or other meat weighing a half pound or more. From this one food he obviously satisfies his daily protein requirement. As a matter of fact, protein deficiency is encountered only under severe economic conditions, in time of war, or among food faddists.

DIET FOR REDUCING

As has been stressed, the individual who is more than about 15 per cent heavier than recommended for his age-height-sex group is obese and in need of treatment. In places where the standard of living is high, as in the United States, this pathological condition is extremely common. Obesity places a greatly increased load upon the circulatory system and other mechanisms. For example, every pound of body tissue contains a quarter of a mile of blood vessels. If an individual is 20 lb overweight, there are 5 extra miles of blood vessels through which blood must be pushed by the action of the heart. It is not surprising that heart disease frequently develops in such people. It has been well demonstrated, for example, that heart failure, hypertension, cancer and diabetes mellitus occur far more frequently in fat people than in normal individuals.

Obese people vehemently insist that they do not overeat. Most of them indignantly maintain that they eat less than most of their friends, that they practically starve themselves. They conclude the discussion, at least to their own satisfaction, by proclaiming that there is nothing they can do about the situation because it is their "glands" or it "runs in the family." This is an untenable viewpoint. A car will not run without gasoline. In the same way, man will not function without fuel, and that fuel is derived only from the ingested or the stored food. If one does not eat, he consumes his stored reserves and must lose weight. If this were not so, the second law of thermodynamics would be breached!

No matter what the activity of one's "glands," the fact remains that the energy utilization must be balanced by energy intake. That is to say, caloric output and input must be the same. If the input is less than the utilization, weight will be lost in every case, without exception. As to the argument that it "runs in the family," there is an element of truth in that vague statement. What the obese individual fails to realize, or is reluctant to admit, is that *eating habits* run in the family. Thus the fat mother and father look upon their cherubic children fully convinced that just as they all have blue eyes, so they all have mounds of fat. The fat has not been inherited, however. It has been acquired at the family festive board.

Obesity is truly a psychological problem. One must ascertain why a patient is overeating. In many cases it is simply an attention-getting device. The child may be the youngest or neglected member of the family and therefore eats startling quantities so as to draw attention and comment in his direction. There are, of course, many other explanations extending throughout the realm of psychology. We are not concerned with that aspect of the problem here. After we are convinced that the only reason for obesity is overeating, we can turn our attention to diets which will rectify that condition. If the obese person adheres to the diet, he will invariably lose weight. The problem, of course, is making him accept and carry out the difficult regime.

As already discussed (page 415), food intake is controlled by the hypothalamus. Normally there is a drive for food, and after an adequate quantity has been consumed, one feels satiated and ceases to eat. Undoubtedly there are individuals with hypothalamic abnormalities that drastically alter their eating habits so that they are too thin or grossly fat. More often, however, eating patterns have developed which simply dominate the hypothalmic mechanism.

In certain exaggerated cases of obesity, rather striking results can be obtained by proper dieting. Such exaggerated cases, of course, should always be handled by a physician. But the average person who is only 10 to 40 lb overweight can usually bring himself to more normal proportions by self-dieting. Tables 25-4 and 25-5 give the ideal weights for men and women. These are average figures compiled by insurance companies and afford a rough measure for the reader to judge his own condition.

TABLE 25-4   Optimal Weight Range for Men. Medium Frame as Ordinarily Dressed

Height, Ft and In.	Weight, Lb
5 1	124–133
5 2	127–136
5 3	130–140
5 4	134–144
5 5	137–147
5 6	141–151
5 7	145–156
5 8	149–160
5 9	153–164
5 10	157–168
5 11	161–173
6 0	166–178
6 1	171–184
6 2	176–189

TABLE 25-5   Optimal Weight Range for Women. Medium Frame as Ordinarily Dressed

Height, Ft and In.	Weight, Lb
4 10	110–118
4 11	112–120
5 0	114–122
5 1	117–125
5 2	120–128
5 3	124–132
5 4	127–135
5 5	130–140
5 6	134–144
5 7	137–147
5 8	141–151
5 9	145–155
5 10	148–158

Caloric Content   The total number of calories in the reducing diet must be regulated so that there is a steady loss of weight. The ideal weight loss is considered to be between 1 and 2 lb per week. Therefore, in most cases the individual need do little more than get a bathroom scale, a piece of graph paper, and a pencil. If he will then mark his actual weight at the top left corner of the graph and the weight to which he desires to reduce in the lower right corner, he need only connect them with a straight line and arrange the time to attain this goal so that the weight loss per week is between 1 and 2 lb. Let us say that our patient weighs 200 lb. He desires to reduce to 180. At 2 lb per week, this will take 10 weeks. Each vertical line on the graph represents a day. Now if he will simply weigh himself each morning at the same time before breakfast and mark his actual weight on the chart, he can see at a glance whether he has eaten too many or too few calories. If the dots remain above the line he must cut down further. Of course, the dots will not follow the line exactly, but they should approximate it so that at the end of each week his actual weight is just about the same as that indicated by the sloping line.

As a rough measure, the dieting individual should begin with a total caloric intake of about 1500 Calories per day and then vary this figure up or down, depending upon whether or not his decrease in weight is progressing too rapidly or too slowly. In some cases it may be necessary to reduce the caloric intake to as low as 1000 Calories. But for the average, active individual it is very rarely necessary to go lower than this.

Protein Content   Unless contraindicated because of some disease condition, every reducing diet shoud have an unusually high protein content. The object of the diet is to rid the body of the fat stores. Protein, it will be recalled, makes up vital tissues. It is not desirable to have these tissues broken down to supply energy demands. Also, the other essential uses by the body of protein make it mandatory that the body fuel used to supplement the low-caloric diet be anything but protein. For this reason the protein content of the food is kept high.

In addition, the high-protein diet, with its high specific dynamic action, keeps the metabolic rate elevated. For reducing purposes, this is highly desirable.

It was noted above that the protein content of the normal diet is usually set at about 20 per cent of the total. In the reducing diet, it is well to take this percentage up to 50 per cent or even higher.

Vitamin Content   There is great danger of vitamin deficiency in a very restricted diet. This eventuality must be avoided. Nutritionists always carefully consider the vitamin content of each food recommended in the diet to be sure that these essential substances are in adequate supply. In many cases, multivitamin tablets are prescribed.

Mineral Content   It is very difficult for the average person to restrict the diet to the point where mineral requirements are not being met. However, in certain cases, such as pregnant women and growing children who are placed on a diet, the mineral content of the diet must be considered. In such cases the concentration of iron, calcium, and iodine should be kept high.

Salt and Water Content   Perhaps no greater confusion has arisen in the entire field of reducing than that concerning the salt and water content. All too many diets, recommended by competent authorities, restrict the use of salt and water. This procedure is undesirable and ineffective. It must be kept clearly in mind that the object of dieting is to remove excessive fat. The fact that weight is lost is secondary. There is clearly little gained by losing weight but not fat. That is precisely what restriction of salt and water accomplishes. Certainly, if an individual takes in no fluid, takes in limited salt, and then sits in an oven and bakes for several hours, he will emerge several pounds lighter. But the weight lost represents only the loss of fluid. The person is dehydrated. No fat has melted, since fat does not melt in the body; it must be metabolized. It is possible to reduce 10 lb or more simply by cutting down the amount of salt in the food. But this weight loss is fluid loss.

In many pathological conditions it is necessary to put a patient on a low-salt diet, but for the person who simply wants to remove fat this procedure is clearly unwise. Normal hydration is essential from both a physiological and a cosmetic viewpoint. The individual should be encouraged to take as much water and salt as he desires.

Exercise   A final word concerning exercise is necessary in this discussion of reducing. Since the weight of an individual must reflect the balance between caloric intake and utilization, it seems apparent that exercise should assist in reducing. This is true. But it is also true that exercise increases the appetite, and therein lies the problem. If an individual can adhere to his low-caloric diet and still exercise moderately, he will lose weight more rapidly and will probably feel better. However, on a low-caloric diet excessive exercise should be avoided. It is far better for the individual to reduce his caloric intake rather than subject his system to the great strains of vigorous exercise. A young person may play a set or two of tennis or a round of golf. The older person had best restrict his exercise to his normal work plus a leisurely walk. In short, the easiest, the best, and the most normal mode of losing weight is to restrict the diet.

SUMMARY

Vitamins are substances found in food which, in small quantities, are essential to health. **Vitamin A** is fat-soluble. The daily requirement is 5,000 units. It is found in carrots, spinach, milk, and liver. Vitamin A is stored in the liver and functions to aid in growth, vision, and the integrity of the epithelial tissues.

Vitamin B is really a complex made up of several distinct substances. They are all water-soluble. **Vitamin B$_1$** or **thiamine hydrochloride** is highly concentrated in yeast and cereals. The recommended daily intake is 0.5 mg. Thiamine plays an essential role in the cellular processes of respiration. Deficiency of this substance results in **beriberi.**

Vitamin B$_2$ or **riboflavin** is found in adequate quantities in milk, broccoli, spinach, eggs, and liver. It is recommended that the adult consume at least 1.5 mg per day. Riboflavin is also involved in the intracellular oxidative processes. A deficiency results in blurred vision, burning and soreness of the eyes and tongue, dermatitis, and cracking and fissuring at the angle of the mouth.

Nicotinic acid is essential to prevent **pellagra,** a condition characterized by skin disorders, digestive upset, irritability, and weakness. A daily intake of 12 to 20 mg suffices. **Folic acid** is another member of the B complex. It is known to be **pteroylglutamic acid. Vitamin B$_6$** is **pyridoxine** and is often referred to as the **antidermatitic factor,** because of its action. **Pantothenic acid** prevents graying of hair in rats, while **vitamin B$_{12}$** relieves **pernicious anemia.**

Vitamin C or **ascorbic acid** is highly concentrated in fresh fruits and potatoes. At least 75 mg of this substance per day should be consumed. It is stored in the adrenal glands, hypophysis, pancreas, and liver and is water-soluble. Vitamin C is essential for the prevention of **scurvy.**

Vitamin D is fat-soluble. It is found principally in fish and milk. It is now known to be identical with **calciferol.** Exposure to sunlight aids the body in synthesizing its own vitamin D, but in addition about 400 units per day should be taken in, and about twice that amount during pregnancy. Vitamin D functions to aid calcium absorption from the intestinal tract. If is it deficient, **rickets** results.

Vitamin E is **alpha-tocopherol.** In small rodents, it seems essential for normal sexual function and reproduction. What influence it exerts in man is conjectural.

Vitamin K is fat-soluble and is identical with **menadione.** It is widely distributed in nature; deficiencies develop usually only in cases of bile shortage. This vitamin is essential for the formation of prothrombin.

The minerals **potassium, sodium, phosphorus, calcium, sulfur, mag-**

nesium, chlorine, iron, copper, iodine, manganese, cobalt, and zinc must be ingested in order to prevent grave disturbances. Most diets contain these minerals in abundance. However, in some regions the iodine content of the water and food may be short, and therefore iodine must be added. Growing children and pregnant women should have food with a high calcium content. The diet requires foods rich in iron so as to maintain the oxygen-carrying capacity of the blood within normal limits.

The normal diet must contain approximately the same number of Calories as the individual utilizes, it should have about 20 per cent or more protein, and it should be adequate in the vitamins and minerals. Protein is required because the other foodstuffs cannot be converted to protein.

QUESTIONS

1. What is a vitamin?
2. Discuss the current theory which purports to explain why thiamine deficiency causes nervous-system alterations.
3. What abnormalities does a shortage of vitamin C cause?
4. Individuals on a normal diet may suffer a vitamin A and D deficiency if there is inadequate bile formation. Why?
5. What role does vitamin A play in vision?
6. If salt and fluids are restricted, an obese individual loses weight. Why?

SUGGESTED READING

"Action of Vitamins," *Therapeutic Notes,* **67:**#3, 67–73, March 1960.

Breehen, R., and Breecher, T. E., "Easy Guide to Family Nutrition," *Parents' Magazine,* **31:** 52–53, 1956.

Cooley, D. G., "What Is a Vitamin?" *Today's Health,* **41:**#1, 20–23, 73–75, 77–78, January 1963.

Griffith, W. H., "The Physiologic Role of Vitamins," *Am. J. Med.,* **25:**#5, 666–672, November 1958.

Kaufman, W., "Doctors' Reports on the Effect of Diet on Fertility, Potency, and Personality," *Coronet,* **41:** 136–139, 1956.

Maddox, G., "Meeting our Mineral Needs," *Today's Health,* **40:**#4, 52–53, April 1962.

Mayer, J., "Appetite and Obesity," *Atlantic Monthly,* **196:** 58–62, 1955.

Mayer, J., "Genetic, Traumatic, and Environmental Factors in the Etiology of Obesity," *Physiol. Revs.,* **33:** 472–508, 1953.

Schneider, H. A., "What Has Happened to Nutrition?" *Persp. Biol. Med.,* **1:**#3, 278–292, Spring 1958.

PART

Endocrine System

Thyroid and Parathyroid Glands

26

STRICTLY SPEAKING, THERE ARE TWO TYPES OF **hormones.** In recent times it has been recognized that hormones may be produced and act locally. These still poorly understood hormones are referred to as **kinins.** Traditionally, the term hormone has been defined as a substance elaborated by a ductless gland and carried by the blood stream to some other part of the body, which it excites. It has already been pointed out that though excitation is, strictly speaking, implicit in that definition, through usage the term hormone has come to embrace any substance elaborated by a ductless gland and carried elsewhere by the blood stream, whether it excites or inhibits the target tissue. Thus, it was noted that secretin *activates* the production of gastric juice, while enterogastrone *inhibits* the gastric glands. Both these substances are now properly called hormones.

All endocrine glands are ductless. That is to say, the substance formed by the secretory cells of these glands is expressed directly into the blood stream instead of into a series of collecting ducts, as in the case of bile, pancreatic juice, and perspiration, for example. The terms **endocrine gland** and **ductless gland** are synonymous. In short, an endocrine gland elaborates a hormone which is secreted directly into the blood stream and carried usually to a particular tissue the activity of which it markedly influences.

A word concerning some of the more common methods of investigating the function of the endocrine glands will be helpful. If a part of the body is removed and the animal dies, not as a result of the surgical procedure but due to extirpation of the part, it is logical to assume that the presence of that particular part is essential to life. If the animal does not die, but very definite and marked alterations occur, by the same reasoning that organ is considered to function in some way to prevent the observed alterations.

The endocrine glands are, for the most part, small discrete organs which in experimental animals can be surgically removed with ease. Following such an operation, the animal is studied carefully. For example, the blood chemistry may be analyzed before and after removal, the basal metabolic rate may be followed, or any of the other various functions outlined in the preceding sections may be scrutinized. Such extirpation studies often give the first clue as to the function of a particular gland.

It has been found that, if the endocrine glands are chemically treated so as to extract the potent substances they contain, the product so prepared can then be injected into experimental animals and the results observed. Generally speaking, the injection of an extract should produce effects just opposite to those observed after removal of that particular gland. Also, the administration of the glandular extract should prevent the alterations usually noted after extirpation of that gland. If the changes have already occurred, the extract should reverse them and return the animal to a normal state.

Finally, animal experimental work finds essential confirmation in the clinic. As will be learned shortly, the endocrine glands often function too leisurely or too energetically. The case history frequently supplies valuable information to supplement our knowledge of endocrinology.

THE THYROID GLAND

Sometimes the endocrine glands are classified according to whether or not they are essential to life. If continued survival depends upon the gland, its removal should result in death. According to this classification, the thyroid gland is not essential; as we shall see, man survives after it is completely removed. But though death does not result, very definite and serious alterations do occur. The thyroid gland is one of the most important endocrine glands, and its normal function is essential to health, if not to life.

ANATOMY OF THE THYROID GLAND

Figure 26-1 shows the gross and microscopic anatomy of the thyroid gland. It is seen to overlie the trachea and larynx to form a shield. It is this configuration which gives to the gland its name, for thyroid means an oblong shield. In man, this organ weighs about 30 gm.

The microscopic view reveals that the thyroid gland is arranged very much like a beehive. The cubicles are formed by so-called cuboid epithelial tissue. Each cubicle is termed a **follicle.** In the normal thyroid gland, the follicles are filled with a **colloid.**

The thyroid gland has an abundant blood supply through the **superior** and **inferior thyroid arteries.** In man, the rate of blood flow is 3 to 7 ml/

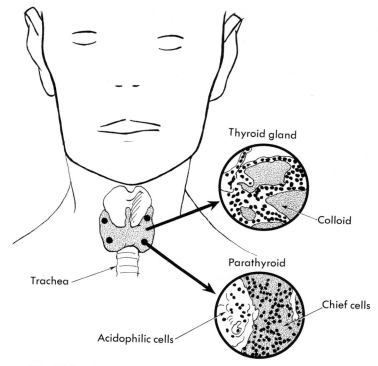

FIG. 26-1   Anatomy of the thyroid and parathyroid glands.

min/gm of tissue. The thyroid gland is innervated by both branches of the autonomic nervous system. It is thought that this innervation controls the blood supply rather than the secretory activity of the cells.

FUNCTION OF THE THYROID GLAND

Extirpation   If the thyroid gland is completely removed from an experimental animal, death does not result. Instead, the animal becomes fat, sleeps inordinately, moves slowly if at all, its skin and fur become dry; and when the basal metabolic rate is determined it is found to be abnormally low. The observed changes—the sluggishness, the gain in weight, the excessive somnolence, the dry skin—are all due to the marked decrease in the metabolic rate. Following complete thyroidectomy (removal of the thyroid gland), the basal metabolic rate may fall to as much as 30 or 40 per cent below normal.

Thyroid Hormones   The thyroid gland is now believed to secrete at least four hormones. All of them are **iodothyronines** (Fig. 26-2). Of the four hormones, **3, 5, 3′-triiodothyronine** is the most active. It has about three times the potency of thyroxin. But the rate of thyroxin formation is by far the greater. The other two forms, shown in Fig. 26-2, are secreted in only very small quantities.

If the thyroid hormones are injected into the thyroidectomized animal, the drop in metabolic rate is thwarted. Further, it is possible to administer these substances to either an intact or a thyroidectomized animal in such amounts that the BMR is elevated far above normal. These experiments, and many others, indicate that the primary function of the thyroid gland is to control the rate at which the various metabolic processes throughout the body proceed.

Iodine Of particular importance is the presence of four atoms of **iodine** in the thyroxin molecule (Fig. 26-2). If the diet is lacking in iodine, the thyroid still secretes a thyroxinlike substance, but it differs in having less than the normal quantity of iodine in the molecule. This ersatz substance is incapable of doing the work of thyroxin, and the individual suffers all the changes associated with thyroid deficiency. Normally the blood contains but 6 μg of iodine per 100 ml of blood (Table 26-1). Since a microgram is a thousand times less than a milligram, it can be seen that it does not take much iodine to maintain normal thyroid function. Only about 1 mg is required per week. That is why the minute quantities added to salt and other products suffice.

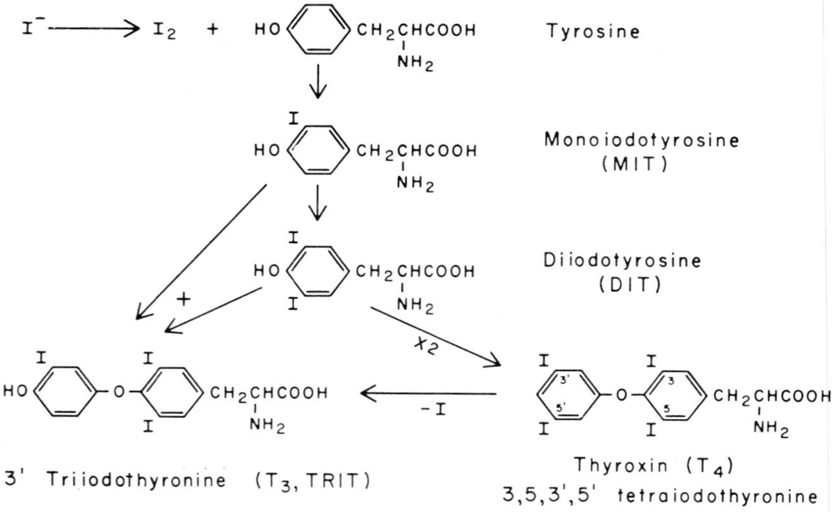

FIG. 26-2 Biosynthesis of thyroid hormones. (Reproduced, with permission, from S. J. Tepperman, "Metabolic and Endocrine Physiology," Year Book Medical Publishers, Chicago, 1962.)

TABLE 26-1   Composition of Plasma Iodine ($\mu g/100$ ml)

Form	Iodine Concentration
All forms	6.0
Inorganic	0.6
Organic	5.4
Free thyroxin	0.2
Protein bound	5.2
Thyroxin + triiodothyronine	4.8
Moniodotyrosine + diiodotyrosine	0.8

Mode of Action   There is no question but that thyroxin strikingly increases metabolic activity in perhaps every cell of the body, but just how this is accomplished is still not certain. It is interesting to observe that following the administration of thyroxin there is a relatively long latent period before any alterations may be discerned. In man, even a very large injection produces no metabolic changes during the first 24 hours. After this period the basal metabolic rate steadily increases until a maximum is reached 8 to 12 days after the single injection. After this peak is attained (Fig. 26-3) the metabolic rate only slowly returns to its former level, the total effect of a single administration of thyroxin persisting for well over a month.

Biosynthesis of Thyroid Hormone   In the intestinal tract, ingested iodine is converted to iodide. The iodide is then absorbed into the blood. When it reaches the thyroid gland, it is actively transported into the gland by the thyroid cells. This is referred to as the **iodide trap.** In the gland, the iodide is oxidized to iodine in which form it reacts with **tyrosine** to form **3-monoiodotyrosine (MIT)** (Fig. 26-2). Some of the MIT molecules are further iodinated to **3, 5-diiodotyrosine (DIT).** MIT and DIT form **3, 5, 3′-triiodothyronine** (T_3 or TRIT). Two molecules of DIT form **3, 5, 3′, 5′-tetraiodothyronine** (thyroxin or T_4). It is believed that tyrosine is bound to globulin and that all of the above transformations occur without altering this bond. Thus, as the iodothyronines are synthesized, they are in the **thyroglobulin** form.

The liberation of the active form of iodothyronine into the blood requires the action of a **proteolytic enzyme.** In the gland, the hormone is stored as thyroglobulin.

The delayed influence of thyroxin is only partly explicable on the basis of slow penetration of the cells. The best current theory postulates that this hormone stimulates enzyme production throughout the body. It will be recalled that enzymes are organic catalysts which speed metabolic processes within living cells. The greater the concentration of a specific enzyme, the faster will that reaction proceed. Thus, though this may not

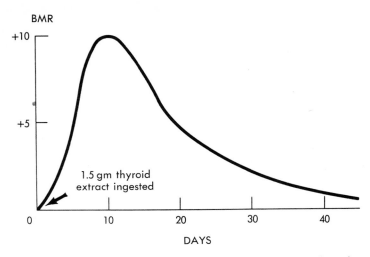

FIG. 26-3   Effect of thyroid extract ingestion. Note that the maximum change is not reached until about 10 days after treatment and some elevation of BMR is still detectable as long as 30 days after the ingestion.

be the complete explanation of thyroxin function, there is growing evidence which indicates that at least one of its functions is to encourage the production of enzymes which in turn speed metabolic processes. Apparently, this sequence of events requires considerable time to reach its maximal influence.

It has now been confirmed that iodothyronines have an uncoupling effect on oxidative phosphorylation. This means that instead of energy being stored in energy-rich phosphate bonds, the energy appears as heat. Because heat is generated under the influence of thyroid hormone, the hormone is said to have a **calorigenic** action.

REGULATION OF THYROID FUNCTION

In the normal individual, the BMR does not vary more than 1 or 2 per cent from day to day, and over a period of years there is but a slow decline. There is no question, however, but that the thyroid hormone can sharply vary this rate. Obviously, there must be some mechanism which regulates the thyroid gland.

The Thyrotropic Hormone   There is an endocrine gland lying at the base of the brain. It is sometimes referred to as the **pituitary gland,** but preferably as the **hypophysis.** As we shall note in some detail in Chap. 30, this gland elaborates many hormones. Some of these hormones do nothing but control other endocrine glands. Such a substance is termed *tropic,* which means to turn or stimulate. Thus, the **thyrotropic hormone** "turns," that is, regulates, the thyroid gland. If the thyroid gland is removed, injection of the thyrotropic hormone has no effect on the BMR. But when the thyroid is present, this substance causes it to grow and to increase its activity. Following these changes, the BMR is elevated. The point to remember is that the thyrotropic hormone influences the metabolic rate only through the thyroid gland. Such indirect action is the crucial test of all tropic hormones.

The thyrotropic hormone, also referred to as **TSH** (thyroid-stimulating hormone), influences the thyroid gland in three ways: (1) *to increase its size,* (2) *to augment the elaboration of thyroglobulin,* and (3) *to elevate the production of the proteolytic enzyme.* It can be seen, therefore, that when this hormone is abundantly secreted by the hypophysis there is more thyroglobulin produced and the excess enzyme quickly converts the thyroglobulin into thyroxin. All the changes associated with hyperthyroidism then occur.

Reciprocal Regulation   There is no doubt but that the thyrotropic hormone regulates thyroid function. The question then arises, what controls the output of TSH?

The preponderance of evidence indicates that there is reciprocal regulation. Just as TSH regulates the amount of thyroxin secreted, so does thyroxin govern the quantity of TSH elaborated. It is now known that specifically it is the iodine in the thyroxin molecule which regulates the output of TSH. So long as there is the normal quantity of iodine in the blood, the production of TSH is kept in check, but when the iodine concentration falls, TSH is unleashed, the thyroid is stimulated, and the iodine concentration of the blood is returned to within the normal range.

Further work has shown that thyroxin not only inhibits the production of TSH but also decreases the action of the proteolytic enzyme. It can be seen, in brief, that there are two very effective self-regulating mechanisms. When there is a deficiency of thyroxin, the thyroid gland is stimulated by TSH, and at the same time the proteolytic enzyme is allowed to function. As soon as the thyroxin concentration of the blood returns to normal, it slows down the production of TSH and inhibits the enzyme. This reciprocal regulation is extremely delicate. Thus, despite the individual's activities and the varying calls for thyroxin, the concentration of this substance in the blood is normally maintained within a very narrow range. This is just one more illustration of the many delicately balanced homeostatic mechanisms.

Thyrotropin-releasing Factor (TRF)   The output of TSH by the anterior lobe of the hypophysis is under the control, not only of the circulating iodothyronines, but also of a **neurohumor** secreted by the **hypothalamus.** By virtue of TRF, there exists a link by which the nervous system can modulate thyroid function. Thus there is an explanation for the long recognized influence that cold environments, and psychic trauma, have on thyroid function.

ABNORMALITIES OF THYROID FUNCTION

We have nòted that clinical cases afford an excellent source of verification of knowledge acquired through animal experimentation. It is for this reason that the more important abnormalities of thyroid function are presented here.

Hypothyroidism   The term **hypothyroidism** means abnormally low activity of the thyroid gland. Too little iodothyronin is secreted into the blood stream. The results of this abnormality depend upon the period in life during which this deficiency persists.

If the thyroid gland does not elaborate enough iodothyronin during the developmental stage of life, or if the intake of iodine is so low as to render the formed hormone impotent, all the child's metabolic processes will be retarded. This will lead to stunted growth, mental backwardness, a dry, wrinkled skin and, of course, a very low BMR. The diagnosis in such cases is made not only on the characteristic appearance but also on the BMR, which may be as much as 30 per cent below normal. Such an individual, shown in Fig. 26-4, is called a **cretin.** The origin of the term cretin is of considerable interest. It seems that Arian refugees settled in the Pyrenees in France, but because of religious persecution they huddled together in remote valleys. Their diet was insufficient, and since the water and available food were deficient in iodine, their children were often stunted and mentally retarded. The French called these children by the term *chrétien* which means "Christian." It was a term of contempt and came to be applied to all children suffering from hypothyroidism.

Cretinism is now almost extinct. Formerly it was prevalent in regions where the water and food contained too little iodine. Such communities now add this element to their drinking water and prevent hypothyroidism. In cases not caused by iodine deficiency, thyroid hormone therapy is usually initiated early enough in life so as to prevent untoward effects.

In many instances, the thyroid gland is perfectly normal throughout the developmental period but then becomes hypoactive in the adult. In such cases, if corrective measures are not instituted, the BMR progressively falls to very low levels. The skin becomes dry, the hair falls out, the individual may gain weight because he continues to consume his usual number of calories despite the lowered metabolic rate, and though the intelligence remains normal, there is a striking reluctance to use it. These persons are considered mentally retarded, but actually are not so.

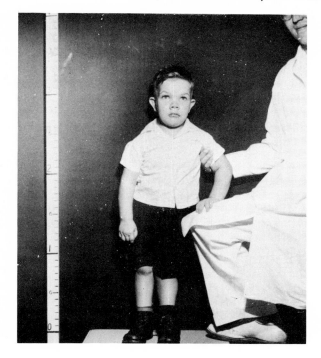

FIG. 26-4   Cretinism. This patient is 17 years old but appears to be but three.

The most characteristic change is the appearance. These individuals become puffy, especially around the eyes. The puffy appearance is due to the deposition of a semifluid albuminous substance in the soft tissue beneath the skin. This hypothyroid condition in the adult is termed **myxedema,** meaning a swelling due to mucus. Another name for the disorder is **Gull's disease,** in honor of the doctor who first described it.

Myxedema can be effectively treated by thyroid medication. The desiccated thyroid is usually given by mouth in tablet form. The dose is regulated according to the BMR so as to keep it within the normal range. When this result has been achieved, the edematous appearance disappears, the hair grows back and regains its usual luster, and once again the individual demonstrates his former vigor and enthusiasm. It is truly a dramatic alteration.

Hyperthyroidism   The term **hyperthyroidism** implies overactivity of the thyroid gland. In such cases, the BMR is unduly high, often reaching 30 per cent above normal or, in rare cases, even higher. These individuals are truly "living fast." Their heart rate is accelerated, their skin is moist, they seem to require little or no sleep, they have insatiable drive and therefore are often the leaders of the community. They are, as might be expected, also hyperirritable. Hyperthyroidism is usually referred to as **thyrotoxicosis** or **Graves' disease.**

Hyperthyroidism is often associated with **exophthalmos,** a bulging of the eyes. Exophthalmos is thought to be due to either a separate secretion from the anterior lobe of the hypophysis, or to a derivative of TSH. At any rate, there is edema, lipid deposition, and cellular infiltration in the extraocular muscles. The net result is that the eyeballs are forced outward (Fig. 26-5). In advanced cases, blindness results from damage to the optic nerve. Because it is difficult or impossible to close the upper lid over the bulging eyeball, there are drying and irreversible changes in the cornea. Elimination of the etiological factors does not cause the eyeball to return to its original position, but it does prevent further bulging.

Hyperthyroidism is treated in several ways, one of which is partial extirpation. The surgeon simply removes a large part of the glandular tissue. The small remaining portion usually manufactures much less thyroxin than did the entire gland. The changes associated with hyperthyroidism are consequently ameliorated. Radioactive iodine can also be used. Iodine has a great affinity for the thyroid gland. As a matter of fact, one-third of all the iodine in the body is found in the thyroid. Thus when radioactive iodine is administered, it quickly makes its way to the thyroid. Here it emits rays which are lethal to the surrounding tissue. This effectively reduces the functional thyroid tissue, thereby decreasing the output of thyroxin.

Goiter When thyroid disorders were far more prevalent than they are today, almost everyone was familiar with the sight of a person with a huge swelling of the neck (Fig. 26-6). The term **goiter** means "throat" and

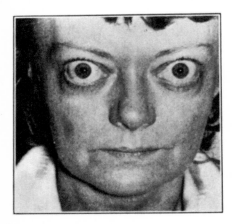

FIG. 26-5 **Severe exophthalmos.** (Reproduced, with permission, from L. J. Soffer, "Diseases of the Endocrine Glands," Lea & Febiger, 1951.)

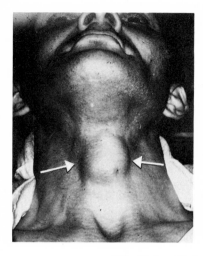 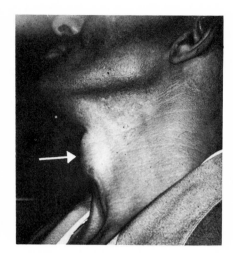

FIG. 26-6   Clinical appearance of a goiter.

refers specifically to the swelling of the throat. This swelling is caused by enlargement of the thyroid gland.

The goiterous patient may be suffering from either hypo- or hyperthyroidism. For example, in regions where the iodine supply is inadequate, the thyroid puts out a substance poor in iodine; as a result, TSH production increases. The excess TSH enlarges the thyroid, causing the goiter. But in the absence of iodine, this effort is frustrated and the individual suffers from hypothyroidism.

On the other hand, the enlargement of the thyroid may represent a hyperplasia; that is to say, there may be an undue growth and multiplication of the thyroid cells caused by a neoplastic or inflammatory process. This gland is usually not only large but also hyperactive. In this case the goiter is associated with hyperthyroidism.

Finally, the excessive thyroid enlargement may reflect hyperactivity of the hypophysis, with a great outpouring of TSH. Accordingly, there will result hyperthyroidism and exophthalmos. For these reasons, this condition is termed **exophthalmic goiter.**

TESTS OF THYROID FUNCTION

Basal Metabolic Rate   In view of the fact that iodothyronins so markedly influence cellular metabolic processes, the evaluation of the basal metabolic rate has long been a standard test for thyroid function. It must be kept in mind, however, that factors other than thyroid hormone are capable of influencing this rate. Therefore the determination of the basal metabolic rate alone is not always diagnostic of thyroid function.

Protein-bound Iodine   Almost all the iodine in the blood is closely bound with protein. An analysis of blood from a person with normal thyroid function discloses between 4 and 7.5 μg of protein-bound iodine (**PBI**) in each 100 ml of plasma. On the other hand, in cases of hyperthyroidism the PBI is significantly higher, ranging up to 15 or even 20 μg per cent. Conversely, in hypothyroidism there is little protein-bound iodine in the plasma.

Radioactive-iodine Uptake   It has already been mentioned that the thyroid has a great avidity for iodine. When a small dose of iodine is administered, it quickly settles in the thyroid gland, where it is incorporated into thyroglobulin and thyroxin. If radioactive iodine is used, its uptake by the thyroid can be easily followed. It is found that in individuals with normal thyroid function 15 to 45 per cent of the small test dose is taken up by the thyroid in 24 hours. As is to be anticipated, much more than this is attracted by the hyperactive thyroid.

THE PARATHYROID GLANDS

As seen in Fig. 26-1, the parathyroids are usually four in number, but they are so small that for a long time their existence was completely unknown. When the early studies of thyroid activity were made, an erroneous concept emerged because the investigators were inadvertently removing the parathyroids as well as the thyroid. In such instances the animal invariably died. Consequently, it was concluded that the thyroid gland is essential to life. We now know that it is the parathyroids which are essential to life, not the thyroid.

ANATOMY OF THE PARATHYROID GLANDS

The smallness of the parathyroids can be seen in Fig. 26-1 by comparing their size with that of the thyroid. The parathyroids are usually less than ¼ in. long. Although the number of them is usually considered to be four, actually this may vary considerably in man, as may their location. For these reasons it is sometimes very difficult to remove all parathyroid tissue.

Upon microscopic examination, the parathyroid tissue is seen to be masses of closely packed cells. These cells are richly supplied with blood. Only a few nerve fibers have been reported to innervate these glands.

FUNCTION OF THE PARATHYROID GLANDS

Extirpation   The experimental animal dies within a few days after complete removal of the parathyroid tissue. Before death occurs, there are drastic alterations in the calcium and phosphate levels in the blood. There are normally about 10 mg of calcium in 100 ml of blood, but only about half, that is, 5 mg per cent, in a freely diffusible, ionized state. The remainder is protein-bound. The normal phosphate concentration, expressed as phosphorus, is approximately 4 mg per cent. After removal of the parathyroids, the calcium content of the blood decreases, while there is a proportionate increase in phosphate.

Following the removal of all parathyroid tissue, the plasma calcium falls to about 7 mg per 100 ml and remains at that level. This base level is apparently maintained by the pool of calcium in the bones. The normal value of 10 mg per 100 ml depends upon the presence of adequate quantities of parathyroid hormone.

This reciprocal alteration between calcium and phosphate is usually explained on the basis of the solubility constant. Ca^{2+} and PO_4^{3-} combine to form the relatively insoluble $Ca_3(PO_4)_2$. Only a small quantity of this calcium phosphate can remain in solution. Therefore if calcium salt and a phosphate compound are placed in a test tube of water and time is allowed for equilibrium to be reached, a subsequent analysis will reveal some calcium phosphate in solution. Let us assume that there are 100 ml of water in the tube and that analysis reveals 5 mg of calcium and the same concentration of phosphate. If a small quantity of $CaCl_2$ is now added to the tube, some of the extra calcium ions will combine with the available phosphate ions to form a precipitate. Once again the product between the two ions equals the solubility product, a constant, but now the calcium is higher and the phosphate is lower. Analysis may reveal, say, 7 mg of calcium and about 3.6 mg of phosphate.

According to this concept, when the parathyroid glands are removed, the kidneys fail to reabsorb the normal load of calcium; therefore the concentration of calcium in the blood decreases. This permits more calcium phosphate to enter solution, and as a result the phosphate concentration of the blood increases.

This is a convenient explanation, but unfortunately there is good evidence which indicates that the concentration of calcium and phosphate in the blood is not at the solubility product. It is now generally conceded that the solubility product may, in certain circumstances function in this way, but the rise and fall of calcium and phosphate ions in the body fluids in accord with parathyroid secretion probably depend upon other mechanisms.

The Parathyroid Hormone   An extract of the parathyroid glands proves effective in altering the metabolism of calcium and phosphate. Thus the parathyroid glands may be removed and, if sufficient quantities of this extract are administered, the blood chemistry will not change. Large injections, however, result in an elevation of blood calcium with a comparable fall in the phosphate level.

The parathyroid hormone has not, as yet, been obtained in the pure crystalline form. Thus its formula is not known. This hormone is sometimes referred to as **parathormone** and also **parathyrin,** although the term **parathyroid hormone** is to be preferred.

The results of extirpation and injection experiments indicate that the parathyroid hormone regulates calcium and phosphate metabolism. The important question for the physiologist to answer is, how does it do this? The answer to this question can still not be given with great certainty, although the weight of experimental work suggests that it functions in three places: (1) the kidneys, (2) bone, and (3) the gut.

Using the method of renal clearance, it has been demonstrated that the hormone acts on the renal tubules in such a way as to decrease their absorption of phosphate. Consequently, the more hormone injected, the more phosphate will appear in the urine (Fig. 26-7). As depicted in Fig. 26-7, this causes a progressive lowering of the phosphate level in the blood.

Granted that the parathyroid hormone does influence the kidneys to excrete more phosphate, a mechanism still must be found to explain the accompanying alterations in plasma calcium. The best evidence seems to indicate that this hormone has a direct influence on bone metabolism. Contrary to popular opinion, bone is continuously being deposited and, at the same rate, reabsorbed. Clearly, if these two processes did not function at the same rate, calcium would be either added to or taken from the blood. It is thought that the parathyroid hormone influences one, or perhaps both. It has been shown that, when parathyroid tissue is brought into direct contact with bone, local dissolution of bone occurs. It has been postulated that the hormone causes the number of **osteoclasts** to increase.

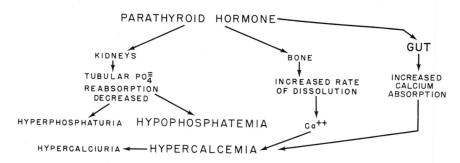

FIG. 26-7 Parathyroid hormone action. By acting on kidneys, bone, and gut, plasma calcium is increased and plasma phosphate decreases.

Osteoclasts are cells responsible for the resorption of bone. Consequently, if there were more of them present, the rate of bone dissolution would be increased and calcium liberated to raise the blood concentration. There is also some evidence that this hormone may, at the same time, inhibit the rate at which new bone is formed. The net result of both of these effects would be to decalcify the bone and to flood the blood with calcium. In such a case the solubility product may well be exceeded and the phosphate level, accordingly, reduced.

Finally, it has been well demonstrated that the parathyroid hormone enhances the absorption of calcium by the gut. Phosphate, apparently, is not influenced. When the hormone is administered over a long period of time, a positive calcium balance results, due, in part, to increased calcium absorption by the gut.

By virtue of the influence the parathyroid hormone has on the kidneys so as to increase phosphate excretion and probably decrease calcium excretion; by virtue of its influence on bone so as to cause liberation of calcium phosphate; and by its effect on gut so as to cause more calcium to be absorbed, it is clear why this hormone brings about an elevation of blood calcium and a decrease in blood phosphate.

REGULATION OF PARATHYROID FUNCTION

There is no good evidence that the hypophysis secretes a hormone which influences parathyroid function. There seems to be another regulatory mechanism, however, and that is the level of calcium in the blood. No matter how the calcium level is altered, parathyroid function is influenced. For example, on a vitamin-D-deficient diet, calcium will not be normally absorbed from the intestine, and the blood-calcium level falls. Likewise, during pregnancy the drain of calcium to the fetus lowers the blood level in the mother. The administration of large quantities of phosphate has the same result. Finally, in certain renal disorders, calcium is lost in excessive quantities, causing the lowering of the blood-calcium concentration. In all these cases the common denominator is low blood calcium, and in every instance the parathyroid glands enlarge and secrete abnormally great quantities of hormone. These same results are seen even in the absence of the hypophysis. This observation is significant because it indicates that the low blood calcium influences the parathyroids directly rather than through the mediation of a tropic hormone from the hypophysis.

Here again, then, is a self-regulating mechanism. The parathyroid hormone controls the blood level of calcium, and as we have just seen, the calcium concentration regulates the output of this hormone. Thus, when there is an inordinate demand for calcium, as during pregnancy, the blood calcium decreases, the parathyroid is activated, the hormone, through the mechanism just outlined, reaches the storehouse of calcium (the bones) and withdraws sufficient calcium to make up the deficit. It is for this reason that the diet under such circumstances should be abundant in calcium and vitamin D. This high intake will prevent the lowering of the blood-calcium level and thus spare the bones.

ABNORMALITIES OF PARATHYROID FUNCTION

Hypoparathyroidism   The decreased activity of the parathyroid glands results in a low blood-calcium level. When the level falls below a critical point, or when there is a sudden decrease from high levels, **tetany** occurs. Tetany is a disorder marked by intermittent muscular contractions, tremors, and muscular pain. The hands are usually held in a characteristic position known as **carpopedal spasm.** The condition can be quickly rectified by elevating the blood-calcium level. It does not matter how this is done. It can be accomplished by calcium injections or by administration of the hormone. Usually, calcium is first injected until tetany ceases, and then the patient is maintained on parathyroid hormone to prevent a recurrence.

Hyperparathyroidism   Excessive quantities of parathyroid hormone result in an elevation of blood calcium. This is accomplished at the expense of the bones. Thus the cardinal finding in cases of long-standing hyperparathroidism is decalcification of the bone, which, upon examination, reveals cystlike areas usually filled in with fibrous tissue. This disorder is known as **osteitis fibrosa cystica generalisata,** a term which describes the condition of the bones, or **von Recklinghausen's disease,** after the pathologist who first reported it. The bones become painful and fracture at the least provocation.

Hyperparathyroidism should be diagnosed early, before the irreversible bone changes take place. The treatment consists of surgical removal of a large part of the hyperactive parathyroid tissue. It is interesting to note that following this operation there is a great and sudden drop in the blood-calcium level. Although the concentration only decreases to within the normal range, nonetheless tetany often results. In other words, tetany seems to be caused by any large and sudden decrease in the blood-calcium level. It does not matter whether the decrease is from an abnormally high level or from the normal concentration. It is for this reason that patients with hyperparathyroidism are given calcium immediately after operation. The calcium administration is then slowly reduced to allow the blood-calcium level to sink gradually, insensibly to within the normal range. This slow retreat prevents tetany.

Since the teeth have much the same structure as bone, a word concerning the influence of the parathyroid hormone upon the teeth is appropriate here. If, during dental development, there is a deficient amount of calcium in the diet, the teeth may be malformed. Likewise, if there is a vitamin-D deficiency, the available calcium will not be absorbed from the intestinal tract and the same malformations will result. Finally, if there is hyperparathyroidism during this developmental period, calcium phosphate will not be deposited in the developing teeth as it normally is; again, the teeth will be poorly calcified. On the other hand, for reasons not yet understood, once the teeth are formed, alterations in parathyroid function do not seem to affect the dental tissue as bone is afflicted. There is no adequate explanation for this difference.

SUMMARY

The **thyroid gland** lies over the larynx and trachea in the neck. It is made up of **follicles** which contain the colloid **thyroglobulin.** The thyroid gland produces a proteolytic enzyme which aids in the liberation of iodothyronin from thyroglobin. Iodothyronin influences the rate of utilization of oxygen by all the cells of the body. Its activity depends upon the presence of **iodine** in its molecule.

The thyroid is controlled by the **thyrotropic hormone** secreted by the hypophysis. There exists a reciprocal relationship between the level of iodine in the blood and the production of TSH. This relationship provides a self-regulatory mechanism. TSH is influenced by the **thyrotropin releasing factor (TRF)** secreted by the hypothalamus.

Hypothyroidism during the developmental stage eventuates in a **cretin,** characterized by being stunted, potbellied, and stupid. The skin is dry, the hair scant, and the BMR very low. Hypothyroidism which develops after puberty causes a condition termed **myxedema.** This state is characterized by a puffy, swollen appearance caused by the deposition of a semifluid albuminous substance in the soft tissue beneath the skin. It is often referred to as **Gull's disease.**

Hyperthyroidism, also known as **thyrotoxicosis** or **Graves' disease,** gives rise to a high BMR and a moist, hot skin. The individual is usually thin, hyperactive, and hyperirritable. In many cases the eyes bulge, a condition termed **exophthalmos.** Hyperthyroidism may be treated by surgical removal of a part of the gland. A **goiter** or swelling of the neck may represent either hypofunction, normal function, or hyperfunction of the thyroid.

Thyroid function may be evaluated by determining the **BMR, protein-bound iodine,** or **radioactive iodine uptake.**

The **parathyroids** are very small, about the size of a pea, and are usually four in number. Removal of these glands severely upsets the calcium and phosphorus metabolism, resulting in death. **Parathyroid hormone** is a protein of unknown structure. This hormone influences kidney function so as to increase the renal excretion of phosphate. As a result, the plasma phosphate level falls. The hormone also activates **osteoclasts** which hasten the rate of bone dissolution. It causes the gut to increase calcium absorption.

The parathyroid glands are regulated by the level of calcium in the blood. When blood calcium falls, the glands are stimulated to put out more parathyroid hormone; consequently, the blood-calcium level is returned to normal.

Hypoparathyroidism causes the calcium concentration in the blood to decrease, resulting in **tetany,** a condition marked by intermittent muscular contractions, tremors, and muscle pain. **Hyperparathyroidism** produces marked changes in the bones so that they develop cavities and become brittle and deformed. This disorder is known as **osteitis fibrosa cystica generalisata** or **von Recklinghausen's disease.**

QUESTIONS

1. What is a hormone?
2. How is thyroxin thought to influence the basal metabolic rate?
3. How is thyroid function regulated?
4. Outline the sequence in the biosynthesis of iodothyronins.
5. By what mechanisms does parathyroid hormone influence calcium and phosphate metabolism?
6. During pregnancy, the parathyroid glands hypertrophy. What is the sequence of events which leads to this end result?

SUGGESTED READING

Aurbach, G. D., and Potts, J. T., Jr., "The Parathyroids," *Adv. Metabolic Disorders,"* **1:** 46–93, 1964.

Collier, H. O. J., "Kinins," *Sci. American,* **207:**#2, 111–118, August 1962.

Hoch, F. L., "Biochemical Actions of Thyroid Hormones," *Physiol. Rev.,* **42:**#4, 605–673, October 1962.

Rasmussen, H., "The Parathyroid Hormone," *Sci. American,* **204:**#4, 56–63, April 1961.

Solomon, D. H., and Dowling, J. T., "The Thyroid," *Ann. Rev. Physiol.,* **22:** 615–650, 1960.

Wilkins, L., "The Thyroid Gland," *Sci. American,* **202:**#3, 119–129, March 1960.

The Gonads

27

THE TERM **gonad** means "seed." It refers to one of the functions of the gonads, namely, to produce the sexual seed. But the gonads also serve another function, and that is to elaborate hormones which are essential to sexual intercourse and reproduction. The gonads in man are termed the **testes.** In the female they are referred to as the **ovaries.** These glands elaborate the hormones which prepare the individual for sexual intercourse. They also produce the sperm and the ova which must unite for conception to occur. Thus, the gonads are only partly endocrine glands. Nonetheless, the physiology of reproduction will be considered in this section. This chapter will concern itself solely with a discussion of the function of the gonads. The next chapter will utilize that knowledge in a comprehensive study of reproduction.

THE OVARIES

ANATOMY OF THE FEMALE SEX ORGANS

The ovaries, two in number, lie deep in the pelvic cavity, one on either side of the uterus (Fig. 27-1). They are small, roughly spherical bodies which weigh about 2 or 3 gm. The blood supply is derived directly from the descending aorta.

In the ovaries **graafian follicles** develop. At birth, the ovaries of the newborn girl contain only immature graafian follicles, often referred to as **primordial follicles.** There are about 400,000 of them. Beginning at puberty, the primordial follicles ripen or mature, one each month. The ripe follicle is seen to contain the **ovum.** Once a month, usually midway between two menstrual periods, the follicle ruptures and expels the ovum, which passes down one of the **fallopian tubes** to the **uterus.** The fallopian tubes (Fig. 27-1) are two small tubes which are continuous at one end with

559

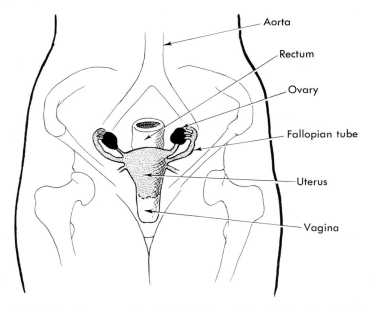

FIG. 27-1 Diagrammatic representation of the relationships of the internal female reproductive organs.

the body of the uterus. The other end, with its fimbriated design, lies free in the abdominal cavity, usually close to the ovary. When the ovum is expelled from the ovary, it is literally caught by the little fingerlike projections of the fallopian tube. The efficacy of this mechanism is illustrated in those individuals who have lost the ovary on one side and the fallopian tube on the other. There are cases on record where such individuals have become pregnant despite the great distance the ovum must travel. Immediately following ovulation, a spot of blood persists in the ruptured follicle. It is therefore termed the **corpus hemorrhagicum** (Fig. 27-2). This structure quickly gives way to a follicle which contains a yellow substance. Consequently, the follicle is now termed the **corpus luteum,** the latter term meaning yellow. If pregnancy does not occur, the corpus luteum disintegrates within a few days and is replaced by a white fibrous structure now called the **corpus albicans.** The follicles that fail to mature degenerate and are called **atretic follicles.** Each is ultimately replaced by fibrous tissue to become a **corpus fibrosum.**

Although both ovaries contain approximately 400,000 immature follicles at birth, it is easy to calculate that only a small percentage of these ever actually mature. The sexual life of the woman extends from about

OVARY

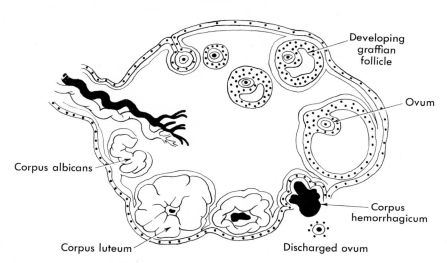

FIG. 27-2   Follicular development. Immature follicles periodically develop and produce the ovum which is discharged. Thereafter the follicle changes to the corpus luteum and then to the corpus albicans.

the fourteenth year to close to age fifty. If only one follicle matures a month, it can be seen that only about 400 follicles are required. The fact that there are 400,000 ready to ripen is simply one more example of the safety factor the body provides in all important functions.

FUNCTION OF THE OVARIES

The ovaries, as already mentioned, serve two functions: (1) to *produce ova* and (2) to *secrete the sex hormones.* There are two types of female sex hormones: (1) **estrogens** and (2) **progesterone.**

Extirpation   The removal of the ovaries produces widespread alterations which depend upon the age of the woman. If the ovaries are removed before puberty, the girl never does develop the secondary sexual characteristics, and the sexual organs remain immature. Secondary sexual characteristics are the changes which occur at puberty and which make women appear different from men. For example, the breasts develop; there is the characteristic deposition of fat around the hips; the hair distribution on the body is limited to the armpits and the pubic region, with just a fine fuzz on the arms and legs. If the ovaries are removed before puberty, these changes do not occur. In addition, there is little or no sexual motivation.

Removal of the ovaries after puberty also causes marked derangements. The breasts usually atrophy, the body configuration becomes more masculine, and there may be some growth of hair over the body and on the face. In addition, the sexual drive usually fades.

Estrogens Figure 27-3 shows the structural formulas for the major estrogens. It is believed that the ovaries secrete **estradiol** which is then converted into **estrone** and then into **estriol** and other nonestrogenic steroids during the process of metabolism. **Diethylstilbestrol** is a synthetic compound that possesses strong estrogen activity and which even retains its potency when given orally. This is of great significance clinically in view of the fact that the naturally occurring estrogens are destroyed by the digestive processes. All these hormones are seen to be **steroids.**

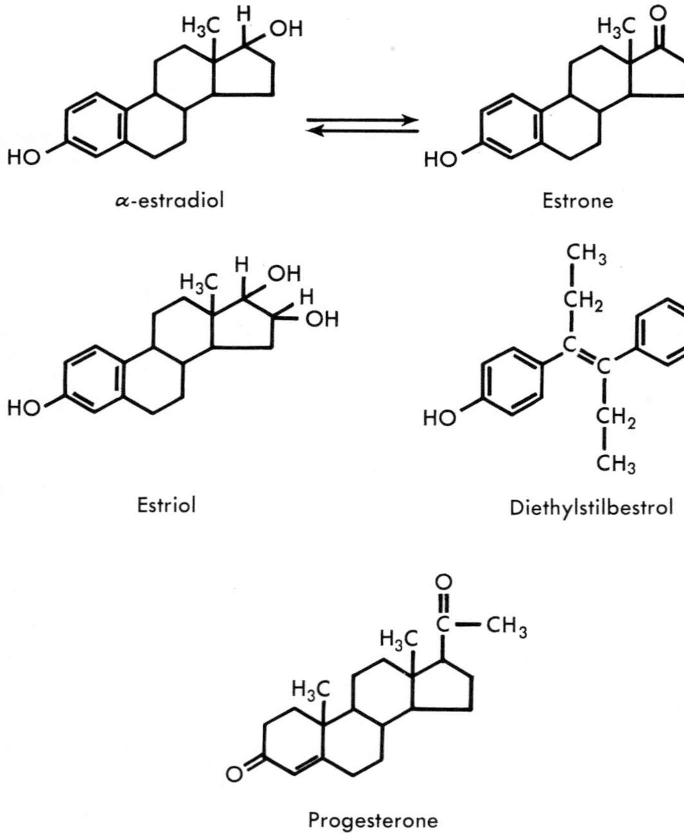

α-estradiol   Estrone

Estriol   Diethylstilbestrol

Progesterone

FIG. 27-3   Structural formulas of the female sex hormones.

It is thought that the estrogens are secreted by the cells of the maturing graafian follicles, although there is some evidence which indicates that other ovarian cells may also contribute. Of the estrogens, by far the most potent is alpha-estradiol, and there are good reasons to believe that this is the hormone secreted by the ovaries.

The administration of the estrogens prevents most of the changes which occur in the mature woman after removal of the ovaries. They have also been used to advantage to accelerate or augment maturation in girls whose ovaries fail to secrete adequate quantities of these hormones. There is no question but that the estrogens are primarily responsible for the maturation of the sexual organs, that is, the vagina and the uterus, and they also play a role in the development of the breasts, the characteristic feminine proportions, and sexual drive. As a matter of fact, the term estrogen is derived from *estrus,* which means "mad desire."

It has long been taught that the estrogens also influence bone growth and are responsible for the characteristic spurt in growth immediately following puberty. Estrogens, however, do not act in this way. The spurt in growth is apparently due to androgen secretion in both boys and girls. In the female, the sole source of androgen is the adrenal cortex. For unknown reasons, androgen secretion increases at puberty. It probably has to do with altered activity of the anterior lobe of the hypophysis at this time. In any event, the long bones grow under this hormonal influence. But the androgens also cause closure of the epiphyseal centers; thus bone development ceases earlier than it does when the ovaries are not present, or when they mature late. It is for this reason that girls who fail to mature sexually, or who do so relatively late in life, are generally taller than the average. They notably have disproportionately long extremities.

The estrogens influence fat metabolism so as to cause fat deposition in the subcutaneous tissues. Fat, in the female, is characteristically deposited in the hips, breasts, and thighs.

Progesterone Progesterone is often referred to as the hormone of pregnancy. Its function is to prepare the uterus for implantation of the fertilized ovum and for maintaining it during pregnancy. Progesterone also helps to prepare the breasts for their function of lactation. The estrogens develop the duct system of the human breast, whereas progesterone is responsible for the development of the alveoli, causing the alveolar cells to become secretory. The estrogens and progesterone act on the kidney, resulting in greater tubular reabsorption of sodium, chloride, and water.

Progesterone prevents ovulation. So long as the corpus luteum remains functional, ovulation does not occur. Progesterone also causes the mucus of the cervix to thicken, whereas the estrogens make it thinner. Because of these functions of progesterone it is highly effective as a contraceptive agent, and is now widely so used in pill form.

Relaxin   During pregnancy the ovaries, at least in some animals, secrete several polypeptides which, collectively, are referred to as relaxin. This name is used because the function of these polypeptides is to cause relaxation of the symphysis pubis and uterus. Whether these substances are secreted by the human ovaries is not certain.

REGULATION OF OVARIAN FUNCTION

The ovaries, like the thyroid gland, are controlled by hormones secreted by the hypophysis. There are believed to be three **gonadotropic** hormones. They are (1) the **follicle-stimulating hormone,** shortened to **FSH,** (2) the **luteinizing hormone,** abbreviated **LH,** and (3) the **luteotropic hormone, LTH.** In addition to these tropic factors, the **placenta,** the organ on the wall of the uterus to which the embryo is attached, also secretes hormones which have many of the functions already ascribed to the gonadotropic hormones. For this reason, the placental hormones are sometimes called collectively the **APL substance,** which means "anterior pituitary-like." This refers to the anterior lobe of the hypophysis or pituitary gland which secretes the gonadotropic hormones.

Follicle-stimulating Hormone   This hormone is carried from the hypophysis to the ovaries by the blood stream. It directs the development and activity of the graafian follicles. If this substance, the formula of which is still unknown, is administered in large quantities, instead of only one follicle maturing, many of them may ripen. The resulting expulsion of several ova has been dynamically described as "a shower of ova."

FSH not only encourages the maturation of the follicles but in so doing increases production of the estrogens. Accordingly, widespread alterations in the primary and secondary sexual characteristics occur as a result of FSH administration. But it is important to remember that these alterations are not due to FSH itself but rather to its influence over the ovary.

It has now been established that the output of FSH is controlled by the concentration of estrogens in the blood. That is to say, here again is a self-regulating reciprocal relationship. When the concentration of the estrogens falls, more FSH is secreted, resulting in an increase of the elaboration of estrogens.

Luteinizing Hormone   Progesterone, secreted by the corpus luteum, is essential for preparation and maintenance of the uterus. If the corpus luteum is allowed to disintegrate, the uterus will not be maintained, the wall will slough off, and if the woman is pregnant, she will suffer a miscarriage. Thus, it is essential that the corpus luteum be protected, and this is the function of the luteinizing hormone. That is why an experimental animal will abort if the hypophysis is removed during the early stages of pregnancy.

The luteinizing hormone is, in turn, regulated by the level of progesterone in the blood. Thus, if the corpus luteum starts to fade, the concentration of progesterone in the blood will decrease. Consequently, the hypophysis will elaborate more LH. This hormone stimulates the corpus luteum and maintains its integrity.

Luteotropic Hormone It has just been explained that progesterone is secreted by the corpus luteum in response to the stimulation of the luteinizing hormone. It is now known that the anterior lobe of the hypophysis secretes still a third substance, the luteotropic hormone, which causes the corpus luteum to elaborate not only progesterone but the estrogens as well.

HYPOTHALAMIC CONTROL

Although it is true that the ovarian hormones are capable of inhibiting the secretion of the gonadotropic hormones by a direct action on the anterior lobe of the hypophysis, their major influence is on the hypothalamus. The hypothalamus is now known to secrete at least two neurohumors which influence secretion of the gonadotropins: (1) **follicle-stimulating-hormone-releasing factor (FSHRF)**, and (2) **luteinizing-hormone-releasing factor (LHRF)**. These neurohumors travel in the **hypothalamico-portal system** (see Chap. 30) to control the release of LH and FSH. It has been shown that it is the hypothalamus which keeps the gonadotropins in check until puberty. The anterior lobe of the hypohysis is quite capable of secreting these hormones and thus bringing on sexual maturity long before puberty. It is also the hypothalamus, no doubt under the control of timing circuits in the brain, that is responsible for the rhythmic nature of the menstrual cycle.

The role of LTH and its control are not yet clear. In some animals LTH appears to be necessary for the maintenance and secretion of the corpus luteum, but whether this is true in women is not certain. Further, the hypothalamus seems to inhibit the secretion of LTH in experimental animals. It has been suggested that LHRF is responsible for its inhibition. If this is true, there should be a reciprocal relationship between LH and LTH, and the evidence does indicate that as one increases the other decreases.

MENSTRUATION

The maturation of a woman is signaled not only by the development of the breasts and other feminine characteristics but also by the onset of the menstrual cycle. The term menstruation refers to the monthly periodicity of this sequence of events. On the average, this cycle is repeated approximately every 28 or 30 days. The **menarche** is the term applied to the first menstrual cycle of puberty.

Destructive Phase The destructive phase of the menstrual cycle is the period during which bleeding occurs. The bleeding is due to the sloughing off of the uterine wall (Fig. 27-4). This phase usually persists for 3 to 7 days, with an average of 4 or 5. The total quantity of the menstrual discharge varies widely, but on the average amounts to about 125 ml, or approximately a cupful, for the entire destructive phase. This discharge consists not only of blood but also of the debris of the uterine wall which is carried away with the flow. It is interesting to note that menstrual blood does not ordinarily clot. This is because the essential clotting elements, fibrinogen and prothrombin, are missing.

The onset of the destructive phase of the menstrual cycle is usually associated with many organic and psychic alterations. There may be frequency of urination and exaggeration of skin disorders, such as acne. The breasts usually become larger and firmer. Many women are unusually irritable at this time and complain of easy fatigue and headaches. The latter changes may be a result of the absorption of toxic substances from the necrotic uterine wall before they can be carried away with the menstrual flow.

Phase of Repair After the menstrual flow ceases, the wall of the uterus is very thin. It now undergoes a process of growth under the stimulation of the estrogens. This is called the phase of repair. It extends for about 9 days. Close to the fourteenth day of the cycle, ovulation takes place. The corpus luteum now begins to develop under the influence of LH and the luteotropic hormone.

Premenstrual Phase The concentration of estrogens in the blood reaches a peak at the time of ovulation. It now begins to decrease, but at this time the corpus luteum becomes active and secretes progesterone and estrogens. Under stimulation of progesterone and the estrogens, the uterine mucosa continues to thicken, to become more vascular and more receptive to the fertilized ovum. But, if conception does not occur, the corpus luteum disintegrates so that the concentration of the sex hormones in the blood now falls sharply. This sudden withdrawal of the two hormones is believed to be the direct cause for the onset of the destructive phase of menstruation. The uterine wall once again is sloughed off. The menstrual flow has been colorfully described as "the weeping of the disappointed womb."

Regulation of the Menstrual Cycle The mechanisms which regulate each phase of the menstrual cycle are now fairly well understood. At the end of the destructive phase the concentration of estrogens in the blood is low; therefore, FSH is secreted in large quantities. This brings about the mat-

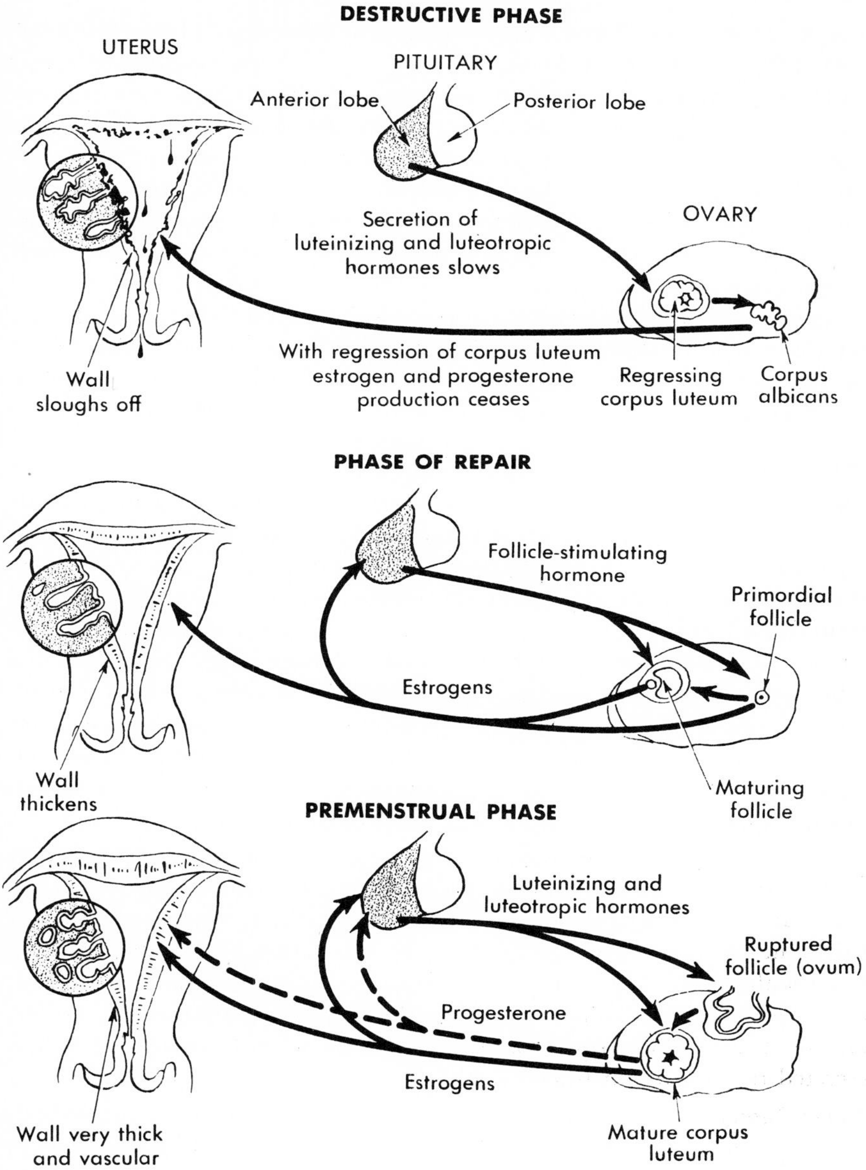

FIG. 27-4 Menstrual cycle. The inhibitory influence of the female sex hormones on the anterior lobe of the hypophysis is probably exerted through the hypothalamus.

uration of the follicle and the production of estrogens. The secretion of FSH is suppressed by the estrogens acting on the hypothalamus. LH and LTH secretion is stimulated by the estrogens; moreover, since the concentration of progesterone at this time is very low, there is no inhibition. Thus, LH and LTH pour forth to form the corpus luteum and to stimulate it to secrete estrogens and progesterone which inhibit the hypothalamus. LH and LTH are now suppressed so the corpus luteum disintegrates and the concentration of estrogen and progesterone falls sharply. The cycle is ready to begin again.

It has been postulated that there is some sort of a neural timing device, perhaps a reverberating circuit, that regulates the secretion of the neurohumors, and therefore the secretion of the gonadotropins. Such a timing circuit could well account for the rhythmicity of menstruation.

THE CLIMACTERIC

The term **climacteric** literally means "rung of a ladder." As used in this connotation, it has to do with the stage of life when the gonads undergo degenerative or senescent changes. This applies to men and women alike. If we view the ladder of life of the female, we learn that she matures sexually at about the fourteenth year, at which time menstruation commences. Then at about the fiftieth year, another great change occurs, called the climacteric. At this time menstruation ceases. This cessation is called the **menopause.** The two terms, climacteric and menopause, are not synonymous. The latter refers to the end of the monthy menstrual cycle. The climacteric embraces all the changes which occur at this time.

The Menopause   Menstruation does not suddenly cease. A period or two may be missed from time to time over a year or more. Finally, the actual flow becomes very scanty, occurs infrequently, and ultimately ceases entirely. It is interesting, from the physiological viewpoint, to note that at this time the concentration of FSH in the blood and urine becomes abnormally high. This may well be because the ovaries have atrophied, there are no mature follicles, and thus the output of estrogens is very low, or absent altogether. In the absence of estrogenic inhibition, FSH is now secreted in large quantities.

Other Changes   At this stage of life there are widespread changes, both physiological and psychological. The ovaries, as noted, undergo progressive wasting so that finally all follicular maturation ceases. Because there is now very little sex hormone produced, both the sexual organs and the secondary sexual characteristics undergo marked alterations. The vaginal secretions diminish, the breasts atrophy, and in some cases the distribution of hair changes, so that elderly women are often seen with a fine growth of hair on their faces.

Psychologically, the climacteric may be a very difficult period of life. Many women become highly irritable, emotional babies so that they cry at the slightest provocation, are very tense and anxious, and usually display many organic as well as psychosomatic complaints, such as elevation of blood pressure, dry and itchy skin, and musculoskeletal aches.

ABNORMALITIES OF OVARIAN FUNCTION

Amenorrhea As the term indicates, this is a condition characterized by the complete absence of menstruation. It may be due to a number of causes. If the menstrual flow has been well established and regular, the most common cause for the sudden cessation is pregnancy. As a matter of fact, amenorrhea is one of the first and most reliable signs that conception has occurred.

But if the menstrual cycle has never been initiated, or if it ceases and pregnancy is not the cause, then the physician usually seeks some hormonal imbalance as the explanation. In some instances, for example, the ovaries are congenitally absent or simply fail to develop. In such cases, the inadequate production of the estrogens is the reason for the failure of menstruation. As might be expected, such women also show other abnormalities. The breasts fail to develop, and a rather boylike figure persists. The sexual inclination of these indivduals is usually subnormal.

Dysmenorrhea Dysmenorrhea is the term applied to difficult or painful menstruation. The chief complaints are cramps, low abdominal pain, aching of the thighs, headache, nausea, perhaps even emotional lability. The explanation of this condition is still not forthcoming. Treatment usually is purely symptomatic.

Hypo- and Hyperactivity of Ovarian Function In view of the fact that the hormones elaborated by the ovaries control the development of the sexual organs and the secondary sexual characteristics, it follows that the degree of development depends upon ovarian activity. Thus, women are seen who appear almost masculine. They have very small breasts and narrow, flat hips, and quite often their sexual inclinations are more masculine than feminine. At the other extreme are the fully developed women with rounded hips, long, luxuriant hair, and soft, exquisitely fair skin. It is true that the physical characteristics of the individual develop in accordance with ovarian function, but as far as sexual inclination and drive are concerned, so many factors play a role that this consideration cannot be placed on a purely physiological basis. However, speaking very generally, it is true that sexual drive is related to ovarian function, and subnormal or supranormal sexual interests may be referable to hypoactivity or hyperactivity of the ovaries.

THE TESTES

The gonads in the male are called the **testes** (Fig. 27-5). In the developing embryo, the testes in the male and the ovaries in the female arise from the same tissue and form at the same site. However, before birth, at about the sixth or seventh month, the testes normally descend through the **inguinal canal** to come to rest in the scrotal sac, where they reside throughout life.

ANATOMY OF THE MALE ORGANS

The testes are egg-shaped. They weigh, together, about 25 gm. This is to be compared with the ovaries, which collectively weigh only 5 or 6 gm.

Closer examination of the testes reveals that they are made up of masses of **seminiferous tubules** (Fig. 27-5). Between these tubules are the so-called **interstitial cells of Leydig.** The seminiferous tubules empty into the **ducti efferentes,** which enter the **epididymis,** a term which means "to lie on the testis"; that is what this structure does. The **vas deferens** then leads from the epididymis to join the urethra. At the point of junction of these two tubes lie the **prostrate gland** and the **seminal vesicles.**

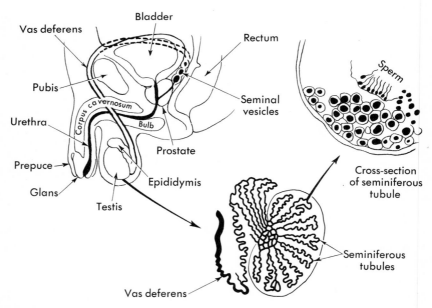

FIG. 27-5 Diagrammatic representation of the anatomy of the male sex organs.

FUNCTION OF THE TESTES

The testes, like the ovaries, have a dual function: (1) to *produce sperm* and (2) to *secrete a hormone.*

Extirpation If the testes are removed before puberty, the individual fails to develop the characteristics associated with manhood. The external genitalia remain infantile, the voice does not deepen, and there is very little growth of hair on the body or face. In short, the person retains the juvenile appearance. It is true that he may grow rather tall. In many Oriental countries it was the practice to castrate (remove the testes) those who were to have the dubious honor of guarding the king's harem. These individuals usually grew well over 6 ft tall and therefore looked quite imposing. Actually, however, a **eunuch,** as one who has had his testicles removed is called, does not possess even the usual degree of strength. Eunuchs are not muscular, but remain soft and somewhat feminine. Undoubtedly the resulting size was only a minor reason for this drastic procedure.

If the testes are removed after puberty, there is of course no change in the size of the individual. His voice remains deep. However, the necessity to shave becomes less urgent, he is infertile because of the lack of sperm, and he usually undergoes a marked reduction in sexual drive.

Testosterone The testes secrete primarily a substance called **testosterone.** Another hormone, termed **androsterone,** is also found in small concentrations. All male hormones, as a group, are labeled **androgens,** the prefix *andro-* meaning man.

Testosterone is secreted by the interstitial cells of Leydig. The administration of this substance evokes striking alterations in the eunuch. Even in the normal male, large doses may produce an exaggeration of the characteristics associated with masculinity. It is clear, therefore, from such experiments and clinical experience, that the testes do have an endocrine function and that the hormones produced by these glands are responsible for the development of the sexual organs as well as the secondary sexual characteristics.

Production of Sperm The seminiferous tubules of the testes produce sperm, shown in Fig. 27-5, at an almost incredible rate. In each milliliter of semen there are in excess of 60,000,000 sperm. When it is realized that an average ejaculation includes 4 ml, a teaspoonful, it can be seen that in the total ejaculate there are over a quarter of a billion sperm. It is true that the size of the ejaculate and the number of sperm therein decrease if sexual relations are indulged in with great frequency. However, it is well within the physiological range for the average man to produce this number of sperm each day. In view of the fact that only one sperm usually fertilizes one ovum, the probability of the race being continued is well assured. It is another example of the defenses in depth with which the body is so well equipped.

Oddly enough, sperm cannot survive very long at body temperature. Nor can they be produced at this temperature. The temperature within the scrotal sac is 3 to 4 degrees below body temperature. It seems to be the optimal temperature for the production of sperm. This fact is demonstrated well by the observation that when the testes fail to descend from the abdominal cavity into the scrotal sac, no viable sperm are produced. Such a condition is termed **cryptorchidism,** *crypt* meaning "hidden," and *orchid* referring to the testes. In other words, the testes are within the abdominal cavity and therefore hidden. Such individuals are quite capable of sexual intercourse. Apparently testosterone is produced in adequate quantities, but since there is no sperm production, these individuals are sterile.

The scrotal sac is suspended primarily by the **cremaster muscles.** These muscles are unique in that they contract and relax in response to temperature changes. They are smooth muscle and are innervated by the autonomic nervous system. Thus they shorten in response to reflex stimuli, but cannot be made to react voluntarily. It is the temperature response which is of interest and importance. When the temperature increases, the muscles relax; when it decreases, the muscles contract. Therefore, in warm weather the scrotal sac is allowed to fall away from the body. This removes the testes from the body heat. On the other hand, cold weather or immersion in cold water will cause the testes to be brought up tight against the body where they can have the benefit of the body heat. Through this effective and unique mechanism, the temperature within the scrotal sac is maintained a few degrees below body temperature at all times. At this temperature, viable sperm are produced in quantity.

REGULATION OF TESTIS FUNCTION

The hypophysis in the male, just as in the female, secretes gonadotropic hormones, probably only two in number. They are (1) the **follicle-stimulating hormone** or **FSH** and (2) the **interstitial-cell-stimulating hormone** or **ICSH.** As previously noted, the chemical nature of these hormones still evades analysis.

Follicle-stimulating Hormone   Since FSH in the female acts upon the follicles which produce ova, it is to be expected that in the male it would act upon the seminiferous tubules which produce sperm. This is the case. If the hypophysis is removed and the testes are examined histologically some time later, it is found that the seminiferous tubules have undergone extensive atrophy and fail to produce sperm except in most inadequate quantities. Conversely, it is possible by use of this hormone to increase sperm production greatly.

Interstitial-cell-stimulating Hormone   This hormone acts upon the interstitial cells of Leydig and regulates the production of testosterone. It is thought to be identical with the luteinizing hormone in the female.

Reciprocal Relationships   There is apparently a reciprocal relationship between ICSH and testosterone, so that this hormone regulates itself. When the androgen concentration of the blood increases, the secretion of ICSH is inhibited. There is also some evidence to indicate that testosterone inhibits the secretion of FSH as well as ICSH. It appears that there is a rhythm of rising and falling androgen secretion in the male just as there are estrogen and progesterone fluctuations in the female. The significance of this rhythm is not known.

As indicated above, the secretion of the gonadotropins is under the control of the so-called releasing factors of the hypothalamus. It is now believed that the inhibition that testosterone exerts on the secretion of ICSH is not a direct one, but rather is exerted via the hypothalamus. The control of FSH secretion in the male, however, is still a very open question. It is possible, of course, that in the male there is a steady production of FSHRF and therefore of FSH, necessitating no feedback control. On the other hand, it has been postulated that the seminiferous tubules secrete a substance, referred to as "inhibin" which inhibits the secretion of FSHRF and therefore of FSH. There is no evidence for such a secretion, however.

ABNORMALITIES OF TESTIS FUNCTION

Hypogonadism   In some men the testes fail to secrete sufficient testosterone; more often, the normal output is unduly delayed, so that the boy fails to mature long past the usual age. There is considerable divergence of opinion as to whether such boys should simply be left untreated until normal testicular function is established or whether testosterone should be administered so as to hurry the process and make it coincide with the usual period of life. Those who favor the latter viewpoint use as their rallying cry: "If he is old enough to be teased, he is old enough to be treated." By this they mean that the psychological damage done to the sexually retarded youth by the insults of his more mature colleagues should be avoided by appropriate hormonal treatment.

The more serious cases, of course, involve those men who never do establish normal hormonal secretion. They usually grow quite tall, with disproportionately long legs. They invariably have thick, luxuriant head hair and practically none on their bodies, and they shave infrequently.

Men suffering from hypogonadism usually have little interest in the opposite sex. Whether or not this disorder may be an important cause of homosexuality has never been clearly established. Many homosexuals have been treated with male sex hormones, but with little alteration in their preference.

Hypergonadism   Authorities usually say that cases of hypergonadism are rare. True, very few such cases are seen in the clinic, but one must doubt if this condition is any rarer than hyperactivity of any of the other endocrine glands. If it is recalled that people usually seek medical advice only when they are in pain or suffering an undesirable abnormality, then perhaps the major reason why these individuals are seldom seen becomes apparent.

It is possible to arrange a large group of men in such a way that the most masculine will be at one extreme and those who approach the feminine at the other end. No doubt normal testicular function embraces the middle group. Those who have unusually broad shoulders and narrow hips, those who have excessive growth of hair over their bodies, and those who possess unusually large sexual organs no doubt have testes which are producing an inordinate quantity of testosterone. It is doubtful whether they would desire corrective treatment for this "abnormality."

We have seen that the distribution of hair is under the control of the sex hormones. Women have long, luxuriant head hair and no face or chest hair. Men, on the other hand, develop a beard and a variable growth over their bodies. Many men after puberty also experience a steady recession of the head hair. This is another one of those subjects about which there has been much confusion. Whether or not **baldness** is an abnormality is a fine point to decide. The important issue is that common baldness results from internal and not external factors. The usual type of baldness is not the result of excessive washing, tight hats, swimming in chlorinated pools, cutting the hair, not cutting the hair, or dandruff or other local skin conditions. Baldness is usually simply a change in hair distribution associated with sexual maturation. It may be caused by undue testosterone secretion. Some men have much hair on their chests, others do not. The thickness of the hair on their heads is caused by exactly the same mechanism. It is interesting and significant to note that eunuchs never become bald. In short, baldness should be considered as a normal sexual change. Baldness has been encouragingly if not accurately described as "a tertiary sexual characteristic."

Cryptorchidism   This condition, in which the testes remain in the abdominal cavity and fail to descend, has already been discussed. It might be mentioned here, however, that cryptorchidism occurs in over 0.1 per cent of the total male population. The majority of cases rectify themselves at puberty. But in other instances it is necessary to institute hormonal therapy to encourage descent or, as a last resort, to use surgery.

SUMMARY

The **gonads** serve a dual function: (1) they produce the germ cells essential for reproduction, and (2) they secrete hormones which bring about sexual maturation. In man the gonads are called the **testes**; in woman, the **ovaries**.

The **ovaries** are found in the pelvic cavity and weigh, together, about 6 gm. Out of some 400,000 **primordial follicles,** only about 400 ripen into mature **graafian follicles,** at the rate of approximately one a month, throughout the sexually active period which lasts from the **menarche** to the **menopause.** After **ovulation,** the follicle becomes progressively the **corpus hemorrhagicum, corpus luteum,** and **corpus albicans.**

The female sex hormones are secreted by the ovaries. They are (1) **estrogens** and (2) **progesterone.** The estrogens are formed chiefly by the maturing follicle. Progesterone is secreted by the corpus luteum. Estrogens cause development of the vagina, thickening of the uterus during the menstrual cycle, growth of the breasts, and other feminine characteristics. Progesterone continues the thickening of the uterus and, during pregnancy, develops the secretory glands of the breasts.

The sex hormones are regulated by the three **gonadotropic** hormones. They are (1) the **follicle-stimulating hormone** or **FSH,** (2) the **luteinizing hormone** or **LH,** and (3) the **luteotropic hormone LTH.** FSH encourages the growth of the ovaries and the maturation of the follicles. It regulates the production of estrogens which, in turn, inhibit FSH secretion. LH and the LTH maintain the corpus luteum and regulate the elaboration of progesterone, which inhibits the production of LH.

The hypothalamus secretes two neurohumors which regulate the gonadotropins: (1) **follicle-stimulating-hormone-releasing factor, FSHRF,** and (2) **luteinizing-hormone-releasing factor, LHRF.**

At about the fiftieth year, menstruation ceases, the ovaries atrophy, and important physiological and psychological changes result. This period of life is termed the **climacteric.** Abnormalities of ovarian function cause menstrual disorders and, in some cases, sterility. Lack of menstruation is termed **amenorrhea;** painful menstruation is called **dysmenorrhea.** Underactivity or overactivity of the ovaries usually is reflected in the appearance and sexual motivation of the woman.

The **testes** develop in the abdominal cavity but descend before birth into the **scrotal sac.** They weigh, together, about 25 gm. The testes consist of masses of **seminiferous tubules** which produce billions of sperm throughout the sexual life. The **interstitial cells of Leydig** elaborate the major male sex hormone **testosterone.** This hormone is responsible for the maturation of the male sex organs as well as the secondary sexual characteristics such as growth of the beard, body hair, perhaps baldness, lowering of the voice, and muscular development.

Sperm can be produced and live only at a temperature a few degrees below body temperature. This environment is maintained through the action of the **cremaster muscle** which is contracted by cold and relaxes when the temperature increases. Sperm production is controlled by the follicle-stimulating hormone. Testosterone secretion is regulated by the **interstitial-cell-stimulating hormone** or **ICSH** also produced by the hypophysis.

QUESTIONS

1. Describe the functions of the ovarian hormones.
2. Discuss the interrelationships between the gonadotropic, ovarian, and hypothalamic hormones.
3. What function do the ovaries have other than hormone production?
4. What alterations occur in a mature woman following extirpation of the ovaries?
5. Describe the alterations that occur in the male at puberty.
6. What mechanism assures an optimal temperature for sperm production?

SUGGESTED READING

Bolton, W., "Why Girls Menstruate," *Today's Health,* **40:**#4, 68–69, April 1962.

Clermont, Y., "The Cycle of the Seminiferous Epithelium in Man," *Am. J. Anat.,* **112:**#1, 35–51, January 1963.

Conner, C. F., "Facts and Fancies about Menstruation," *Today's Health,* **28:**#3, 18–19, March 1950.

Jensen, E. V., "On the Mechanism of Estrogen Action," *Persp. Biol. Med.,* **6:**#1, 47–59, Autumn 1962.

Vath, W. R., "Man's Oldest Fallout Problem: Baldness," *Today's Health,* **41:**#8, 46–50, August 1963.

Physiology of Reproduction

28

PERHAPS THE MOST OUTSTANDING CHARACTERISTIC OF ALL LIVING MATTER is its ability to reproduce itself. The lowly ameba carries out this function simply by dividing in two, with the subsequent growth and development of each half. As the phylogenetic scale is ascended, reproduction becomes increasingly more complex. In man, a study of the physiology of reproduction must include a consideration of (1) *sexual intercourse*, (2) *fertilization and pregnancy*, (3) *the physiology of the newborn infant*, and (4) *lactation*.

SEXUAL INTERCOURSE

Reproduction requires the union of the sperm and the ovum. In order for this union to occur, viable sperm must be delivered into the vagina. Sexual intercourse accomplishes this purposes. However, a woman may be made pregnant in the absence of sexual relations simply by the introduction of the male ejaculate deep into the vagina. This procedure is termed **artificial insemination.** There are many instances in which the husband is infertile. If the wife is capable of bearing children, the couple may desire to have a child by the wife rather than adopt one. For this reason artificial insemination has grown in popularity in recent years. The technique of artificial insemination has improved to the point where most cases are successful. However, as can well be imagined, the entire problem is beset with moral and legal complications.

MALE ROLE

Erection The **penis,** which normally is flaccid and shrunken, becomes firm and enlarged during sexual relations. In this state it can most effectively be introduced into the vagina.

Figure 28-1 shows a cross section of the penis. It can be seen to be

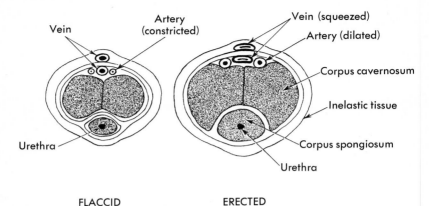

Vein

Artery (constricted)

Vein

Vein (squeezed)

Artery (dilated)

Corpus cavernosum

Inelastic tissue

Corpus spongiosum

Urethra

Urethra

FLACCID   ERECTED

FIG. 28-1   Cross section of the penis in the flaccid and erected states. Dilatation of the artery permits blood to enter the organ. As it enlarges the veins are squeezed between the cavernous tissue and the inelastic envelope, thereby limiting outward blood flow.

composed of three pillars of cavernous tissue called **corpora** or **bodies.** They may be further classified as **corpora cavernosa** and **spongiosum.** These pillars are bound together by connective tissue. Special attention should be paid to the location of the blood vessels. It will be noted that the veins lie between the cavernous structures and the inelastic connective-tissue envelope and skin. This is of fundamental importance, because when the organ becomes erect the swelling of the cavernous pillars squeezes the veins and reduces blood drainage to a minimum. At the same time the arteries and arterioles which supply the penis are dilated. A large quantity of blood under high pressure enters the cavernous pillars. They expand and squeeze the veins; thus, more blood enters than leaves. For this reason the pillars become expanded and rigid and remain in that state until the arteries and arterioles once again constrict. Now the blood supply to the penis is reduced below the drainage rate, and therefore the organ once again becomes flaccid and shrunken.

The erection of the penis is brought about by flooding the cavernous tissue with blood under high pressure. But what causes these local circulatory alterations? The **glans penis** has the most liberal nerve supply, an innervation which diminishes as the base is approached. These fibers convey sensory impulses initiated by tactile receptors in the skin of the organ. The impulses are conducted to the spinal cord where they then activate efferent fibers, belonging to the parasympathetic nervous system, which innervate the penile arteries and arterioles. There is thus a reflex mechanism. The effective stimulus is tactile stimulation of the penis; the response is dilation of the blood vessels; the result is an erection.

This is not to say that tactile stimulation of the penis itself is the only means for producing this end result. Impulses may arise from higher centers. One may simply entertain erotic thoughts with the same consequence. Also stimulation of other parts of the body may well produce an erection. It is true that the basic reflex mechanism has its receptors in the skin of the penis, but through conditioning practically any part of the body may serve the same function. Whatever the stimulus, the ultimate result is dilation of the arterial blood vessels which permits blood to fill the cavernous tissues.

A word might properly be added here concerning **circumcision**. A **foreskin** or **prepuce** overhangs the glans penis in the flaccid state (Fig. 27-5). Circumcision means "to cut around." This operation cuts around so as to remove this foreskin. It is a procedure which is now being widely practiced on most male infants. It is highly desirable from a hygienic standpoint.

The size of the penis, in the erected state, varies from 8 or 10 cm in length up to as much as 30 cm. The average for white men is 15 to 18 cm. The average for colored races is somewhat greater. The diameter varies from 3 to 7 cm. The size of the organ, in part, reflects the production of testosterone, although other factors may play a role.

Ejaculation   The sperm are formed in great numbers by the **seminiferous tubules.** They are moved along by cilia and later by their own motility into the **vas deferens.** They are stored there and not in the **seminal vesicles,** as the name indicates. It is found that the number of sperm in the ejaculate increases with decreasing frequency of intercourse until there are about 120,000,000 to 200,000,000 sperm per milliliter of semen. After this point is reached, decreasing frequency of ejaculation does not increase the sperm count.

Tactile stimulation of the penis sets off another reflex mechanism. As a result, the smooth muscle of the vas deferens contracts and propels the sperm into the urethra. At the same time, the seminal vesicles and the **prostate gland** contract and add their secretions. Semen, then, contains sperm plus the secretions of the seminal vesicles and the prostate gland. Next, by a series of wavelike muscular contractions, the semen is ejected from the urethra. This complex but coordinated series of muscular reflex contractions, which results in the expulsion of the semen, is called **ejaculation.** It serves effectively to bathe the uterus with the seminal fluid and thus place the sperm in a position to fertilize the ovum.

Ejaculation, like the erection, is a reflex mechanism which is complete at the lower-spinal-cord level. However, it may be impinged upon by impulses arising elsewhere in the body. Thus an erection followed by an ejaculation may occur in the complete absence of tactile stimulation to the penis. This reflex can also be brought under higher-center control, so that despite the usual stimulus, the onset of the reflex may be retarded or prevented. In view of the fact that the sexual responses of the female are usually slower than those of the male, desirable relations demand development of control of the ejaculation reflexes.

Orgasm   Ejaculation is normally accompanied by widespread sensations and movements. This total response, one of intense excitement, is termed the **orgasm.** Thus, strictly speaking, an orgasm and an ejaculation are not the same. The latter is only a part of the orgasm. In man, there follows a sudden and rapid muscular relaxation, a startling and dramatic change of interest, and usually a profound but pleasant sensation of fatigue which is far out of proportion to the effort expended during the act.

FEMALE ROLE

In order for pregnancy to occur, the woman need take no active part in the sexual act. She need not even be conscious. So long as the sperm are introduced into a favorable position at the proper time of the month, pregnancy can occur. It is true that in some animals, such as the rabbit, sexual excitement is necessary to induce ovulation, but this is not true of woman. Nonetheless, in most instances, the female plays an active and important role.

Erection of the Clitoris   The **clitoris** is the homologue of the penis. As seen in Fig. 28-2, it lies within the vaginal folds just above the urethral opening. It contains cavernous tissue which, during sexual excitement,

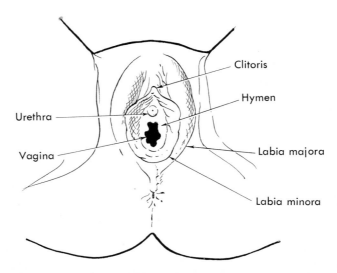

FIG. 28-2   Relationships of the female external sexual organs.

becomes engorged and causes erection of this organ. Like the penis, it is exquisitely sensitive to tactile stimulation. Thus it plays an important role in sexual excitement and satisfaction.

Ejaculation   There are rhythmic, reflex contractions at the peak of sexual intercourse which correspond with the ejaculation in the male. But there is no actual production or expulsion of fluid at this time. In response to sexual play, **Bartholin's glands,** which line the vagina, secrete. This viscous fluid serves to lubricate the penis and thus facilitate the sexual act. Production is continuous and does not increase during the muscular responses.

Orgasm   A very definite orgasm is experienced by the majority of women as a result of sexual relations. It involves not only the rhythmic contraction of the muscles of the vagina and anus but also a rapidly spreading, diffuse sensation of relaxation and pleasurable exhaustion.

FERTILIZATION AND PREGNANCY

FERTILIZATION

Either through the normal sexual act or by artificial insemination, a tremendous number of sperm are introduced into the vaginal vault. The sperm, by their own motility, enter the **uterus** and travel up the **fallopian tubes** at a rate of about 3 mm per minute. Fertilization usually takes place in one or the other of the tubes. The fertilized egg is then carried down the fallopian tube to the uterus. Approximately 6 or 7 days after fertilization it becomes implanted in the uterine wall.

Hyaluronidase   It is known that the semen must contain a great number of sperm in order for fertilization to take place. If the semen contains less than about 60,000,000 sperm per milliliter, fertilization rarely occurs. One wonders why this great number is required, since only one sperm actually penetrates the ovum. One answer to this question points out that the sperm, after being deposited in the vagina, move in all directions completely at random. If all the possible directions are taken into consideration and the distances involved calculated, it can be shown that purely on the basis of "random walking," as it has been called, this huge number is required to assure that at least one will reach the ovum.

Another theory emphasizes the fact that the ovum is surrounded by granulosa cells. For the sperm to enter the ovum, these cells must be separated. The sperm contain a proteolytic enzyme **hyaluronidase.** According to this theory, a large number of sperm is required to provide adequate hyaluronidase to separate the cells and thereby permit the sperm to enter the ovum. Whatever the explanation, the fact remains that a great number of sperm is required for fertilization.

Time of Fertilization   Contrary to popular opinion, there is only a very short period of time during the menstrual cycle when fertilization can occur. In the woman with a normal menstrual cycle, ovulation takes place approximately 14 days before the onset of the menses. The ovum is normally fertilized while it is being carried down one of the fallopian tubes. If it is not fertilized here, it continues on into the uterus. At this time conception can still take place, but if it does not, the ovum undergoes rapid degeneration. From this time until the next ovulation, there can be no fertilization.

Some authorities insist that the time limit of conception is less than 24 hours, while others place it closer to 36 hours. Whatever the exact figure, the indisputable fact remains that there is a remarkably short period of time during which pregnancy can be initiated.

It is true that there are reliable cases of women becoming pregnant following sexual relations at times other than the middle of the menstrual month. But such instances are rare and probably are explicable on the basis of multiple or irregular ovulation. The average woman, however, ovulates only once in each cycle, and it is only at this time that fertilization can occur. The length of time is somewhat extended by the fact that the sperm may survive in the vagina, uterus, and fallopian tubes for a day or two. Thus if sexual relations take place just before ovulation, pregnancy may ensue. Taking all these possibilities into consideration, it is safe to estimate that there is a period of less than 4 days, in the middle of the menstrual cycle, during which fertilization can be successful.

TESTS OF PREGNANCY

Most tests for pregnancy are based on the finding that placenta produces gonadotropins which are excreted in the urine. The urine is then administered to a female animal; some time later, the animal's ovaries are examined. If the woman is pregnant, the urine will contain the gonadotropins, and therefore the ovaries of the test animal will undergo significant maturation.

Aschheim-Zondek Test   In this procedure, which is one of the oldest and most reliable tests for pregnancy, 3- to 4-week-old mice are used. For a 3-day period they are given a total of six evenly spaced injections of about 0.4 ml of urine. One hundred hours later the mice are sacrificed and the ovaries examined. If they are dilated, if they show many hemorrhagic points, indicating follicular rupture, and if there are corpora lutei, the test is considered positive; that is, the woman is pregnant. The test is accurate in over 98 per cent of cases.

Friedman Test   The principle is the same as in the Aschheim-Zondek test, but a slightly different procedure is used because it saves time and the results can be read without a microscope. In the Friedman test, mature female rabbits which weigh about 2 kg are used. They must be kept isolated for about 4 weeks before being used, however, so as to assure that sexual excitement has not been the cause of the observed changes. Only one injection is given, consisting of 10 ml of the urine. Usually two animals are injected, one being examined 24 hours later, the second in 2 days. If hemorrhagic follicles are seen, the test is positive. About the same accuracy is obtained with this test as with the Aschheim-Zondek test.

PREGNANCY

Development of the Ovum   As soon as the sperm penetrates the ovum, the latter begins to divide and subdivide with ever-increasing frequency, so that it quickly becomes a mass of cells now called the "mulberry mass" or **morula** (Fig. 28-3). The membrane covering the morula is termed the **trophoblast.** It is believed that the trophoblast releases a proteolytic en-

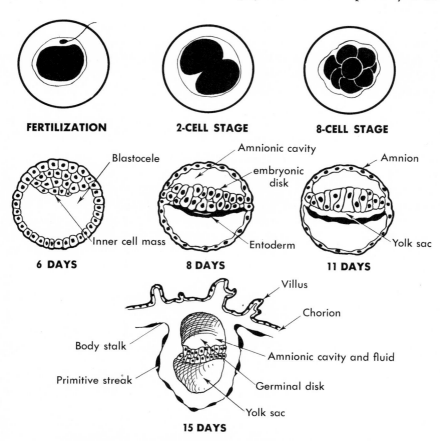

FERTILIZATION   **2-CELL STAGE**   **8-CELL STAGE**

Blastocele

Amnionic cavity

Amnion

embryonic disk

Inner cell mass

Entoderm

Yolk sac

6 DAYS   **8 DAYS**   **11 DAYS**

Villus

Chorion

Body stalk

Amnionic cavity and fluid

Primitive streak

Germinal disk

Yolk sac

15 DAYS

FIG. 28-3   Early development of the fertilized ovum.

zyme which facilitates the implantation of the developing ovum in the thick, vascular, receptive uterine wall. After implantation, the remarkable and extensive development continues for approximately 270 days, that is, about 9 months (Fig. 28-4). The duration of the gestation period varies considerably, however. There are authentic pregnancies of over 300 days.

Sex Differentiation   When the sperm and the ovum come together, the genetic pattern of the embryo is determined. Each gamete has 23 chromosomes; thus, the embryo will have 46. One pair of chromosomes is termed the **sex chromosomes.** They are usually referred to as the X and Y chromosomes. Females have two X chromosomes whereas males have the XY pattern. Accordingly, the sex of the child is determined at the time of fertilization. However, hormonal abnormalities during the period of gestation can cause the embryo to develop sexual organs at variance to its genetic makeup. In order for male sexual organs to develop, the testes of the embryo must become functional. If they fail to do so, or if there are ovaries instead of testes, then female organs develop. Thus it is that sometimes an embryo with male chromosomes will develop female sexual organs (**pseudohermaphroditism**). The reverse also occurs when the female embryo is subjected to androgens.

Changes in the Mother   During pregnancy there are significant alterations in almost all the physiological mechanisms. The most outstanding change, of course, is in the appearance of the woman. The abdomen grows very large because of the development of the fetus within the uterus. The breasts also become enlarged and sometimes painful. The nipples become erect, enlarged, and dark (Fig. 28-10).

The maternal thyroid increases in size and secretes more thyroxin. This is reflected is an increased BMR, especially in the later months of pregnancy. Actually, there is little or no increase in the mother's metabolic rate alone. The increase observed represents the total for the mother and embryo. Apparently the mother's thyroid functions for both at this stage.

The parathyroid glands also become hyperactive. As a result, more calcium is made available for the developing embryo. As already pointed out, it is for this reason that the diet must be high in calcium so as to spare the maternal bones. During pregnancy there is a positive balance not only for calcium, but for nitrogen, phosphorus, iron, and many other substances as well. Thus, the diet must be abundant in these substances to prevent an undue drain on the mother.

The hypophysis increases its activity during pregnancy. It furnishes a good supply of the luteinizing hormone to maintain the corpus luteum. In addition, it secretes the luteotropic hormone for the same purpose and also for lactation. Finally, it produces a third substance which evokes strong contractions of the uterus, thus facilitating birth.

In the cardiovascular system, there is a progressively increasing circulatory rate with a rise in the white-blood-cell count. The blood pressure remains normal, although the venous pressure in the lower extremities may rise sufficiently to produce edema. Apparently the pressure of the embryo on the abdominal veins is responsible for this increase.

The only noteworthy alterations in respiration occur late in pregnancy when some women experience difficulty in breathing. This is purely a mechanical effect reflecting the increase in pressure on the diaphragm.

Women gain a varying amount of weight during pregnancy. At first there may a weight loss because of nausea, vomiting, and the inability to eat adequately. However, after this initial period there is then a progressive gain, normally amounting to about 24 lb. A significantly greater weight gain indicates that the mother is overeating and depositing adipose tissue. The normal 24-lb weight gain is distributed as follows:

	Pounds
Fetus	7
Fluid and membranes	4
Uterine enlargement	2
Breast enlargement	3
Maternal fluid increase	8

The increase in maternal body fluid representing about 8 lb of the total weight gain is probably a manifestation of the high concentration of steroid hormones which act on the renal tubules to encourage fluid retention. After birth, the concentration of these hormones diminishes, and during this period there is an accelerated production of urine which serves to return body fluid to the normal volume.

The Placenta The placenta, as has been pointed out, is attached to the uterus and furnishes the means for nutrition of the embryo. The maternal and fetal circulatory systems are related in the placenta. The maternal and fetal blood are separated by only two thin membranes. Eventually these membranes fuse into one. Across this barrier all the fetal nutrition must pass.

Not only is the placenta the means of fetal nourishment, but it also actively produces hormones which are essential to the successful completion of pregnancy. Very early in fetal development the placenta elaborates substances which are very similar to the gonadotropic hormones of the anterior lobe of the hypophysis. Closer examination discloses that these gonadotropins function more like the luteinizing and luteotropic hormones than like FSH. Accordingly, under the influence of this placental secretion the corpus luteum does not involute as it normally does during the menstrual cycle. Instead it actually increases in size and forms

FIG. 28-4 Photographs of normal human fetal development. These remarkable photographs were made available through the courtesy of the Department of Embryology, Carnegie Institution of Washington. Chester F. Reather, FBPA, was the photographer. All the ages given date from the time of ovulation. The menstrual age, then, is about two weeks longer in each instance.

a. Thirteen paired somites, 2.5 mm long, 23 days old.

b. Chorion, 28 days old.

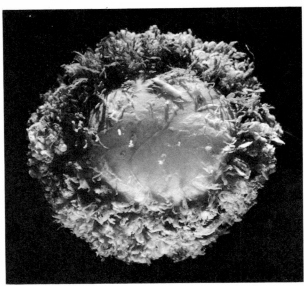

c. Chorion opened to shown embryo in yolk sac, 28 days old.

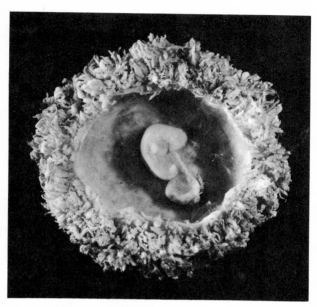

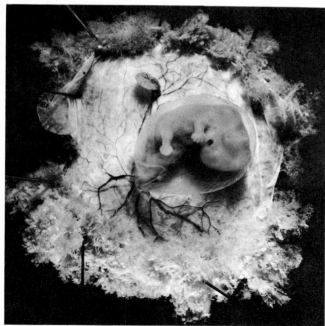

d. Chorion opened to show 39-day-old embryo.

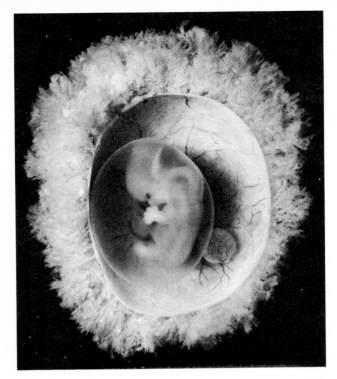

e. Chorion opened to show 40-day-old embryo within the intact amnion. Yolk sac at lower right.

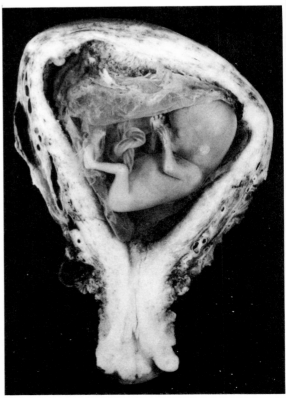

f. Uterus containing 70-day-old embryo.

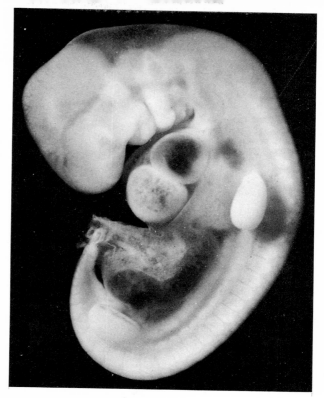

g. Embryo, 30 days old, 7.3 mm long.

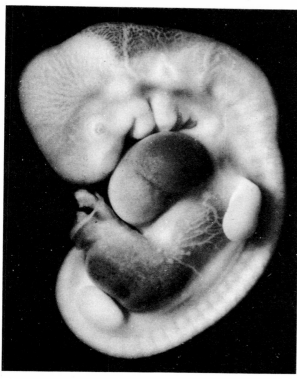

h. Embryo, 31 days old, 7.8 mm long.

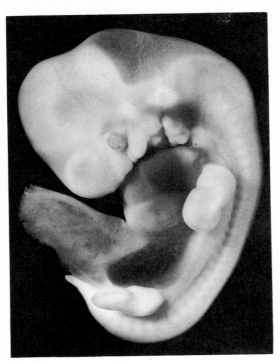

i. Embryo, 34 days old, 11.6 mm long.

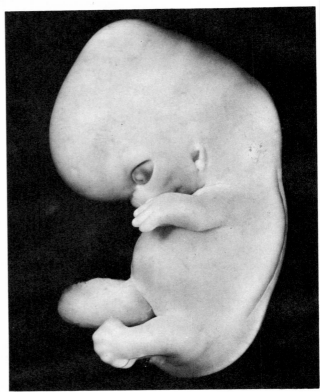

j. Embryo, 40 days old, 19.0 mm long.

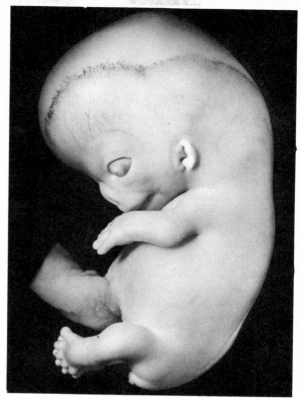

k. Embryo, 44 days old,
   23.0 mm long.

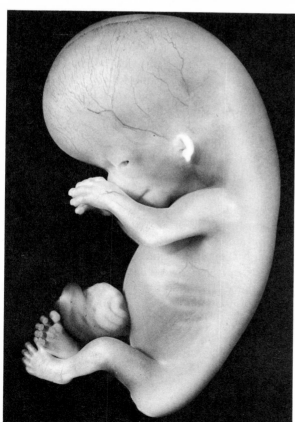

l. Embryo, 56 days old,
   37.0 mm long.

591

large quantities of progesterone which aids in the maternal alterations essential to pregnancy. After about 3 or 4 months, however, the corpus luteum does decrease in size and then becomes inactive, but by this time the placenta is secreting large quantities of estrogens and progesterone. These compounds are essential for the continued development of the embryo. Since the placenta can obviously manufacture them adequately, there is no longer a necessity for the corpus luteum, and it now becomes completely functionless.

The marvelous hormonal interplay is nowhere more dramatically illustrated than in the pregnant woman. Even before fertilization occurs, the uterus is made ready under the influence of the estrogens and progesterone which, in turn, are controlled by the gonadotropic hormones of the hypophysis. After fertilization, the ovum is implanted in this receptive uterus and a placenta forms which first secretes gonadotropins to maintain the corpus luteum and therefore assure an adequate supply of female sex hormones until the placenta itself can take over that task. Finally, the placenta becomes truly autonomous and secretes all the active hormones required for the continuance of pregnancy.

PARTURITION

The term **parturition** is derived from *partitio,* meaning "a dividing." As used in this sense, it means the dividing of the embryo from the mother, that is, the act of giving birth. Parturition is conveniently separated into three stages.

First Stage of Labor At term, the uterine muscles begin to contract rhythmically and with ever-greater force. The cause of the onset of labor is still not clear. The best evidence indicates that it is hormonally inspired. These contractions give rise to the typical labor pains.

The contractions of the uterine wall exert considerable pressure on the **amniotic sac,** or, as it is popularly called, the bag of waters. Since the fluid is not compressible, the bag bulges into the opening of the uterus and tends to dilate that opening. When the opening has been well enlarged, there is no longer any support to the bag and it bursts, releasing the amniotic fluid. This marks the completion of the first stage of labor.

Second Stage of Labor As shown in Fig. 28-5, the opening of the uterus is dilated and the head of the child begins to descend through it. This movement of the child through the vagina exerts considerable pressure. As a result, the mother strains much as in a difficult bowel movement. Straining markedly increases the intra-abdominal pressure which aids in moving the child along. The pressure, the slow movement of the child, and the periodic straining efforts continue until the child is born. This signals the end of the second stage of labor.

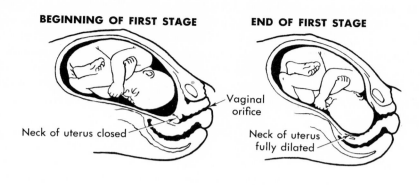

BEGINNING OF FIRST STAGE

END OF FIRST STAGE

Vaginal orifice

Neck of uterus closed

Neck of uterus fully dilated

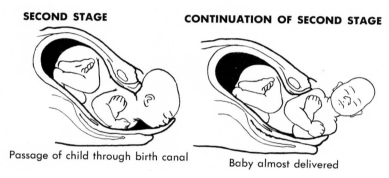

SECOND STAGE

CONTINUATION OF SECOND STAGE

Passage of child through birth canal

Baby almost delivered

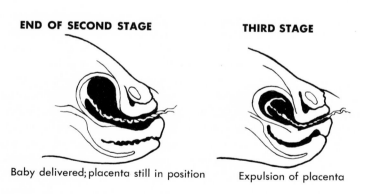

END OF SECOND STAGE

THIRD STAGE

Baby delivered; placenta still in position

Expulsion of placenta

FIG. 28-5   Parturition. The three stages of delivery are portrayed diagrammatically.

Third Stage of Labor   After the birth of the child, the mother usually relaxes while the uterus slowly contracts, thus taking up the huge slack left by the expulsion of the child. However, a few minutes later the uterus vigorously and rhythmically contracts once again, thus ridding itself of the placenta. This is often referred to as the **afterbirth.** In addition, the contraction of the uterine muscles serves to constrict the various vessels which have been ruptured during parturition, thus reducing hemorrhage to a minimum.

PHYSIOLOGY OF THE NEWBORN INFANT

The extremely low mortality rate among newborn infants is apt to blind the student to the truly cataclysmic physiological changes which occur at birth. While the child was carried in the womb, the placenta functioned as both lungs and kidneys. At birth, this service is abruptly ended. Even more drastic, more urgent, are the alterations in circulation.

Not only is the physiology of the newborn baby of interest and importance, but a consideration of the more significant peculiarities will offer, at this time, a review of major physiological concepts.

CIRCULATION

Fetal Circulation   Figure 28-6 illustrates the path of the fetal circulation. It can be seen that the blood is oxygenated in the placenta and then passes through the **umbilical vein** to enter the **ductus venosus** which bypasses the liver. The blood now enters the **inferior vena cava** to flow into the right atrium. The **superior vena cava** also empties into this atrium. Thus, in the fetus, the blood which fills the right atrium has an oxygen content that is higher than in the adult right atrium, because of the addition of the oxygenated blood from the placenta.

The blood next flows into the right ventricle, or it may go through the open **foramen ovale** to enter the left atrium. The percentage of the total blood flow which goes by one route or the other has not been determined. Some of the blood which makes its way to the right ventricle is pumped through the lungs, but of course in this passage it is not oxygenated. Most of the blood which traverses the pulmonary artery is deflected to the aorta via the **ductus arteriosus.** In the fetus, the lungs are collapsed. Therefore, there is great resistance to blood flow and, as a result, the pressure in the pulmonary artery is higher than it is in the aorta. It is for this reason that blood will flow through the ductus arteriosus from the pulmonary artery to the aorta.

It can be seen from a study of this circulatory pathway that blood with a relatively low oxygen content is delivered to all the tissues of the

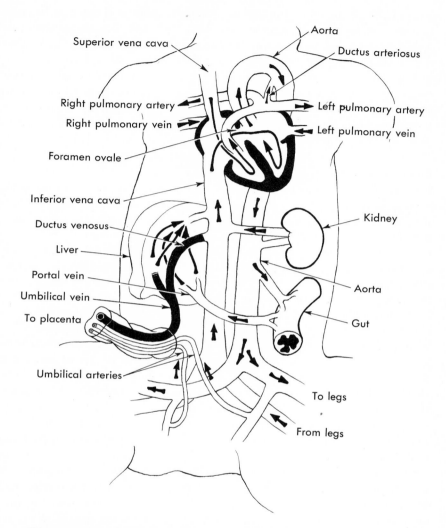

FIG. 28-6 Circulation in the fetus. The black area indicates the most highly oxygenated blood. This enters the fetus via the ductus venosus, a continuation of the umbilical vein. Note that the blood can bypass the lungs by flowing from the right to left heart through the foramen ovale. Blood that does enter the pulmonary system is shunted, at least in part, to the aorta by the ductus arteriosus.

body. It has been well demonstrated that the greatest danger to life and mental development is oxygen deficiency. For this reason considerable work has been done on this aspect of fetal physiology. We now know that the fetal hemoglobin has a greater affinity for oxygen than does the hemoglobin found in the adult. This means that fetal blood contains more oxygen at any oxygen partial pressure than does adult blood. But, by the same token, fetal blood surrenders its oxygen load more reluctantly than does adult blood. However, because of the very low partial pressures of oxygen prevailing in the fetus, this system assures an adequate oxygen supply to the tissues even under these adverse conditions.

Circulation in the Newborn Infant   At birth, the child begins to breathe. The blood which flows through the lungs is now oxygenated. In the fetus a large part of the blood never enters the lungs but flows directly into the left side of the heart through the foramen ovale. This opening must now be closed.

At birth, the lungs expand and therefore the resistance to blood flow decreases. As a result, more blood flows through the pulmonary system than was the case in the fetus. Because of this decrease in resistance, the pressure throughout the pulmonary system decreases and falls below that of the left ventricle and aorta. Blood, which in the fetus, flowed from the right atrium through the foramen ovale into the left atrium, is now reversed. There is a flap present in the wall of the left atrium which, because of this reversal of flow, closes the foramen ovale. In addition, the ductus venosus becomes obliterated and, in the adult circulation, is retained as a ligament. The obliteration of this vessel begins with the tying of the umbilical cord.

Other changes in the circulation are made apparent by a study of Fig. 28-7. The umbilical arteries become, in the newborn infant, the **umbilical ligaments,** and the obliterated umbilical vein is now called the **teres ligament.** *Teres,* meaning "round," describes the ultimate shape of the ligament. Finally, attention should be paid to the ductus arteriosus in the fetal circulation. This duct transfers blood directly from the pulmonary artery to the aorta. In other words, there are two ways of bypassing the fetal lungs: (1) via the foramen ovale and (2) by means of the ductus arteriosus. In the newborn infant, both of these short circuits must be quickly closed so as to take advantage of oxygenation in the lungs. The ductus arteriosus, which has been functioning in the fetus to shunt blood from the pulmonary artery to the aorta, functionally closes when the lungs expand at birth. However, it takes about two months for the ductus arteriosus to become obliterated and become the **arteriosus ligament.**

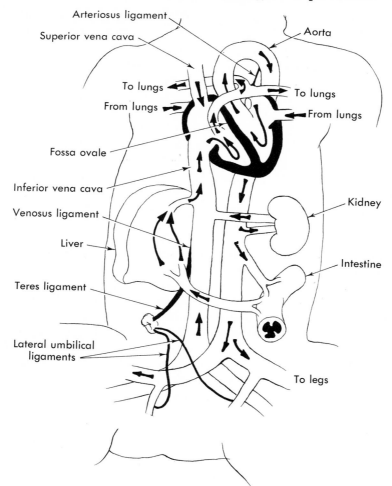

Arteriosus ligament

Superior vena cava

Aorta

To lungs

From lungs

To lungs

From lungs

Fossa ovale

Inferior vena cava

Kidney

Venosus ligament

Liver

Intestine

Teres ligament

Lateral umbilical
ligaments

To legs

FIG. 28-7   Circulation in the newborn. Note that the ductus venosus, the foramen ovale, and the ductus arteriosus have all closed.

RESPIRATION

Fetal Respiration   It is believed that the fetus undertakes some breathing movements before birth. In the placental circulation, the carbon dioxide, oxygen, and pH values are all usually within the normal range, so that there is very little, if any, provocation of the respiratory center. But evidence indicates that occasional rhythmic breathing movements do occur.

Since the fetus is immersed in the amniotic fluid, these intrauterine breathing gestures simply move a small amount of the fluid through the fetal lungs.

Respiration in the Newborn Infant When the child is deprived of the placenta, the oxygenation of the blood as well as the removal of carbon dioxide ceases. In addition, acid metabolites are continuously expelled into the blood stream. It is clear that it is only a matter of time before the stimulus to the respiratory center as a result of these alterations will be strong enough to initiate breathing. It is the practice to spank the newborn baby in order to start breathing; no doubt this procedure is effective. It has been claimed that the shock of sudden exposure to air produces the same result. But whether these claims are valid or not, the fact remains that the usual and normal mechanisms will quickly suffice to initiate this important function.

THE KIDNEYS

Renal Function in the Fetus It is believed that the kidneys function to a limited extent before birth. But the main excretory role is carried out by the placenta. The ability of the fetal kidneys to excrete various substances is shown by experiments in which inulin, for example, was injected into the mother and then detected within 2 hours in the amniotic fluid. The only way it could have reached the amniotic fluid was via the urine. Likewise, it is found that the osmotic pressure and concentration of urea in the amniotic fluid progressively decrease. This is believed to be explicable on the basis that the fetal urine contains a low concentration of urea and has a low osmotic pressure. It is eliminated by the fetus into the amniotic fluid.

Renal Function in the Newborn Infant The kidneys, which function somewhat during intrauterine life, quickly assume their full responsibilities immediately after birth. The urine is found to become progressively more concentrated after birth and, as the intake of fluids increases, so does the urinary volume.

It is of interest to learn that the administration of the antidiuretic hormone to the newborn baby is without effect. In line with this fact is the observation that the hypophysis of the newborn infant produces very little of the hormone. Thus it is found that the infant does not respond to large quantities of water as do adults.

In general, it can be said that though the kidneys of the newborn baby function quite adequately to maintain the internal environment fairly constant, their full capability in this respect is not attained until about the first year.

LACTATION

The child is brought into the world quite incapable of caring for itself. In addition to the obvious maternal care, the most desirable form of nutrition during the first stages of life is maternal milk, as secreted by the mammary glands.

MAMMARY GLANDS

Most mammals have several pairs of mammary glands. Women normally have only one pair, although in rare cases small accessory mammae are present.

Development of the Breasts   The breasts of the newborn child, whether male or female, exhibit definite activity. A small amount of milklike fluid can be expressed at this time and is known popularly as **witch's milk.** The mammary activity at this stage is caused by the influence of the maternal hormones upon the fetal breasts. These hormones which circulate in the

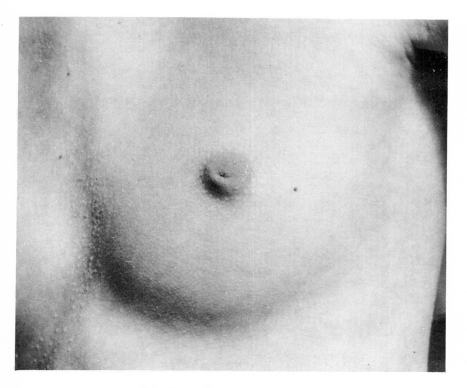

FIG. 28-8   The adolescent breast.

blood stream are apparently freely transferred across the placenta to enter the fetal circulation.

At puberty the female breasts begin to grow rapidly (Fig. 28-8). Within a year or two after the onset of menstruation, the breasts reach their full growth (Fig. 28-9). At this time the duct system develops but there is very little maturation of the glandular tissue. It is known that the breasts undergo cyclic changes associated with menstruation. Just before the destructive phase, the breasts become firmer and somewhat enlarged and may be unusually tender.

It is during pregnancy that the most pronounced breast alterations occur (Fig. 28-10). During the first few months of pregnancy there is fat deposition and further duct development. Later the glandular tissue also partakes in this process. In the latter months of pregnancy, the glandular cells swell and begin to secrete. The noticeable enlargement of the breasts at this time is caused by the accumulation of milk.

Hormonal Regulation   The development of the breasts, as just outlined, is under the control of the various sex hormones. The growth at puberty is due primarily to the action of estrogens. These hormones cause thickening of the nipple and marked growth and branching of the ducts.

Progesterone seems to be without effect on the breasts if administered by itself. But when it is given along with estrogens, a striking develop-

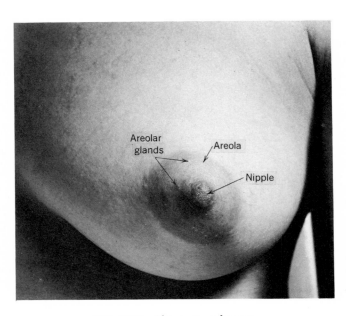

FIG. 28-9   The mature breast.

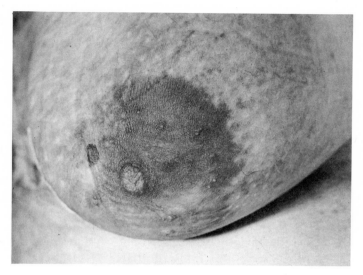

FIG. 28-10   The breast during pregnancy.

ment follows. The breast changes which occur during the few days just preceding menstruation are probably a result of the high concentration of both these hormones in the blood at that time. Likewise the great growth during the first half of pregnancy seems to be attributable to the combined action of these substances. It should be kept in mind that during pregnancy the main source of the sex hormones is the placenta, as little if any is formed during this time in the ovary.

The hypophysis secretes a substance which has been designated **prolactin,** also called the luteotropic hormone. This hormone no doubt contributes to the development of the breasts in the later phases of pregnancy.

MILK SECRETION

The secretion of milk is under the control of the luteotropic hormone (prolactin). Prolactin is chemically very similar to growth hormone and, in man, the two may be identical. The initiation of milk secretion, that is, lactation, is termed **lactogenesis.** The maintenance of lactation is known as **galactopoiesis.**

During pregnancy, the breasts develop, but they do not produce milk, probably because the secretion of prolactin is inhibited by the estrogens and progesterone, which are in high concentration until loss of the placenta at parturition.

Other hormones obviously also play roles in milk secretion. It has been reported that thyroid activity increases during lactation in proportion to the milk yield. In addition, secretion is seriously impaired by adrenalectomy.

Sympathetic nerve stimulation can reduce the blood flow through the mammary glands to zero. And when this occurs, milk secretion stops. This probably explains why emotional states can so drastically alter milk production.

MILK EJECTION

The milk that is secreted by the alveoli cells does not simply pour through the ducts and out of the nipple. To the contrary, it accumulates and if not ejected will build up sufficient pressure to stop the secretion of additional milk. Milk secretion ceases when the pressure rises to about 25 to 40 mm Hg.

The ejection of milk is thought to be due to the contraction of the mammary **myoepithelial cells** which surround the alveoli cells and the small ducts. Apparently, the impulses initiated by the suckling act are propagated to the hypothalamus, and, as a result, **oxytocin** is released from the posterior lobe of the hypophysis. Oxytocin is carried by the blood to the mammary glands where it evokes contraction of the myoepithelial cells. As a result, milk is ejected. Suckling also reflexly stimulates the release of prolactin. Prolactin not only is responsible for the secretion of milk but it also delays mammary involution. Thus, if the child is not breast-fed, if there is no suckling, milk will not be formed and secretion will halt. Mammary involution will therefore occur far earlier than when suckling is active.

HUMAN MILK

Quantity   The amount of milk secreted increases progressively after parturition. The maximal flow is usually attained at about the sixth month and then decreases to cease altogether within the following year. The length of the feeding period is highly variable and seems to depend more upon social custom than upon physiological factors. In some societies it is the practice to feed the offspring for 2 to 4 years. But in the United States, few children are fed for more than 12 months.

The total daily output during the peak production amounts to about 1 liter. Again the quantity produced seems to bear a relationship to the demand. Women who have twins or triplets secrete, in some cases, as much as 2 to 3 liters daily.

Composition   The composition of human milk is indicated in Table 28-1. For comparison, the composition of cow's milk is also presented.

In considering the vitamin content of human milk, it is found that all vitamins with the exception of vitamin D are present in sufficient quantities. For this reason most diets for children have a high vitamin-D supplement.

TABLE 28-1   Composition of Milk

Constituent	Human, gm per 100 ml	Cow, gm per 100 ml
Water	89.0	87.0
Protein	1.2	3.5
Casein	0.8	2.4
Lactalbumin	0.4	0.6
Lactose	6.5	4.8
Calories	67.0	69.0

The argument as to whether a baby should be breast or bottle fed has never been completely resolved. Since the milk of one species differs from that of another, it is probably best for a mother to feed her child. However, this insistence can be carried too far in cases where the mother's milk is clearly insufficient. But aside from the relative nutritive value of mother's milk, there are undeniable psychological advantages, for both mother and child, in breast feeding. Therefore both physiological and psychological factors should be taken into consideration when one is confronted with this extremely important decision.

SUMMARY

Human reproduction requires the union of the **sperm** and the **ovum.** Sexual intercourse usually accomplishes this purpose, but the same results may be had through **artificial insemination.** A reflex mechanism evoked by a variety of stimuli causes **erection** of the penis. Another set of reflexes, aroused by the sexual act, bring about **ejaculation.** Up to a half billion sperm in a fluid medium contributed by the **seminal vesicles** and **prostate gland** are forcibly expelled by a series of muscular contractions at this time. The accompanying sense of relaxation, well-being, and fatigue is termed the **orgasm.** After being deposited in the vaginal vault, the sperm move in all directions under their own power. Some of them enter the uterus and make their way up the **fallopian tubes. Fertilization,** the union of sperm and ovum, usually occurs here.

Tests of pregnancy depend upon the presence of gonadotropic hormones in the urine which are formed by the placenta. The suspect urine is injected into mice in the **Aschheim-Zondek test** and into rabbits in the **Friedman test.** Some time later the ovaries of the animal are examined for evidence of maturing follicles which indicates that the woman is pregnant. The tests are accurate in over 98 per cent of the cases.

The duration of pregnancy, or **gestation,** is approximately 270 days. During this period there is marked growth of the breasts and, of course, the uterus. The thyroid, hypophysis, and parathyroid glands become more active. The white-blood-cell count rises, and the circulatory rate usually increases somewhat. Total weight gain is normally about 24 lb.

The **placenta** is attached to the uterus and nourishes the fetus while, at the same time, playing an excretory role. It also secretes gonadotropins and the female sex hormones.

Parturition or birth occurs in three definite phases. In the first stage of labor, the uterus is dilated and the **amniotic sac** bursts, freeing the amniotic fluid. In the second stage, the child passes through the dilated uterus and vagina and is born. In the third stage, the placenta is expelled.

The **breasts** develop during puberty under the influence of estrogens. During the first half of pregnancy, stimulated by both estrogens and progesterone, there is further mammary growth. **Prolactin** activates the secretory cells and milk is produced. The actual expression of milk from the breast does not occur until after parturition, probably because of estrogenic inhibition and perhaps because the suckling movements are required for this function. Human milk is produced in steadily increasing quantities, reaching a maximum at about the sixth month after delivery. At this time, 1 or 2 liters per day may be secreted.

QUESTIONS

1. Outline the sequence of physiological events leading to an erection.
2. Why is the woman fertile for only a day or two during each menstrual cycle?
3. Describe the essential hormonal interplay associated with pregnancy.
4. What is the physiological basis of tests for pregnancy?
5. Describe the circulatory changes which occur in the child immediately following parturition.
6. What hormones are required for breast development and lactation?

SUGGESTED READING

Allen, R. D., "The Moment of Fertilization," *Sci. American,* **201:**#1, 124–134, July 1959.

Bishop, D. W., "Sperm Motility," *Physiol. Rev.,* **42:**#1, 1–59, January 1962.

Dean, S. R., "Man and Wife," *Today's Health,* **33:**#8, 26–28, August 1955.

Linzell, J. L., "Physiology of the Mammary Glands," *Physiol. Rev.,* **39:**#3, 534–576, July 1959.

Mittwoch, V., "Sex Differences in Cells," *Sci. American,* **209:**#1, 54–62, July 1963.

Pincus, G., "Reproduction," *Ann. Rev. Physiol.,* **24:** 57–84, 1962.

The Pancreas and Adrenal Glands

29

MANY INSTANCES OF THE VARIOUS ORGANS OF THE BODY possessing a dual function have been encountered. We have just learned that the gonads not only give rise to the germ cells essential for reproduction but also serve as very important endocrine glands. The pancreas also has a dual function. The digestive role of the pancreas has already been studied. Here we shall analyze another essential function of the pancreas, that of an endocrine gland.

We now know that the pancreas is intimately associated with a disorder termed **diabetes mellitus.** This is a disease which has been recognized since antiquity. Its history is worthy of note. Chinese medical literature as long ago as about A.D. 600 contains descriptions of a disease with the characteristic signs and symptoms of diabetes mellitus. The search of medical writings from other civilized centers also indicates that diabetes was quite prevalent. But although the disorder was accurately described throughout many centuries, it remained for the Greek, Aretaeus, to name this disorder, the name which persists today. He called it *diabetes* because, in Greek, this term implies "to run through a siphon," which refers to the great volume of urine formed in this condition. In 1675, it was found that the urine was characteristically sweet. Thus the condition became known as diabetes mellitus, *mellitus* meaning "sweet." It then took another century before it was recognized that the sweetness of the diabetic urine was caused by the presence in it of glucose.

Carbohydrate metabolism, however, is not influenced solely by insulin. The adrenal glands also secrete hormones which are vitally important in the regulation of blood sugar. Actually, as will be presently described, the adrenal glands consist of (1) an outer shell called the **adrenal cortex** and (2) the inner core known as the **adrenal medulla.** Both parts secrete distinct hormones, and since they influence carbohydrates significantly, it is advisable to consider both the pancreas and the adrenal glands in this chapter.

ISLETS OF LANGERHANS

Although, as we have just seen, the disease diabetes mellitus has been recognized for centuries, knowledge of the role that the pancreas plays in this disorder really dates from 1869, the year in which Langerhans published his classic work. Langerhans accurately described the islet-cell formation in the pancreas. It is now known that these cells are the ones which secrete the pancreatic hormone. Today, they are rightly termed the **islets of Langerhans** (Fig. 29-1).

EXTIRPATION

The most complete way to remove the islet cells is to extirpate the entire pancreas. Although the animal will then suffer from the loss of the pancreatic juice, other distinct changes are observed.

As a result of this procedure, the animal undergoes a progressive deterioration which is ultimately culminated by death. A day-by-day examination discloses that first the blood sugar increases, then sugar begins to appear in the urine. The urinary output now becomes copious and, because of the thirst mechanism, the intake of fluid keeps step with the increasing urine output. The animal progressively loses weight. There is an unusually low RQ. Both the breath and the urine acquire a characteristic acetone odor. The normal alkalinity of the blood slowly but

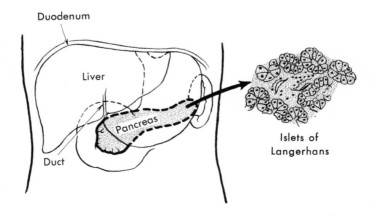

FIG. 29-1   Anatomical relationships of the pancreas.

steadily decreases, and the animal soon dies of respiratory paralysis. In short, the loss of the islet cells is associated with grave alterations in metabolism, primarily carbohydrate metabolism.

INSULIN

Much of our basic knowledge of carbohydrate metabolism we owe to the great French physiologist Claude Bernard who published his important work just before the beginning of this century. At about the same time, in 1889 to be exact, experiments reporting the results following the removal of the pancreas established conclusively that the ancient disorder of diabetes is associated with pancreatic deficiency. However, progress in this field was severely retarded by the consistent failure of all investigators to obtain a pancreatic extract which would prevent or reverse the alterations of diabetes after experimental removal of the pancreas. In brief, the frustrating situation which prevailed for some 30 years was this: the pancreas must produce a hormone essential to carbohydrate metabolism, but all extracts of the pancreas proved impotent.

Discovery   It remained for the Canadian scientist Banting and his student Best to prepare a potent extract. This team is credited with the discovery of **insulin,** a term which means "island." Insulin is a protein. It is destroyed by the digestive juices. Thus when the whole pancreas is extracted, the pancreatic juice therein quickly inactivates the insulin during the extraction process. Banting and Best prevented this by first ligating the pancreatic duct which caused the pancreatic cells to die. The islet cells, however, remain functional in this procedure. They then removed the pancreas and made an extract. Since there was no longer any pancreatic juice present, the insulin was preserved and the extract proved potent.

Secretion   The **beta cells** of the islets contain granules which are packets of insulin. These granules are secreted from the cells by **emeiocytosis** (Fig. 1-7). Under the electron microscope it can be seen that each granule is surrounded by a membrane. In the process of secretion by emeiocytosis, the membrane surrounding the granule and the cell membrane appear to join (Fig. 1-7). This double membrane now disappears leaving the granule free to be extruded. The inner half of the granule membrane then becomes a part of the cell membrane.

It is important to realize that insulin is secreted into the portal blood stream. Thus, it reaches the liver in high concentration, and it is here that it exerts a major influence on carbohydrate metabolism. It has been shown that the injection of insulin into the portal vein has different consequences from the injection of the same amount in a peripheral vein.

The circulating form of insulin is a polypeptide with a molecular weight of 6000. The molecule is made up of two chains of amino acids. One contains 21 amino acids, the other 30. The two chains are connected by two disulfide linkages. It is thought that insulin is inactivated by breaking the disulfide linkages and by shortening of the peptide chains. In the blood, insulin is bound to globulin.

Function of Insulin Because insulin is a protein it cannot be administered orally, since the digestive juices inactivate it before absorption into the blood stream. Therefore, it must be given by injection. Insulin, when administered to a pancreatectomized animal, prevents all the changes just described. The animal can be maintained in a normal state indefinitely with daily injections of this hormone. On the other hand, large injections of insulin are capable of lowering the blood sugar far below the normal range.

Figure 29-2 illustrates that the blood-sugar level represents a balance between the amount of carbohydrate ingested or formed from protein, on the one hand, and the storage or utilization of carbohydrate, on the other. Insulin lowers the blood sugar. If there is too little insulin present, the blood sugar rises. It seems clear that insulin, in lowering blood sugar, must do it by (1) decreasing the conversion of protein to carbohydrate, (2) increasing the utilization of blood glucose, or (3) a combination of both. Extensive experimentation indicates that a combination of both follows insulin administration. However, the increased utilization of blood glucose seems to be the more important action of the two.

Even though a tremendous amount of research has been carried out in

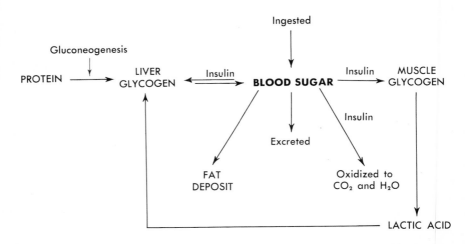

FIG. 29-2 Regulation of blood sugar. Insulin is shown to enhance the formation of glycogen and to hasten the oxidation of blood sugar.

an attempt to clarify exactly how insulin influences carbohydrate metabolism, it must be admitted that its mode of action still remains uncertain. There is growing evidence, however, that its primary role is to regulate the rate of glucose transfer across the cell membrane. It is possible to study carbohydrate metabolism in tissues removed from the living organism. When this is done, it is found that the rate of glucose utilization in the tissue cells is directly related to the amount of insulin present. On the other hand, if the cell membranes are destroyed, then the rate of glucose utilization is completely independent of the presence of insulin. These results suggest, of course, that insulin does not control glucose utilization directly but, rather, the transfer of glucose into the cell where it is oxidized. There are other experiments which lead to the same conclusion. If this theory is correct, then the action of insulin in lowering blood sugar can be explained by visualizing the enhanced transfer of glucose into liver and muscle cells where it is converted to glycogen and into other cells where it is oxidized for energy. In both instances, the blood sugar would be diminished.

One problem with this theory is the observation that insulin does not increase the transport of glucose into all cells. It has this influence primarily in skeletal and cardiac muscle. The brain and the intestine are not affected. Surprisingly neither is the liver. Yet, beyond any question, insulin markedly alters liver function. If the transport of glucose into the liver cells is not increased by insulin, then this hormone must have still another mechanism of action.

Insulin also alters protein and fat metabolism. Whether this is a direct influence, or secondary to deranged carbohydrate metabolism, is still an open question. Normally the concentration of ketone bodies in the blood is less than 1 mg per cent. But in severe cases of insulin lack, the concentration may rise as high as 90 mg per cent. Clearly there is an overproduction because of excessive fat catabolism. As a result, the kidneys excrete the ketone bodies in great quantities in combination with base, mostly sodium. The **ketonemia** plus sodium loss causes acidosis.

Just as there is excessive fat catabolism so is there excessive protein catabolism. In addition, in the absence of insulin, the entrance of amino acids into the cells is impaired, thereby limiting protein anabolism.

Regulation of Insulin Secretion The production of insulin by the islet cells is apparently controlled by the level of the blood sugar. This is very similar to the self-regulating mechanism for the secretion of parathyroid hormone. It has been noted that this hormone regulates blood calcium and that the blood calcium controls the output of parathyroid hormone. In the case of the pancreas, insulin regulates the level of blood sugar which, in turn, controls insulin production. For an understanding of the etiology of diabetes mellitus, this relationship is important. It can be seen that, whenever the blood sugar goes up, the islet cells are stimulated. If the blood sugar is kept high constantly by the continuous ingestion of carbohydrate, there will be a strong and steady stimulation of the islet cells. If this provocation is great enough and persists long enough, there is evidence to indicate that the cells may become exhausted and disintegrate. Eventually, then, the production of insulin must decrease below the demands placed upon it. Thus, frank diabetes mellitus results.

Ordinarily, this reciprocal relationship functions admirably. Between meals, the blood sugar slowly diminishes, and therefore the production of insulin decreases. This then permits other hormones to increase the production of glucose, thereby maintaining the blood level fairly constant. Following a high-carbohydrate meal, as the glucose is absorbed from the intestine into the blood stream, the stimulation to the islet cells progressively increases. There is now insulin available to assure prompt storage or utilization of the blood glucose, thereby preventing an undue rise in the glucose level. Through this self-regulating mechanism, the blood-sugar concentration varies only within a narrow range despite the great fluctuation in carbohydrate ingestion and the irregular time intervals between meals.

The hypophysis also liberates a hormone which plays an important role in carbohydrate metabolism. But this is clearly not a tropic hormone; it only indirectly influences pancreatic activity. Certainly, if the hypophysis secretes much of this substance, the blood sugar will tend to rise; therefore more insulin will be produced. But it must be understood that the increased secretion of insulin does not result from the direct action of this hypophyseal secretion. In so far as we know, the regulation of pancreatic function is exercised solely through the blood-sugar concentration.

GLUCAGON

It is now known that the **alpha cells** of the islets of Langerhans secrete glucagon which elevates blood sugar. Glucagon is a straight chain polypeptide with 29 amino acid units.

Function of Glucagon   Glucagon is termed the **hyperglycemic hormone** because it elevates blood sugar. It does this by speeding the conversion of liver glycogen to glucose. It also increases the rate of gluconeogenesis from protein. Increased gluconeogenesis, however, may result from the depletion of liver glycogen, but the present consensus is that increased gluconeogenesis is a direct effect of glucagon action.

Glucagon is thought to decrease glycogenolysis by converting inactive **phosphorylase** to the active form. Phosphorylase is an enzyme that catalyzes glycogenolysis.

When glucagon is administered, the metabolic rate increases. This calorigenic action is probably the end result of increased deamination of amino acids in the process of gluconeogenesis.

Regulation of Glucagon Secretion   Low blood sugar stimulates the alpha cells of the islets of Langerhans to secrete glucagon. High blood sugar inhibits them. There is thus a similar feed-back mechanism to that which controls insulin secretion, but it works in the opposite direction.

Under normal circumstances, only fasting lowers the blood sugar low enough to stimulate glucagon secretion. For this reason glucagon is sometimes referred to as the **fasting hormone.**

ABNORMALITIES OF ISLET-CELL FUNCTION

As in the case of all the other endocrine glands, the islet cells in many cases secrete either too little or too much insulin. The underproduction of insulin results in **diabetes mellitus.** Overproduction of insulin is termed **hyperinsulinism.**

Diabetes Mellitus   It is estimated that in the United States there are at least 1,000,000 people afflicted with this disorder. It has also been stated, based upon reliable evidence, that over 4,000,000 people now living will eventually develop this disease. When we realize that there are many individuals suffering from milder forms of this disorder who escape detection, we first begin to appreciate just how serious the problem is. And its occurrence is rapidly increasing. Fortunately, the death rate from this disease is steadily being whittled away, but still some 20 out of every 100,000 deaths are caused by diabetes. It occurs at all ages, but most commonly in late middle life, usually in the fifth and sixth decade. Diabetes seem to afflict women far more frequently than men.

If there should be a hormonal imbalance so that there is relatively too little insulin, the sequence of events portrayed in Fig. 29-3 results. The utilization of carbohydrate is severely impaired. Consequently, glucose accumulates in the blood. This gives rise to **hyperglycemia.** In classic diabetes, blood-sugar levels of 200 to 300 mg per cent, or even higher, are encountered. This is to be compared with the normal fasting range of 70 to 90 mg per cent. In Chap. 25 it was emphasized that at normal glucose levels no glucose appears in the urine. Glucose freely filters through Bowman's capsule, but all that passes through is reabsorbed by the tubules. The tubules have a definite limitation on how much glucose they can reabsorb per unit time. As the blood-glucose concentration increases, so does the concentration in the tubules. Finally, a point is reached at which the tubule cells cannot reabsorb all the glucose presented to them. Therefore the unabsorbed glucose appears in the urine. **Glycosuria,** glucose in the urine, begins when the blood sugar increases

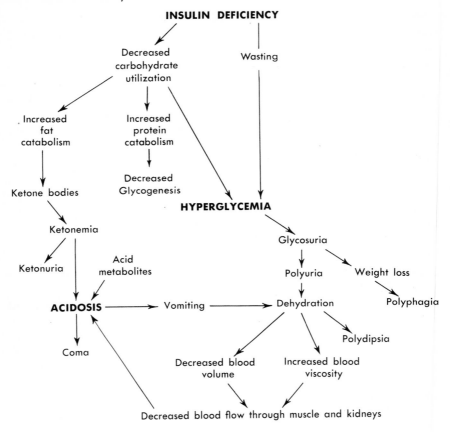

FIG. 29-3 Sequence of events resulting from insulin deficiency.

above about 160 mg per cent. It is, of course, a characteristic finding in diabetes mellitus.

Water is normally reabsorbed by the kidney collecting duct cells. The more concentrated the filtrate, the less water reabsorbed. The large quantity of glucose in the filtrate by this mechanism decreases the amount of water reabsorbed, and so another characteristic finding in diabetes is **diuresis** or **polyuria.** The great urine production causes dehydration, excites thirst, and therefore people with diabetes always consume abnormal quantities of fluids, a condition termed **polydipsia.** The unsatisfactory utilization of foodstuffs and the loss of glucose via the urine naturally lead to weight loss. The individual then eats more and more. This highly characteristic finding in diabetes mellitus is termed **polyphagia.**

All these changes are brought about by the impaired carbohydrate metabolism. The fact that in diabetes carbohydrate cannot be normally utilized is well shown by the RQ, which is characteristically low. In other words, the energy requirements of the individual must be supplied by the metabolism of protein and fat. Large stores of fat are mobilized and carried to the liver where they are started through the catabolic processes. This mechanism liberates **ketone bodies.** Ordinarily, ketone bodies are oxidized as rapidly as they are formed. Thus the concentration of ketone bodies in the blood remains low and constant. But under these abnormal conditions, the production of ketone bodies is so great that not all of them can be oxidized. Consequently, they accumulate in the blood and spill over in the urine. There is thus **ketonemia** (ketone bodies in the blood) and **ketonuria** (ketone bodies in the urine). These ketone bodies, one of which is acetone, give to the breath and the urine their characteristic odor.

Protein is also catabolized at an abnormal rate. The products of protein catabolism are acidic. Because of these acid metabolites and the ketone bodies, the alkalinity of the blood steadily decreases until it becomes incompatible with life. Death ends the sequence.

Insulin, of course, is the mainstay in the treatment of diabetes mellitus. But there are other important considerations. The weight of the individual plays a vital role. The incidence of diabetes among obese people is so much greater than among otherwise normal individuals that obesity is usually considered to be one of the predisposing causes of the disease. Therefore an obese individual with diabetes should be placed upon a reducing diet. There is a severe negative nitrogen balance in untreated diabetes. Consequently, the diet should be high in protein to make up these depleted stores. The diet should also be substantial in carbohydrate. This may be surprising, but so long as insulin is being given, the carbohydrate metabolism will be normal. Enough must then be ingested so as to reduce the abnormal catabolism of fat.

Insulin is so rapidly taken up from the subcutaneous spaces where it is normally injected that small frequent injections must be given to avert a precipitous fall in the blood sugar. To obviate frequent administration, insulin is now available combined with protamine and zinc. This **protamine zinc insulin** is absorbed into the blood stream much more slowly than regular insulin. Thus larger injections can be given less often. In actual practice a mixture of regular and protamine zinc insulin is used.

Quite understandably, the necessity of regular injections proves very unpleasant to the diabetic individual. For this reason, scientists have continued to seek for an effective substance that could be taken by mouth. **Tolbutamine** is currently being used. It is thought to lower blood sugar by stimulating the production of insulin from the beta cells. It is, therefore, of value only if the beta cells retain some capacity for secretion of insulin. **Phenethylbiguanide** is also of value in that it seems to encourage the various tissues to increase their utilization of glucose. However, it in no way mimics the action of insulin in this respect. The ideal oral substance to control diabetes mellitus has yet to be found.

Hyperinsulinism   Occasionally, because of tumorous growth of the islets of Langerhans, there is an overproduction of insulin. As might be expected, such cases are characterized by abnormally low blood sugar, a condition termed **hypoglycemia.**

Hypoglycemia, if severe—if the blood sugar falls below about 50 mg per cent—causes marked alterations of the nervous system. In such a state the individual may appear to be under the influence of alcohol, and often such people have been misdiagnosed. If the hypoglycemia is not corrected promptly, convulsions and death result.

It is of interest to note that the persistent low blood sugar gives rise to marked hunger contractions, so that these individuals have an insatiable craving for food. This is fortunate, since they respond by eating almost constantly, thus maintaining their blood sugar above the critical level. However, if they are prevented by circumstances from eating for several hours, they may well pass into hypoglycemic convulsions.

The treatment of this disorder is surgical, although milder forms have been successfully resolved with adrenocortical extracts.

ADRENAL CORTEX

Of the two parts of the adrenal gland (Fig. 29-4), the cortical cells seem to be the more important. If this tissue is removed, the animal steadily disintegrates and dies within about a week. The medulla can be destroyed with little or no apparent distress.

EXTIRPATION

The adrenal cortex is essential to life. Following removal of these glands there is loss of appetite with a resulting steady reduction in weight and great wasting. Carbohydrate metabolism is altered so that the blood sugar decreases to subnormal levels; if the animal is fasted, it is likely to go into hypoglycemic shock. In addition to these alterations, there is progressive hemoconcentration which leads to a reduced blood pressure and ultimate renal failure. There are also marked changes in sodium and potassium metabolism. Perhaps most significantly, adrenalectomized animals are extremely susceptible to adverse conditions like high or low temperatures, hemorrhage, and severe exercise. Such stress usually precipitates a fatal crisis in an adrenalectomized animal.

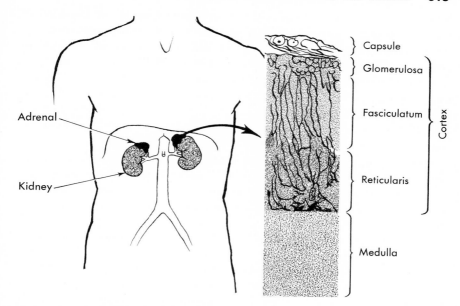

FIG. 29-4 Anatomical relationships of the adrenal glands. On the right is a cross section which shows the cortical zones.

ADRENOCORTICAL HORMONES

The extract of adrenocortical tissue is efficacious in preventing all the above alterations. Thus, an adrenalectomized animal may be maintained indefinitely with daily injections. As is to be expected, the administration of large quantities of this substance can bring about alterations in the sodium and potassium metabolism which are just opposite to those observed in the adrenalectomized animal. Likewise, the blood-sugar and liver-glycogen stores may be greatly increased.

From these observations it can readily be seen that there is no single, well-defined function attributable to the adrenal cortex. For example, in the case of the thyroid we concluded that its function was to regulate the metabolic rate. We learned that the parathyroid glands control calcium and phosphate metabolism. But the adrenal cortex is a far more complex gland.

Many distinct adrenocortical hormones have been isolated. All of them are steroids (Fig. 29-5). They are very similar in structure to the sex hormones and in some functions actually simulate them. In an attempt to simplify the terminology of this great mass of substances, the ones which act mainly upon the metabolism of potassium and sodium have been named **mineralocorticoids,** those which affect carbohydrate metabolism are termed **glucocorticoids.** The most potent of the mineralocorticoids is **aldosterone** (Fig. 29-5). However, there is so little of this hormone available that **desoxycorticosterone acetate (DOCA),** although it is far less effective than aldosterone, is still widely used in the clinic. Of the glucocorticoids, **cortisol,** also termed **hydrocortisone,** or **compound "F,"** and **corticosterone,** or **compound "B,"** appear to be the major components of the mixture secreted by the human adrenal cortex. The adrenal cortex also secretes varying amounts of **testosterone** and **estradiol.**

Metabolism of the Cortical Hormones The biosynthesis of the adrenal corticosteroids is shown in Fig. 29-6. The precursor of all of them is cholesterol. It is of considerable interest that progesterone is an intermediary product necessary for the synthesis of aldosterone, corticosterone, and cortisol. Progesterone is an important sex hormone formed by the ovary. Triphosphopyridine nucleotide (TPNH) is obviously necessary for the synthesis of these steroids.

There is good evidence that aldosterone is formed primarily by the **zona glomerulosa.** It has been claimed that cortisol and corticosterone are formed in the **zona fasciculata,** and **dehydroepiandrosterone** (similar to testosterone) is synthesized in the **zona reticularis.** The evidence for this distinction, however, is not too compelling.

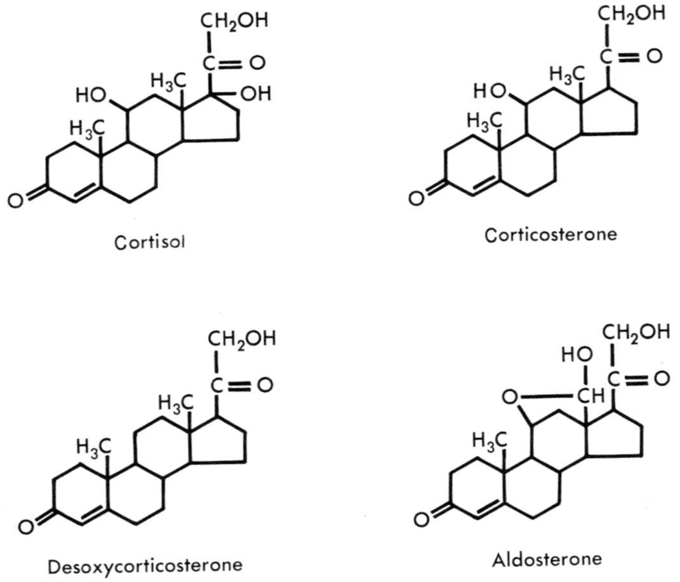

FIG. 29-5 Structural formulas of corticosteroids.

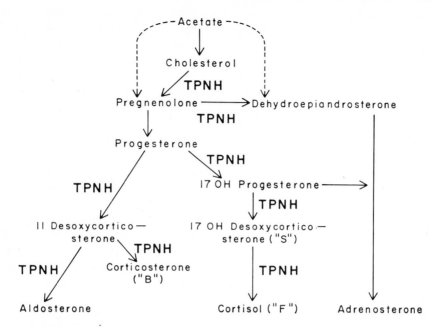

FIG. 29-6 Biosynthesis of the adrenocortical hormones. (Reproduced, with permission, from S. J. Tepperman, "Metabolic and Endocrine Physiology," Year Book Medical Publishers, Chicago, 1962.)

Cortisol and corticosterone are carried in the plasma bound to a specific globulin termed **transcortin** or **corticosteroid-binding globulin (CBG).** While the steroids are bound, they are physiologically inactive. They can only exert their influence in the free, or unbound state. Thus, if there is excessive transcortin, all of the steroid may be bound, and this would give rise to findings characteristic of adrenal insufficiency. Aldosterone is not protein bound.

Mineralocorticoid Action   Extirpation of the adrenal glands results in a decreased plasma sodium and an increase in the potassium concentration. In the intact animal it has been found that the administration of mineralocorticoids influences the renal tubular reabsorption of these two elements so that sodium is reabsorbed to a greater extent while potassium reabsorption is depressed. Consequently, the plasma is depleted of potassium and the sodium concentration increases. These results are, of course, just the opposite of that observed in the adrenalectomized animal. Thus it may be concluded that the mineralocorticoids act to influence renal tubular reabsorption of sodium and potassium. But it has also been reported that these hormones alter plasma potassium concentration even in an animal deprived of its kidneys. This clearly means that the mineralocorticoids must act not only on the renal tubules, but elsewhere as well. The evidence is growing that these hormones regulate the transfer of potassium through the cell membrane. Therefore, in the adrenalectomized animal potassium accumulates in the plasma instead of entering the cells. When the hormones are administered, the plasma potassium passes rapidly into the cells.

The influence that the mineralocorticoids exert on sodium and potassium levels strikingly controls the volume of body fluids. In the adrenalectomized animal, sodium is lost from the body because of its failure to be reabsorbed by the renal tubules. As a consequence, the extracellular fluid, which includes the blood volume, decreases, the cardiac output is diminished, the blood pressure falls, there is hemoconcentration and a sluggish blood flow, and finally renal failure and death occur (Fig. 29-7).

Glucocorticoid Action   It has been well established that the glucocorticoids are capable of increasing the store of liver glycogen and opposing the action of insulin in so far as the blood sugar is concerned. The evidence strongly suggests that the major effect of these hormones is to increase the rate of gluconeogenesis, that is, the conversion of protein to carbohydrate.

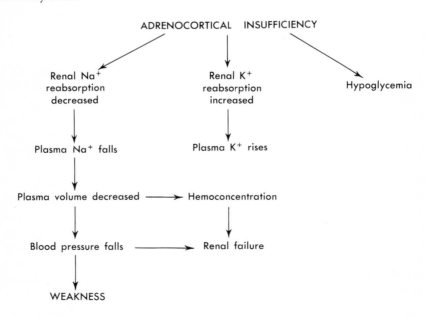

FIG. 29-7   Sequence of events resulting from adrenocortical insufficiency.

It can be seen, then, that the blood sugar is maintained within relatively narrow limits by the opposing action of insulin on the one hand and of the glucocorticoids on the other. Insulin, by facilitating the entry of glucose into the cells, lowers blood sugar. The glucocorticoids, by encouraging gluconeogenesis, elevate blood sugar.

Other Corticosteroid Functions In view of the fact that the glucocorticoids elevate blood sugar by enhancing gluconeogenesis from protein, it follows that protein metabolism is influenced by these steroids. The glucocorticoids also cause excessive fat catabolism with the development of ketonemia and ketonuria.

While aldosterone decreases urine output, the glucocorticoids are necessary for normal water excretion. If there is glucocorticoid deficiency, the kidneys do not eliminate a water load. It is said that the glucocorticoids exert this influence through regulation of the rate of glomerular filtration. A better explanation is probably the regulation by these steroids of the permeability of the collecting ducts and distal tubules.

The glucocorticoids alter the erythrocyte, lymphocyte, and eosinophil counts. The steroids decrease the number of lymphocytes and eosinophils, but increase the erythrocytes.

Cortisol, corticosterone, and many other steroids have a remarkable effect on inflammatory reactions. It does not seem to matter what gives rise to the inflammation, the steroids exert a beneficial influence. The most dramatic use of these steroids has been to ameliorate **rheumatoid arthritis.** Very large, unphysiological doses of the steroid must be given in these cases. For this reason a concentrated effort is being made to synthesize steroids that will have anti-inflammatory properties but will not influence carbohydrate and electrolyte metabolism.

Anything, or any situation, which threatens the survival of the organism constitutes **stress.** It has been observed that the adrenal steroids provide a defense in such circumstances. In contradistinction, the adrenalectomized animal quickly succumbs to even moderate stress. There is considerable knowledge concerning the mechanism by which stress activates the adrenal cortex, but there is practically nothing known of the means by which the consequent outpouring of the steroids protects the organism.

In the absence of the glucocorticoids, the permeability of the capillaries increases and the arterioles fail to respond to stimuli which normally evokes constriction.

Finally, it is well known that abnormalities of the adrenal cortex may markedly influence the secondary sexual characteristics. It is now known that testosterone and estradiol can be secreted by the adrenal cortex.

REGULATION OF THE ADRENAL CORTEX

The anterior lobe of the hypophysis secretes a hormone, termed the **adrenocorticotropic hormone (ACTH)**, which regulates the zona fasciculata. It can also influence the zona glomerulosa. What influence it has on the zona reticularis is not clear. The glucocorticoids form a reciprocal relationship with ACTH. When the steroids decrease, more ACTH is secreted. On the other hand, the administration of steroids inhibits the secretion of ACTH. If one adrenal gland is removed, the cortex of the remaining gland hypertrophies. This is due to the decrease in steroid following the loss of one gland; the consequent increase in ACTH causes hypertrophy of the remaining gland so that once again the normal blood level of the steroids is achieved and equilibrium established.

The hypothalamus secretes a neurohumor called **corticotropin-releasing factor (CRF)**, which releases ACTH from the anterior lobe of the hypophysis. By virtue of this link the nervous system can regulate the activity of the adrenal cortex. There is evidence that the glucocorticoids can directly inhibit the secretion of CRF and thus form an additional feed-back system.

The control of the zona glomerulosa and the secretion of aldosterone is still a very open problem. ACTH can alter the activity of this zone of the cortex, but there are reasons to believe that there are other, more important regulatory forces. Some authorities believe that the concentration of sodium and/or potassium in the circulating blood directly controls the output of aldosterone. Others insist that there is a neurohumor produced by some part of the brain, perhaps the diencephalon, which is responsible for its regulation. The **pineal gland** has also been suggested as being important in this role.

The best current evidence suggests that **angiotensin** is the most important factor controlling aldosterone secretion. Angiotensin forms in the blood from the reaction of **angiotensinogen** and **renin.** Renin is secreted by the kidney. The control of the renal secretion of renin is believed to involve a change in mean blood pressure, or pulse pressure. It has been observed that most anything that reduces mean or pulse pressure results in increased angiotensin production and increased aldosterone secretion. Aldosterone increases sodium and water retention, thereby elevating both mean and pulse pressure. This would therefore constitute an important self-regulating mechanism.

It is thought that the **juxtamedullary cells** of the kidney are responsible for renin secretion. It is possible that these cells are stretch receptors which would be stretched by increased pressure in the afferent arterioles of the kidney. Whatever the specific mechanism, it results in an effective feed-back arrangement which maintains the volume of the extracellular fluid through regulation of aldosterone secretion.

ABNORMALITIES OF ADRENOCORTICAL FUNCTION

Hypofunction   In man, the inadequate secretion of adrenocortical hormones give rise to a disorder called **Addison's disease.** It is characterized by weight loss, weakness, easy fatigability, hypoglycemia, hypotension, altered sodium and potassium metabolism, and a striking bronze pigmentation of the skin.

Addison's disease, if diagnosed early enough, can usually be successfully treated, with the various cortical preparations. One such compound, **desoxycorticosterone acetate,** is often used in this condition because pellets of the pure crystalline material can be implanted beneath the skin. In this position the hormone is slowly absorbed into the body, and the necessity of frequent injections is avoided.

Hyperfunction   The excessive production of the adrenal steroids causes the expected alterations in carbohydrate and electrolyte metabolism. In addition, findings include obesity, especially in the back of the neck, giving rise to the characteristic "buffalo hump." The face becomes round (moon face) and is usually flushed. There is general weakness. This combination of findings due to hyperfunction of the adrenal cortex is termed **Cushing's syndrome.**

There are cases in which the adrenal cortex secretes excessive amounts of aldosterone, a situation referred to as **aldosteronism.** This may result from an adrenal cortical tumor or it may occur in the absence of a tumor. In either case the excessive hormone causes hypokalemia because of increased renal loss of potassium. The blood sodium is usually somewhat elevated. And due to the retention of sodium and water with expansion of the blood volume, there is generally hypertension. In some patients the cardinal finding is edema.

Cushing's syndrome may, or may not, be associated with sexual changes. It depends upon whether or not the zona reticularis is also hyperactive. If it is, there is usually exaggeration of the male characteristics. A young boy may undergo maturity with enlarged penis, lowering of the voice, development of chest hair, and sexual desire. This is referred to as the **adrenogenital syndrome.** Male adults show overgrowth of body hair, enlargement of the sexual organs, and increased sexual drive. Adult women may undergo virilism. The breasts atrophy, the clitoris enlarges, body hair increases, and baldness may ensue. Young girls afflicted with this disorder often become sexually mature at a very early age.

ADRENAL MEDULLA

Embryological and histological studies indicate that the adrenal medulla is actually modified nervous tissue. Preganglionic sympathetic fibers innervate the adrenal medulla. The medullary cells are said to be modified postganglionic sympathetic tissue.

EXTIRPATION

In view of the fact that the entire sympathetic nervous system can be destroyed without causing any very drastic results, it is not surprising that if both adrenal medullas are extirpated the animal may quickly recover and seem to be quite normal. But as we learned in discussing the autonomic nervous system, this result does not warrant the conclusion that the adrenal medulla has no function. Rather it indicates that it is a reserve organ, partaking little or not at all in normal functions but ever ready to swing into action in case of an emergency. Thus it can be shown that after the adrenomedullary tissue is removed the animal is far more vulnerable to stress than is a normal animal, especially in the immediate responses to adverse conditions.

ADRENOMEDULLARY HORMONES

Epinephrine This hormone, also called adrenaline, is secreted by the adrenal medulla. It is powerless when given orally, but when injected it influences almost every physiological mechanism we have studied thus far.

Epinephrine is a potent pressor substance. It acts upon the smooth muscle of the arterioles, causing them to constrict. Consequently, the peripheral resistance is increased and the arterial blood pressure is elevated. Epinephrine also stimulates the heart. It augments the rate and vigor of the beat. This substance inhibits intestinal activity and the urinary bladder. Yet it causes contraction of the gallbladder, the uterus and most sphincters. The pupil of the eye is dilated. It even influences skeletal muscle, so that when there is a high concentration of epinephrine in the blood the person fatigues less easily and seems to possess a greater capacity for work.

Epinephrine plays a cardinal role in carbohydrate metabolism. If the liver contains glycogen, the injection of this hormone will rapidly convert it to blood glucose. This one function alone emphasizes the emergency role of epinephrine, for it serves to make available carbohydrate in a form in which it can be rapidly oxidized for energy.

Finally, it is found that epinephrine decreases the clotting time and causes contraction of the spleen which increases blood volume. There is evidence that it also stimulates the hypophysis to secrete ACTH.

How are these widespread and confusing results to be interpreted? If the reader will stop and think just what physiological alterations would be desirable in an emergency, as, for example, when he is suddenly challenged and must fight, he will find that most of these physiological alterations are speeded or enhanced by epinephrine. For example, it is found that the blood pressure is raised. This forces more blood to the active muscles when the arterioles dilate. Epinephrine enlarges the pupil of the eye and permits more available light to strike the retina. This hormone inhibits peristalsis, which is not needed under such circumstances, and thus releases blood for use in the active muscles. Carbohydrate is mobilized and made available for energy. The muscles are given that small but desirable extra push. It is also found that the coronary blood vessels are caused to dilate, thus permitting more blood to flow to the hard-working heart which is itself stimulated by epinephrine. Such an analysis should quickly convince one that in a fight, in an emergency, it is well to have the adrenomedullary tissue pouring epinephrine into the blood stream.

Norepinephrine The reports regarding the effect of epinephrine are often conflicting, probably because commercial preparations usually contain two distinct substances: (1) **epinephrine** and (2) **norepinephrine**. For the most part the two hormones possess similar actions with differences only in the degree of response. However, in some respects the two have antagonistic effects. In Fig. 29-8 the structural formulas of the two hormones are depicted. It can be seen that they are quite similar.

REGULATION OF THE ADRENAL MEDULLA

The medullary tissue is completely under the domination of the sympathetic nervous system. Thus when a person is placed in a threatening situation, the nervous system is fired, the sympathetic fibers conduct impulses to the adrenal medulla, and epinephrine is secreted.

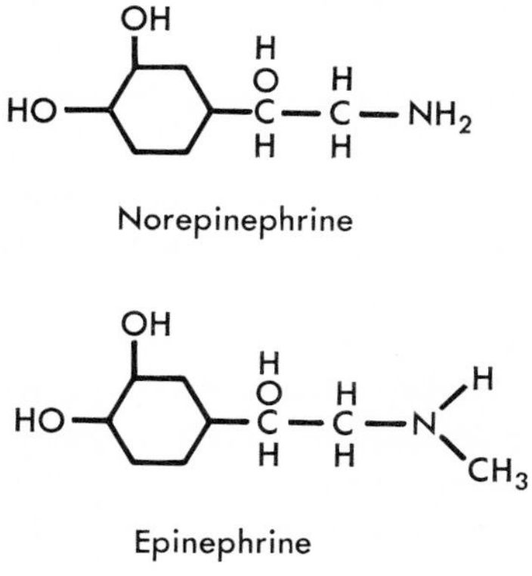

Norepinephrine

Epinephrine

FIG. 29-8 Structural formulas of norepinephrine and epinephrine.

It is doubtful if anything like the reciprocal relationships noted in the case of the other glands exists here. Epinephrine seems to be liberated simply in response to nervous stimulation and continues to be formed so long as the sympathetic nervous system is firing. When the emergency has passed, the nervous activity subsides, and the secretion of the adrenomedullary hormone probably becomes very slight or ceases altogether.

ABNORMALITIES OF ADRENOMEDULLARY FUNCTION

Very few clinical cases of abnormalities of medullary function have been reported. Since this endocrine gland is important only in unusual circumstances, its failure to respond under those conditions is seldom noted or appreciated. However, the abnormal production of epinephrine, as in the case of tumors of this tissue, has been studied.

Should a medullary tumor develop, great quantities of epinephrine would be poured into the blood stream continuously instead of only during emergencies. The situation could be likened to a car parked at the curb with the motor racing. This is precisely the case with **pheochromocytoma,** a term used to designate a tumor of the medullary tissue. Individuals with such a tumor develop all the manifestations of an "excitable" sympathetic nervous system. Thus, we find elevated blood pressure, dilated pupils, and fast heartbeat.

SUMMARY

In the **pancreas,** the **islets of Langerhans** secrete **insulin.** Insulin deficiency results in **diabetes mellitus.** This condition is characterized by (1) **hyperglycemia,** (2) **glycosuria,** (3) **polyuria,** (4) **polydipsia,** (5) **polyphagia,** (6) **ketonemia,** (7) **ketonuria,** and (8) **acidosis.** The primary function of insulin is thought to be to regulate the transfer of glucose through the cell membrane. In this way it quickly lowers blood sugar. Insulin production is regulated by the blood glucose concentration. When the blood sugar falls, more insulin is produced. **Hyperinsulinism** usually results from tumors of the islet cells. The abnormally low blood sugar leads to convulsions and respiratory failure.

The **alpha cells** of the islets of Langerhans secrete **glucagon** which elevates blood sugar. Glucagon secretion is controlled by the level of the blood sugar; the lower the blood sugar the greater the secretion of glucagon.

The **adrenal glands** consist of two distinct endocrine organs: (1) the **adrenal cortex** and (2) the **adrenal medulla.** The adrenal cortex secretes **mineralocorticoids** which regulate sodium and potassium blood levels and **glucocorticoids** which influence carbohydrate metabolism. Extirpation of the adrenal cortices results in an elevation of plasma potassium and a decrease in sodium. The mineralocorticoids act on the renal tubules as well as the cell membrane. The glucocorticoids elevate blood sugar by facilitating the conversion of protein to carbohydrate.

The major mineralocorticoid is **aldosterone.** The major glucocorticoids are **cortisol** and **corticosterone.** The adrenal cortex can also secrete male and female sex hormones.

The growth and activity of the adrenal cortex are regulated by the **adrenocorticotropic hormone (ACTH).** ACTH is controlled by the glucocorticoid blood level and also by hypothalamic **corticotropin-releasing factor (CRF).** Aldosterone secretion is regulated by **angiotensin,** the product of **renin** from the kidney and **angiotensinogen** which is in the blood. ACTH also plays a role.

Hypofunction of the adrenal cortex in man produces **Addison's disease.** It is characterized by loss of weight, weakness, easy fatigue, low blood pressure, altered sodium and potassium metabolism, and bronze pigmentation of the skin. Hormonal treatment is usually effective. Hyperfunction of the adrenal cortex in children markedly speeds sexual maturation, whereas the same disorder in the adult often causes a bizarre reversal of sex. These changes can usually be ameliorated by surgical removal of the active tissue.

The adrenal medulla consists of modified postganglionic sympathetic nervous tissue. In response to nervous stimulation it secretes **epinephrine** and **norepinephrine.** These hormones mobilize many physiological mechanisms which better prepare the individual to protect himself in an emergency situation.

A tumor of the adrenal medulla, a so-called **pheochromocytoma,** causes the continuous liberation of epinephrine with its attendant findings such as high blood pressure and fast heart rate.

QUESTIONS

1. Outline the sequence of events that occurs in the absence of insulin.
2. What is the mechanism for the control of insulin secretion?
3. How does insulin influence blood sugar?
4. What is the difference between the mineralocorticoids and the glucocorticoids?
5. What is the function of the adrenal medulla?
6. Discuss the hormonal interrelationships responsible for the regulation of blood sugar.

SUGGESTED READING

Berson, S. A., and Yalow, R. S., "Plasma Insulin in Health and Disease," *Am. J. Med.,* 31:#6, 874–881, December 1961.

Cooley, D. G., "Hormones: Your Body's Chemical Rousers," *Today's Health,* **40:** #11, 28–33, 72–74, November 1962.

Flink, E. B., "Adenohypophysis and Adrenal Cortex," *Ann. Rev. Physiol.,* **23:** 229–262, 1961.

Forsham, P. H., "The Adrenal Gland," *Clin. Symposia,* **15:** #1, 6–21, January-March, 1963.

Malmejac, J., "Activity of the Adrenal Medulla and Its Regulation," *Physiol. Rev.,* **44:** #2, 186–218, April 1964.

Ratcliff, J. D., "Victory over the Sugar Sickness," *Today's Health,* **42:** #3, 56–58, 60–61, 64, March 1964.

The Hypophysis

30

FROM THE VERY FIRST CHAPTER IN THIS PART, which dealt with the thyroid gland, we have become familiar with the often repeated theme that the hypophysis regulates the action of many of the other endocrine glands. This widespread and important function has won for the hypophysis the appellative **master gland.** The intimate relationship of the hypophysis with the other endocrine glands makes a consideration of this organ an ideal way to review the entire subject of endocrinology.

ANATOMY OF THE HYPOPHYSIS

The hypophysis is a remarkably small gland, in view of the great number of important hormones which it elaborates. It is, in the adult, only about 1 cm in diameter, that is, about the size of a lima bean. It resides underneath the brain and is protected by a saddlelike depression in the base of the skull. The shape of this depression has given rise to its name, **sella turcica,** which means "Turkish saddle."

Part of the hypophysis develops in conjunction with the oral structures. In the embryo there is an upward outpouching from the roof of the mouth which becomes the anterior portion of the hypophysis. This oral projection grows up to meet and unite with an evagination of the brain which grows downward. These two bodies fuse and form the hypophysis. The origin convinced early investigators that this gland had, as its major function, the production of phlegm. Phlegm or mucus gave rise to the term **pituitary** and the gland is often referred to by this name. The term **hypophysis** now seems preferable because it means "to grow under," which accurately describes the position of the gland under the brain.

LOBES OF THE HYPOPHYSIS

Anatomically, the hypophysis is divided into (1) the **anterior lobe** and (2) the **posterior lobe.**

Anterior Lobe   Histological section of the anterior lobe reveals that it is composed of irregularly anastomosing cords of epithelial cells. Between these cords are large sinusoids which permit blood to flow freely and copiously around these secreting cells. This part of the hypophysis is called the anterior lobe, simply because in the normal position of this gland the anterior lobe is in front, or facing forward. It is also commonly referred to as the **adenohypophysis.**

The adenohypophysis consists of three types of cells: (1) **chromophobes** which constitute about 50 per cent of the cells and are thought to be non-secretory; (2) **acidophils,** about 40 per cent and which are believed to secrete luteinizing hormone, luteotrophic hormone, and the growth hormone; and (3) **basophils,** 10 per cent and which probably secrete follicle-stimulating hormone, thyrotropic hormone, and adrenocorticotropic hormone.

Posterior Lobe   The posterior lobe of the hypophysis is a good-sized lobe which, upon histological examination, proves to resemble nervous tissue. The principal cell is called a **pituicyte.** Because the posterior lobe is made up of modified nervous tissue, it is referred to as the **neurohypophysis.** Actually, the term neurohypophysis embraces more than merely the posterior lobe of the hypophysis. Strictly speaking, it includes the median eminence of the tuber cinereum, the infundibular stem, and the infundibular process. These three parts form a functional unit. The upper part of the infundibular stem, together with the surrounding pars tuberalis tissue, forms the hypophyseal stalk.

INNERVATION OF THE HYPOPHYSIS

The posterior lobe is richly innervated. The fibers arise in the **hypothalamus** and course down the **hypophyseal stalk** to the posterior lobe.

It is the innervation of the anterior lobe which has brought anatomists and physiologists to the firing line. Anatomically, there is little evidence of innervation of this lobe; yet physiologically there must be some connection. For example, rabbits ovulate only as a result of sexual excitement. Experiments indicate that ovulation is brought about by the sudden secretion of gonadotropic hormones by this lobe in response to nervous stimuli. Numerous other observations could be given which combine to form strong circumstantial evidence for the control of the anterior lobe by the nervous system. Recently, however, the problem has been resolved by the recognition of the role of the **hypothalamico-hypophyseal portal system** (Fig. 30-1). The hypothalamus, which receives impulses from all areas of the body, secretes **neurohumors.** The exact nature of these substances has not been established, but they are carried by the hypothalamico-hypophyseal portal system to the anterior lobe of the hypophysis

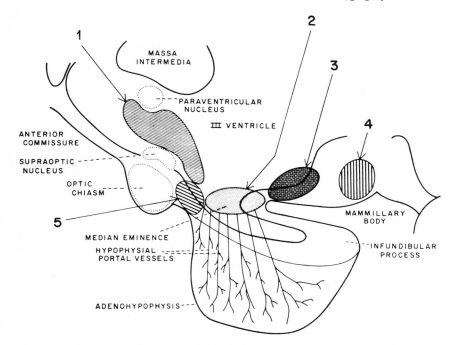

FIG. 30-1 Hypothalamico-hypophyseal system. Illustration also shows the results of lesions in various areas. (Reproduced, with permission, from S. J. Tepperman, "Metabolic and Endocrine Physiology," Year Book Medical Publishers, Chicago, 1962.)

where they exert important control over the elaboration of the various hormones. In this way the nervous system is able to influence almost all the endocrine glands.

FUNCTION OF THE HYPOPHYSIS

The anterior and posterior lobes not only are anatomically distinct but also serve different functions. Thus, just as in the case of the adrenal glands, we are here dealing really with two endocrine organs.

ANTERIOR LOBE

Extirpation Removal of this gland causes widespread alterations. Yet, strangely, the animal survives. But if about 2 weeks or more are permitted to elapse after removal of the hypophysis and then the other endocrine glands are examined, striking changes will be observed.

The gonads, the thyroid, and the adrenal glands all atrophy. One need only remove these organs, weigh them, and compare the weights with normal glands to see the difference. Not only do these glands waste away, but their output of hormones is sharply reduced. It is true that they continue to secrete, but they elaborate a very inadequate quantity of their specific hormones. Consequently, following hypophysectomy, all the changes to be expected of inadequate adrenal, thyroid, and gonadal function are observed. Thus the animal has a very low BMR and suffers from hypoglycemia, hypotension, weakness, disturbed sodium and potassium metabolism, and sexual inadequacy. If the gland is removed very early in pregnancy, the animal will abort. If removed later, pregnancy will continue but lactation will not take place.

Not all the changes observed following ablation of the hypophysis are due to reduced function of the adrenals, the thyroid, and the gonads. For example, if the gland is removed in the young, there is very definite stunting of growth. This occurs even though the animal is maintained on sufficient thyroxin to hold the BMR normal. In a similar way it can be shown that the loss of the hypophysis interferes with carbohydrate metabolism, not only because of the reduced activity of the adrenal but also because of the loss of a hormone, normally secreted by the anterior lobe, which plays an important role in blood-glucose regulation.

In short, the removal of the anterior lobe results in many alterations, some direct and others indirect. It can be concluded that this gland secretes hormones which regulate the adrenals, the thyroid, and the gonads. It also produces hormones which are essential to lactation and normal growth and which aid in maintaining blood glucose constant. There are, then, several distinct hormones secreted by this amazing gland.

Thyrotropic Hormone   TSH influences only the growth and activity of the thyroid gland (Fig. 30-2). If the thyroid gland is missing, this hormone exerts no effect, with the possible exception of causing **exophthalmos.** But clearly its primary function is to regulate thyroid activity. TSH encourages the growth of the thyroid gland and the manufacture of thyroglobulin, and it also excites the proteolytic enzyme to convert thyroglobulin to thyroxin, the active circulating form of the thyroid hormone. Through this combination of actions, TSH administration can cause all the changes associated with hyperthyroidism, particularly an elevated BMR.

The thyrotropic hormone is itself regulated by the level of iodine in the blood. Thus a balance is reached, so that thyroxin keeps TSH in check. There is, therefore, a steady blood-thyroxin level, but if this hormone is suddenly and rapidly utilized, TSH is removed from its inhibition and pours forth to stimulate the thyroid gland to liberate more thyroxin. TSH is also controlled by the hypothalamus.

Adrenocorticotropic Hormone   ACTH regulates the growth and activity of the adrenal cortices (Fig. 30-2). Just as in the case of TSH and thyroxin,

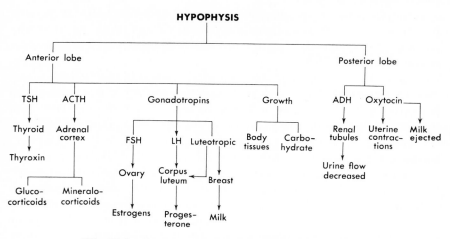

FIG. 30-2   Functions of the hypophyseal hormones.

there is a reciprocal relationship between the adrenocortical hormones and ACTH. The use of ACTH in stress conditions and for rheumatoid arthritis is based upon its proved ability to cause a marked increase in the secretion of the adrenocortical hormones.

More detailed analysis of the function of the adrenocorticotropic hormone discloses that it exerts most of its influence on the secretion of glucocorticoids and very little on the production of mineralocorticoids. Histological examination of the adrenal cortex reveals three distinct layers of cells. One layer, the **zona fasciculata,** is thought to produce the glucocorticoids, whereas the **zona glomerulosa** secretes mainly mineralocorticoids. Following the extirpation of the hypophysis it is found that the zona fasciculata atrophies far more than does the zona glomerulosa. This observation is in keeping with the theory that ACTH is primarily concerned with the control of glucocorticoid secretion.

Gonadotropic Hormones   There are three hormones secreted by the anterior lobe of the hypophysis which regulate ovarian function (Fig.30-2). One of these hormones, the so-called **luteotropic hormone,** is also essential to lactation. The other two gonadotropic hormones, **FSH** and **LH,** also influence the testes in man. In the male, however, LH is termed **ICSH.** The follicle-stimulating hormone is responsible for the monthly maturation of one **graafian follicle.** This follicle then liberates **estrogens.** The luteinizing and luteotropic hormones, on the other hand, govern the **corpus luteum.** The corpus luteum secretes **progesterone.**

Just as in the case of the other tropic hormones, there is a reciprocal relationship between the gonadotropins and the female sex hormones. But in this case a steady production does not result. The sex hormones wax and wane, and this oscillation is responsible for the rhythmicity of the menstrual cycle.

In man, FSH regulates the activity of the **seminiferous tubules** which produce the **sperm.** ICSH, on the other hand, controls the activity of the **interstitial cells.** These cells elaborate the male sex hormone **testosterone.** It is not known whether testosterone is produced steadily or in rhythmic fashion.

Lactogenic Hormone   The luteotropic hormone, also known as **prolactin,** acts lactogenically to stimulate the production of milk in the prepared breast (Fig. 30-2). The mammary glands develop at puberty under the influence of the estrogens. These glands have many ducts but very little secretory tissue. During pregnancy, under the stimulation of both estrogens and progesterone, especially the latter, the breasts grow larger, more ducts develop, but significantly now the secretory cells proliferate and ready themselves for the elaboration of milk. At this point, prolactin takes over and provokes the cells into forming copious quantities of milk.

Growth Hormone   The anterior lobe of the hypophysis secretes a hormone which plays a very important role in determining the size of the organism (Fig. 30-2). Figure 30-3 shows two hypophysectomized animals. One dog received hypophyseal extract without the growth hormone. The other animal was given the growth substance. The difference is striking. It will be recalled that the thyroid gland also influences the size of an individual. Thus **cretins** are stunted, but they are also disproportionate, whereas **hypophyseal dwarfs** are small but well-proportioned individuals.

Growth hormone has now been obtained in pure form. So potent are its growth-promoting qualities that only a very minute quantity is required to maintain normal growth in hypophysectomized rats. In this respect it is well to point out that growth is more than mere gain in weight. There are many substances which cause salt and water to accumulate and in this way produce a gain in size and weight, but that is not true growth. The best indication of growth, aside from weight, is the accumulation of body protein. For this reason any analysis of growth must include nitrogen-balance studies. When the growth hormone is administered to experimental animals, there are (1) a gain in weight, (2) significant changes in bone development, and (3) marked nitrogen retention. As a matter of fact, the presence of this hormone is essential for the normal retention of body protein.

Diabetogenic Hormone   It was discovered some time ago, if the anterior lobe of the hypophysis were to be removed at the same time that extirpation of the pancreas was done, diabetes mellitus did not develop. This

FIG. 30-3. Effect of hypophyseal growth hormone. The dachshunds are litter-mates about eleven months old. The dog in the lower figure was injected with growth hormone for 35 weeks. (After H. M. Evans and associates.)

result is not simply due to the reduction in adrenocortical function. There is good evidence to show that the anterior lobe liberates a hormone which opposes insulin, mobilizes carbohydrate stores, and elevates blood sugar. Because of these actions, the substance is termed **diabetogenic,** which means "to produce diabetes."

For some time it has been postulated that the diabetogenic hormone was a distinct entity. There is now, however, general concurrence that the growth hormone is responsible for the carbohydrate effects. So potent is the growth hormone in this respect that the continued injection of sufficient quantities in experimental animals ultimately leads to permanent diabetes mellitus. Apparently, under the influence of this substance, carbohydrate is mobilized, hyperglycemia ensues, insulin is secreted in great quantities, and eventually the islet cells become exhausted. At this point, insulin can no longer be elaborated and the animal becomes diabetic.

Part of the influence upon carbohydrate metabolism possessed by the anterior lobe is exerted through the production of ACTH and the consequent secretion of the glucocorticoids. But the glucocorticoids and the growth hormone do not act in precisely the same manner. As just outlined, growth hormone inhibits protein catabolism and thus slows the rate of gluconeogenesis, whereas the glucocorticoids definitely speed this process. On the other hand, the growth hormone markedly slows glucose utilization, and this may well be its major effect on carbohydrate metabolism. Interestingly enough, then, though the glucocorticoids and growth hormone yield the same end result, namely, the mobilization of carbohydrate as opposed to insulin, this picture is brought about in different ways. The former produces more carbohydrate, the latter prevents its utilization.

REGULATION OF ANTERIOR-LOBE FUNCTION

Reciprocal Relationships   All the tropic hormones are regulated by the blood level of the particular hormone with which they are concerned. That is, thyroxin controls TSH; the adrenocortical hormones, especially the glucocorticoids, regulate ACTH; and the sex hormones have a reciprocal relationship with the gonadotropins. But what about the lactogenic and growth hormones? This question cannot be answered definitely. There is some evidence that the estrogens regulate to a degree the lactogenic substance. The control of the growth hormone is still puzzling. There is evidence that the blood concentration of the sex hormones may have something to do with the secretion of this substance. It is known, for example, that boys and girls who sexually mature early usually are of average or below-average size. Thus a high correlation exists between the height of a woman and the time at which she begins to menstruate. Very tall girls, particularly those whose great stature comes from long extremities, often report the menarche at a relatively late year. Very tall men usually exhibit hypogonadism. These observations, however, are merely suggestive. The final answer is unknown.

Hypothalamic Control   One of the most important developments in endocrinology in recent years has been the discovery that the hypothalamus secretes neurohumors which influence the activity of the adrenohypophysis. The discovery of this "missing link" goes a long way in explaining many observations of the apparent affect of the nervous system on the endocrine system. Both are of vital importance in the regulation of the many physiological mechanisms discussed in this book. They may now be considered to be but two parts of a single integrating system.

Just how many neurohumors the hypothalamus secretes, the chemical nature of each, and the means by which they influence the adenohypophysis are all unanswered questions. There does, however, seem to be ample evidence for the belief that the hypothalamus secretes neurohumors which regulate TSH, ACTH, FSH, and LH. These are referred to as the **thyrotropin-releasing factor (TRF)**, **corticotropin-releasing factor (CRF)**, **follicle-stimulating-hormone-releasing factor (FSHRF)**, and **luteinizing-hormone-releasing factor (LHRF)**.

The control of luteotropic hormone and growth hormone by the hypothalamus has not yet been established.

ABNORMALITIES OF ANTERIOR-LOBE FUNCTION

In view of the fact that this lobe produces so many hormones with such widespread activities, a full discussion of the clinical cases involving abnormalities of the anterior lobe would fill a volume in itself. Only a few of the simpler and more obvious cases will be briefly mentioned.

Hypofunction The effects of hypofunction of the anterior lobe depend upon the age at which the malfunction occurred. If there is inadequate production during childhood, the individual will not be likely to attain normal stature. In extreme cases, a **dwarf** results. Such individuals are very small but well proportioned, are of average intelligence, and seem to develop sexually quite normally. Of course, there are cases where there is congenital absence of the anterior lobe, in which instance not only is the individual's growth stunted, but the thyroid, gonads, and adrenals all fail to develop normally. They suffer from hypofunction of all these glands.

Likewise, in the adult, many distinct disorders are caused by hypofunction of the anterior lobe. The great wasting and profound weakness and apathy are apparent. In such cases the BMR is very low, suggesting thyroid hypofunction, and there is almost total absence of sexual function. It is referred to as **Simmonds' disease.**

Hyperfunction The reader need only look at a basketball team to observe the results of hyperfunction of the anterior lobe during the developmental period. These individuals grow remarkably tall, some of them reaching well over 7 and sometimes 8 ft in height. Strangely enough, however, many hypophyseal giants have subnormal sexual development. One would expect a hyperactive gland to stimulate the gonads as well as the growth mechanisms, but such does not seem to be the case. It is possible that the great outpouring of the growth hormone may result from a failure of the gonads to produce sex hormones which normally exert some inhibition over the anterior lobe. However, it is not invariably true that tall individuals suffer from sexual inadequacy. The condition of unusual growth is termed **gigantism** or **giantism** (Fig. 30-4).

FIG. 30-4   Giantism. The man in the center is 8 ft 6½ in. tall and weighs 375 lb. The other two men are almost 6 ft tall. A tumor involving the adeno-hypophysis was found. (Reproduced, with permission, from R. I. Franks, *Am. J. Orthodont.*, **28**:580, 1942.)

If the anterior lobe first becomes hyperactive after puberty, there are also noticeable changes. The growth centers of the long bones have closed, and thus the increased production of the growth hormones cannot bring about an increase in height of the person, but soft tissues are stimulated and the flat bones do spread somewhat. Thus, as seen in Fig. 30-5, these people show a thickened nose, heavy lips, large, spadelike hands, and an underslung jaw. The disorder is called **acromegaly,** which means "great extremities." It is interesting to learn that many of these individuals also have hyperglycemia and glycosuria due to excessive secretion of growth hormone. Sexual and thyroid function may or may not be altered.

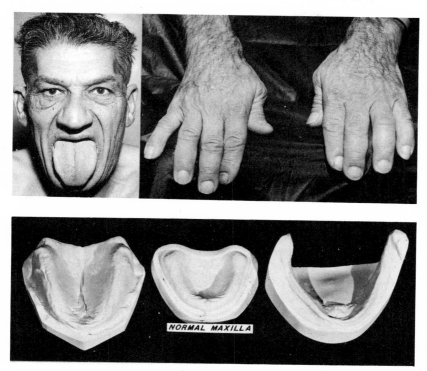

FIG. 30-5 Acromegaly. This is a typical case showing coarse facial features, an enlarged tongue, and heavy hands. Casts of his jaws are shown in the lower figure compared with a normal maxilla.

THE POSTERIOR LOBE

Extirpation   The posterior lobe can be removed or inactivated without interference with the function of the anterior lobe. In such preparations, the most outstanding alteration is in the volume of urine produced. Some twenty times the normal urine volume may be elaborated in the absence of the posterior lobe. The specific gravity of this great urine volume is very low, closely approaching that of water.

At one time it was taught that the pituicytes of the posterior lobe were responsible for formation and secretion of the hormones. Then it was proposed that the hormones were actually formed in the hypothalamus and transported by the axons of the supraoptic-hypophyseal pathway to the posterior lobe where they were stored for later release. This concept never met with much favor. Now there is good evidence that the hormones can be formed all along the axons which make up the pathway to enter the circulation at the sites of formation. The major site of formation appears to be the axon ending in the posterior lobe.

From a crude extract of the posterior lobe at least 2 purified hormones have been obtained. They are: (1) **vasopressin,** also known as the **antidiuretic hormone (ADH),** and (2) **oxytocin.**

Vasopressin   Vasopressin is a polypeptide containing 8 amino acids and a disulfide ring. Its major function is to enhance the reabsorption of water by the kidneys. For this reason vasopressin is popularly referred to as the antidiuretic hormone.

It will be recalled that in man about 125 ml of filtrate are formed by the glomeruli each minute. Approximately 124 ml of this filtrate are reabsorbed. The greater load is reabsorbed isosmotically, the remainder due to an osmotic gradient. This lesser fraction is influenced by ADH by alteration of the permeability of the distal tubules and collecting ducts. Variations in the quantity of urine excretion can be varied from about 0.35 ml per minute to close to 15 ml per minute. This broad range usually suffices to regulate body water volume.

Vasopressin, in large quantities, elevates the arterial pressure by constriction of the arterioles and precapillaries, thus its name. It is also one of the few substances that constricts the coronary arterioles. It seems to have a similar effect on the pulmonary vessels. The role of vasopressin in the normal physiological control of circulation is not clear. The quantities required to produce a pressor response are so large that there is a profound antidiuretic effect. For this reason its role in regulating circulation has been questioned. The suggestion has been made that it does play a significant role in the control of circulation through the vasa recta, the countercurrent circulatory loops essential for the maintenance of the osmotic state of the renal medullary tissue. Constriction of these vessels would slow the flow of blood and thus decrease the rate of removal of solutes from the medullary tissue.

Oxytocin   Oxytocin has reference to "rapid birth." This hormone acts on the uterus to evoke powerful contractions (Fig. 30-6). It is, therefore, used to assist in parturition. However, parturition appears to occur quite normally after extirpation of the neurohypophysis. Accordingly, there is considerable doubt as to the importance of oxytocin in childbirth. Oxytocin, however, is also secreted as a consequence of sexual excitement. It has therefore been suggested that the resulting uterine contractions facilitate the movement of sperm through the uterine lumen and into the fallopian tubes.

Suckling initiates impulses which result in the release of oxytocin. Oxytocin is carried by the blood to the breasts where it causes the ejection of milk from the nipples.

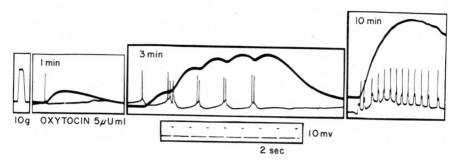

FIG. 30-6   Influence of oxytocin on the myometrium. The action potentials and mechanical activity are shown in each record. Note that oxytocin causes more rapid firing and a sustained, forceful contraction. (Reproduced, with permission, from H. Kuriyama, and A. Casapo, *Endocrinology,* **68:**1010, 1961.)

REGULATION OF POSTERIOR-LOBE FUNCTION

The posterior lobe of the hypophysis is innervated by neurons arising in the hypothalamus. The cells which give rise to these neurons have been shown to be very sensitive to the osmotic attraction of the blood. For this reason they are termed **osmoreceptors.** The osmotic state of the blood reflects the degree of hydration of the body as a whole. Thus when one perspires freely and fails to ingest comparable quantities of fluid, there will be generalized dehydration with some hemoconcentration. As a result, the osmoreceptors will be stimulated to fire impulses into the posterior lobe. The posterior lobe then secretes more of the antidiuretic hormone. This substance is carried by the blood to the kidneys where it encourages the greater reabsorption of water from the filtrate. Consequently, the urine volume is decreased and water conserved to combat the dehydration.

Conversely, if one consumes several bottles of beer or large quantities of other fluids, the blood is diluted, the activity of the osmoreceptors is inhibited, and the output of the posterior lobe decreases. In this case less fluid is reabsorbed by the renal tubules, and so the urine volume increases. This again assures the maintenance of body-water balance.

ABNORMALITIES OF POSTERIOR-LOBE FUNCTION

The only important known clinical manifestation of posterior-lobe malfunction is termed **diabetes insipidus.** This name refers to the great quantities of urine produced when too little antidiuretic hormone is secreted. It will be recalled that *diabetes* means "to run through a siphon." The pancreatic disorder was thus labeled because of the characteristically large urine flow. That disorder was further qualified as *mellitus,* which means "sweet," because the diabetic urine is made sweet by the glucose present. But the shortage of the antidiuretic hormone also results in a large urine volume; for that reason this disorder has likewise been termed diabetes. But it is classified as "insipidus," because this urine is not sweet but flat. Insipidus means flat or tasteless.

A man with diabetes insipidus may produce as much as 18 liters of urine per day. It will be remembered that the normal individual puts out only little more than a liter daily. Because of this great loss of fluid, these patients suffer from insatiable thirst. They therefore drink almost continuously. Since the bladder can hold comfortably only about 300 to 500 ml of urine, it can be seen that they must urinate with great frequency. Thus, they have been described as "standing over a stream."

Fortunately, diabetes insipidus, in many cases, can be controlled by administration of the antidiuretic hormone. Such people are severely limited, for they must be careful to control their loss of fluids in perspiration and must also carefully regulate the quantity of fluids they drink. Normally the posterior lobe adjusts itself to body-water-balance needs. If this function has been taken over by hormone administration, then no such fine regulation can exist.

Strangely, cases of hyperfunction of the posterior lobe are rarely reported. Apparently if too much of the antidiuretic hormone is being produced, the individual adequately compensates by reducing fluid intake to a minimum. In severe cases, when this compensation is overwhelmed, the resulting disorders from inadequate renal function are in all probability diagnosed as other than hyperfunction of the posterior lobe.

SUMMARY

The **hypophysis** or **pituitary** gland is a small structure situated in the cranial vault just under the brain. It is divided anatomically and physiologically into the **anterior lobe** and the **posterior lobe.**

The anterior lobe secretes many distinct hormones. The **thyrotropic hormone** regulates the thyroid gland. The **adrenocorticotropic hormone** controls the adrenal cortices. Three **gonadotropins—follicle-stimulating hormone, luteinizing hormone,** and **luteotropic hormone—**influence the gonads. **FSH** and **ICSH** regulate testicular function. There is, in addition, a **growth hormone** that is also **diabetogenic.** The anterior lobe is controlled by the thyroid, adrenocortical, and sex hormones. Additional regulation is exerted through the hypothalamus by **neurohumors.**

Hypofunction of the anterior lobe before puberty results in **dwarfism,** after puberty in **Simmonds' disease.** In either instance, there may be other alterations associated with loss of any one or more of the anterior-lobe hormones. Hyperfunction before puberty produces **giantism,** after puberty **acromegaly. Cushing's disease** is caused by abnormal hypophyseal stimulation of adrenal activity.

The posterior lobe of the hypophysis is innervated by fibers arising in the hypothalamus. Cell bodies act as **osmoreceptors** and thus regulate the secretion of this gland in accordance with the osmotic state of the blood. The **antidiuretic** hormone acts on the renal tubules and controls the quantity of urine excreted. Hypofunction of this lobe produces a disorder termed **diabetes insipidus.** It is characterized by urine volumes as great as 18 liters per day. The posterior lobe also secretes **oxytocin** which causes vigorous contractions of the uterus and ejection of milk from the breasts.

QUESTIONS

1. Why is the hypophysis sometimes referred to as the "master gland"?
2. What hormones are known to be secreted by the anterior lobe of the hypophysis?
3. How is the activity of the anterior lobe of the hypophysis controlled?
4. Discuss the roles of insulin, the glucocorticoids, growth hormone, and epinephrine in the regulation of blood sugar.
5. How does the posterior lobe of the hypophysis control body-fluid balance?
6. What alterations occur following complete extirpation of the hypophysis?

SUGGESTED READING

Cooley, D. G., "Hormones: Your Body's Chemical Rousers," *Today's Health,* **40:**#12, 28–31, 86, December 1962.

Danowski, T. S., "The Thyroid-pituitary Relationship," *N.Y. J. Med.,* **63:**#1, 50–55, January 1, 1963.

Ezrin, C., "The Pituitary Gland," *Clin. Symposia,* **15:**#3, 71–100, 1963.

Finkel, M. J., "Human Growth Hormone. Metabolic Effects and Experimental and Therapeutic Applications," *Am. J. Med.,* **32:**#4, 588–598, April 1962.

Hamwi, G. J., Skillman, T. G., and Tufts, K. C., Jr., "Acromegaly," *Am. J. Med.,* **29:**#4, 690–699, October 1960.

Li, C. H., "The ACTH Molecule," *Sci. American,* **209:**#1, 46–53, July 1963.

Index